PROBABILISTIC
THEORY OF
STRUCTURAL DYNAMICS

PROBABILISTIC THEORY OF STRUCTURAL DYNAMICS

Y. K. LIN
Professor of Aeronautical
and Astronautical Engineering
University of Illinois

McGRAW-HILL BOOK COMPANY

New York / St. Louis / San Francisco / Toronto / London / Sydney

PROBABILISTIC THEORY OF STRUCTURAL DYNAMICS

Library of Congress Catalog Card Number 67-10624

37878

1234567890 M P 7321069876

to Ying-yuh

PREFACE

"Probabilistic Theory of Structural Dynamics" is the outgrowth of lecture notes for a graduate course entitled Stochastic Structural Dynamics that I have taught at the University of Illinois since 1961. Hence, one of the purposes of this book is to serve as a textbook for graduate students in structural engineering. As a structural engineering textbook in random vibrations—as the general field is now more widely known—it emphasizes analyses of the responses of practical structures, such as beams, plates, and their combinations, to random excitations of known probability descriptions or known statistical properties. The number of examples introduced herein make this book also suitable as a reference for research workers.

Briefly, the organization is as follows: Chapter 1 is an explanation of the scope of the probabilistic theory of structural dynamics. Chapters 2 through 4 present the elements of probability theory necessary to the subsequent structural analyses. Chapters 5 through 8 consider in turn the random vibration of single-degree-of-freedom, multiple-degrees-of-freedom, continuous, and nonlinear structures. Chapter 9 discusses structural reliability and related topics. A knowledge of calculus, differential equations, matrices, strength of materials, and mechanical vibrations is the prerequisite for the complete use of this book.

It is a pleasure to acknowledge the help I received during the preparation of the manuscript. Among my colleagues at the Aeronautical and Astronautical Engineering Department of the University of Illinois, I am indebted to Prof. H. S. Stillwell, head of the department, for giving me warm and constant encouragement and to Prof. H. H. Hilton, who convinced me of the need for a course in stochastic structural dynamics at the University of Illinois. I am grateful for the invaluable and comprehensive suggestions and criticisms of Prof. S. H. Crandall of the Massachusetts Institute of Technology, who reviewed the manuscript. Among my students, my special thanks are due B. K. Donaldson, who painstakingly checked over the entire manuscript and with whom I have had many stimulating discussions, and T. J. McDaniel, who ably assisted in a number of computations. I also wish to thank Miss Dorothy Nugent and her staff for their unfailing assistance in putting the manuscript in proper order, and especially Mrs. R. E. Richardson, who typed the major part of the manuscript.

Y. K. LIN

CONTENTS

1 | INTRODUCTION

The realm of structural dynamics has been considerably enlarged since the introduction of probabilistic methods. Previously, the structural engineer would always cope with design needs by use of a deterministic analysis. In such an analysis, he would assume a complete knowledge of the dynamic properties and the initial state of a structure and the exact time history of its excitation. Consider, for example, the simplest situation in which a structure is idealized as a spring-mass-damper system excited by an external force acting on the mass, as shown in Fig. 1.1. If at time $t = 0$, the displacement and velocity of the mass are, respectively,

$$x(0) = x_0 \qquad \dot{x}(0) = v_0 \tag{1-1}$$

then the general expression for the displacement $x(t)$ may be written as follows:

$$x(t) = g(x_0, v_0, m, k, c, t) + \int_0^t f(\tau) h(m, k, c, t, \tau) \, d\tau \tag{1-2}$$

If it is assumed that the value of every element on the right-hand side of Eq. (1-2) is precisely known, then the motion of the mass $x(t)$ can be computed exactly. In a probabilistic analysis we admit uncertainty of knowledge of one or several elements on the right-hand side of Eq. (1-2). For the sake of discussion, let it be uncertainty about the spring rate. We shall call an uncertain quantity *random*. If we pick and carefully calibrate one particular spring, we cannot help but find that it has a definite extension-contraction rate. Therefore, as far as one particular spring is concerned, the probabilistic viewpoint is not appropriate, or at most it is only trivial. Suppose, however, that we are interested in any such spring manufactured from a certain process. Since not all springs

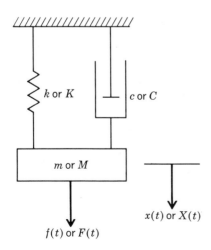

Fig. 1.1 Spring-mass-damper system. Small letters denote deterministic quantities; capital letters denote random quantities.

so manufactured are identical, before one sample is picked from a batch and tested it is not possible to foretell the exact spring rate. From this example we see that the adjective *random* implies a collection of samples none of which has been separated from the others, and that once an individual sample has been taken from the collection, it is deterministic. Similarly, when we say that the forcing function is random, we mean that the analysis is for a collection of exciting forces, each one of which is generally different from the others, but any one of which can be encountered in the actual service of the structure. Obviously, when one or more of the elements of the right-hand side of Eq. (1-2) are random, the displacement must also be random. It is possible, however, to deduce the random nature of the displacement from the random nature of the spring rate, the excitation, etc.

Since no material is perfectly homogeneous, no beam is perfectly uniform, and no rivet perfectly fits a hole, etc., it is clear that the probabilistic viewpoint is more realistic, although in those cases where the uncertainties involved are small and are not the major issue, the simpler deterministic approach may well be satisfactory. For example, by adequate specification and supervision, the fabrication of a structure may be controlled so that the uncertainty about the dynamic properties of the structure may be overlooked. The uncertainty about the excitation is generally greater, although sometimes a wise choice of a representative load or the choice of the most severe load can be made and the consequent deterministic analysis may lead to a useful design although perhaps not to the optimum design. Nevertheless, the primary incentive for the adaptation of probabilistic methods in structural dynamics analyses has been random excitations. In aerospace engineering applications, jet or rocket engine noise and gusts are two representative sources of excitations which should be treated by probabilistic methods. The efflux of a jet or rocket engine is a turbulent flow. It is known that turbulence is a phenomenon of flow instability and that there is a complicated energy exchange taking place which has not been fully understood. A small portion of the energy is converted into acoustic pressure, and this excites the nearby structural component of the flight vehicle. The undesirable consequences of this type of excitation are the fatigue failure of the nearby structure, now generally known as acoustic fatigue, and the malfunction of electronic equipment mounted on the structure. When an airplane flies into a gusty region, the irregularly fluctuating portion of the total lift can produce higher stresses in the wing structure than those resulting from the steady portion of the lift. For certain wing configurations, it has been found that such fluctuating stresses may become the major consideration in the structural design. If records were taken of jet noise pressure at a given location on an airplane fuselage, we should find that they are very erratic and that one record differs from another. The same unpredictability and lack of resemblance to each other are also characteristics of the records of gust velocity. Figure 1.2 depicts some such records placed side by side. It is easy to see that this type of physical phenomenon must be regarded as being random.

Examples of excitations which are essentially random and which act upon other than aerospace structures are plentiful. Earthquake, blast, and wind loads acting on architectural structures fall into this general category. The excitation experienced by a ship hull in a confused sea is similar to that of an airplane in a gusty atmosphere. Nevertheless, it has been primarily the applications in aerospace engineering which have speeded the development of the probabilistic techniques in the area of structural dynamics. It is worth mentioning that these techniques are being accepted more and more by the government purchasing and certifying agencies as being more suitable for the analysis of the structural integrity of a product. It may not be too long before probabilistic design requirements for earthquake, blast, and wind loads will be incorporated in most building codes.

Fig. 1.2 Typical records of a random phenomenon.

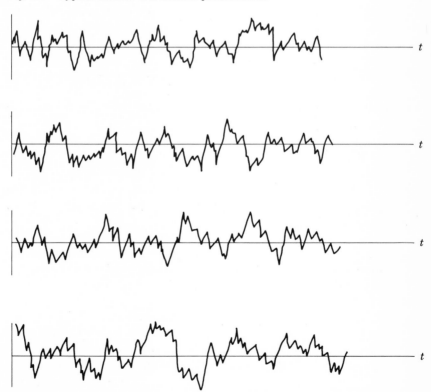

Although structural applications have provided the immediate incentive for developing the probabilistic theory of structural dynamics on a broad base, it is well to mention that structural engineers have inherited a considerable amount of knowledge from the early work of physicists on the subject of Brownian motion. The first paper treating Brownian motion as a random process was published by Einstein in 1905. It is interesting to note that Einstein's problem may be considered as a special case of the spring-mass-damper system with both the spring rate and the mass of the system negligibly small. Later, Einstein's work was extended by many others, notably Ornstein (1917), Uhlenbeck and Ornstein (1930), Van Lear and Uhlenbeck (1931), and Wang and Uhlenbeck (1945). However, from the standpoint of Brownian motion, one is generally more interested in the behavior of closed systems, closed in the sense that either the simple mass particle or the complicated continuum, say a beam, is surrounded by a fluid medium which is in a state of so-called statistical equilibrium. The main objective is to study how the Brownian motion of the mass particle or the beam tends to statistical equilibrium. Since, for such cases, the excitation and the dissipation forces are both provided by the fluid medium, the two types of force are related. On the other hand, structural engineers are interested in excitations and dissipations which are essentially independent. Structural engineers also have benefited from the work of electrical engineers, in particular from those in the fields of information theory and control theory. These groups have made extensive use of probability theory since the early 1930s and have developed techniques useful to structural engineers. Also notable is the rich literature on the theory of turbulence. It was in the development of this theory that the important concept of correlation in random phenomena was evolved. Finally, of course, we must not forget the contribution of the mathematicians who furthered the development of the common tool, probability theory, and put it on a rigorous foundation.

In spite of the healthy cross-fertilizations between different disciplines, certain features and difficulties are unique in some structural dynamics problems. A unified approach is, therefore, warranted to discuss such problems. In the chapters which follow, an attempt has been made to accomplish this objective. Roughly one-third of the volume is devoted to familiarizing the reader with certain aspects of probability theory, and two-thirds is devoted to applications. The treatment of probability theory is limited to what is needed for our purposes, but it adheres to the basic viewpoint of the modern textbooks on this theory so that the reader can easily refer to such books for additional background. In the applications portion of this volume, the exposition is divided according to tradition into single-degree-of-freedom linear systems, multiple-degrees-of-freedom linear systems, continuous linear systems, and nonlinear systems. In all cases the dynamic characteristics of a system are assumed to be deterministic, and the excitation is assumed to be random. The objective is to compute the probability law which governs the behavior of the random response of the system or, in various orders of completeness, statistical properties possessed by the response. However, from an engineering standpoint the final goal is the ability to make statements regarding the reliability of a structure to withstand random excitations. Therefore, the concluding chapter is devoted to a discussion of structural failure.

Since this book deals solely with the methods of analysis, the design aspects of structures are not considered in this volume. An analysis is usually based on a mathematical model which is an idealization of the real situation. For example, we often use the descriptions uniform cross sections, homogeneous material, sinusoidal excitations, etc., for deterministic models. Here, we shall describe probabilistic models by probability laws or by statistical properties. It is clear that ideal models, either deterministic or probabilistic, never actually exist. To justify the suitability of a model in representing a real situation we must resort to measurements. Since measured results of a random phenomenon are erratic and dissimilar to one another, the justification of a probabilistic model is not a simple matter; it belongs to the realm called statistical inference. The following diagram shows that a probabilistic model and a physical random phenomenon would be unrelated if not linked by measurements and

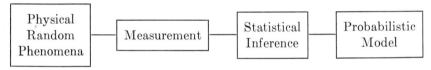

statistical inference. Unfortunately, a proper exposition of the theoretical background and techniques of statistical inference for structural dynamic problems would double the size of this book.‡

The procedures of taking measurements and of data processing are not covered since the operating information can be found in the brochures of most commercial devices; but the optimum use of such devices requires, again, an understanding of the principles of statistical inference. In short, the scope of the present book is confined to the analysis of the probabilistic models of structural dynamics problems.

‡ The following references are suggested for readers who are interested in this aspect. R. B. Blackman and J. W. Tukey, The Measurement of Power Spectra from the Point of View of Communications Engineering, *Bell System Tech. J.*, **37**:185–282, 485–569 (1958); reprinted by Dover, New York, 1959. J. S. Bendat and A. G. Piersol, "Measurement and Analysis of Random Data," Wiley, New York, 1966.

2 | SOME ASPECTS OF PROBABILITY THEORY

It is not possible nor necessary to give a thorough exposition here of modern probability theory. Chapters 2 through 4 will sketch, however, certain aspects of this theory required for our study of the probabilistic theory of structural dynamics, for the sake of being self-contained as well as for building a common language for later discussion.

2.1 / SAMPLE SPACE, EVENTS, AND SIGMA ALGEBRA

We shall call a single observation of a random phenomenon a *trial*. The outcome of a trial of a random phenomenon is, of course, unknown in advance. However, we can always identify the set‡ whose elements consist of all the possible outcomes of a trial. This set is called the *sample space* of the random phenomenon. For example, the sample space of tossing a coin is the set $\{H, T\}$, that of throwing a die is the set $\{1, 2, 3, 4, 5, 6\}$, and that of measuring the extension-contraction rate of a spring from a batch of springs is the set of, say, all positive real numbers, i.e., the open interval $(0, \infty)$. Every element in a sample space representing an outcome is called a *sample point*. We shall denote a sample space by Ω, a sample point by ω.

We can distinguish three types of sample spaces. A finite sample space contains a finite number of sample points, such as $\{H, T\}$ and $\{1, 2, 3, 4, 5, 6\}$. A countably infinite sample space contains a countably infinite number of sample points, such as the set of all integers, denoted by $\{n: n = \text{integer}\}$. Finally, an uncountable sample space contains uncountably many sample points such as the intervals $[0, \infty)$ and $[a, b]$.

Next, we introduce the concept of an *event*. Suppose that the outcome of a trial of throwing a die is 4. We may say that several events have occurred: (*a*) number 4, (*b*) an even number, (*c*) a number greater than 2, (*d*) a number smaller than 5, (*e*) a number equal to or smaller than 6, etc. Note that any of the events (*b*) through (*e*) may also occur when the outcome is not 4. Since the sample space contains all the outcomes, every event is a subset of the sample space. Event (*a*), containing only a single sample point, is called an *elementary* event; and events (*b*) through (*e*), each containing more than one sample point, are called *compound* events. An event is called a *certain* event when it contains *all* the elements in the sample space. Thus, event (*e*) is a certain event. Opposite to a certain event is an *impossible* event which contains *no* sample point. In the present example, the event a number smaller than 1 is impossible. Regarding both a certain event and an impossible event

‡ Readers unfamiliar with the terminology and the algebra of simple set theory may consult Appendix IV.

as subsets of the sample space is consistent with the usual practice in set theory of regarding a set as a subset of itself, and the empty set as a subset of any set.

Although every event is a subset of the sample space, it is not always true that every subset of the sample space is an event. We postulate that an event must be one for which a probability of occurrence can be specified. It is known in advanced probability theory that by use of certain complicated limiting procedures we can obtain some subsets of an uncountable sample space about which we cannot make consistent probability statements. Fortunately, these sets have no engineering interest, and a useful probability theory can still be formulated by excluding such ill-conditioned sets from consideration. In short, it is enough for our purposes to know that we can include as events all finite and countably infinite subsets and those uncountable subsets which are composed of intervals.

We state without proof that the family $\mathcal{F}$ of the probabilizable subsets E of a sample space Ω satisfies the following statements:

1. If $E \in \mathcal{F}$, then $\bar{E} \in \mathcal{F}$, where an upper bar denotes complementation; that is, $\bar{E}$ means E does not occur.

2. If $E_i \in \mathcal{F}$, $i = 1, 2, \ldots$, then $\bigcup_{i=1}^{\infty} E_i \equiv E_1 \cup E_2 \cup \cdots \in \mathcal{F}$.

Since the intersection and the difference operations can be indirectly performed by use of the operations of complementation and union, a family of probabilizable subsets of a sample space is closed under these set operations. (By the adjective *closed* we mean that the result of the set operation on members of the family $\mathcal{F}$ must also belong to this family.) A family of subsets of a set which satisfies statements 1 and 2 is called a *sigma algebra*.

2.2 / AXIOMS AND SOME THEOREMS OF PROBABILITY THEORY

With the above background, we can now state the following axioms of probability theory:

Axiom 1. For each member E belonging to a sigma algebra $\mathcal{F}$

$$0 \leq \mathcal{P}(E) \leq 1$$

Here $\mathcal{P}(E)$ denotes the probability of occurrence of the event E. It reads "the probability measure of E," or simply "the probability of E."

Axiom 2. $\mathcal{P}(\Omega) = 1$.

Axiom 3. If E_1, E_2, . . . , E_n are mutually exclusive, then

$$\mathcal{P}\left(\bigcup_{j=1}^{n} E_j\right) = \sum_{j=1}^{n} \mathcal{P}(E_j)$$

where n may be finite or infinite.

A few observations are worth special attention. We first note that a probability measure $\mathcal{P}$ is a *set function*, since its argument is generally a set which may contain more than one point. Secondly, the probability associated with the entire sample space Ω, a certain event, is unity; thus the assignment of probability measures to different events is analogous to the distribution of a unit mass over the sample space. For this reason some authors have aptly called $\mathcal{P}$ the probability mass function. Thirdly, in order that Axiom 3 may be satisfied, the probabilities assigned to individual sample points in the case of an uncountable sample space must be either all zero or nearly all zero except possibly for a subset of countable sample points in the sample space. The third observation is not surprising if we compare this situation with the distribution of a finite load over a continuous structure, say a flat plate. If the total load is limited to unity, then there can be at most a countable number of concentrated loads acting on the plate. The nonconcentrated portion of the total load is distributed in a prescribed manner over the surface of the plate. Since a single point occupies a *zero* area on the surface, it is subjected to a zero load if not directly under one of the concentrated loads.

Theorems and definitions

1. Theorem of the Complementary Event.

$$\mathcal{P}(\bar{E}) = 1 - \mathcal{P}(E) \tag{2-1}$$

Corollary:

$$\mathcal{P}(\phi) = 0 \tag{2-2}$$

where $\phi = \bar{\Omega}$ represents nothing happens, an impossible event.

2. Theorem of the Total Event.

$$\mathcal{P}(E_1 \cup E_2) = \mathcal{P}(E_1) + \mathcal{P}(E_2) - \mathcal{P}(E_1 \cap E_2) \tag{2-3}$$

Note that $E_1 \cup E_2$ is the occurrence of either E_1 or E_2, and $E_1 \cap E_2$ is the occurrence of both E_1 and E_2.

Corollary:

$$\begin{aligned}
\mathcal{P}(E_1 \cup E_2 \cup \cdots \cup E_n) = {} & \Sigma\mathcal{P}(E_i) - \Sigma\mathcal{P}(E_i \cap E_j) \\
& + \Sigma\mathcal{P}(E_i \cap E_j \cap E_k) - \cdots \\
& + (-1)^{n-1}\mathcal{P}(E_1 \cap E_2 \cap \cdots \cap E_n)
\end{aligned} \tag{2-4}$$

where each summation includes all distinct combinations of distinct events.

3. Definition of Conditional Probability. The probability of the occurrence of event E_2 conditional upon the occurrence of event E_1, denoted by $\mathcal{P}(E_2|E_1)$, is defined as

$$\mathcal{P}(E_2|E_1) = \frac{\mathcal{P}(E_1 \cap E_2)}{\mathcal{P}(E_1)} \qquad \text{if } \mathcal{P}(E_1) > 0 \qquad (2\text{-}5)$$

If $\mathcal{P}(E_1) = 0$, the conditional probability is undefined.

4. Definition of Independence. Event E_2 is said to be independent of event E_1 if

$$\mathcal{P}(E_2|E_1) = \mathcal{P}(E_2) \qquad (2\text{-}6)$$

5. Theorem of Joint Events.

$$\begin{aligned}
\mathcal{P}(E_1 \cap E_2) &= \mathcal{P}(E_1)\mathcal{P}(E_2|E_1) \\
&= \mathcal{P}(E_2)\mathcal{P}(E_1|E_2) \qquad (2\text{-}7)
\end{aligned}$$

$$\mathcal{P}(E_1 \cap E_2 \cap \cdots \cap E_n) = \mathcal{P}(E_1)\mathcal{P}(E_2|E_1)\mathcal{P}(E_3|E_1 \cap E_2) \\ \cdots \mathcal{P}(E_n|E_1 \cap E_2 \cap \cdots \cap E_{n-1}) \qquad (2\text{-}8)$$

There are $n!$ ways of expressing the same joint probability in (2-8) corresponding to the different permutation of $E_1, E_2, \ldots, E_n$.

Corollary:

If $E_1, E_2, \ldots, E_n$ are independent one with the others, then

$$\mathcal{P}(E_1 \cap E_2 \cap \cdots \cap E_n) = \mathcal{P}(E_1)\mathcal{P}(E_2) \cdots \mathcal{P}(E_n) \qquad (2\text{-}9)$$

Although the probability of a certain event is 1 and the probability of an impossible event is zero, the reverse is not necessarily true; that is, an event with probability 1 is not always certain, nor is an event with probability zero always impossible. This observation becomes clear if we recall that generally we can only assign zero probability to a sample point in a uncountable sample space. It is also important to note that Eq. (2-9) may be true without the events E_i being independent of each other as a system. For all the events E_i to be independent, all the following equations would have to be satisfied:

$$\mathcal{P}(E_i \cap E_j) = \mathcal{P}(E_i)\mathcal{P}(E_j)$$
$$\mathcal{P}(E_i \cap E_j \cap E_k) = \mathcal{P}(E_i)\mathcal{P}(E_j)\mathcal{P}(E_k)$$
$$\cdots \cdots \cdots \cdots \cdots \cdots \cdots \cdots \cdots \qquad (2\text{-}10)$$
$$\mathcal{P}(E_1 \cap E_2 \cap E_3 \cap \cdots \cap E_n) = \mathcal{P}(E_1)\mathcal{P}(E_2)\mathcal{P}(E_3) \cdots \mathcal{P}(E_n)$$

However, when only two events are considered, then

$$\mathcal{P}(E_1 \cap E_2) = \mathcal{P}(E_1)\mathcal{P}(E_2)$$

will lead to both

$$\mathcal{P}(E_1|E_2) = \mathcal{P}(E_1) \qquad \text{and} \qquad \mathcal{P}(E_2|E_1) = \mathcal{P}(E_2)$$

and the conclusion that they are truly mutually independent.

2.3 / STATISTICAL REGULARITY

The foregoing sections have been devoted to the development of a modern concept of probability without being unduly rigorous. So far we have remained unconcerned with physical realities. In particular, the question of how to assign probabilities to physical events has been untouched.

It is not difficult to determine at least the general form of the probability measure $\mathcal{P}$ for a simple random experiment such as flipping a coin or tossing a die. In the example of flipping a coin, it is obvious that $\mathcal{P}(H) = \mathcal{P}(T) = \frac{1}{2}$ if the coin is fair. Even when the coin is not fair we can still write $\mathcal{P}(H) = p$ and $\mathcal{P}(T) = q = 1 - p$, and proceed to determine the more interesting probability for the number of H's (or T's) obtained from flipping the same coin N times. The die-tossing problem is similar. Both problems are treated extensively in elementary books on probability theory. It seems reasonable to assume, however, that readers of this book are not interested merely in flipping coins or tossing dice. An immediate question in each mind more likely will be, How can probabilities be determined for events associated with more complicated engineering problems? Unfortunately, nature is generally reluctant to reveal the exact probabilistic mechanism of a physical phenomenon, and man has to exercise his best judgment based upon some available clues.

Our daily experiences show that repeated trials of a random experiment exhibit a certain regularity such that averages of the outcomes tend to recognizable limits when the number of trials becomes large. This tendency is called *statistical regularity*. It is important to note that we speak of statistical regularity for each random experiment; i.e., the trials are repeated under an identical set of conditions. Obviously, it would be fruitless to attempt to establish any regularity for trials under different sets of conditions.

Let N be the total number of trials of a random experiment, and N_E the number of occurrences of an event E. We define the relative frequency of the event E as

$$r_N(E) = \frac{N_E}{N} \tag{2-11}$$

One version of statistical regularity is stated as follows:

$$\lim_{N \to \infty} \mathcal{P}\{|r_N(E) - p| \geq \epsilon\} = 0 \tag{2-12}$$

where $p = \mathcal{P}(E)$ and ϵ is an arbitrarily small positive number. Equation (2-12) is often referred to as Bernoulli's *law of large numbers*. The type of limit specified in this equation is called the *limit in probability*.‡

In terms of *other* types of limit we can write down other versions of statistical regularity or other versions of the law of large numbers. We remark that various versions of the law of large numbers can be proved,¶ but we shall not attempt the proofs here.

The fact that no trial can be repeated indefinitely indicates that an exact probability associated with a physical event can never be found. Sometimes, even a reasonably large number of trials is prohibitive because of practical considerations. The usual practice is to *assume* a probability distribution for various events and *justify* the assumption by some established techniques, using the results from a limited number of trials. (In an engineering problem such trials are usually experimental measurements.) These techniques belong to the general area of statistical inference, a subject closely related to probability theory (cf. page 5).

2.4 / RANDOM VARIABLES

For most physical problems, outcomes are numerical values. Other types of outcomes, while not originally numerical values, can be made to correspond to numbers by a suitable choice. For example, in the game of flipping a coin, we may assign the value 1 to the outcome H and the value zero to the outcome T. Therefore, it is completely general to say that we can represent a random phenomenon by a random number, say X. Since the value of X depends on the trial outcome which is represented by a sample point ω, X is clearly a function defined on a sample space. More specifically, we write $X = X(\omega)$, $\omega \in \Omega$. The function $X(\omega)$ is called a *random variable*. To ensure that consistent probability statements can be made about a random variable, we give a formal definition as follows:

A random variable $X(\omega)$, $\omega \in \Omega$, is a function defined on a sample space Ω, such that for every real number x there exists a probability $\mathcal{P}[\omega : X(\omega) \leq x]$.

The existence of the probabilities $\mathcal{P}[\omega : X(\omega) \leq x]$ means that the sets $\{\omega : X(\omega) \leq x\}$ belong to a sigma algebra (cf. Sec. 2.1) of events of Ω. We note here that if the sets $\{\omega : X(\omega) \leq x\}$ are used as a basis to generate (i.e., to make complete) a sigma algebra by set operations, this sigma

‡ Compare with Eq. (3-25).

¶ See, for example, A. Papoulis, "Probability, Random Variables, and Stochastic Processes," pp. 263–266, McGraw-Hill, New York, 1965.

algebra will include the events $\{\omega\colon x_1 < X(\omega) \leq x_2\}$, $\{\omega\colon x_1 \leq X(\omega) \leq x_2\}$, $\{\omega\colon X(\omega) = x\}$, etc.

For simplicity the argument ω in the functional form $X(\omega)$ of a random variable is usually omitted in physical science literature. The probabilities $\mathcal{P}[\omega\colon X(\omega) \leq x]$, $\mathcal{P}[\omega\colon X(\omega) = x]$, etc., are usually abbreviated as $\mathcal{P}(X \leq x)$, $\mathcal{P}(X = x)$, etc.

There are two basic types of random variables: the discrete random variables are capable of taking on only a finite or countably infinite number of distinct values, whereas the continuous random variables are capable of taking on any values within one or several given intervals. A continuous random variable is necessarily associated with an uncountable sample space.

A random variable may be vectorially valued. To be more descriptive it will be called a random vector or a random n-tuple.

2.5 / PROBABILITY FUNCTION, PROBABILITY DISTRIBUTION FUNCTION, AND PROBABILITY DENSITY FUNCTION

We shall now undertake to give probability descriptions for random variables. If a random variable is discrete, then the most direct way is to specify the probabilities for the random variable to take on these discrete values, i.e., specify

$$P_X(x) = \mathcal{P}(X = x) \qquad x = a_1, a_2, \ldots, a_n \tag{2-13}$$

where n may be finite or infinite. We restate here that $\mathcal{P}(X = x)$ is an abbreviation of $\mathcal{P}[\omega\colon X(\omega) = x]$. The notation $P_X(x)$ reflects that this function is a *point* function since $a_1, a_2, \ldots, a_n$ are points on the real line. It is known as the *probability function* of the random variable X, and the argument x is called the *state variable* or the range variable of X. Note the distinction‡ between a random variable and its state variable. The latter is an arbitrary conceivable value which the former may emerge to be.

From the way it is defined (page 11), either a discrete or a continuous random variable can be described by the probability for it to be smaller than or equal to a state variable. Called the *probability distribution function* of the random variable X and denoted by $F_X(x)$, this function is related to the probability function as follows if X is discrete:

$$F_X(x) = \mathcal{P}(X \leq x) = \sum_{x_i \leq x} P_X(x_i) \tag{2-14}$$

---

‡ In early literature, a random variable and its state variable were often denoted by the same symbol. However, the use of different symbols is desirable since otherwise the right-hand side of Eq. (2-13) would become $\mathcal{P}(x = x)$, which is confusing.

For a discrete random variable it has an appearance of a staircase when plotted against the state variable x, and the staircase may or may not have an infinite number of steps. Figure 2.1 compares the representations of a discrete random variable by its probability function and its probability distribution function.

Some important properties of probability distribution functions may be noted. By definition, a probability distribution function must satisfy

$$F_X(-\infty) = 0 \qquad \text{and} \qquad F_X(+\infty) = 1$$

Since the sequence of the subsets $\{X \leq x\}$ of the sample space is a monotonically increasing sequence, and since a probability measure is nonnegative, a probability distribution function is nondecreasing. Furthermore, it is always continuous from the right.

We recall that a continuous random variable is associated with an uncountable sample space, and the probability for it to assume a specific value is generally zero. Therefore probability functions cannot be used to describe continuous random variables, but probability distribution functions are suitable. It is more convenient, however, to deal with the derivative of the probability distribution function, called the *probability density function*

$$p_X(x) = \frac{dF_X(z)}{dx}$$
$$= \lim_{\Delta x \to 0} \frac{F_X(x + \Delta x) - F_X(x)}{\Delta x} \tag{2-15}$$

assuming that this derivative exists. From the definition of a probability distribution function

$$F_X(x + \Delta x) - F_X(x) = \mathcal{P}(x < X \leq x + \Delta x) \tag{2-16}$$

Fig. 2.1 (*a*) Probability function and (*b*) probability distribution function of a discrete random variable.

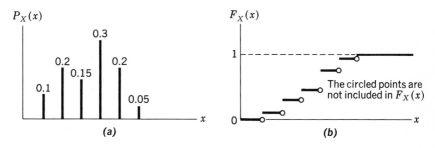

For the case where the probability of a continuous random variable to take on a particular value is zero, that is, $\mathcal{P}(X = x) = 0$, the right-hand side of (2-16) may be changed to

$$\mathcal{P}(x \leq X \leq x + \Delta x) = \Delta P$$

The ratio $\Delta P / \Delta x$ represents the average rate at which the probability is increased within the range $[x, x + \Delta x]$; and in the limit as Δx approaches zero, this ratio approaches the probability density $p_X(x)$.

The above reasoning shows that a probability density exists at a point x only if $\mathcal{P}(X = x) = 0$; and when this is true

$$p_X(x)\, dx = \mathcal{P}(x \leq X \leq x + dx)$$

Since a probability distribution function is nondecreasing, a probability density function is nonnegative. The inversion of Eq. (2-15) gives

$$F_X(x) = \int_{-\infty}^{x} p_X(x')\, dx' \tag{2-17}$$

where the condition $F_X(-\infty) = 0$ has been used. As the upper limit of the integral goes to ∞, we have

$$\int_{-\infty}^{\infty} p_X(x)\, dx = F_X(\infty) = 1 \tag{2-18}$$

Equation (2-18) is often referred to as the normalization condition of a probability density function. Figure 2.2 depicts the probability density function and the probability distribution function of a possible continuous random variable.

By limiting our attention to random variables, we usually need not be concerned with the abstract sample space and events, but shall deal with the functions $P_X(x)$, $F_X(x)$, and $p_X(x)$. Of course, when a random

Fig. 2.2 (a) Probability density function and (b) probability distribution function of a continuous random variable.

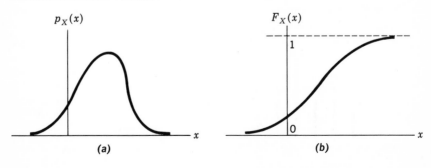

(a)   (b)

phenomenon is originally numerically valued, the sample space Ω is identical to the range of the functions $P_X(x)$, $F_X(x)$, and $p_X(x)$, and their conceptual difference can be overlooked very easily by casual readers.

2.6 / THE PROBABILITY DENSITY REPRESENTATION EXTENDED

It has been shown that a random variable may be defined by a probability density function if $\mathcal{P}(X = x) = 0$ is true over the entire range of x. However, this restriction can be *formally* removed since we require only a probability density function from which the distribution function can be recovered by use of Eq. (2-17). When a continuous random variable admits a countable number of discrete values of nonzero probability, we write the probability density function as

$$p_X(x) = p_X^*(x) + \sum_i P_X(x_i)\, \delta(x - x_i) \qquad (2\text{-}19)$$

where $p_X^*(x)$ = probability density disregarding discrete components
$\quad P_X(x_i)$ = probability function evaluated at $x = x_i$
$\quad \delta(x - x_i)$ = a Dirac delta function‡

Substitution of (2-19) into (2-17) then gives

$$F_X(x) = \int_{-\infty}^{x} p_X^*(x')\, dx' + \sum_{x_i \leq x} P_X(x_i) \qquad (2\text{-}20)$$

In obtaining Eq. (2-20) the upper limit of the integral in Eq. (2-17) must be changed to $x + \epsilon$ if $P_X(x) \neq 0$ in order to preserve the right continuity of the distribution function. As $x \rightarrow \infty$, we obtain the normalization condition

$$\int_{-\infty}^{\infty} p_X^*(x)\, dx + \sum_i P_X(x_i) = 1 \qquad (2\text{-}21)$$

It is seen that expression (2-19) for the probability density includes those of the purely continuous and purely discrete random variables as special cases. Figure 2.3 illustrates a probability density function and the corresponding probability distribution function of a mixed continuous-discrete type of random variable.

Another irregular situation arises when the distribution function does not possess a unique derivative at a certain point, although the distribution function itself is continuous at that point. In this case the probability density at the point considered is defined by two expressions, each of which holds for one of the adjacent intervals. To recover the probability distribution function, however, it is permissible to use either

‡ See Appendix V.

of the expressions. The probability density and the probability distribution for such a random variable are shown in Fig. 2.4.

2.7 / JOINTLY DISTRIBUTED RANDOM VARIABLES

Frequently we need to know the joint behavior of two or more random variables. In the spring-mass-damper problem, for example, the random excitation must be described at different times; and it is reasonable to anticipate that, although they are random, the excitation at one time may not be entirely unrelated to that at another time.

Let random variables X_1 and X_2 be the values of the excitation at times t_1 and t_2, respectively. The joint behavior of X_1 and X_2 is described by the *joint probability distribution function*

$$F_{X_1 X_2}(x_1, x_2) = \mathcal{P}[\{X_1 \leq x_1\} \cap \{X_2 \leq x_2\}] \tag{2-22}$$

Fig. 2.3 (*a*) Probability density function and (*b*) probability distribution function of a mixed-type random variable.

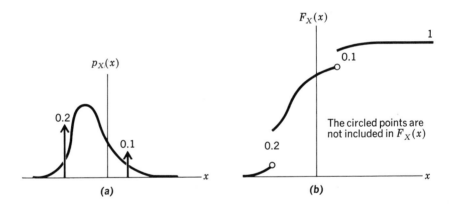

Fig. 2.4 (*a*) Discontinuous probability density function and (*b*) the corresponding probability distribution function of a continuous random variable.

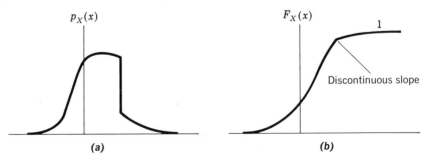

We may also regard X_1 and X_2 as the components of a random vector $\mathbf{X}$. The joint distribution function may then be denoted alternatively by $F_{\mathbf{X}}(\mathbf{x})$, where $\mathbf{x} = (x_1, x_2)$ is a conceivable vector whose value may be taken by $\mathbf{X}$. This notion is especially convenient when many random variables are considered.

A joint probability distribution function is nondecreasing and right-continuous with respect to each of the multiple dimensions. For two random variables, it satisfies the following obvious relations:

$$
\begin{aligned}
F_{X_1X_2}(-\infty, x_2) &= F_{X_1X_2}(x_1, -\infty) = 0 \\
F_{X_1X_2}(\infty, \infty) &= 1 \\
F_{X_1X_2}(x_1, \infty) &= F_{X_1}(x_1) \\
F_{X_1X_2}(\infty, x_2) &= F_{X_2}(x_2)
\end{aligned}
\tag{2-23}
$$

The *joint probability density* is defined as the mixed derivative of the joint probability distribution function. In the two-dimensional case, for example,

$$
p_{X_1X_2}(x_1, x_2) = \frac{\partial^2}{\partial x_1\,\partial x_2} F_{X_1X_2}(x_1, x_2)
\tag{2-24}
$$

and it is always nonnegative. The inverse of (2-24) is

$$
F_{X_1X_2}(x_1, x_2) = \int_{-\infty}^{x_1} \int_{-\infty}^{x_2} p_{X_1X_2}(x_1', x_2')\, dx_1'\, dx_2'
\tag{2-25}
$$

If we let one of the upper limits of the double integration approach infinity, we obtain the distribution function for a single random variable, i.e.,

$$
\int_{-\infty}^{\infty} dx_2' \int_{-\infty}^{x_1} p_{X_1X_2}(x_1', x_2')\, dx_1' = \mathcal{P}(X_1 \leq x_1) = F_{X_1}(x_1)
\tag{2-26}
$$

If both the upper limits on the right-hand side of (2-25) approach infinity, the integration then covers the entire two-dimensional sample space and

$$
\int_{-\infty}^{\infty} \int_{-\infty}^{\infty} p_{X_1X_2}(x_1, x_2)\, dx_1\, dx_2 = 1
\tag{2-27}
$$

Differentiation of both sides of (2-26) with respect to x_1 results in

$$
p_{X_1}(x_1) = \int_{-\infty}^{\infty} p_{X_1X_2}(x_1, x_2)\, dx_2
\tag{2-28}
$$

Similarly,

$$
p_{X_2}(x_2) = \int_{-\infty}^{\infty} p_{X_1X_2}(x_1, x_2)\, dx_1
\tag{2-29}
$$

Thus the joint probability density $p_{X_1 X_2}(x_1, x_2)$ contains more information than $p_{X_1}(x_1)$ and $p_{X_1}(x_2)$ separately, since the latter can be obtained from the former.

The two-dimensional case can be readily generalized. Starting from

$$F_{X_1 X_2 \cdots X_n}(x_1, x_2, \ldots, x_n) = \mathcal{P}[\{X_1 \leq x_1\} \cap \cdots \cap \{X_n \leq x_n\}] \tag{2-30}$$

and

$$p_{X_1 X_2 \cdots X_n}(x_1, x_2, \ldots, x_n)$$
$$= \frac{\partial^n}{\partial x_1 \, \partial x_2 \, \cdots \, \partial x_n} F_{X_1 X_2 \cdots X_n}(x_1, x_2, \ldots, x_n) \tag{2-31}$$

we are led to, for example, the extended version of (2-28):

$$\int_{-\infty}^{\infty} \underset{k\text{-fold}}{\cdots} \int_{-\infty}^{\infty} p_{X_1 X_2 \cdots X_n}(x_1, x_2, \ldots, x_n) \, dx_{n-k} \, dx_{n-k+1} \cdots dx_n$$
$$= p_{X_1 X_2 \cdots X_{n-k-1}}(x_1, x_2, \ldots, x_{n-k-1}) \tag{2-32}$$

Analogous expressions can also be written for (2-23), (2-25), (2-26), and (2-27).

Joint probability density functions may be used to describe discrete or mixed continuous-discrete random vectors if the Dirac delta functions are permitted in the representation. In certain purely discrete cases it may be convenient to deal with the joint probability function defined as

$$P_{X_1 X_2 \cdots X_n}(x_1, x_2, \ldots, x_n)$$
$$= \mathcal{P}[\{X_1 = x_1\} \cap \{X_2 = x_2\} \cap \cdots \cap \{X_n = x_n\}] \tag{2-33}$$

2.8 / CONDITIONAL DISTRIBUTION

If two jointly distributed random variables X and Y are both discrete, then the probability for $X = x$ on the condition that $Y = y$ is given by

$$P_{X|Y}(x|y) = \frac{P_{XY}(x, y)}{P_Y(y)} \tag{2-34}$$

Equation (2-34) is merely a special case of Eq. (2-5). It too is valid only when $P_Y(y) > 0$. From the definition of independence of two events, Eq. (2-6), the random variable X is said to be independent of the random variable Y if $P_{X|Y}(x|y) = P_X(x)$.

In the case of continuous random variables defined on an uncountable sample space, Eq. (2-34) becomes meaningless since $P_Y(y) = 0$ almost everywhere. In order to overcome this difficulty, we replace

(2-34) by

$$\mathcal{P}[\{x \leq X \leq x + \Delta x\} | \{y \leq Y \leq y + \Delta y\}]$$
$$= \frac{\mathcal{P}[\{x \leq X \leq x + \Delta x\} \cap \{y \leq Y \leq y + \Delta y\}]}{\mathcal{P}[\{y \leq Y \leq y + \Delta y\}]} \quad (2\text{-}35)$$

When the limit as Δx, $\Delta y \to 0$ is taken on both sides of Eq. (2-35), the right-hand side becomes

$$\frac{p_{XY}(x, y)\, dx\, dy}{p_Y(y)\, dy} = \frac{p_{XY}(x, y)\, dx}{p_Y(y)} \quad (2\text{-}36)$$

The limiting form is the probability for X to be in the infinitesimal interval $[x, x + dx]$ conditional on $Y = y$.‡   On this basis it is plausible to define a *conditional probability density* as

$$
\begin{aligned}
p_{X|Y}(x|y) &= \frac{p_{XY}(x, y)}{p_Y(y)} \\
&= \frac{p_{XY}(x, y)}{\displaystyle\int_{-\infty}^{\infty} p_{XY}(x, y)\, dx} \quad (2\text{-}37)
\end{aligned}
$$

Again, the definition is meaningful so long as $p_Y(y) > 0$.   For completeness we define $p_{X|Y}(x|y) = 0$ whenever $p_Y(y) = 0$.   The second part of (2-37) indicates that the conditional probability density is derivable from the joint probability density.   The definition of independence in the case of two continuous random variables reads as

$$p_{X|Y}(x|y) = p_X(x) \quad (2\text{-}38)$$

which implies

$$p_{XY}(x, y) = p_X(x)p_Y(y) \quad (2\text{-}39)$$

Note that the first part of (2-37) can be rearranged to calculate the joint probability density; i.e.,

$$p_{XY}(x, y) = p_Y(y)p_{X|Y}(x|y) \quad (2\text{-}37a)$$

Integration of (2-37a) gives

$$p_X(x) = \int_{-\infty}^{\infty} p_{XY}(x, y)\, dy = \int_{-\infty}^{\infty} p_{X|Y}(x|y)p_Y(y)\, dy \quad (2\text{-}40)$$

which shows how the unconditional probability density may be computed from the conditional probability density.

The validity of (2-38) through (2-40) is extended to the discrete or

‡ More exactly, conditional on the limit of a set, say $\{y \leq Y \leq y + 1/2^n\}$, as n approaches infinity.

mixed continuous-discrete random variable by admitting the Dirac delta functions in the representation of the various probability densities.

The conditional distribution function is obtained from an integration of (2-37):

$$F_{X|Y}(x|y) = \frac{\int_{-\infty}^{x} p_{XY}(x', y) \, dx'}{p_Y(y)} \tag{2-41}$$

Transposing and further integrating gives us

$$F_X(x) = \int_{-\infty}^{\infty} F_{X|Y}(x|y) p_Y(y) \, dy \tag{2-42}$$

2.9 / FUNCTIONS OF RANDOM VARIABLES

Let X be a random variable. Then a function of X, say $Y = f(X)$, is also a random variable, provided that the probability $\mathcal{P}(\{\omega: f[X(\omega)] \leq y\})$ exists‡ for every real number y. From advanced probability theory it is known that the existence of the probabilities $\mathcal{P}(\{\omega: f[X(\omega)] \leq y\})$ is guaranteed if f is a *Borel function*. We shall not give a precise definition of a Borel function. For our purposes, it suffices to know that a function with at most a finite number of discontinuities is a Borel function.

It is not at all inconvenient to consider the general case of m functions of n random variables. Let $X_1, X_2, \ldots, X_n$ be random variables; then

$$Y_k = f_k(X_1, X_2, \ldots, X_n) \qquad k = 1, 2, \ldots, m; \, m \leq n \tag{2-43}$$

are also random variables if the f_k's are Borel functions. It will be shown that in certain cases the joint probability density of the Y's can be obtained from that of the X's.

The simplest case is the one in which $n = m$ and the functions f_k define a one-to-one mapping. These restrictions ensure the existence of the inverse relations

$$X_k = g_k(Y_1, Y_2, \ldots, Y_m) \qquad k = 1, 2, \ldots, m \tag{2-44}$$

The joint probability densities for both initial and derived random variables must satisfy the normalization condition

$$\int \cdots \int_{\text{range of } x\text{'s}} p_{X_1 X_2 \cdots X_m}(x_1, x_2, \ldots, x_m) \, dx_1 \, dx_2 \cdots dx_m$$

$$= \int \cdots \int_{\text{range of } y\text{'s}} p_{Y_1 Y_2 \cdots Y_m}(y_1, y_2, \ldots, y_m) \, dy_1 \, dy_2 \cdots dy_m = 1 \tag{2-45}$$

‡ Compare with page 11 for the definition of a random variable.

It follows from a well-known result in coordinate transformation that

$$p_{Y_1Y_2\cdots Y_m}(y_1, y_2, \ldots, y_m) = p_{X_1X_2\cdots X_m}(x_1, x_2, \ldots, x_m)|J_m| \qquad (2\text{-}46)$$

where J_m is the Jacobian of the transformation, and it is defined by

$$J_m = \begin{vmatrix} \dfrac{\partial x_1}{\partial y_1} & \dfrac{\partial x_1}{\partial y_2} & \cdots & \dfrac{\partial x_1}{\partial y_m} \\[2mm] \dfrac{\partial x_2}{\partial y_1} & \dfrac{\partial x_2}{\partial y_2} & \cdots & \dfrac{\partial x_2}{\partial y_m} \\[2mm] \cdots & \cdots & \cdots & \cdots \\[2mm] \dfrac{\partial x_m}{\partial y_1} & \dfrac{\partial x_m}{\partial y_2} & \cdots & \dfrac{\partial x_m}{\partial y_m} \end{vmatrix} \qquad (2\text{-}47)$$

In the application of (2-46) the x state variables on the right-hand side must be expressed in terms of the y state variables by using the relations (2-44), i.e.,

$$x_k = g_k(y_1, y_2, \ldots, y_m) \qquad k = 1, 2, \ldots, m \qquad (2\text{-}44a)$$

It is important to point out that besides the condition for a one-to-one mapping, the validity of Eq. (2-46) further requires that the functions g_k be continuous in each of the arguments and that the partial derivatives in J_m exist and be continuous.

An example of one-to-one mapping is that in which the f_k functions are monotone with respect to each of the arguments. For $n = m = 1$, Eq. (2-46) reduces to

$$p_Y(y) = p_X(x) \left| \dfrac{dx}{dy} \right| \qquad (2\text{-}48)$$

where dx/dy is positive or negative depending on whether y is monotonically increasing or decreasing with respect to x.

The technique just described may be modified to treat the case where $m < n$, provided that the functions f_k in (2-43) specify a one-to-one mapping of the remaining initial random variables, if any $n - m$ initial random variables are held fixed. Without loss of generality, let the fixed random variables be $X_{m+1}, \ldots, X_n$. Then an application of Eq. (2-46) results in a transformation which is subject to the condition $X_{m+1} = x_{m+1}, \ldots, X_n = x_n$. Symbolically,

$$p_{Y_1Y_2\cdots Y_m|X_{m+1}\cdots X_n}(y_1, y_2, \ldots, y_m|x_{m+1}, \ldots, x_n)$$
$$= p_{X_1X_2\cdots X_m|X_{m+1}\cdots X_n}(x_1, x_2, \ldots, x_m|x_{m+1}, \ldots, x_n)|J_m| \qquad (2\text{-}49)$$

If we multiply both sides of this equation by $p_{X_{m+1}\cdots X_n}(x_{m+1}, \ldots, x_n)$ and integrate, we obtain as our solution

$$p_{Y_1Y_2\cdots Y_m}(y_1, y_2, \ldots, y_m)$$
$$= \int \cdots \int p_{X_1X_2\cdots X_n}(x_1, x_2, \ldots, x_n)|J_m| \, dx_{m+1} \cdots dx_n \qquad (2\text{-}50)$$

As an example, consider

$$Y = X_1 + X_2$$

and assume that X_1 and X_2 are independent random variables. Application of Eq. (2-50) gives

$$p_Y(y) = \begin{cases} \int_{R_1} p_{X_1}(x_1) p_{X_2}(y - x_1) \, dx_1 \\ \int_{R_2} p_{X_2}(x_2) p_{X_1}(y - x_2) \, dx_2 \end{cases} \qquad (2\text{-}51)$$

where R_1 and R_2 are the ranges of x_1 and x_2, respectively.

Equation (2-51) is known as the *convolution theorem* for the sum of independent random variables. In view of the symmetrical appearance of its two alternative forms, it is often abbreviated as

$$p_Y(y) = p_{X_1}(x_1) * p_{X_2}(x_2) \qquad (2\text{-}51a)$$

For the sum of n independent random variables,

$$Y = X_1 + X_2 + \cdots + X_n$$

repeated application of (2-51a) results in

$$p_Y(y) = p_{X_1}(x_1) * p_{X_2}(x_2) * \cdots * p_{X_n}(x_n) \qquad (2\text{-}52)$$

When it is possible to identify the set of sample points of the X's which are mappings (not necessarily one-to-one) of the set $\{Y_1 \le y_1\} \cap \{Y_2 \le y_2\} \cap \cdots \cap \{Y_m \le y_m\}$, we can always determine the joint distribution function of the Y's. The joint probability density function then follows from straightforward differentiations.

Consider, for example,

$$Y = X^2$$

Here the mapping is *not* one-to-one, but it can be seen that

$$F_Y(y) = \mathscr{P}[\{Y \le y\}] = \mathscr{P}[\{-\sqrt{y} \le X \le \sqrt{y}\}]$$
$$= \int_{-\sqrt{y}}^{\sqrt{y}} p_X(x) \, dx \qquad (2\text{-}53)$$

It follows from differentiation of both sides of this expression with respect to y that

$$p_Y(y) = \frac{p_X(\sqrt{y}) + p_X(-\sqrt{y})}{2\sqrt{y}} \qquad (2\text{-}54)$$

The transformation of random variables will be discussed further in Sec. 2.12.

2.10 / EXPECTED VALUES

Let X be a random variable; the *expected value* of X is defined as

$$E[X] = \int_{-\infty}^{\infty} x p_X(x) \, dx \qquad (2\text{-}55)$$

In a comparison of the distribution of probability measure with the distribution of a unit mass, the expected value of a random variable is analogous to the location of the mass centroid. The expected value is well defined only when

$$\int_{-\infty}^{\infty} |x| p_X(x) \, dx < \infty \qquad (2\text{-}56)$$

An expected value is synonymously called an *ensemble average* (or mean), or *statistical average* (or mean), or *mathematical expectation*.

The expected value of a function of a random variable $Y = f(X)$ can be computed without first determining the complete probability structure of Y. It is known from advanced probability theory that if f is a Borel function, then

$$E[Y] = \int_{-\infty}^{\infty} y p_Y(y) \, dy = \int_{-\infty}^{\infty} f(x) p_X(x) \, dx = E[f(X)] \qquad (2\text{-}57)$$

if either of the expectations is well defined. Similarly, the expectation of a Borel function of several random variables may be computed from

$$E[f(X_1, X_2, \ldots, X_n)] = \int_{-\infty}^{\infty} \cdots \int_{-\infty}^{\infty} f(x_1, x_2, \cdots, x_n) p_{X_1 X_2 \cdots X_n}$$
$$(x_1, x_2, \ldots, x_n) \, dx_1 \, dx_2 \cdots dx_n \qquad (2\text{-}58)$$

provided that the multifold integral remains finite if the function f is replaced by $|f|$.

Application of Eq. (2-58) to the special case

$$f(X_1, X_2, \ldots, X_n) = \sum_{i=1}^{n} f_i(X_i)$$

leads to

$$E\left[\sum_{i=1}^{n} f_i(X_i) \right] = \sum_{i=1}^{n} E\left[f_i(X_i) \right] \qquad (2\text{-}59)$$

regardless of the form of the joint probability density as long as each expectation on the right-hand side is well defined. This equation states that the *operations of mathematical expectation and summation are commutative*. When n is infinite, it is also necessary that the right-hand side of (2-59) converge to a limit.

Consider another special case,

$$f(X_1, X_2, \ldots, X_n) = \prod_{i=1}^{n} f_i(X_i)$$

An examination of Eq. (2-58) reveals that the operations of mathematical expectation and multiplication commute when $X_1, X_2, \ldots, X_n$ are independent random variables; otherwise these operations generally cannot be interchanged.

2.11 / MOMENTS

An important class of expected values is that of the various powers of one or several random variables. These expected values are called the *moments*. In the case of a single random variable, $E[X]$ is also known as the first moment, $E[X^2]$ the second moment, etc., and $E[X^n]$ the nth moment of X. For two or more random variables $E[X_1{}^m X_2{}^n]$ is called the *joint moment* of X_1 and X_2 of the $(m + n)$th order, and $E[X_1{}^{n_1} X_2{}^{n_2} \cdots X_k{}^{n_k}]$ the joint moment of $X_1, X_2, \ldots, X_k$ of the $(n_1 + n_2 + \cdots + n_k)$th order. While the first moment of a random variable is analogous to the location of the centroid of a unit mass, the second moment is comparable to the mass moment of inertia, the joint second moment of two random variables to the mass product of inertia, etc. The analogy makes it clear that moments of an arbitrary order can be computed from the probability distribution; but without additional information, moments of *all* orders are generally required to recover the knowledge of the probability distribution.

Let μ_X be the first moment of X; then $E[(X - \mu_X)^n]$ is called the *nth central moment* of X, $E[(X_1 - \mu_{X_1})^m (X_2 - \mu_{X_2})^n]$ the $(m + n)$th joint central moment of X_1 and X_2, etc. Of foremost importance are the second central moments, which are referred to frequently by special names and are denoted by special symbols. In particular,

$$E[(X - \mu_X)^2] = E[X^2] - \mu_X{}^2 = \sigma_X{}^2$$

is known as the *variance* of X. The positive square root of the variance, namely, σ_X, is called the *standard deviation* of X. In the case of two random variables

$$E[(X_1 - \mu_{X_1})(X_2 - \mu_{X_2})] = E[X_1 X_2] - \mu_{X_1}\mu_{X_2} = \kappa_{X_1 X_2}$$

is called the *covariance* of X_1 and X_2.

The importance of the variance in characterizing a random variable is demonstrated by the well-known Chebyshev's inequality

$$\mathcal{P}[|X - \mu_X| \geq h\sigma_X] \leq \frac{1}{h^2} \qquad h > 0 \qquad\qquad (2\text{-}60)$$

This inequality gives a crude estimate of the portion of the probability measure which is located farther than $h\sigma_X$ from the expected value. To prove this inequality, we note that since a probability density is nonnegative,

$$\sigma_X{}^2 = \int_{-\infty}^{\infty} (x - \mu_X)^2 p_X(x)\, dx \geq \int_{-\infty}^{\mu_X - h\sigma_X} (x - \mu_X)^2 p_X(x)\, dx$$
$$+ \int_{\mu_X + h\sigma_X}^{\infty} (x - \mu_X)^2 p_X(x)\, dx \quad (2\text{-}61)$$

Furthermore, for $x \leq \mu_X - h\sigma_X$ or $x \geq \mu_X + h\sigma_X$ we have

$$(x - \mu_X)^2 \geq h^2\sigma_X{}^2$$

Therefore,

$$\sigma_X{}^2 \geq h^2\sigma_X{}^2 \left[\int_{-\infty}^{\mu_X - h\sigma_X} p_X(x)\, dx + \int_{\mu_X + h\sigma_X}^{\infty} p_X(x)\, dx \right] \quad (2\text{-}62)$$

The quantity within the square brackets of inequality (2-62) represents

$$\mathcal{O}[X - \mu_X \leq -h\sigma_X] + \mathcal{O}[X - \mu_X \geq h\sigma_X] = \mathcal{O}[|X - \mu_X| \geq h\sigma_X]$$

The Chebyshev inequality follows from dividing inequality (2-62) by the positive quantity $h^2\sigma_X{}^2$. We note that the Chebyshev inequality applies to all random variables.

Two random variables are said to be *uncorrelated* or *linearly independent* if their covariance is zero. From the definition of a covariance it is clear that two *independent random variables are uncorrelated*. Being uncorrelated, however, is not sufficient for being independent. Consider, for example, two random variables $Y = \sin 2\pi X$ and $Z = \cos 2\pi X$, both of which are derived from an initial random variable X. Clearly, Y and Z are not independent since they are related by $Y^2 + Z^2 = 1$; however, if $p_X(x) = 1$, $0 \leq x \leq 1$, then $E[YZ] = E[Y] = E[Z] = 0$, showing that they are uncorrelated.

If X_1 and X_2 are uncorrelated, then the variance of $Y = X_1 + X_2$ satisfies

$$\sigma_Y{}^2 = \sigma_{X_1}{}^2 + \sigma_{X_2}{}^2 \quad (2\text{-}63)$$

By induction, if $X_1, X_2, \ldots, X_n$ are linearly independent of each other,

$$\sigma_{X_1+X_2+\cdots+X_n}^2 = \sigma_{X_1}{}^2 + \sigma_{X_2}{}^2 + \cdots + \sigma_{X_n}{}^2 \quad (2\text{-}64)$$

It is sometimes convenient to deal with the normalized covariance called the *correlation coefficient*

$$\rho_{X_1 X_2} = \frac{\kappa_{X_1 X_2}}{\sigma_{X_1}\sigma_{X_2}} \quad (2\text{-}65)$$

The value of a correlation coefficient for real-valued random variables‡ always lies between -1 and 1.

2.12 / CHARACTERISTIC FUNCTIONS

Another important expected value is that of an exponential function of a real random variable X. It is defined as follows:

$$E[e^{i\theta X}] = M_X(\theta) = \int_{-\infty}^{\infty} e^{i\theta x} p_X(x) \, dx \qquad (2\text{-}66)$$

This special expected value is called the *characteristic function* of X, and it is in general a complex function of the real parameter θ. Recognize that the characteristic function is the Fourier transform of the probability density. As such, the characteristic function exists provided that $p_X(x)$ is absolutely integrable, i.e.,

$$\int_{-\infty}^{\infty} |p_X(x)| \, dx < \infty \qquad (2\text{-}67)$$

This criterion is always satisfied, since it has been shown that any probability density function is nonnegative, and the value of the integral in (2-67) is actually equal to unity.

An inversion theorem in Fourier transform theory asserts that if $p_X(x)$ is piecewise continuous and of bounded variation, then

$$\hat{p}_X(x, A) = \frac{1}{2\pi} \int_{-A}^{A} M_X(\theta) e^{-i\theta x} \, d\theta \qquad (2\text{-}68)$$

converges to $p_X(x)$ as $A \to \infty$ at every point where $p_X(x)$ is continuous and converges to $\frac{1}{2}[p_X(x+) + p_X(x-)]$ at every point where $p_X(x)$ is discontinuous. This type of convergence is sufficient to ensure a unique probability distribution function if the distribution function is continuous. For brevity we write

$$p_X(x) = \frac{1}{2\pi} \int_{-\infty}^{\infty} M_X(\theta) e^{-i\theta x} \, d\theta \qquad (2\text{-}69)$$

without further qualification as to the exact mode of convergence.

When the probability density function of a discrete random variable is represented by use of the Dirac delta functions, the condition of bounded variation is not satisfied. However, if the formal representation

$$p_X(x) = \Sigma P_X(x_i) \, \delta(x - x_i) \qquad (2\text{-}70)$$

is substituted into Eq. (2-66), the resulting characteristic function is a Fourier series

$$M_X(\theta) = \Sigma P_X(x_i) e^{i\theta x_i} \qquad (2\text{-}71)$$

‡ A certain type of complex-valued random variable will be considered in Chap. 3.

Equation (2-70) can be recovered from the inverse transformation of Eq. (2-71) if the following form‡ of the Dirac delta function is used:

$$\lim_{A \to \infty} \frac{\sin A (x - x_i)}{\pi (x - x_i)} = \delta(x - x_i)$$

Therefore a random variable can be defined by a characteristic function as well as by a probability density function regardless of whether the random variable is continuous, discrete, or mixed continuous and discrete.

The moments of a random variable X can be computed conveniently from the characteristic function. Specifically,

$$E[X] = \mu_X = \frac{1}{i} \left(\frac{dM_X}{d\theta} \right)_{\theta=0}$$

. . . .

$$E[X^n] = \frac{1}{i^n} \left(\frac{d^n M_X}{d\theta^n} \right)_{\theta=0} \tag{2-72}$$

. . . .

assuming that these moments exist. Conversely, if the nth moment of X does not exist, it is necessarily implied that the nth derivative of the characteristic function does not exist. The foregoing observation suggests that a characteristic function may have a Maclaurin series expansion

$$M_X(\theta) = 1 + \sum_{n=1}^{\infty} \frac{(i\theta)^n}{n!} E[X^n] \tag{2-73}$$

provided that all the moments of X exist and that (2-73) converges for some $|\theta| > 0$. Equation (2-73) agrees with an earlier comment (page 24) that all moments are generally required to specify a random variable. Sometimes it is more convenient to deal with the principal value of the logarithm of a characteristic function, to be called a *log-characteristic function*, which can be expanded as follows:

$$\ln M_X(\theta) = \sum_{n=1}^{\infty} \frac{(i\theta)^n}{n!} \kappa_n[X] \tag{2-74}$$

where

$$\kappa_n[X] = \frac{1}{i^n} \frac{d^n}{d\theta^n} \ln M_X(\theta) \tag{2-75}$$

is called the nth *cumulant* or *semi-invariant* of X. It is interesting to note that the nth cumulant of a random variable is related to the nth

‡ See Eq. (V-7), Appendix V.

and lower-order moments. The relations for the first three cumulants are especially simple:

$$\kappa_1[X] = E[X] = \mu_X$$
$$\kappa_2[X] = E[(X - \mu_X)^2] = \sigma_X{}^2 \qquad (2\text{-}76)$$
$$\kappa_3[X] = E[(X - \mu_X)^3]$$

Obviously we can also define a random variable by its cumulants. This is especially desirable when only a few lower-order cumulants are nonzero (cf. the discussion of Gaussian random variables, page 80).

The characteristic function of several jointly distributed random variables is similarly defined as

$$M_{X_1 X_2 \cdots X_n}(\theta_1, \theta_2, \ldots, \theta_n)$$
$$= E\{\exp[i(\theta_1 X_1 + \theta_2 X_2 + \cdots + \theta_n X_n)]\}$$
$$= \int_{-\infty}^{\infty} \cdots \int p_{X_1 X_2 \cdots X_n}(x_1, x_2, \ldots, x_n)$$
$$\exp[i(\theta_1 x_1 + \theta_2 x_2 + \cdots + \theta_n x_n)] \, dx_1 \, dx_2 \cdots dx_n \qquad (2\text{-}77)$$

Its derivatives are related to the various joint moments as follows:

$$E[X_1{}^{m_1} X_2{}^{m_2} \cdots X_n{}^{m_n}] = \frac{1}{i^{m_1 + m_2 + \cdots + m_n}}$$
$$\left(\frac{\partial^{m_1 + m_2 + \cdots + m_n}}{\partial \theta_1{}^{m_1} \partial \theta_2{}^{m_2} \cdots \partial \theta_n{}^{m_n}} M_{X_1 X_2 \cdots X_n} \right)_{\theta_1 = \theta_2 = \cdots = \theta_n = 0} \qquad (2\text{-}78)$$

provided that these moments exist. When a characteristic function for several random variables is expandable in a Maclaurin series, it has the form

$$M_{X_1 X_2 \cdots X_n}(\theta_1, \theta_2, \ldots, \theta_n)$$
$$= 1 + (i\theta_j)E(X_j) + \frac{1}{2!}(i\theta_j)(i\theta_k)E(X_j X_k) + \cdots \qquad (2\text{-}79)$$

where the indices j, k, etc., range from 1 to n and a repeated index denotes a summation over this range. This summation convention will be used frequently in this book when it is convenient and will cause no confusion.

The expansion of a log-characteristic function for several random variables is a generalization of Eq. (2-74),

$$\ln M_{X_1 X_2 \cdots X_n} = i\theta_j \kappa_1[X_j] + \frac{1}{2!}(i\theta_j)(i\theta_k)\kappa_2[X_j X_k] + \cdots \qquad (2\text{-}80)$$

where

$$\kappa_{m_1 + m_2 + \cdots + m_n}[X_1 X_2 \cdots X_n] = \frac{1}{i^{m_1 + m_2 + \cdots + m_n}}$$
$$\left(\frac{\partial^{m_1 + m_2 + \cdots + m_n}}{\partial \theta_1{}^{m_1} \partial \theta_2{}^{m_2} \cdots \partial \theta_n{}^{m_n}} \ln M_{X_1 X_2 \cdots X_n} \right)_{\theta_1 = \theta_2 = \cdots = \theta_n = 0} \qquad (2\text{-}81)$$

is the *joint cumulant* of $X_1, \ldots, X_n$ of the $(m_1 + \cdots + m_n)$th order. It has been noted before that $\kappa_1[X_j] = E[X_j]$. The second and the third joint cumulants are the same as the joint central moments, i.e.,

$$
\begin{aligned}
\kappa_2[X_j X_k] &= E[(X_j - \mu_{X_j})(X_k - \mu_{X_k})] = \kappa_{X_j X_k} \\
\kappa_3[X_j X_k X_l] &= E[(X_j - \mu_{X_j})(X_k - \mu_{X_k})(X_l - \mu_{X_l})]
\end{aligned} \tag{2-82}
$$

A higher-order joint cumulant is related to the joint moments of the same and lower orders, but the relation is more complicated.

If $\kappa_m[X_1 X_2 \cdots X_m] = 0$, it implies‡ that at least one of the m random variables is uncorrelated with any of the others; therefore, one way to specify that any m random variables are mutually uncorrelated is to require that all the joint cumulants of orders 2 through m for distinct random variables be zero.

The transformation of random variables can be accomplished by use of the characteristic function. Return to Eqs. (2-43):

$$
Y_k = f_k(X_1, X_2, \ldots, X_n) \qquad k = 1, 2, \ldots, m; n \geq m \tag{2-43}
$$

The characteristic function for the Y's is given by

$$
M_{Y_1 \cdots Y_m}(\theta_1, \ldots, \theta_m) = \underbrace{\int_{-\infty}^{\infty} \cdots \int}_{n\text{-fold}} p_{X_1 \cdots X_n}(x_1, \ldots, x_n)
$$

$$
\exp\left(i \sum_{j=1}^{m} \theta_j f_j\right) dx_1 \cdots dx_n \tag{2-83}
$$

The joint probability density for the Y's results from the transformation of (2-83):

$$
p_{Y_1 \cdots Y_m}(y_1, \ldots, y_m) = \frac{1}{(2\pi)^m} \underbrace{\int_{-\infty}^{\infty} \cdots \int}_{m\text{-fold}} M_{Y_1 \cdots Y_m}
$$

$$
\exp\left(-i \sum_{j=1}^{m} \theta_j y_j\right) d\theta_1 \cdots d\theta_m
$$

$$
= \underbrace{\int_{-\infty}^{\infty} \cdots \int}_{n\text{-fold}} p_{X_1 \cdots X_n}(x_1, \ldots, x_n)
$$

$$
\prod_{j=1}^{m} \delta(f_j - y_j) \, dx_1 \cdots dx_n \tag{2-84}
$$

‡ See R. L. Stratonovich, "Topics in the Theory of Random Noise," vol. 1, pp. 13–15, English translation by R. A. Silverman, Gordon and Breach, Science Publishers, New York, 1963.

Either Eq. (2-83) or Eq. (2-84) defines the derived random variables $Y_1, \ldots, Y_m$; the choice depends on which multifold integration is easier to carry out. Both equations are valid even when the mapping of the sample points is not one-to-one.

2.13 / CONDITIONAL EXPECTATIONS

Let X and Y be jointly distributed random variables. The expected value of X on the condition that Y takes on a value y is given by

$$E[X|Y = y] = \int_{-\infty}^{\infty} x p_{X|Y}(x|y) \, dx \qquad (2\text{-}85)$$

This expectation is obviously a function of the state variable y, and it is well defined if

$$\int_{-\infty}^{\infty} |x| p_{X|Y}(x|y) \, dx < \infty$$

It is useful to introduce the concept of another conditional expectation $E[X|Y]$. We regard this expectation as a random variable which has the value on the right-hand side of (2-85) if Y is given the value y. The expectation of $E[X|Y]$ is

$$E\{E[X|Y]\} = \int_{-\infty}^{\infty} \left\{ \int_{-\infty}^{\infty} x p_{X|Y}(x|y) \, dx \right\} p_Y(y) \, dy$$
$$= E[X] \qquad (2\text{-}86)$$

In advanced probability theory the conditional expectation $E[X|Y]$ is defined implicitly as

$$E[Xg(Y)] = E\{g(Y)E[X|Y]\} \qquad (2\text{-}87)$$

assuming that the expectation on the left-hand side of this equation exists. Note that Eq. (2-87) includes Eq. (2-86) as a special case.

Equations (2-85) through (2-87) remain valid if X is replaced by a Borel function of X. A further generalization can include multiple random variables under multiple conditions. We define

$$E[g(X_1, X_2, \ldots, X_n)|Y_1 = y_1, \ldots, Y_m = y_m]$$
$$= \int \cdots \int g(x_1, x_2, \ldots, x_n)$$
$$p_{X_1 \cdots X_n|Y_1 \cdots Y_m}(x_1, \ldots, x_n|y_1, \ldots, y_m) \, dx_1 \cdots dx_n \qquad (2\text{-}88)$$

for a Borel function g for which $E[g(X_1, \ldots, X_n)]$ exists. Then

$$E\{E[g(X_1, X_2, \ldots, X_n)|Y_1, Y_2, \ldots, Y_m]\}$$
$$= E[g(X_1, X_2, \ldots, X_n)] \qquad (2\text{-}89)$$

as long as the right-hand side is well defined.

As an example, consider

$$p_{X_1 X_2}(x_1, x_2) = \frac{1}{2\pi\sigma_1\sigma_2\sqrt{1-\rho^2}} \exp\left\{-\frac{1}{2(1-\rho^2)}\left[\left(\frac{x_1-\mu_1}{\sigma_1}\right)^2\right.\right.$$
$$\left.\left. -2\rho\frac{x_1-\mu_1}{\sigma_1}\frac{x_2-\mu_2}{\sigma_2} + \left(\frac{x_2-\mu_2}{\sigma_2}\right)^2\right]\right\} \quad (2\text{-}90)$$

where $\mu_1 = E[X_1]$, $\mu_2 = E[X_2]$, $\sigma_1{}^2 = E[(X_1-\mu_1)^2]$, $\sigma_2{}^2 = E[(X_2-\mu_2)^2]$, and $\rho = E[(X_1-\mu_1)(X_2-\mu_2)]/\sigma_1\sigma_2$. It follows from integration on x_2 that

$$p_{X_1}(x_1) = \frac{1}{\sqrt{2\pi}\,\sigma_1}\exp\left[-\frac{(x_1-\mu_1)^2}{2\sigma_1{}^2}\right] \quad (2\text{-}91)$$

Dividing (2-90) by (2-91), we obtain

$$p_{X_2|X_1}(x_2|x_1) = \frac{1}{\sqrt{2\pi}\,\sigma_2\sqrt{1-\rho^2}}$$
$$\exp\left\{-\frac{[x_2-\mu_2-(\sigma_2/\sigma_1)\rho(x_1-\mu_1)]^2}{2\sigma_2{}^2(1-\rho^2)}\right\} \quad (2\text{-}92)$$

Equation (2-92) can be used to compute conditional expectations. For example,

$$E[X_2|X_1 = x_1] = \mu_2 + \frac{\sigma_2}{\sigma_1}\rho(x_1-\mu_1)$$
$$E\{[X_2 - E(X_2)|X_1 = x_1]^2\} = \sigma_2{}^2(1-\rho^2) \quad (2\text{-}93)$$

EXERCISES

2-1. Let $p_{XY}(x, y) = x/\pi a^2$, $0 \le x \le a$, $0 \le y \le 2\pi$. Compute $p_{X|Y}(x|y)$ and $p_{Y|X}(y|x)$. Are X and Y independent?

2-2. Given

$$p_X(x) = \frac{1}{\sigma_X\sqrt{2\pi}}\exp\frac{-(x-\mu_X)^2}{2\sigma_X{}^2} \qquad -\infty < x < \infty$$

prove that the probability density for $Y = a + bX$, $b \ne 0$, has the same form as that for X with $\mu_Y = a + b\mu_X$ and $\sigma_Y = |b|\sigma_X$.

2-3. Let X_1 and X_2 be independent and

$$p_{X_1}(x_1) = \frac{1}{\sigma_{X_1}\sqrt{2\pi}}\exp\frac{-(x_1-\mu_{X_1})^2}{2\sigma_{X_1}{}^2} \qquad -\infty < x_1 < \infty$$

$$p_{X_2}(x_2) = \frac{1}{\sigma_{X_2}\sqrt{2\pi}}\exp\frac{-(x_2-\mu_{X_2})^2}{2\sigma_{X_2}{}^2} \qquad -\infty < x_2 < \infty$$

Prove that the probability density for $Y = aX_1 + bX_2$ has the same form as that for X_1 or X_2 with

$$\mu_Y = a\mu_{X_1} + b\mu_{X_2}$$
$$\sigma_Y{}^2 = a^2\sigma_{X_1}{}^2 + b^2\sigma_{X_2}{}^2$$

2-4. Given

$$p_X(x) = \frac{1}{\sqrt{2\pi}\,\sigma_X} \exp\left[-\frac{(x-\mu_X)^2}{2\sigma_X^2}\right] \qquad -\infty < x < \infty$$

and $Y = e^{aX}$, determine $p_Y(y)$.

2-5. Given $p_X(x) = 1/\pi$, $0 \leq x \leq \pi$, and $Y = \sin X$, show that

$$p_Y(y) = \begin{cases} \dfrac{2}{\pi\sqrt{1-y^2}} & \text{for } 0 \leq y < 1 \\ 0 & \text{otherwise} \end{cases}$$

2-6. Given

$$p_X(x) = \frac{1}{\sqrt{2\pi}} \exp\left(-\frac{x^2}{2}\right) \qquad -\infty < x < \infty$$

and $Y = |X|$, show that

$$p_Y(y) = \sqrt{\frac{2}{\pi}} \exp\left(\frac{-y^2}{2}\right) \qquad 0 \leq y < \infty$$

2-7. Let X and Y be independent random variables and

$$p_X(x) = \frac{1}{\pi\sqrt{1-x^2}} \qquad -1 < x < 1$$

$$p_Y(y) = y \exp-\left(\frac{y^2}{2}\right) \qquad 0 \leq y < \infty$$

Show that the probability density for $Z = XY$ equals

$$\frac{1}{\sqrt{2\pi}} \exp\left(-\frac{z^2}{2}\right) \qquad -\infty < z < \infty$$

2-8. Let X_1, X_2, . . . , X_n be n independent random variables and

$$p_{X_i}(x_i) = \frac{1}{\sqrt{2\pi}\,\sigma} \exp\left(-\frac{x_i^2}{2\sigma^2}\right) \qquad -\infty < x_i < \infty$$

for all i. Show that the probability density function for

$$Y = \sum_{i=1}^{n} \left(\frac{X_i}{\sigma}\right)^2$$

is

$$p_Y(y) = \frac{1}{2^{n/2}\Gamma(n/2)} y^{n/2-1} \exp\left(-\frac{y}{2}\right) \qquad 0 \leq y < \infty$$

2-9. Given $p_{XY}(x, y) = 120y(x-y)(1-x)$, $0 \leq x \leq 1$, $0 \leq y \leq x$, determine the probability density function or $Z = Y/\sqrt{X}$.

2-10. Given $p_{XY}(x\ y) = p_X(x)p_Y(y) = 1/x^2y^2$, $1 \leq x$, $y < \infty$, show that $p_{UV}(u, v) = (2u^2v)^{-1}$, $u^{-1} \leq v \leq u$, $1 \leq u < \infty$, where $U = XY$ and $V = X/Y$.

2-11. Let the random variable X be gamma distributed; that is,

$$p_X(x) = \frac{1}{\delta^{\alpha+1}\Gamma(\alpha+1)} x^\alpha \exp\left(-\frac{x}{\delta}\right) \qquad \alpha > -1, \delta > 0, 0 \le x < \infty$$

Show that the mean and the variance of X are $\mu_X = \alpha\delta + \delta$ and $\sigma_X^2 = \delta^2(\alpha+1)$, respectively.

2-12. Find the characteristic function of X defined in Exercise 2-11 and then determine the nth moment by using the characteristic function.

Solution:

$$M_X(\theta) = (1 - i\theta\delta)^{-(\alpha+1)} \qquad E[X^n] = \delta^n(\alpha+1)(\alpha+2)\cdots(\alpha+n)$$

2-13. The Pareto distributed random variable is defined by its probability density function

$$p_X(x) = \begin{cases} rA^r \dfrac{1}{x^{r+1}} & \text{for } x \ge A \\ 0 & \text{for } x < A \end{cases}$$

Find the nth moment of X. Under what condition does the nth moment exist?

Solution:

$$E[X^n] = \frac{r}{r-n} A^n \qquad \text{for } n < r$$

2-14. The stresses recorded at a critical location on a structure are considered to be independent realizations of a random stress X. The sample mean μ and the sample variance σ are then computed and used as estimates for the true mean and variance of X. Estimate the upper bound of $\mathcal{P}[|X| > a]$ assuming that

$$\mathcal{P}[X - \mu < -a] = \mathcal{P}[X - \mu > a],$$

where a is a specified stress level (a positive number) and $a > |\mu|$.

2-15. If in Exercise 2-14 an additional assumption is made that

$$p_X(x) = \frac{1}{\sqrt{2\pi}\,\sigma} \exp\left[-\frac{(x-\mu^2)}{2\sigma^2}\right] \qquad -\infty < x < \infty$$

then what is $\mathcal{P}[|x| > a]$?

2-16. Let $Y = aX + bX^2$ and

$$p_X(x) = \frac{1}{\sqrt{2\pi}} \exp\left(-\frac{x^2}{2}\right) \qquad -\infty < x < \infty$$

Find (a) the characteristic function of Y and (b) the probability density function of Y.

2-17. Given

$$p_{XY}(x, y) = ye^{-xy} \frac{\beta^\alpha}{\Gamma(\alpha)} y^{\alpha-1} e^{-\beta y} \qquad x, y > 0$$

compute the expectation and the variance of X conditional on $Y = y$.

3 | RANDOM PROCESSES

3.1 / DEFINITION   In the example of the spring-mass-damper system of Chap. 1, we are concerned with the random displacement not only at one time but also at other times, i.e., with a family of random variables $X(t_1)$, $X(t_2)$, ...   The entire family may be denoted by $\{X(t): t \in T\}$ or, more simply, by $X(t)$, where the removal of the subscript from the t means that t is now free to assume any value belonging to a set T. Similarly, when the random motion of a beam is of interest, we shall deal with a family of random variables $\{X(t, s): t \in T, s \in S\}$, or simply $X(t, s)$.   Here t and s have the usual meanings of time and space coordinates.   Such families of random variables are called *random processes*.   A formal definition of a random process is as follows:

A random process is a parametered family of random variables with the parameter (or parameters) belonging to an indexing set (or sets).

For convenience, the general discussion to follow will refer to singly parametered random processes unless there is a need to emphasize the possible multiplicity of the parameters.

A random process is synonymously called a *stochastic process* or a *random function*.   The name *time series* is also used for time-parametered random processes which are frequently encountered in physical problems. If the indexing set is finite, a random process is a random vector; if the indexing set is countably infinite, it is a random sequence.   For example, when a structure is approximated by a system with springs and lumped masses, the spatial indexing set becomes countable (either finite or countably infinite).   If we are concerned only with the random displacements of this structure at times 0, 1, 2, 3, . . . sec, then the temporal indexing set also becomes countable.   A random process is said to be *discrete* or *continuous* depending upon whether it is a family of discrete or continuous *random variables*.   Note that in this context the adjective *continuous* does not refer to the continuity of a random function with respect to its *parameter* [cf. Eq. (3-46)].   Since the parameter may belong to a countable or an uncountable indexing set, a random process can be classified in one of four broad categories, namely, continuously parametered continuous random processes, continuously parametered discrete random processes, discretely parametered continuous random processes, and discretely parametered discrete random processes.

3.2 / SPECIFICATION OF RANDOM PROCESSES

Since a random process is a family of random variables, its specification is the same as that for jointly distributed random variables except that the number of random variables may be infinite or even uncountable.

Specification by probability functions is suitable only for discrete random processes, whereas probability distribution functions are appropriate for both discrete and continuous random processes. By admitting the Dirac delta functions in representing probability densities, either continuous or discrete or mixed-type random processes can also be specified by probability densities.

In the increasing order of completeness, the probability structure of a random process is described by

$$p_{X(t_1)}(x_1)$$
$$p_{X(t_1)X(t_2)}(x_1, x_2)$$
$$\cdot \quad \cdot \quad \cdot \quad \cdot \quad \cdot \quad \cdot \quad \cdot \quad \cdot$$
$$p_{X(t_1)X(t_2)\cdots X(t_n)}(x_1, x_2, \ldots, x_n)$$
$$\cdot \quad \cdot \quad \cdot \quad \cdot \quad \cdot \quad \cdot \quad \cdot \quad \cdot \quad \cdot \quad \cdot \quad \cdot \quad \cdot \quad \cdot \quad \cdot$$

$$(3\text{-}1)$$

where $t_1, t_2, \ldots \varepsilon T$. These are called the probability densities of the random process $X(t)$ of the first order, the second order, etc. In general, these density functions change when $t_1, t_2, \ldots$ change. Thus, they are not only functions of the state variables $x_1, x_2, \ldots$ but also functions of $t_1, t_2, \ldots$. It is more explicit to rewrite (3-1) as

$$p_{\{x\}}(x_1, t_1) \quad \text{or} \quad p_{\{x\}}(x, t)$$
$$p_{\{x\}}(x_1, t_1; x_2, t_2)$$
$$\cdot \quad \cdot \quad \cdot \quad \cdot \quad \cdot \quad \cdot \quad \cdot \quad \cdot \quad \cdot$$
$$p_{\{x\}}(x_1, t_1; x_2, t_2; \ldots; x_n, t_n)$$
$$\cdot \quad \cdot \quad \cdot \quad \cdot \quad \cdot \quad \cdot \quad \cdot \quad \cdot \quad \cdot \quad \cdot \quad \cdot$$

$$(3\text{-}1a)$$

The lower-order probability densities can be obtained from the higher-order ones by use of the compatibility condition

$$\int \cdots \int_{k\text{-fold}} p_{\{x\}}(x_1, t_1; x_2, t_2; \ldots; x_{n+k}, t_{n+k}) \, dx_{n+1} \cdots dx_{n+k}$$
$$= p_{\{x\}}(x_1, t_1; x_2, t_2; \ldots; x_n, t_n) \quad (3\text{-}2)$$

Equation (3-2) is valid irrespective of the values of $t_{n+1}, \ldots, t_{n+k}$. Probability densities describing several jointly distributed random processes are analogous to those in expressions (3-1a). For example, for random processes $X(t)$ and $Y(s)$ they are

$$p_{\{x\}\{y\}}(x_1, t_1; y_1, s_1)$$
$$p_{\{x\}\{y\}}(x_1, t_1; x_2, t_2; y_1, s_1)$$
$$p_{\{x\}\{y\}}(x_1, t_1; y_1, s_1; y_2, s_2)$$
$$p_{\{x\}\{y\}}(x_1, t_1; x_2, t_2; y_1, s_1; y_2, s_2)$$
$$\cdot \quad \cdot \quad \cdot \quad \cdot \quad \cdot \quad \cdot \quad \cdot \quad \cdot \quad \cdot \quad \cdot \quad \cdot \quad \cdot$$

$$(3\text{-}3)$$

For simplicity the following discussion will be based primarily on one random process. Any exceptions to this will be noted.

A random process may also be specified by a sequence of characteristic functions which are the Fourier transforms of (3-1a):

$$M_{\{X\}}(\theta_1, t_1) = E\{\exp [i\theta_1 X(t_1)]\}$$
$$M_{\{X\}}(\theta_1, t_1; \theta_2, t_2) = E\{\exp [i\theta_1 X(t_1) + i\theta_2 X(t_2)]\}$$
$$\dots \dots \dots \dots \dots \dots \dots \dots \dots \dots \dots \dots \qquad (3\text{-}4)$$
$$M_{\{X\}}(\theta_1, t_1; \dots ; \theta_n, t_n) = E\{\exp [i\theta_1 X(t_1) + \cdots + i\theta_n X(t_n)]\}$$
$$\dots \dots \dots \dots \dots \dots \dots \dots \dots \dots \dots \dots$$

A higher-order characteristic function can be reduced to a lower-order one by setting some of the θ's to zero:

$$M_{\{X\}}(\theta_1, t_1; \dots ; \theta_n, t_n; 0, t_{n+1}; \dots ; 0, t_{n+k})$$
$$= M_{\{X\}}(\theta_1, t_1; \dots ; \theta_n, t_n) \quad (3\text{-}5)$$

The validity of Eq. (3-5) is ensured by the compatibility condition of the probability densities. Thus, Eqs. (3-2) and (3-5) are equivalent.

If the parameter t is continuous, the random process $X(t)$ is an uncountable family of random variables. It is useful to introduce the concept of a characteristic functional

$$M_{\{X\}}[\theta(t)] = E\left\{\exp\left[i \int_T \theta(t) X(t) \, dt\right]\right\} \qquad (3\text{-}6)$$

where the function $\theta(t)$ belongs to a class for which the integral

$$\int_T \theta(t) X(t) \, dt$$

is meaningful. More will be said about the meaning of such an integral in Sec. 3.7. The sequence of characteristic functions in (3-4) may be obtained from (3-6) if we choose

$$\theta(t) = \Sigma \theta_j \, \delta(t - t_j) \qquad (3\text{-}7)$$

Conversely, (3-6) may be viewed intuitively as a limiting characteristic function as the neighboring points $t_1, t_2, \dots$ chosen from the indexing set T tend to be infinitely close.

A random process can also be described by moment functions of various orders, which are defined as

$$E[X(t_1)] = \int x p_{\{X\}}(x, t_1) \, dx$$
$$E[X(t_1) X(t_2)] = \int \int x_1 x_2 p_{\{X\}}(x_1, t_1; x_2, t_2) \, dx_1 \, dx_2 \qquad (3\text{-}8)$$
$$\dots \dots \dots \dots \dots \dots \dots \dots \dots \dots$$

when these moments exist. These are generally functions of t_1, t_2, etc. The fact that all the moment functions are required to completely describe a random process can be seen from the Maclaurin series expansion of a characteristic function:

$$M_{\{X\}}(\theta_1, t_1; \ldots ; \theta_n, t_n) = 1 + i\theta_j E[X(t_j)]$$

$$+ \frac{1}{2!} (i\theta_j)(i\theta_k) E[X(t_j)X(t_k)] + \cdots \quad (3\text{-}9)$$

The first- and second-order moment functions are especially important in practical applications. They will be denoted by special symbols

$$\mu_X(t) = E[X(t)] \qquad \phi_{XX}(t_1, t_2) = E[X(t_1)X(t_2)]$$

and called the *mean function* and the *autocorrelation function*, respectively. The mean function describes the first-order statistical property of a random process, and the autocorrelation function describes the second-order property. The importance of these two functions will be cited later. The prefix *auto-* modifying *correlation function* indicates that the two random variables considered, $X(t_1)$ and $X(t_2)$, belong to the same random process. The counterpart is the *crosscorrelation function*, defined as

$$\phi_{XY}(t_1, t_2) = E[X(t_1)Y(t_2)]$$

where $X(t_1)$ and $Y(t_2)$ belong to different (perhaps related) random processes.

Instead of using moment functions, a description of a random process can also be made by the use of *cumulant functions* of various orders when they exist:

$$\kappa_1[X(t_1)], \kappa_2[X(t_1)X(t_2)], \ldots$$

These functions are related to log-characteristic functions as follows:

$$\ln M_{\{X\}}(\theta_1, t_1; \ldots ; \theta_n, t_n) = i\theta_j \kappa_1[X(t_j)]$$

$$+ \frac{1}{2!} (i\theta_j)(i\theta_k)\kappa_2[X(t_j)X(t_k)] + \cdots \quad (3\text{-}10)$$

The first cumulant function is the same as the first moment function, and the second and third cumulant functions are identical with the second and third central moment functions, i.e.,

$$\kappa_1[X(t_1)] = E[X(t_1)] = \mu_X(t_1)$$
$$\kappa_2[X(t_1)X(t_2)] = E\{[X(t_1) - \mu_X(t_1)][X(t_2) - \mu_X(t_2)]\}$$
$$= \phi_{XX}(t_1, t_2) - \mu_X(t_1)\mu_X(t_2)$$
$$\kappa_3[X(t_1)X(t_2)X(t_3)] = E\{[X(t_1) - \mu_X(t_1)][X(t_2) - \mu_X(t_2)][X(t_3) - \mu_X(t_3)]\}$$

The higher cumulant functions, however, cannot be so simply identified, although the nth cumulant function can be expressed in terms of the nth- and lower-order moment functions. Conversely, the nth moment function can be computed from the nth- and lower-order cumulant functions.

This is a useful observation since in many cases it is simpler to deal with the cumulant functions than with the moment functions. In particular, the first and second cumulant functions contain the information about the first and second statistical properties; therefore, they are especially important in practical applications. The second cumulant function will be given a special symbol

$$\kappa_{XX}(t_1, t_2) = \kappa_2[X(t_1)X(t_2)]$$

and called the *autocovariance function* or *autocovariance kernel*. The prefix *auto-* suggests the counterpart *cross-covariance function* or *cross-covariance kernel*

$$\kappa_{XY}(t_1, t_2) = E\{[X(t_1) - \mu_X(t_1)][Y(t_2) - \mu_Y(t_2)]\}$$
$$= \phi_{XY}(t_1, t_2) - \mu_X(t_1)\mu_Y(t_2)$$

which is associated with two random processes. Without a prefix, the term *covariance function* refers to an autocovariance function. When $t_1 = t_2 = t$, an autocovariance function becomes a *variance function*

$$\sigma_X^2(t) = \kappa_{XX}(t, t)$$

The normalized covariance functions are called *correlation-coefficient functions*; they are denoted by

$$\rho_{XX}(t_1, t_2) = \frac{\kappa_{XX}(t_1, t_2)}{\sigma_X(t_1)\sigma_X(t_2)}$$

$$\rho_{XY}(t_1, t_2) = \frac{\kappa_{XY}(t_1, t_2)}{\sigma_X(t_1)\sigma_Y(t_2)}$$

The expansions (3-9) and (3-10) can be generalized to the following representation of the characteristic functional and the log-characteristic functional

$$M_{\{X\}}[\theta(t)] = 1 + i \int \theta(t)E[X(t)]\,dt$$
$$+ \frac{i^2}{2!} \iint \theta(t_1)\theta(t_2)E[X(t_1)X(t_2)]\,dt_1\,dt_2 + \cdots \quad (3\text{-}11)$$

and

$$\ln M_{\{X\}}[\theta(t)] = i \int \theta(t)\kappa_1[X(t)]\,dt$$
$$+ \frac{i^2}{2} \iint \theta(t_1)\theta(t_2)\kappa_2[X(t_1)X(t_2)]\,dt_1\,dt_2 + \cdots \quad (3\text{-}12)$$

The importance of the first- and second-order statistical properties of a random process as described by the mean functions and the correlation (or, equivalently, the covariance) functions has been mentioned previously. There are a number of reasons for their being especially important. Firstly, for some random processes, the statistical properties of an order higher than the second can be computed if the first and second ones are known. (Such random processes are, of course, completely characterized by the first and second statistical properties.) The Gaussian random processes (cf. Sec. 4.4), which are most frequently used in engineering analyses, belong to this group. Secondly, by use of the Chebyshev inequality (2-60), an upper-bound estimate of the probability of the event $|X(t) - \mu_X(t)| \geq \epsilon$ at any t can be made from the mean and variance functions for an arbitrary random process $X(t)$. It is also possible to estimate the probability of the event $|X(t) - \mu_X(t)| \geq \epsilon$ for *some* t in an interval $a \leq t \leq b$. Let $\sigma_X{}^2(t)$ and $\sigma_{\dot{X}}{}^2(t)$ be the variance functions of $X(t)$ and its derivative‡ $d/dt[X(t)]$, respectively. It can be shown that

$$\mathcal{P}[|X(t) - \mu_X(t)| \geq \epsilon \text{ for some } t \text{ in } a \leq t \leq b]$$

$$\leq \frac{1}{2\epsilon^2}[\sigma_X{}^2(a) + \sigma_X{}^2(b)] + \frac{1}{\epsilon^2}\int_a^b \sigma_X(t)\sigma_{\dot{X}}(t)\,dt \qquad \epsilon > 0 \qquad (3\text{-}13)$$

Therefore, even when the first- and second-order statistical properties do not characterize a random process completely, they still contain the most important information about that process. Thirdly, from the standpoint of computing estimated statistical properties from the records of a random process, the higher-order results are much more scattered than the lower-order results. In fact, practically all experimental data reported in the literature have been just the first- and second-order estimates.

The proof of inequality (3-13) can be obtained in a few simple steps. ¶ We note that for a random process $Y(t)$ with a zero mean,

$$\mathcal{P}[\sup_{a \leq t \leq b} |Y(t)| \geq \epsilon] \leq \frac{1}{\epsilon^2} E[\sup_{a \leq t \leq b} Y^2(t)]$$

where sup (reads "supremum") denotes a least upper bound. Now

$$Y^2(t) = Y^2(a) + 2\int_a^t \left[\frac{d}{du} Y(u)\right] Y(u)\,du$$

$$= Y^2(b) - 2\int_t^b \left[\frac{d}{du} Y(u)\right] Y(u)\,du$$

Therefore, at any t within the interval $[a, b]$,

$$Y^2(t) \leq \tfrac{1}{2}[Y^2(a) + Y^2(b)] + \int_b^a \left|\left[\frac{d}{du} Y(u)\right] Y(u)\right| du$$

‡ The meaning of such a derivative will be discussed in Sec. 3.6.

¶ See E. Parzen, "Stochastic Processes," p. 85, Holden-Day, San Francisco, 1962. See also P. Whittle, Continuous Generalizations of Chebyshev's Inequality, *Theory Probability Appl.*, **3**:386–394 (1958).

In particular,

$$\sup_{a \leq t \leq b} Y^2(t) \leq \tfrac{1}{2}[Y^2(a) + Y^2(b)] + \int_b^a \left| \left[\frac{d}{du} Y(u) \right] Y(u) \right| du$$

Taking mathematical expectations on both sides of this inequality and noting that‡

$$E[|UV|] \leq (E[U^2]E[V^2])^{\frac{1}{2}}$$

we obtain

$$E[\sup_{a \leq t \leq b} Y^2(t)] \leq \tfrac{1}{2}[Y^2(a) + Y^2(b)] + \int_a^b \left(E \left\{ \left[\frac{d}{du} Y(u) \right]^2 \right\} E[Y^2(u)] \right)^{\frac{1}{2}} du$$

Then inequality (3-13) follows from substituting $Y(t) = X(t) - \mu_X(t)$.

Quite frequently the mean function of a random process is equal to zero or another constant. For such a case the correlation function or the covariance function becomes the most important description of the random process. This is often true in structural dynamics problems. Special emphasis on the second-order statistical properties is, therefore, evident in Chaps. 5 through 8 when the response of structures to random excitations is discussed.

3.3 / HOMOGENEOUS RANDOM PROCESSES

A random process $X(t)$ is said to be *strongly homogeneous* if its complete probability structure is independent of a shift of the parametric origin. By using a probability-density description of a random process, strong homogeneity implies that

$$p_{\{X\}}(x_1, t_1) = p_{\{X\}}(x_1, t_1 + a)$$
$$p_{\{X\}}(x_1, t_1; x_2, t_2) = p_{\{X\}}(x_1, t_1 + a; x_2, t_2 + a)$$
$$\cdots\cdots\cdots\cdots\cdots\cdots\cdots\cdots\cdots\cdots\cdots\cdots\cdots \quad (3\text{-}14)$$
$$p_{\{X\}}(x_1, t_1; \ldots ; x_n, t_n) = p_{\{X\}}(x_1, t_1 + a; \ldots ; x_n, t_n + a)$$
$$\cdots\cdots\cdots\cdots\cdots\cdots\cdots\cdots\cdots\cdots\cdots\cdots\cdots$$

Consider the special case $a = -t_1$. Then expressions (3-14) state in effect that the first order probability density is independent of the parameter t and that the higher order probability densities are independent of the t origin but dependent on the difference in t values. When the first two equations in (3-14) are satisfied, the random process is said to be *weakly homogeneous.* ¶

When the parameter t stands for time, a homogeneous random process is more commonly called a *stationary* random process. Since time-parametered random processes arise quite naturally in dynamic problems,

---

‡ This is one form of the well-known Schwarz inequality.

¶ The expressions *homogeneity in the strict sense* and *homogeneity in the wide sense* are used frequently to indicate strong and weak homogeneity, respectively.

we shall, at times, use the term *stationarity* even when the discussion applies to all homogeneous random processes. A definition of a homogeneous random process may also be based on the forms of the characteristic functions, since they are the Fourier transforms of the probability densities.

If a random process is weakly homogeneous, then for arbitrary n and m, $E[X^n(t)]$ is independent of t and $E[X^n(t_1)X^m(t_2)]$ is dependent only on $t_1 - t_2$, if these moment functions exist. These properties of a weakly homogeneous random process will often be used, particularly in the case $n = m = 1$, that is, when we refer to the mean function and the correlation function. It can be readily deduced that the covariance function of a weakly homogeneous random process is also a function of the parametric difference $t_1 - t_2$, but the reverse implication is not necessarily true.

The above discussion can be extended to several jointly distributed random processes. For example, two time-parametered random processes, $X(t)$ and $Y(u)$, are said to be jointly stationary in the strict sense if

$$p_{\{X\}\{Y\}}(x_1, t_1; y_1, u_1) = p_{\{X\}\{Y\}}(x_1, t_1 + a; y_1, u_1 + a)$$

$$p_{\{X\}\{Y\}}(x_1, t_1; x_2, t_2; y_1, u_1)$$
$$= p_{\{X\}\{Y\}}(x_1, t_1 + a; x_2, t_2 + a; y_1, u_1 + a)$$

$$p_{\{X\}\{Y\}}(x_1, t_1; y_1, u_1; y_2, u_2) \qquad (3\text{-}15)$$
$$= p_{\{X\}\{Y\}}(x_1, t_1 + a; y_1, u_1 + a; y_2, u_2 + a)$$

$$p_{\{X\}\{Y\}}(x_1, t_1; x_2, t_2; y_1, u_1; y_2, u_2)$$
$$= p_{\{X\}\{Y\}}(x_1, t_1 + a; x_2, t_2 + a; y_1, u_1 + a; y_2, u_2 + a)$$

. . . .

Equivalent specifications can be made for joint characteristic functions. When the first four equations in (3-15) are true, the random processes are said to be jointly stationary in the wide sense. It can be seen from integrations of expressions (3-15) to obtain probability densities for individual random processes that joint stationarity implies individual stationarity.

In physical problems involving several random processes, joint stationarities beyond the level of the cross-covariance are seldom considered. At the level of cross-covariance stationarity we are limited to the cases where

$$\kappa_{XY}(t_1, t_2) = \Gamma_{XY}(t_1 - t_2)$$

is just a function of $t_1 - t_2$.

3.4 / PROPERTIES OF CORRELATION FUNCTIONS

In this section we shall describe some properties of the correlation functions

$$\phi_{XX}(t_1, t_2) = E[X(t_1)X(t_2)] \qquad \phi_{XY}(t_1, t_2) = E[X(t_1)Y(t_2)]$$

By their definitions, these functions are symmetric, i.e.,

$$\phi_{XX}(t_1, t_2) = \phi_{XX}(t_2, t_1)$$
$$\phi_{XY}(t_1, t_2) = \phi_{YX}(t_2, t_1)$$

(3-16)

For an arbitrary function $h(t)$ the autocorrelation function satisfies

$$\phi_{XX}(t_j, t_k)h(t_j)h^*(t_k) \geq 0$$

(3-17)

where the asterisk denotes the complex conjugate, a repeated index indicates a summation, and j and k range from 1 to any finite integer n.‡ The validity of (3-17) follows from the fact that upon interchange of the operations of expectation and summation, the left-hand side of (3-17) may be replaced by $E[|X(t_j)h(t_j)|^2]$, which is the expectation of a nonnegative random variable. A function of two variables, such as $\phi_{XX}(t_1, t_2)$, which satisfies the relation (3-17) is said to be *nonnegative definite*. If $X(t)$ and $Y(t)$ are jointly stationary in the wide sense, which, again, implies individual stationarity, then

$$\phi_{XX}(t_1, t_2) = R_{XX}(t_1 - t_2)$$
$$\phi_{XY}(t_1, t_2) = R_{XY}(t_1 - t_2)$$

i.e., they are functions of $t_1 - t_2$ rather than t_1 and t_2 separately. Denote $\tau = t_1 - t_2$; then the symmetric properties (3-16) are

$$R_{XX}(\tau) = R_{XX}(-\tau)$$
$$R_{XY}(\tau) = R_{YX}(-\tau)$$

(3-18)

The first of Eqs. (3-18) shows that the autocorrelation function of a real-valued weakly stationary random process is an even function of the difference in times at which the correlation is considered. For a weakly stationary random process, the nonnegative definiteness of the auto-correlation is stated as

$$R_{XX}(t_j - t_k)h(t_j)h^*(t_k) \geq 0$$

(3-17a)

A theorem due to S. Bochner¶ asserts that every nonnegative-definite function which satisfies (3-17a) has a nonnegative Fourier transform, if

---

‡ This inequality is also satisfied by a complex-valued random process for which the autocorrelation function is defined as

$$\phi_{XX}(t_1, t_2) = E[X(t_1)X^*(t_2)]$$

Then the symmetric property becomes hermitian, i.e.,

$$\phi_{XX}(t_1, t_2) = \phi_{XX}^*(t_2, t_1)$$

¶ S. Bochner, "Lectures on Fourier Integrals," p. 326, English translation by M. Tenenbaum and H. Pollard, Princeton, Princeton, N.J., 1959. An alternative proof will be given in Sec. 3.8 [cf. Eq. (3-80)].

such a transform exists, i.e.,

$$\Phi_{XX}(\omega) = \frac{1}{2\pi} \int_{-\infty}^{\infty} R_{XX}(\tau) \exp(-i\omega\tau)\, d\tau \geq 0 \qquad (3\text{-}19)$$

We remark in passing that the function $\Phi_{XX}(\omega)$ plays a dominant role in the theory of weakly stationary random processes. It is called the *mean-square spectral density function*, or, briefly, the *spectral density* of the random process $X(t)$. This function will be studied further in Sec. 3.8.

Another important property of the correlation functions of weakly stationary random processes is stated in the following inequality:

$$|R_{XY}(\tau)| \leq \sqrt{R_{XX}(0)R_{YY}(0)} \qquad (3\text{-}20)$$

This inequality can readily be proved by taking the expectation of the nonnegative random variable

$$\left[\frac{X(t_1)}{\sqrt{R_{XX}(0)}} \pm \frac{Y(t_2)}{\sqrt{R_{YY}(0)}}\right]^2$$

By replacing $Y(t)$ by $X(t)$, (3-20) becomes

$$|R_{XX}(\tau)| \leq R_{XX}(0) \qquad (3\text{-}21)$$

Inequality (3-21) indicates that the autocorrelation function of a weakly stationary random process attains its maximum at $\tau = 0$. Therefore the first and second derivatives of $R_{XX}(\tau)$, when they exist, must be zero and nonpositive at the origin, respectively. Figure 3.1 shows a possible autocorrelation function of a weakly stationary random process.

Since covariance functions and correlation-coefficient functions are special types of correlation functions, they possess the same properties as

Fig. 3.1 A typical autocorrelation function of a weakly stationary random process.

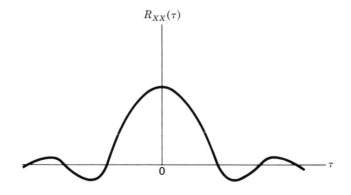

those discussed for correlation functions. In addition, except for random processes containing periodic components (cf. Sec. 3.9) an autocovariance function diminishes as the parametric separation increases, i.e.,

$$\lim_{|t_1 - t_2| \to \infty} \kappa_{XX}(t_1, t_2) = 0 \qquad (3\text{-}22)$$

This is to be expected since, in the absence of periodic contributions, $X(t_1)$ and $X(t_2)$ become uncorrelated for sufficiently large difference in t_1 and t_2. When $X(t)$ is weakly stationary, Eq. (3-22) is replaced by

$$\lim_{\tau \to \infty} \Gamma_{XX}(\tau) = 0 \qquad (3\text{-}23)$$

3.5 / MODES OF CONVERGENCE

In this section we shall introduce the important concept of the convergence of a sequence of random variables which will be required in the analytical treatment of random processes. Motivation may be supplied by applying the definition of the differentiation of a deterministic function to a random process $X(t)$:

$$\frac{d}{dt} X(t) = \lim_{h \to 0} \frac{X(t + h) - X(t)}{h}$$

Under what conditions and in what sense does this limit exist at t? For each choice of h the quotient $[X(t + h) - X(t)]/h$ at a given t is a random variable. Then this limit is one of a sequence of random variables if it exists. Since such a sequence is random, there are different ways to interpret its convergence to a limit.

The first interpretation is represented by

$$\lim_{n \to \infty} \mathcal{P}[X_n = X] = 1 \qquad (3\text{-}24)$$

We say that the sequence X_n converges to X *with probability 1*. We state without proof that a statement equivalent to (3-24) is

$$\lim_{n \to \infty} \mathcal{P}\Big[\bigcup_{k \geq n} \{|X_k - X| \geq \epsilon\} \Big] = 0 \qquad (3\text{-}24a)$$

for every $\epsilon > 0$. This mode of convergence is also known as an almost sure convergence, or convergence almost everywhere; and, in words, it guarantees that $\lim_{n \to \infty} X_n = X$ except for a set of events with probability zero. The second type of convergence is defined by

$$\lim_{n \to \infty} \mathcal{P}[|X_n - X| \geq \epsilon] = 0 \qquad (3\text{-}25)$$

for every $\epsilon > 0$; the sequence of random variables X_n is said to converge to X *in probability*. The third type is *convergence in distribution* and is represented by

$$\lim_{n \to \infty} F_{X_n}(x) = F_X(x) \tag{3-26}$$

That is, the sequence of probability distribution functions $F_n(x)$ converges pointwise to the probability distribution function $F_X(x)$.   Finally, if

$$\lim_{n \to \infty} E[|X_n - X|^2] = 0 \tag{3-27}$$

then the sequence X_n is said to *converge in mean square* to X.   Convergence in mean square is often expressed as

$$\text{l.i.m.}_{n \to \infty} X_n = X \tag{3-28}$$

where the symbol l.i.m. reads *the limit in the mean.*

Recall that only finite expectations are well defined (cf. Sec. 2.10). For (3-27) to be meaningful we require that, for every n,

$$E[X_n^2] < \infty \tag{3-29}$$

This condition must also be satisfied by the limit X if the limit is not included in the sequence.   When (3-29) is satisfied, a random variable is called a second-order random variable.   Therefore, the term *convergence in mean square* is meaningful only with regard to second-order random variables.

A random process which generates second-order random variables is called a second-order random process.   It satisfies

$$E[X^2(t)] < \infty \qquad t \in T \tag{3-30}$$

From the inequality

$$|E[X(t_1)X(t_2)]| \le E[|X(t_1)X(t_2)|]$$

and the following form of the Schwarz inequality

$$E[|X(t_1)X(t_2)|] \le \{E[X^2(t_1)]E[X^2(t_2)]\}^{\frac{1}{2}}$$

we see that (3-30) implies

$$-\infty < \phi_{XX}(t_1, t_2) < \infty \qquad t_1, t_2 \in T \tag{3-31}$$

Conversely, let $t_1 = t_2 = t$, (3-31) reduces to (3-30).   Thus conditions (3-30) and (3-31) are equivalent.   Furthermore, the mean function of a second-order random process always exists; i.e., (3-30) implies

$$-\infty < E[X(t)] < \infty \qquad t \in T \tag{3-32}$$

The validity of (3-32) can be seen from

$$|E[X(t)]| \le E[|X(t) \cdot 1|] \le \{E[X^2(t)]E[1^2]\}^{\frac{1}{2}} < \infty$$

The class of second order random processes is closed under addition; i.e., if $X(t)$ and $Y(t)$ are both of the second order, then so is $X(t) + Y(t)$.

Frequently the limit of a sequence of random variables is not known. Then to test convergence in any of the four modes, it is convenient to use Cauchy's criterion[‡] of mutual convergence. For example, to prove convergence in mean square, we should show

$$\lim_{n,m \to \infty} E[|X_n - X_m|^2] = 0 \qquad (3\text{-}33)$$

Analogous criteria may be written for (3-24) to (3-26).

The statement *convergence with probability 1* is stronger than the statement *convergence in probability*. This is seen from

$$\mathcal{P}[\bigcup_{k \geq n} \{|X_k - X| \geq \epsilon\}] \geq \mathcal{P}[|X_n - X| \geq \epsilon] \qquad (3\text{-}34)$$

Therefore (3-25) holds whenever (3-24a) does. To show that convergence in probability is also implied by convergence in mean square, we use the following form of Chebyshev's inequality:

$$\mathcal{P}[|X_n - X| \geq \epsilon] \leq \frac{1}{\epsilon^2} E[|X_n - X|^2] \qquad (3\text{-}35)$$

If $E[|X_n - X|^2]$ approaches zero, then the left-hand side also vanishes for every $\epsilon > 0$.

The weakest mode of convergence among the four is convergence in distribution, which is satisfied if convergence in probability is satisfied. First we note that the distribution function $F_X(x - \epsilon)$ may be expressed as follows:

$$F_X(x - \epsilon) = \mathcal{P}[\{X \leq x - \epsilon\}] = \mathcal{P}[\{X \leq x - \epsilon\} \cap \{X_n \leq x\}]$$
$$+ \mathcal{P}[\{X \leq x - \epsilon\} \cap \{X_n > x\}] \qquad (3\text{-}36)$$

since the event $\{X \leq x - \epsilon\}$ may occur simultaneously with either of the two mutually exclusive events $\{X_n \leq x\}$ and $\{X_n > x\}$. Similarly,

$$F_{X_n}(x) = \mathcal{P}[\{X \leq x - \epsilon\} \cap \{X_n \leq x\}]$$
$$+ \mathcal{P}[\{X > x - \epsilon\} \cap \{X_n \leq x\}] \qquad (3\text{-}37)$$

Subtracting (3-37) from (3-36), we obtain

$$F_X(x - \epsilon) - F_{X_n}(x) = \mathcal{P}[\{X \leq x - \epsilon\} \cap \{X_n > x\}]$$
$$- \mathcal{P}[\{X > x - \epsilon\} \cap \{X_n \leq x\}] \leq \mathcal{P}[\{X \leq x - \epsilon\} \cap \{X_n > x\}] \qquad (3\text{-}38)$$

The inequality portion in (3-38) follows from the fact that all probabilities

---

‡ Cauchy's criterion is commonly used to test convergence of ordinary number sequences. See, for example, J. M. H. Olmsted, "Real Variables," p. 62, Appleton-Century-Crofts, New York, 1959.

are nonnegative. Since the joint event $\{X \leq x - \epsilon\} \cap \{X_n > x\}$ is just one of the several ways in which $|X_n - X| \geq \epsilon$ may occur,

$$\mathcal{P}[\{X \leq x - \epsilon\} \cap \{X_n > x\}] \leq \mathcal{P}[|X_n - X| \geq \epsilon] \qquad (3\text{-}39)$$

Therefore,

$$F_{X_n}(x) \geq F_X(x - \epsilon) - \mathcal{P}[|X_n - X| \geq \epsilon] \qquad (3\text{-}40)$$

By considering the distribution functions $F_{X_n}(x)$ and $F_X(x + \epsilon)$, we obtain analogously

$$F_{X_n}(x) \leq F_X(x + \epsilon) + \mathcal{P}[|X_n - X| \geq \epsilon] \qquad (3\text{-}41)$$

From the hypothesis $\mathcal{P}[|X_n - X| \geq \epsilon]$ vanishes as n increases. In the limit

$$F_X(x - \epsilon) \leq \lim_{n \to \infty} F_{X_n}(x) \leq F_X(x + \epsilon)$$

for any $\epsilon > 0$. Thus (3-26) holds at every point where $F_X(x)$ is continuous. Since all distribution functions are right-continuous, at points‡ of discontinuity,

$$\lim_{n \to \infty} F_{X_n}(x+) = F_X(x+) \qquad (3\text{-}26a)$$

The relation between the different modes of convergence may be summarized as follows:

Convergence with probability 1
$$\downarrow$$
Convergence in probability $\rightarrow$ Convergence in distribution
$$\uparrow$$
Convergence in mean square

The two highest modes, the convergence with probability 1 and the convergence in mean square, do not necessarily imply each other.

The concept of convergence in mean square will be used in Secs. 3.6 and 3.7, where differentiation and integration of random processes will be considered. An example of convergence in distribution will be discussed in Sec. 4.1.

For later applications in Secs. 3.6 and 3.7, we introduce here the following two theorems on mean-square convergence:

    1. If l.i.m. $X(t) = X$ and l.i.m. $Y(s) = Y$, then
$$\lim_{\substack{t \to t_0 \\ s \to s_0}} E[X(t)Y(s)] = E[XY] \qquad (3\text{-}42)$$

‡ Necessarily countable.

The proof of this theorem is obtained by writing

$$E[X(t)Y(s) - XY] = E\{[X(t) - X][Y(s) - Y]\} \\ + E\{[X(t) - X]Y\} + E\{[Y(s) - Y]X\} \quad (3\text{-}43)$$

and noting that, by use of the Schwarz inequality, each of the three terms of the right hand side vanishes in the limit as $t \to t_0$ and $s \to s_0$.

2. A second order random process $X(t)$ converges in mean square to some random variable X as $t \to t_0$ if, and only if, the limit as $t, t' \to t_0$ of the functions $E[X(t)X(t')] = \phi_{XX}(t, t')$ exists and is finite, no matter how t and t' approach t_0.

The "if" assertion can be proved by applying the Cauchy mutual convergence criterion in the mean-square sense; i.e., we compute $E\{[X(t) - X(t')]^2\}$:

$$E\{[X(t) - X(t')]^2\} = \phi_{XX}(t, t) - \phi_{XX}(t, t') \\ - \phi_{XX}(t', t) + \phi_{XX}(t', t') \quad (3\text{-}44)$$

By hypothesis, the right-hand side of Eq. (3-44) tends to zero as t and t' tends to t_0. The "only if" assertion can be deduced from Theorem 1. By replacing $Y(s)$ by $X(t')$ and s_0 by t_0 in Eq. (3-42), we see that if $X(t)$ converges to X in mean square, then $E[X(t)X(t')]$ converges to a limit which is, in fact, $E[X^2]$.

Theorem 2 is often referred to as the theorem of *mean-square-convergence criterion*.

Theorem 1 can be used to show that the operations of *expectation* and *l.i.m.* (limit in the mean) are commutative, provided, of course, that the expectations in question exist and are continuous at the limit points. To show this, we write

$$\underset{t \to t_0}{\text{l.i.m.}} X(t) = X \quad \text{and} \quad \underset{t \to t_0}{\text{l.i.m.}} 1 = 1$$

Then from Theorem 1, we obtain

$$\lim_{t \to t_0} E[X(t)] = E[X] = E[\underset{t \to t_0}{\text{l.i.m.}} X(t)] \quad (3\text{-}45)$$

3.6 / DIFFERENTIATION OF A RANDOM PROCESS

When a physical problem is formulated as a differential equation, the derivatives of the unknown quantity appear in the equation. If the unknown quantity is a random process, then the differential equation is a valid representation of the physical phenomenon only if all the derivatives of the unknown random process present in the equation exist in the sense of one of the limits discussed in Sec. 3.5. The existence of a derivative of a random process can easily be investigated if the derivative is interpreted as a limit in mean square.

It is reasonable to anticipate that a derivative of a random process exists only at a point where the random process is continuous with respect to its parameter.‡ In the sense of mean-square convergence, continuity of a random process with respect to its parameter means that

$$\text{l.i.m.}_{h \to 0} X(t + h) = X(t) \tag{3-46}$$

The necessary and sufficient condition for Eq. (3-46) to be true follows from the mean square convergence criterion. In the present case we require that $E[X(t + h)X(t + h')] = \phi_{XX}(t + h, t + h')$ approaches to a finite limit as h and h' approach to zero in any fashion. In other words, the necessary and sufficient condition for the mean square continuity of a random process $X(t)$ at t is that its autocorrelation function $\phi_{XX}(t, s)$ be finite and continuous on the diagonal $t = s$.

It is interesting to remark that if the correlation function $\phi_{XX}(t, s)$ is continuous on the diagonal, then it is continuous over the entire product space $T \times T$. The proof will be left as an exercise for the reader.

Turn now to the definition of the mean-square derivative of a random process:

$$\frac{d}{dt} X(t) = X'(t) = \text{l.i.m.}_{h \to 0} \frac{X(t + h) - X(t)}{h} \tag{3-47}$$

It follows from the mean-square convergence criterion that (3-47) is valid if and only if the following limit exists and is continuous:

$$\lim_{h,h' \to 0} E \frac{X(t + h) - X(t)}{h} \frac{X(t + h') - X(t)}{h'} \tag{3-48}$$

This limit can be rewritten as

$$\lim_{h,h' \to 0} \left\{ \frac{1}{h} \left[\frac{\phi_{XX}(t + h, t + h') - \phi_{XX}(t + h, t)}{h'} \right. \right.$$
$$\left. \left. - \frac{\phi_{XX}(t, t + h') - \phi_{XX}(t, t)}{h'} \right] \right\} = \frac{\partial^2}{\partial t \, \partial s} \phi_{XX}(t, s) \qquad \text{at } t = s \tag{3-49}$$

Therefore the necessary and sufficient condition for $X(t)$ to be differentiable in mean square is that the correlation function $\phi_{XX}(t,s)$ has a continuous mixed second derivative on the diagonal $t = s$.

The existence of the limit (3-48) includes the special case

$$\lim_{h \to 0} E \left[\frac{X(t + h) - X(t)}{h} \right]^2 < \infty \tag{3-48a}$$

‡ Not to be confused with the name *continuous random process,* which stands for a parametered family of continuous random variables.

which in turn implies that‡

$$-\infty < \lim_{h \to 0} E \frac{X(t+h) - X(t)}{h} = \frac{d}{dt} \mu_X(t) < \infty \qquad (3\text{-}50)$$

Since the operations of expectation and l.i.m. commute, the limit in (3-50) is just the mean function of the derivative $X'(t)$, that is,

$$\frac{d}{dt} \mu_X(t) = \mu_{X'}(t) \qquad (3\text{-}51)$$

Again by changing the order of expectation and mean-square differentiation, we obtain

$$\frac{\partial^2}{\partial t\, \partial s} \phi_{XX}(t, s) = E[X'(t)X'(s)] = \phi_{X'X'}(t, s)$$

$$\frac{\partial}{\partial t} \phi_{XX}(t, s) = E[X'(t)X(s)] = \phi_{X'X}(t, s) \qquad (3\text{-}52)$$

These derivatives exist and are continuous on the entire product space $T \times T$ if the first exists and is continuous on the diagonal. Generalization of (3-52) gives

$$\frac{\partial^{n+m}}{\partial t^n\, \partial s^m} \phi_{XX}(t, s) = E[X^{(n)}(t)X^{(m)}(s)]$$

$$= \phi_{X^{(n)}X^{(m)}}(t, s) \qquad (3\text{-}53)$$

if the mixed derivative exists and is continuous on $t = s$.

If $X(t)$ is weakly stationary, then

$$\phi_{XX}(t, s) = R_{XX}(t - s) = R_{XX}(s - t)$$

Application of (3-52) yields

$$\phi_{X'X'}(t, s) = -R''_{XX}(t - s) = R_{X'X'}(t - s)$$
$$\phi_{X'X}(t, s) = R'_{XX}(t - s) = R_{X'X}(t - s) \qquad (3\text{-}54)$$

where a prime associated with R represents one differentiation with respect to the argument. Since R is an even function, we have from the second of (3-54)

$$R_{X'X}(0) = R'_{XX}(0) = 0$$

Therefore a weakly stationary random process is *orthogonal*¶ to its derivative when evaluated at the same time.

In principle, the second-order probability density of a random process can be used to find the first-order probability density of the first deriva-

---

‡ Analogous to the inequality (3-32), which is deduced from (3-30).

¶ Orthogonality is defined as $E[XY] = 0$.

tive process, etc. Consider the difference quotient

$$Y(t, h) = \frac{X(t + h) - X(t)}{h}$$

For a given t and h, Y is the algebraic sum of two random variables. The probability density of Y can be determined by use of Eq. (2-50):

$$p_{\{Y\}}(y; t, h) = \int h p_{\{X\}}(x_2 - yh, t; x_2, t + h) \, dx_2 \qquad (3\text{-}55)$$

The first-order probability density of $X'(t)$ is the limit of (3-55) as h approaches to zero, provided that such a limit exists; i.e.,

$$p_{\{X'\}}(x', t) = \lim_{h \to 0} \int h p_{\{X\}}(x_2 - x'h, t; x_2, t + h) \, dx_2 \qquad (3\text{-}56)$$

As an example, let

$$p_{\{X\}}(x_1, t; x_2, t + h)$$
$$= \frac{1}{2\pi\sigma_1\sigma_2 \sqrt{1 - \rho^2}} \exp\left[-\frac{\sigma_2{}^2 x_1{}^2 - 2\rho\sigma_1\sigma_2 x_1 x_2 + \sigma_1{}^2 x_2{}^2}{2\sigma_1{}^2\sigma_2{}^2(1 - \rho^2)} \right] \qquad (3\text{-}57)$$

It can be shown that

$$E[X(t)] = E[X(t + h)] = 0$$
$$E[X^2(t)] = \sigma_1{}^2$$
$$E[X^2(t + h)] = \sigma_2{}^2$$
$$\frac{E[X(t)X(t + h)]}{\sigma_1\sigma_2} = \rho$$

Note that $\sigma_1{}^2$ is a function of t, and $\sigma_2{}^2$ and ρ are functions of t and h. An application of (3-56) yields

$$p_{\{X'\}}(x', t) = \frac{1}{\sqrt{2\pi}} \lim_{h \to 0} \frac{h}{\sqrt{\sigma_1{}^2 - 2\rho\sigma_1\sigma_2 + \sigma_2{}^2}}$$
$$\exp\left[-\frac{h^2(x')^2}{2(\sigma_1{}^2 - 2\rho\sigma_1\sigma_2 + \sigma_2{}^2)} \right] \qquad (3\text{-}58)$$

To evaluate the limit we represent $\rho(t, t + h)$ by use of Taylor's formula with a remainder at the point (t, t):

$$\rho(t, t + h) = 1 + h\rho'(t, t) + \frac{h^2}{2} \rho''(t, t)$$
$$+ \frac{h^3}{3!} \rho'''(t, t + \theta h) \qquad 0 < \theta < 1 \quad (3\text{-}59)$$

where a prime indicates one differentiation with respect to the *second* argument. As h vanishes, σ_2 tends to σ_1, the term involving h^3 becomes small relative to the term involving h^2, and

$$\lim_{h \to 0} \frac{h^2}{\sigma_1{}^2 - 2\rho\sigma_1\sigma_2 + \sigma_2{}^2} = \lim_{h \to 0} \frac{h^2}{2\sigma_1{}^2[-h\rho'(t, t) - (h^2/2)\rho''(t, t)]} \qquad (3\text{-}60)$$

Since $\rho(t, t) = 1$ is the maximum value of any correlation-coefficient function, $\rho'(t, t) = 0$ if it exists, and $\rho''(t, t) \leq 0$ if it exists. Then Eq. (3-58) becomes‡

$$\begin{aligned}
p_{\{x'\}}(x', t) &= \frac{1}{\sqrt{2\pi} \sqrt{-\sigma_1{}^2\rho''(t, t)}} \exp \frac{(x')^2}{2\sigma_1{}^2\rho''(t, t)} \\
&= \frac{1}{\sqrt{2\pi} \sqrt{-\kappa''(t, t)}} \exp \frac{(x')^2}{2\kappa''(t, t)} \qquad (3\text{-}61)
\end{aligned}$$

In the last expression, $\kappa''(t, t) = \sigma_1{}^2\rho''(t, t)$ is the second derivative of the covariance function with respect to the second argument. Note that in obtaining (3-61) we have used Taylor's formula (3-59), which here requires the differentiability of $\rho(t, s)$ or $\kappa(t, s)$ with respect to the second argument up to the third order. This requirement is more restrictive than that for mean-square differentiability of the random process $X(t)$, that is, the requirement of the existence and continuity of $(\partial^2/\partial t\, \partial s)\kappa(t, s)$ at $t = s$.

3.7 / INTEGRATION OF A RANDOM PROCESS

We inquire next into the nature of an integral of a random process:

$$Y = \int_a^b X(t)\, dt \qquad (3\text{-}62)$$

Approximate this integral by a Riemann sum:

$$Y_n = \sum_{j=1}^n X_j(t_{j+1} - t_j) \qquad (3\text{-}63)$$

where $a = t_1 < t_2 < \cdots < t_{n+1} = b$
$X_j = X(t_j') \qquad t_j \leq t_j' \leq t_{j+1}$

Being the sum of n random variables, Y_n is a random variable; therefore, convergence of (3-63) to (3-62) must be interpreted as convergence of a sequence of random variables, as discussed in Sec. 3.5.

In the sense of convergence in mean square, the integral (3-62) is said to exist if

$$\underset{n \to \infty}{\text{l.i.m.}}\; Y_n = Y \qquad (3\text{-}64)$$

---

‡ Note that (3-61) would correspond to the trivial case $p_{\{x'\}}(x', t) = \delta(x')$ if $\rho''(t, t)$ were zero. This trivial case may be stated as $X'(t) = 0$ with probability 1.

Here, to satisfy the mean square convergence criterion is to require the existence of the following limit:

$$\lim_{n,m \to \infty} E\left[\sum_{j=1}^{n} X_j(t_{j+1} - t_j) \sum_{k=1}^{m} X_k(t_{k+1} - t_k) \right]$$

Upon interchanging the order of summation and expectation, we find that the necessary and sufficient condition for (3-64) to be true is the existence of the double Riemann integral of the autocorrelation function, i.e.,

$$\left| \int_a^b \int_a^b \phi_{XX}(t_1, t_2)\, dt_1\, dt_2 \right| < \infty \tag{3-65}$$

Under this condition expectation and mean-square integration commute; thus,

$$E\left[\int_a^b X(t)\, dt \right] = \int_a^b E[X(t)]\, dt = \int_a^b \mu_X(t)\, dt$$
$$E\left[\int_a^b X(t)\, dt \right]^2 = \int_a^b \int_a^b E[X(t_1)X(t_2)]\, dt_1\, dt_2$$
$$= \int_a^b \int_a^b \phi_{XX}(t_1, t_2)\, dt_1\, dt_2 \tag{3-66}$$

A useful generalization is to include a weighting function in the integrand of (3-62); for example,

$$Y = \int_a^b X(t)f(t)\, dt$$
$$Z(\tau) = \int_a^b X(t)h(t, \tau)\, dt \tag{3-67}$$

where f and h are bounded deterministic functions, possibly complex-valued. The first integral in (3-67) is a random variable, whereas the second integral gives rise to a transformed random process with the parameter τ. Since the second integral includes the first as a special case, it suffices to state that the second integral exists in mean square if and only if

$$-\infty < \int_a^b \int_a^b \phi_{XX}(t_1, t_2)h(t_1, \tau_1)h^*(t_1, \tau_2)\, dt_1\, dt_2 < \infty \tag{3-68}$$

for all τ_1 and τ_2. When (3-68) is satisfied, the mean and autocorrelation functions of $Z(\tau)$ are

$$\mu_Z(\tau) = \int_a^b \mu_X(t)h(t, \tau)\, dt$$
$$\phi_{ZZ}(\tau_1, \tau_2) = \int_a^b \int_a^b \phi_{XX}(t_1, t_2)h(t_1, \tau_1)h^*(t_2, \tau_2)\, dt_1\, dt_2 \tag{3-69}$$

The validity of (3-69) can also be demonstrated by computing the characteristic functional of $Z(\tau)$:

$$M_{\{Z\}}[\theta(\tau)] = E\left\{\exp\left[i\int_{-\infty}^{\infty}\theta(\tau)Z(\tau)\,d\tau\right]\right\}$$

$$= E\left\{\exp\left[i\int_{-\infty}^{\infty}\theta(\tau)\,d\tau\int_{-\infty}^{\infty}X_T(t)h(t,\tau)\,dt\right]\right\} \tag{3-70}$$

where

$$X_T(t) = \begin{cases} X(t) & a \le t \le b \\ 0 & \text{elsewhere} \end{cases}$$

Assume that the interchange of the order of integration in the second expression of (3-70) is permissible; then

$$M_{\{Z\}}[\theta(\tau)] = M_{\{X_T\}}\left[\int_{-\infty}^{\infty}\theta(\tau)h(t,\tau)\,dt\right] \tag{3-71}$$

If both sides of (3-71) are expanded according to (3-11), we have the relation

$$E[Z(\tau_1)\cdots Z(\tau_n)]$$

$$= \int_{-\infty}^{\infty}\cdots\int E[X_T(t_1)\cdots X_T(t_n)]h(t_1,\tau_1)\cdots h(t_n,\tau_n)\,dt_1\cdots dt_n$$

$$= \int_a^b\cdots\int_a^b E[X(t_1)\cdots X(t_n)]h(t_1,\tau_1)\cdots h(t_n,\tau_n)\,dt_1\cdots dt_n$$

$$\tag{3-72}$$

provided that the right-hand side exists. This relation includes (3-69) as special cases.

Similarly, by expanding log-characteristic functionals according to (3-12), we obtain

$$\kappa_n[Z(\tau_1)\cdots Z(\tau_n)] = \int_a^b\cdots\int_a^b \kappa_n[X(t_1)\cdots X(t_n)]h(t_1,\tau_1)$$

$$\cdots h(t_n,\tau_n)\,dt_1\cdots dt_n \tag{3-73}$$

Integrals of the type (3-62) or, more generally, (3-67), having random processes in the integrands, are called stochastic integrals. A stochastic integral is said to be improper if the upper limit is ∞ or the lower limit is $-\infty$, or both. Similar to the case of the proper stochastic integral, the existence of an improper stochastic integral in mean square depends on the existence of the corresponding improper double Riemann integral of a correlation function.

3.8 / SPECTRAL DECOMPOSITION OF A RANDOM PROCESS

If the weighting function in a stochastic integral of the type of the second equation in (3-67) is chosen to be $[1/(2\pi)]\exp(-i\omega t)$, where ω is a parameter, then the transformed random process

$$\bar{X}(\omega) = \frac{1}{2\pi} \int_{-\infty}^{\infty} X(t) \exp(-i\omega t)\, dt \qquad (3\text{-}74)$$

exists in mean square if and only if

$$E[\bar{X}(\omega_1)\bar{X}^*(\omega_2)] = \frac{1}{(2\pi)^2} \int_{-\infty}^{\infty} \int_{-\infty}^{\infty} \phi_{XX}(t_1, t_2)$$
$$\exp\left[-i(\omega_1 t_1 - \omega_2 t_2)\right] dt_1\, dt_2 \qquad (3\text{-}75)$$

is bounded for all values of ω_1 and ω_2. We caution that this condition is not met by some random processes, in particular the weakly stationary random processes, as will be shown later. The inversion of Eq. (3-74) in the mean-square sense is expressed as

$$E\left\{ \left| X(t) - \int_{-\infty}^{\infty} \bar{X}(\omega) \exp(i\omega t)\, d\omega \right|^2 \right\} = 0 \qquad (3\text{-}76)$$

wherever $X(t)$ is mean-square-continuous. Intuitively, (3-76) states that $X(t)$ may be replaced, up to a mean-square equivalence, by a sum of harmonic components, and that $\bar{X}(\omega)\, d\omega$ is the random *complex amplitude* of the component with frequency ω. Analogous to the case of deterministic functions, $\bar{X}(\omega)$ and $X(t)$ may be considered as Fourier transform pairs. It will be seen that this interpretation is useful in the analysis of excited random motions of linear structures. In such an analysis the left-hand side of (3-75) is often easy to determine; and when the autocorrelation $\phi_{XX}(t_1, t_2)$ is desired, it can be obtained from

$$\phi_{XX}(t_1, t_2) = \int_{-\infty}^{\infty} \int_{-\infty}^{\infty} E[\bar{X}(\omega_1)\bar{X}^*(\omega_2)] \exp[i(\omega_1 t_1 - \omega_2 t_2)]\, d\omega_1\, d\omega_2 \qquad (3\text{-}77)$$

The validity of (3-75) and (3-77) requires the absolute integrability, piecewise continuous and bounded variation of $\phi_{XX}(t_1, t_2)$ over the domain of t_1 and t_2.

To show that $\bar{X}(\omega)$ does not exist when $X(t)$ is weakly stationary, we first replace (3-74) by the truncated Fourier transform

$$\bar{X}(\omega, T) = \frac{1}{2\pi} \int_{-T}^{T} X(t) \exp(-i\omega t)\, dt \qquad (3\text{-}74a)$$

Then the existence of $\bar{X}(\omega, T)$ in mean square requires that the following be bounded for all ω_1 and ω_2:

$$E[\bar{X}(\omega_1, T)\bar{X}^*(\omega_2, T)]$$
$$= \frac{1}{(2\pi)^2} \int_{-T}^{T} \int_{-T}^{T} R_{XX}(t_1 - t_2) \exp[-i(\omega_1 t_1 - \omega_2 t_2)]\, dt_1\, dt_2 \qquad (3\text{-}75a)$$

It suffices to show that in the special case $\omega_1 = \omega_2$ the right-hand side of (3-75a) diverges as T approaches infinity.

Let $\tau = t_1 - t_2$ and $\omega_1 = \omega_2 = \omega$. Equation (3-75a) becomes

$$E[|\bar{X}(\omega, T)|^2] = \frac{1}{(2\pi)^2} \int_{-T}^{T} \left[\int_{-T-t_2}^{T-t_2} R_{XX}(\tau) \exp(-i\omega\tau)\, d\tau \right] dt_2 \qquad (3\text{-}78)$$

The domain of integration for the right-hand side of (3-78) is shown in Fig. 3.2. Reversing the order of integration,

$$E[|\bar{X}(\omega, T)|^2] = \frac{1}{(2\pi)^2} \left[\int_{0}^{2T} R_{XX}(\tau) \exp(-i\omega\tau) \left(\int_{-T}^{T-\tau} dt_2 \right) d\tau \right.$$
$$\left. + \int_{-2T}^{0} R_{XX}(\tau) \exp(-i\omega\tau) \left(\int_{-T-\tau}^{T} dt_2 \right) d\tau \right]$$
$$= \frac{1}{(2\pi)^2} \int_{-2T}^{2T} (2T - |\tau|) R_{XX}(\tau) \exp(-i\omega\tau)\, d\tau \qquad (3\text{-}79)$$

The last integral diverges as T increases; therefore, (3-74) does not exist if the random process $X(t)$ is weakly stationary.

It is intuitively clear why the mathematical model of a weakly stationary random process does not possess a Fourier transform. For this mathematical model, every sample function extends from the infinite

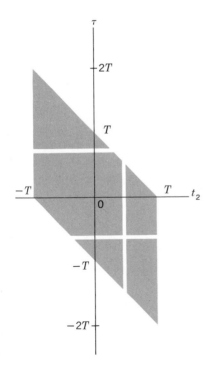

Fig. 3.2. Domain of integration in Eq. (3.78).

past to the infinite future.   Since the distribution of values of the sample functions over the ensemble of sample functions is the same at any time t, we can state with the confidence of probability 1 that every sample function does not vanish at $+\infty$ and $-\infty$ on the time axis.   Therefore, almost all sample functions are not absolutely integrable, and their Fourier transforms do not exist.

Now if (3-79) is multiplied by π/T prior to taking the limit, we obtain

$$\lim_{T\to\infty} \frac{\pi}{T} E[|\bar{X}(\omega, T)|^2] = \lim_{T\to\infty} \frac{1}{2\pi} \int_{-2T}^{2T} \left(1 - \frac{|\tau|}{2T}\right) R_{XX}(\tau) \exp(-i\omega\tau)\, d\tau$$

$$= \Phi_{XX}(\omega) - \lim_{T\to\infty} \frac{1}{2\pi} \int_{-2T}^{2T} \frac{|\tau|}{2T} R_{XX}(\tau) \exp(-i\omega\tau)\, d\tau$$

where we have assumed that the autocorrelation function $R_{XX}(\tau)$ is absolutely integrable from $-\infty$ to ∞; therefore, the mean-square spectral density $\Phi_{XX}(\omega)$ defined in Eq. (3-19) exists.   It will be shown that the integral

$$\int_{-2T}^{2T} \frac{|\tau|}{2T} R_{XX}(\tau) \exp(-i\omega\tau)\, d\tau$$

tends to zero as T increases indefinitely.   Then

$$\lim_{T\to\infty} \frac{\pi}{T} E[|\bar{X}(\omega, T)|^2] = \Phi_{XX}(\omega) \tag{3-80}$$

To prove‡ that for an arbitrarily small number $\epsilon > 0$ there exists a T_0 such that

$$\left| \int_{-2T}^{2T} \frac{|\tau|}{2T} R_{XX}(\tau) \exp(-i\omega\tau)\, d\tau \right| < \epsilon \qquad T > T_0$$

we note first that since $R_{XX}(\tau)$ is absolutely integrable, there exists a $\tau_0 > 0$ such that

$$\int_{\tau_0}^{\infty} |R_{XX}(\tau)|\, d\tau \le \frac{\epsilon}{4}$$

Secondly,

$$\left| \int_{-2T}^{2T} \frac{|\tau|}{2T} R_{XX}(\tau) \exp(-i\omega\tau)\, d\tau \right| \le \int_0^{2T} \frac{|\tau|}{T} |R_{XX}(\tau)|\, d\tau$$

The right hand side of this inequality can be split into

$$\frac{1}{T} \int_0^{\tau_0} |\tau||R_{XX}(\tau)|\, d\tau + \int_{\tau_0}^{2T} \frac{|\tau|}{T} |R_{XX}(\tau)|\, d\tau$$

$$\le \frac{1}{T} \int_0^{\tau_0} |\tau||R_{XX}(\tau)|\, d\tau + \frac{\epsilon}{2} \qquad 2T > \tau_0$$

‡ This proof is due to M. Shinozuka, private communication.

The proof is complete if we choose $T > T_0$, where

$$T_0 = \frac{2}{\epsilon} \int_0^{T_0} |\tau| \|R_{XX}(\tau)\| \, d\tau$$

The existence of the spectral density function requires only that the autocorrelation function $R_{XX}(\tau)$ be absolutely integrable, a condition met by most weakly stationary random processes of interest. There are some cases where absolute integrability does not strictly hold, but formal application of (3-19) still leads to useful results. Such cases will be considered in Sec. 3.9. Note that on the left-hand side of (3-80) the operations of expectation and taking the limit cannot be interchanged. Furthermore, this limit is one of a sequence of nonnegative numbers. Therefore, (3-80) gives an alternative proof of the nonnegativity of an arbitrary spectral density function.‡

In many practical problems, the function $\Phi_{XX}(\omega)$ of an unknown random process $X(t)$ can be more readily computed, and the autocorrelation function $R_{XX}(\tau)$, if required, is obtained from the inversion formula¶

$$R_{XX}(\tau) = \int_{-\infty}^{\infty} \Phi_{XX}(\omega) \exp{(i\omega\tau)} \, d\omega \tag{3-81}$$

The integral in (3-81) exists for all τ if it does at $\tau = 0$.

The physical significance of the function $\Phi_{XX}(\omega)$ can be revealed by letting $\tau = 0$ in Eq. (3-81), i.e.,

$$R_{XX}(0) = \int_{-\infty}^{\infty} \Phi_{XX}(\omega) \, d\omega \tag{3-82}$$

Now $R_{XX}(0) = E[X^2(t)]$ is the mean-square value of the weakly stationary random process under consideration. The right-hand side of Eq. (3-82) is the same mean-square value obtained as a sum of the infinitesimal components $\Phi_{XX}(\omega) \, d\omega$. Thus $\Phi_{XX}(\omega)$ describes the distribution of the total mean-square value over the frequency domain, hence the name *mean-square spectral density*. An alternative name for the function $\Phi_{XX}(\omega)$, the *power spectrum*, is also used in the literature since $E[X^2(t)]$ is often a measure of average energy. For example, if $X(t)$ stands for the random displacement of a linear single-degree-of-freedom mechanical system, then $E[X^2(t)]$ is proportional to the average potential energy in the system. If $X(t)$ represents the random velocity, then $E[X^2(t)]$ is proportional to the average kinetic energy.

Equations (3-19) and (3-81) give a mathematical statement of the well-known Wiener-Khintchine theorem, which asserts that for a weakly stationary random process *the autocorrelation function and the spectral density function are related to each other by Fourier transformations.*

‡ See footnote, page 42.

¶ Strictly speaking, the right-hand side of (3-81) only coincides with $R_{XX}(\tau)$ at points of continuity provided that $R_{XX}(\tau)$ is piecewise continuous and of bounded variation.

Analogous to (3-80) we define a *cross spectral density* of two random processes $X(t)$ and $Y(t)$, which are jointly stationary in the wide sense, as follows:

$$\Phi_{XY}(\omega) = \lim_{T \to \infty} \frac{\pi}{T} E[\bar{X}(\omega, T) \bar{Y}^*(\omega, T)]$$

$$= \frac{1}{2\pi} \int_{-\infty}^{\infty} R_{XY}(\tau) \exp(-i\omega\tau) \, d\tau \tag{3-83}$$

Again the expectation and the limit operations in (3-83) are not inter-changeable. The cross spectral density $\Phi_{XY}(\omega)$ exists if both $\Phi_{XX}(\omega)$ and $\Phi_{YY}(\omega)$ exist, since

$$|E[\bar{X}(\omega, T) \bar{Y}^*(\omega, T)]| \leq E[|\bar{X}(\omega, T) \bar{Y}^*(\omega, T)|]$$
$$= E[|\bar{X}(\omega, T)| \, |\bar{Y}(\omega, T)|] \leq E^{\frac{1}{2}}[|\bar{X}(\omega, T)|^2] E^{\frac{1}{2}}[|\bar{Y}(\omega, T)|^2] \tag{3-84}$$

Frequently a cross spectral density function can be more readily deter-mined, and the crosscorrelation function may be obtained from‡

$$R_{XY}(\tau) = \int_{-\infty}^{\infty} \Phi_{XY}(\omega) \exp(-i\omega\tau) \, d\omega \tag{3-85}$$

The following properties of spectral density and cross spectral density functions are worth noting. Firstly, a spectral density function for a real-valued weakly stationary random process must be real and even in view of Eq. (3-19) and the fact that $R_{XX}(\tau)$ is an even function. For this reason (3-19) and (3-81) may be replaced by

$$\Phi_{XX}(\omega) = \frac{1}{\pi} \int_{0}^{\infty} R_{XX}(\tau) \cos \omega\tau \, d\tau \tag{3-19a}$$

and

$$R_{XX}(\tau) = 2 \int_{0}^{\infty} \Phi_{XX}(\omega) \cos \omega\tau \, d\omega \tag{3-81a}$$

Secondly, a spectral density function is nonnegative, as noted before. Finally, as can be seen from Eq. (3-82), a spectral density function must decrease faster than ω^{-1} as ω approaches either $+\infty$ or $-\infty$ in order that the weakly stationary random process represented have a finite second moment. In contrast, a cross spectral density function is generally complex. However, it is hermitian; i.e.,

$$\Phi_{XY}(\omega) = \Phi_{XY}^*(\omega) \tag{3-86}$$

A cross spectral density function must also die down faster than ω^{-1} in order that the joint moment $E[X(t) Y(t)]$ be finite.

The concept of spectral density as described above does not apply in the case of a nonstationary random process since the autocorrelation function is no longer a function of $\tau = t_1 - t_2$. However, when the

‡ See footnote referring to Eq. (3-81).

Fourier transform of a nonstationary random process, i.e.,

$$\bar{X}(\omega) = \frac{1}{2\pi} \int_{-\infty}^{\infty} X(t) \exp(-i\omega t) \, dt \qquad (3\text{-}74)$$

exists in mean square, it is convenient to call the following expression the *generalized spectral density*‡ of $X(t)$:

$$\hat{\Phi}_{XX}(\omega_1, \omega_2) = E[\bar{X}(\omega_1)\bar{X}^*(\omega_2)] - E[\bar{X}(\omega_1)]E[\bar{X}^*(\omega_2)] \qquad (3\text{-}87)$$

Then the Fourier transform pair, Eqs. (3-75) and (3-77), may be rewritten as

$$\hat{\Phi}_{XX}(\omega_1, \omega_2)$$
$$= \frac{1}{(2\pi)^2} \int_{-\infty}^{\infty} \int_{-\infty}^{\infty} \kappa_{XX}(t_1, t_2) \exp[-i(\omega_1 t_1 - \omega_2 t_2)] \, dt_1 \, dt_2 \qquad (3\text{-}75b)$$

$$\kappa_{XX}(t_1, t_2) = \int_{-\infty}^{\infty} \int_{-\infty}^{\infty} \hat{\Phi}_{XX}(\omega_1, \omega_2) \exp[i(\omega_1 t_1 - \omega_2 t_2)] \, d\omega_1 \, d\omega_2 \qquad (3\text{-}77a)$$

These equations are analogous to the Wiener-Khintchine theorem in the stationary case. Note that $\hat{\Phi}_{XX}(\omega_1, \omega_2)$ and $\kappa_{XX}(t_1, t_2)$ are a Fourier transform pair of deterministic functions. Thus $\hat{\Phi}_{XX}(\omega_1, \omega_2)$ exists if $\kappa_{XX}(t_1, t_2)$ is absolutely integrable. Equation (3-77a) is just an abbreviated version of the Fourier transform inversion theorem. If $\kappa_{XX}(t_1, t_2)$ is at least piecewise continuous and of bounded variation, then strict equality in (3-77a) is guaranteed where $\kappa_{XX}(t_1, t_2)$ is continuous, but the right-hand side of (3-77a) converges to the average value of $\kappa_{XX}(t_1, t_2)$ where it is discontinuous. Similarly, by defining a *generalized cross spectral density*

$$\hat{\Phi}_{XY}(\omega_1, \omega_2) = E[\bar{X}(\omega_1)\bar{Y}^*(\omega_2)] - E[\bar{X}(\omega_1)]E[\bar{Y}^*(\omega_2)] \qquad (3\text{-}88)$$

if it exists, we obtain the pair

$$\hat{\Phi}_{XY}(\omega_1, \omega_2)$$
$$= \frac{1}{(2\pi)^2} \int_{-\infty}^{\infty} \int_{-\infty}^{\infty} \kappa_{XY}(t_1, t_2) \exp[-i(\omega_1 t_1 - \omega_2 t_2)] \, dt_1 \, dt_2 \qquad (3\text{-}89)$$

and

$$\kappa_{XY}(t_1, t_2) = \int_{-\infty}^{\infty} \int_{-\infty}^{\infty} \hat{\Phi}_{XY}(\omega_1, \omega_2) \exp[i(\omega_1 t_1 - \omega_2 t_2)] \, d\omega_1 \, d\omega_2 \qquad (3\text{-}90)$$

3.9 / PERIODIC RANDOM PROCESSES

A weakly stationary random process $X(t)$ is said to be *periodic in mean square* if there exists a period T such that

$$E[|X(t) - X(t + T)|^2] = 0 \qquad (3\text{-}91)$$

‡ See J. S. Bendat et al., Advanced Concepts of Stochastic Processes and Statistics for Flight Vehicle Vibration Estimation and Measurement, p. 4-7, ASD-TDR-62-973, Aeronautical Systems Division, Wright-Patterson Air Force Base, 1962. In this reference, however, the generalized spectral density is defined as $E[\bar{X}(\omega_1)\bar{X}^*(\omega_2)]$.

It follows from straightforward expansion and taking expectations that the necessary and sufficient condition for (3-91) to be true is

$$R_{XX}(0) = R_{XX}(T) < \infty \qquad (3\text{-}92)$$

Moreover, from the following form of Schwarz's inequality,

$$E^2\{X(t)[X(t+\tau) - X(t+T+\tau)]\}$$
$$\leq E[|X(t)|^2]E[|X(t+\tau) - X(t+T+\tau)|^2] \qquad (3\text{-}93)$$

we see that (3-91) implies that

$$R_{XX}(\tau) = R_{XX}(T+\tau) \qquad (3\text{-}94)$$

Therefore the autocorrelation function of a mean-square periodic random process is also periodic with the same period T.

Since a periodic autocorrelation function is *not* absolutely integrable from $-\infty$ to ∞, the power spectral density of a mean-square periodic random process does not exist in the usual sense. However, such an autocorrelation function can be expanded in a Fourier series if it is absolutely integrable and of bounded variation within each period; i.e.,

$$R_{XX}(\tau) = \sum_{n=-\infty}^{\infty} g(n\omega_0) \exp(in\omega_0\tau) \qquad \omega_0 = \frac{2\pi}{T} \qquad (3\text{-}95)$$

and

$$g(n\omega_0) = \frac{1}{T} \int_T R_{XX}(\tau) \exp(-in\omega_0\tau) \, d\tau \qquad (3\text{-}96)$$

Formally substituting (3-95) into (3-19) and interchanging the order of integration and summation, we obtain

$$\Phi_{XX}(\omega) = \sum_{n=-\infty}^{\infty} g(n\omega_0) \, \delta(\omega - n\omega_0) \qquad (3\text{-}97)$$

The inverse Fourier transform of (3-97) yields (3-95). The Wiener-Khintchine theorem is seen to be valid also for mean-square periodic random processes if the spectral density function is represented formally by an infinite number of impulses uniformly spaced at every ω_0 in the frequency domain. Note that

$$R_{XX}(0) = \int_{-\infty}^{\infty} \Phi_{XX}(\omega) \, d\omega = \sum_{n=-\infty}^{\infty} g(n\omega_0) \qquad (3\text{-}98)$$

Each term $g(n\omega_0)$, in the infinite sum, represents the contribution of a component with a frequency $n\omega_0$ to the total value of $R_{XX}(0) = E[X^2(t)]$, which is the expectation of an energy-like random quantity. For a physically realizable random process, $R_{XX}(0)$ is finite; therefore every term in the infinite sum of (3-98) is at most finite. Since the spectral density of a real-valued random process is an even function, (3-98) may be replaced by

$$R_{XX}(0) = 2 \int_0^\infty \Phi_{XX}(\omega) \, d\omega$$
$$= g(0) + 2 \sum_{n=1}^\infty g(n\omega_0)$$

$(3\text{-}98a)$

The term $g(0)$ gives the amount of expected energy contained in the zero-frequency component. The same fact is also evidenced by a constant term in the autocorrelation function.

There is a strong similarity between the two formal representations, the representation for the spectral density of a mean-square periodic random process and the representation for the probability density of a discrete random variable. The comparison suggests that we can use a *spectral distribution function* defined as

$$\Psi_{XX}(\omega) = \int_{-\infty}^\omega \Phi_{XX}(\omega') \, d\omega'$$

$(3\text{-}99)$

to characterize either a mean-square periodic or a nonperiodic weakly stationary random process or a combination of these two types.‡ However, the spectral density characterization could serve the same purpose if the Dirac delta functions were permitted to formally represent the periodic component of a weakly stationary random process.

3.10 / ERGODIC THEOREM

For the theory of random processes to be useful in practical applications we must be able to estimate the characteristics, for example, the mean and correlation functions, of a physical random process by measurements. Let $x_1(t)$, $x_2(t)$, . . . be the sample functions of a random process $X(t)$. Then the mean function $E[X(t_1)]$ is the average of $x_1(t_1)$, $x_2(t_1)$, . . . , and the correlation function $E[X(t_1)X(t_2)]$ is the average of the products $x_1(t_1)x_1(t_2)$, $x_2(t_1)x_2(t_2)$, . . . over the entire ensemble of the sample functions. When the ensemble is countably infinite or uncountable, the limited number of sample functions which can be recorded in experiments is generally inadequate to provide reliable estimates. However, if a random process is stationary, then its probabilistic structure is invariant with respect to a shift of the time origin. For such a case we may take a sufficiently long record, cut it into several shorter portions, and treat each portion separately as one part of a new sample function. The above heuristic argument suggests the possibility of estimating the mean func-

‡ The last case arises, for example, in

$$Z(t) = X(t) + Y(t)$$

where $X(t)$ and $Y(t)$ are uncorrelated weakly stationary random processes, one of which is mean-square periodic.

tion, the correlation function, and even higher-order statistical properties of a stationary random process by the following parametric averages using a long record of a sample function, say $x_1(t)$:

$$a_1 = \frac{1}{T} \int_0^T x_1(t) \, dt$$

$$b_1(\tau) = \frac{1}{T - \tau} \int_0^{T-\tau} x_1(t + \tau) x_1(t) \, dt \qquad (3\text{-}100)$$

· · · · · · · · · · · · · · · · · · · ·

where T is the length of the record. The choice of T must be such that further increase of T does not affect appreciably the values of a_1, $b_1(\tau)$, etc.

For the a_1, $b_1(\tau)$, etc., so obtained to be good estimates of the mean, the correlation function, etc., of a stationary random process, it is necessary that essentially the same results could be obtained if a different sample function, say $x_2(t)$, were used. Unfortunately, this necessity is realized only for some but not for all stationary random processes. The conditions under which the parametric averages a_1, $b_1(\tau)$, etc., regardless of the choice of a particular sample function, approach the corresponding ensemble averages as the sample length T increases are contained in the *ergodic theorem* of probability theory. In the following we shall give a brief account of this theorem as it pertains to the mean and correlation functions.

Let us begin with the parametric average a_1. Note that a_1 is just a sample point of the random variable

$$\frac{1}{T} \int_0^T X(t) \, dt \qquad (3\text{-}101)$$

This integral will be interpreted in the mean-square sense. By gradually increasing T, a sequence of random variables can be generated. The mean-square limit of such a sequence, denoted by

$$\langle X(t) \rangle_t = \underset{T \to \infty}{\text{l.i.m.}} \frac{1}{T} \int_0^T X(t) \, dt \qquad (3\text{-}102)$$

is generally a random variable. Therefore, we should expect that the sample means a_1, a_2, . . . computed from different sample functions would be generally different even if every sample function could be infinitely long. It is now clear that in order for a random process to have essentially the same sample means, we simply require that

$$\langle X(t) \rangle_t = E[X(t)] = \mu \qquad (3\text{-}103)$$

A random process $X(t)$ is said to be *ergodic in first moment* when (3-103) is true. Since $\langle X(t) \rangle_t$ is a mean-square limit, we apply the mean-square convergence criterion. In the present case this criterion states that

$$\lim_{T \to \infty} E\left[\frac{1}{T^2} \int_0^T \int_0^T X(t_1) X(t_2) \, dt_1 \, dt_2 \right] - \mu^2 = 0 \qquad (3\text{-}104)$$

Upon the interchange of the operations of expectation and mean-square integration, we have

$$\lim_{T \to \infty} \frac{1}{T^2} \int_0^T \int_0^T R_{XX}(t_1 - t_2)\, dt_1\, dt_2 - \mu^2 = 0 \tag{3-105}$$

This equation may be replaced by

$$\lim_{T \to \infty} \frac{1}{T^2} \int_0^T \int_0^T \Gamma_{XX}(t_1 - t_2)\, dt_1\, dt_2 = 0 \tag{3-106}$$

Using a procedure similar to the one leading from (3-75a) to (3-79), we obtain

$$\lim_{T \to \infty} \frac{2}{T} \int_0^T \left(1 - \frac{\tau}{T}\right) \Gamma_{XX}(\tau)\, d\tau = 0 \tag{3-107}$$

Therefore, the necessary and sufficient conditions for $X(t)$ to be ergodic in first moment are that $E[X(t)]$ be a constant, that $E[X(t + \tau)X(t)]$ be just a function of τ, and that Eq. (3-107) be satisfied. It will be shown that the requirement Eq. (3-107) can be replaced by the requirement

$$\lim_{T \to \infty} \frac{1}{T} \int_0^T \Gamma_{XX}(\tau)\, d\tau = 0 \tag{3-108}$$

that is, Eq. (3-108) implies

$$\lim_{T \to \infty} \frac{1}{T^2} \int_0^T \tau \Gamma_{XX}(\tau)\, d\tau = 0$$

The validity of the above statement can be seen by noting that, firstly,

$$\frac{1}{T^2} \int_0^T \tau \Gamma_{XX}(\tau)\, d\tau = \frac{1}{T^2} \int_0^T \Gamma_{XX}(\tau) \left(\int_0^\tau dt\right) d\tau$$
$$= \frac{1}{T} \int_0^T \left[\frac{1}{T} \int_t^T \Gamma_{XX}(\tau)\, d\tau\right] dt$$

and that, secondly, for an arbitrary t, the limit of

$$\frac{1}{T} \int_t^T \Gamma_{XX}(\tau)\, d\tau$$

must be zero as T approaches infinity, lest Eq. (3-108) be violated; and that, thirdly,

$$\frac{1}{T} \int_0^T dt = 1$$

Similarly, for a parametric average $b_1(\tau)$ computed from a sufficiently long record to be a good estimate of an autocorrelation function, we require that

$$\langle X(t + \tau)X(t) \rangle_t = R_{XX}(\tau) \tag{3-109}$$

for every τ, where

$$\langle X(t + \tau)X(t) \rangle_t = \text{l.i.m.} \frac{1}{T \to \infty} \frac{1}{T - \tau} \int_0^{T-\tau} X(t + \tau)X(t) \, dt \tag{3-110}$$

A random process $X(t)$ is said to be *ergodic in correlation* when (3-109) is true. Note that, for a given τ, the product $X(t + \tau)X(t)$ may be viewed as a new random process. Therefore, Eq. (3-109) is a restatement of Eq. (3-103) in terms of this new random process. From this viewpoint, it is clear that the necessary and sufficient conditions for $X(t)$ to be ergodic in correlation are that $E[X(t + \tau)X(t)]$ be just a function of τ, that

$$S_{XX}(\tau, u)$$
$$= E\{[X(t + \tau)X(t) - R_{XX}(\tau)][X(t + \tau + u)X(t + u) - R_{XX}(\tau)]\} \tag{3-111}$$

be independent of t, and that

$$\lim_{T \to \infty} \frac{1}{T} \int_0^T S_{XX}(\tau, u) \, du = 0 \tag{3-112}$$

That is, the ergodicity of $X(t)$ in correlation is just the ergodicity of the product process $X(t + \tau)X(t)$ in first moment. Equations (3-111) and (3-112) involve the function $S_{XX}(\tau, u)$, which is essentially the fourth moment function of $X(t)$.

More generally, if

$$\langle g[X(t), X(t + \tau_1), \ldots, X(t + \tau_n)] \rangle_t$$
$$= E\{g[X(t), X(t + \tau_1), \ldots, X(t + \tau_n)]\} \tag{3-113}$$

where n is an arbitrary integer and g a Borel function, then $X(t)$ is said to be *strictly ergodic*. A strictly ergodic random process must be strictly stationary, but the reverse may or may not be true.

EXERCISES

3-1. (a) Let

$$Y(t) = \sum_{n=1}^{N} X_n(t)$$

where all the $X_n(t)$ are jointly stationary random processes in the wide sense. Obtain the general expression for the autocorrelation function of $Y(t)$.

(b) Reduce the general expression for the special case in which the $X_n(t)$ are uncorrelated and $E[X_n(t)] = 0$ for all n.

3-2. ‡Show that if an autocorrelation function $\phi_{XX}(t, s)$, $t, s \in T$, is continuous on the diagonal $t = s$, then it is continuous over the entire product space $T \times T$.

‡ See M. Loéve, "Probability Theory," 3rd ed., p. 470, Van Nostrand, Princeton, N.J., 1963.

3-3. From the given autocorrelation functions (a) to (e), determine in each case whether $X'(t)$ exists in the sense of convergence in mean square; and if it does, determine also $R_{X'X'}(\tau)$.

(a) $R_{XX}(\tau) = \left(1 - \dfrac{a}{2}|\tau|\right) \exp\,(-a|\tau|)$ $a > 0$

(b) $R_{XX}(\tau) = \exp\,(-a\tau^2)$ $a > 0$

(c) $R_{XX}(\tau) = \dfrac{\sin\, b\tau}{\tau}$ $b > 0$

(d) $R_{XX}(\tau) = J_0(a\tau)$

(e) $R_{XX}(\tau) = \dfrac{a^2}{a^2 + \tau^2}$

3-4. Determine in each of the following cases whether the stochastic integral

$$Y(s) = \int_{-\infty}^{\infty} X(t)h(t,\,s)\,dt$$

exists in the sense of mean square.

(a) $R_{XX}(\tau) = \dfrac{a^2}{a^2 + \tau^2}$ $h(t,\,s) = \begin{cases} s - t, & s > t \\ 0, & s \le t \end{cases}$

(b) $R_{XX}(\tau) = \exp\,(-a|\tau|)$ $a > 0$ $h(t,\,s) = \begin{cases} (s - t)^{\frac{1}{2}}, & s > t \\ 0, & s \le t \end{cases}$

3-5. Two random processes $X(t)$ and $Y(t)$ are independent, and both are weakly stationary.

(a) Find the general expression for the spectral density of $Z(t) = X(t)Y(t)$ in terms of the spectral densities of $X(t)$ and $Y(t)$.

(b) Apply the general expression to the special case where

$R_{XX}(\tau) = A^2 \exp\,(-a|\tau|)$
$R_{YY}(\tau) = B^2 \cos\,(b\tau)$

3-6. Specify the admissible values for the parameters in the following autocorrelation functions so that the associated weakly stationary random processes are physically realizable.

(a) $|\tau|^{-a}$ (b) $\dfrac{\cosh\,(b\tau)}{\cosh\,(\pi\tau)}$ (c) $\dfrac{\sinh\,(c\tau)}{\sinh\,(\pi\tau)}$

3-7. Show that the following autocorrelation functions are not realistic.

(a) $R_{XX}(\tau) = \begin{cases} A^2(1 - \tau^2)^p & -1 < \tau < 1,\, p > \dfrac{-3}{2} \\ 0 & \text{otherwise} \end{cases}$

(b) $R_{XX}(\tau) = A^2[\cos\,(\tau^2) \pm \sin\,(\tau^2)]$

(c) $R_{XX}(\tau) = \dfrac{A^2}{1 + \tau^4}$

3-8. Show that the random process $X(t) = a \sin\,(\omega t + Y)$ is ergodic in first moment as well as in correlation, where a and ω are constants and Y is a random variable with

$$pr(y) = \dfrac{1}{2\pi}   0 \le y < 2\pi$$

4 | GAUSSIAN, POISSON, AND MARKOV RANDOM PROCESSES

Previously we classified a random process to be either discretely or continuously valued, discretely or continuously parametered, singly or multiply parametered, homogeneous or inhomogeneous. So far we have postponed a detailed discussion of probability laws or distributions which describe more fully the random nature of the different processes. Indeed, random processes may be better classified according to their probability distributions. In this chapter we shall give a brief account of the probability laws of Gauss, Poisson, and Markov. They are frequently encountered in the study of physical phenomena.

4.1 / GAUSSIAN DISTRIBUTION AND CENTRAL LIMIT THEOREM

A random variable X is said to be *Gaussian distributed* if its probability density can be written in the form

$$p_X(x) = \frac{1}{\sqrt{2\pi}\,\sigma} \exp\left[-\frac{(x-\mu)^2}{2\sigma^2}\right] \qquad -\infty < x < \infty \qquad (4\text{-}1)$$

The graphs of two particular Gaussian probability densities corresponding to different pairs of values of μ and σ are plotted in Fig. 4.1. It can be shown that the constants μ and σ are the mean and the standard deviation of X, respectively, and that these constants completely characterize a Gaussian random variable. The name *unit Gaussian random variable* refers to the special case for which $\mu = 0$ and $\sigma = 1$.

Fig. 4.1 Gaussian probability densities.

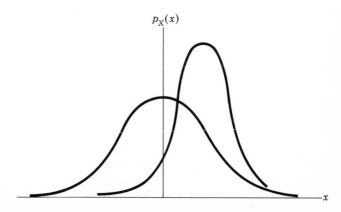

$p_X(x)$

x

An alternative definition of a Gaussian random variable is that it has a characteristic function of the form

$$M_X(\theta) = \exp\left(i\mu\theta - \frac{\sigma^2\theta^2}{2}\right) \tag{4-2}$$

or a log-characteristic function of the form

$$\ln M_X(\theta) = i\mu\theta - \frac{\sigma^2\theta^2}{2} \tag{4-2a}$$

Equations (4-1) and (4-2) are Fourier transform pairs.

One of the reasons that the Gaussian random variables are often assumed in analyses of physical phenomena is the following theorem:

The Central Limit Theorem: The sum of independent random variables

$$S_n = \sum_{k=1}^{n} X_k$$

when centralized and normalized to a zero mean and a unit standard deviation, tends to the unit Gaussian random variable as n tends to infinity, regardless of the individual distributions of the X_k, provided that the following conditions hold:

$$E[|X_k|] < \infty \qquad E\{|X_k - E[X_k]|^{2+\delta}\} < \infty \tag{4-3}$$

and

$$\lim_{n \to \infty} (\sigma_{S_n})^{-(2+\delta)} \sum_{k=1}^{n} E\{|X_k - E[X_k]|^{2+\delta}\} = 0 \tag{4-4}$$

where $\delta > 0$ and

$$\sigma_{S_n}^2 = \sum_{k=1}^{n} \sigma_{X_k}^2$$

is the variance of the sum.

Equation (4-4) is known as *Lyapunov's condition.*

The proof of the central limit theorem can be effected by a determination of the log-characteristic function of the centralized and normalized S_n, that is,

$$U_n = \frac{S_n - E[S_n]}{\sigma_{S_n}} = \frac{\sum_{k=1}^{n} \{X_k - E[X_k]\}}{\sigma_{S_n}}$$

The characteristic function of U_n is

$$M_{U_n}(\theta) = E[\exp(i\theta U_n)]$$

$$= E\left[\exp\left(i\theta \frac{\sum_{k=1}^{n}\{X_k - E[X_k]\}}{\sigma_{S_n}}\right)\right]$$

$$= E\left[\prod_{k=1}^{n}\exp\left(\frac{i\theta\{X_k - E[X_k]\}}{\sigma_{S_n}}\right)\right]$$

$$= \prod_{k=1}^{n} E\left[\exp\left(\frac{i\theta\{X_k - E[X_k]\}}{\sigma_{S_n}}\right)\right] \tag{4-5}$$

The interchange of the order of multiplication and expectation in the last line in (4-5) follows from the independence of the X_k.   Let

$$Y_k = \{X_k - E[X_k]\}/\sigma_{S_n}$$

Equation (4-5) is then abbreviated as

$$M_{U_n}(\theta) = \prod_{k=1}^{n} M_{Y_k}(\theta) \tag{4-5a}$$

Thus

$$\ln M_{U_n}(\theta) = \sum_{k=1}^{n} \ln M_{Y_k}(\theta) \tag{4-6}$$

Since $E[Y_k] = 0$ and $E[Y_k^2] < \infty$, we have the equality

$$M_{Y_k}(\theta) = 1 - r \tag{4-7}$$

where

$$r = \tfrac{1}{2}\theta^2 E[Y_k^2] + \theta^2 \int_0^1 (1 - t)E\{Y_k^2[\exp(it\theta Y_k) - 1]\}\,dt \tag{4-8}$$

The validity of (4-7) can be verified by carrying out the integration in (4-8).   The value for r depends, of course, on the value chosen for θ. Since $|\exp(it\theta Y_k) - 1| \leq 2$, it can be shown that

$$|r| \leq \tfrac{3}{2}\theta^2 E[Y_k^2] \tag{4-9}$$

But $E[Y_k^2] = E\{|X_k - E[X_k]|^2\}/\sigma_{S_n}^2$ decreases as n increases.   Therefore, it is always possible to choose an n sufficiently large that $3\theta^2 E[Y_k^2] \leq 1$. Then $|r| \leq \tfrac{1}{2}$.   For such a value of r

$$\ln M_{Y_k}(\theta) = \ln(1 - r) = -r\int_0^1 \frac{dt}{1 - rt}$$

$$= -r - r^2\int_0^1 \frac{t}{1 - rt}\,dt \tag{4-10}$$

Moreover,

$$\left| \int_0^1 \frac{t}{1 - rt} \, dt \right| \le \int_0^1 \frac{t}{|1 - rt|} \, dt \le \int_0^1 2t \, dt = 1 \tag{4-11}$$

Therefore,

$$\ln M_{Y_k}(\theta) = -\tfrac{1}{2}\theta^2 E[Y_k^2] - \theta^2 \int_0^1 (1 - t)E\left\{Y_k^2[\exp(it\theta Y_k) - 1]\right\} dt$$
$$+ \alpha\theta^4 E^2[Y_k^2] \tag{4-12}$$

where α is a complex number with a finite modulus, that is, $|\alpha| < \infty$. Now for any real quantity w, and for $0 \le \delta \le 1$,

$$|\exp(iw) - 1| = \sqrt{2}\sqrt{1 - \cos w} \le 2|w|^\delta.$$

Consequently,

$$\left| \int_0^1 (1 - t)E\{Y_k^2[\exp(it\theta Y_k) - 1]\} \, dt \right|$$
$$\le 2|\theta|^\delta E[|Y_k|^{2+\delta}] \int_0^1 t^\delta(1 - t) \, dt \tag{4-13}$$

Equation (4-12) can be rewritten as

$$\ln M_{Y_k}(\theta) = -\tfrac{1}{2}\theta^2 E[Y_k^2] + \beta|\theta|^{2+\delta}E[|Y_k|^{2+\delta}] + \alpha\theta^4 E^2[Y_k^2]$$
$$|\alpha|, |\beta| < \infty \tag{4-14}$$

Substituting (4-14) into (4-6) and noting that

$$\sum_{k=1}^n E[Y_k^2] = 1$$

we obtain

$$\ln M_{U_n}(\theta) = -\tfrac{1}{2}\theta^2 + \beta|\theta|^{2+\delta} \sum_{k=1}^n E[|Y_k|^{2+\delta}] + \alpha\theta^4 \sum_{k=1}^n E^2[Y_k^2] \tag{4-15}$$

According to condition (4-4),

$$\sum_{k=1}^n E[|Y_k|^{2+\delta}] = \sigma_{S_n}^{-(2+\delta)} \sum_{k=1}^n E\{|X_k - E[X_k]|^{2-\delta}\}$$

which tends to zero as n increases. Since $E[Y_k^2] \le 1$,‡

$$E^2[Y_k^2] = \left(\frac{\sigma_{X_k}}{\sigma_{S_n}}\right)^4 \le \left(\frac{\sigma_{X_k}}{\sigma_{S_n}}\right)^{2+\delta} \le \frac{E\{|X_k - E[X_k]|^{2+\delta}\}}{\sigma_{S_n}^{(2+\delta)}} \tag{4-16}$$

‡ In obtaining (4-16) use has been made of the inequality

$$E^a[|Z|^b] \le E[|Z|^{ab}] \qquad a > 1$$

This inequality follows directly from Jensen's inequality.

Therefore,

$$\lim_{n \to \infty} M_{U_n}(\theta) = -\tfrac{1}{2}\theta^2 \tag{4-17}$$

which is the log-characteristic function of a unit Gaussian random variable. The central limit theorem is thus proved.

Clearly, the original sum S_n tends to a Gaussian random variable with a mean

$$\mu = \lim_{n \to \infty} E[S_n] = \lim_{n \to \infty} \sum_{k=1}^{n} E[X_k] \tag{4-18}$$

and a variance

$$\sigma^2 = \lim_{n \to \infty} \sigma_{S_n}{}^2 = \lim_{n \to \infty} \sum_{k=1}^{n} \sigma_{X_k}{}^2 \tag{4-19}$$

provided that these limits exist. This observation justifies the assumption of a Gaussian distribution of a physical phenomenon if the phenomenon is a consequence of many independent causes of random nature and if none of the individual causes contributes significantly‡ to the overall behavior of the phenomenon.

4.2 / PROPERTIES OF GAUSSIAN RANDOM VARIABLES

Another reason for the appeal of Gaussian random variables to engineers and scientists is their simple mathematical properties. The most important one is that the class of Gaussian random variables is closed under linear operations; i.e., linear functions of Gaussian random variables remain Gaussian distributed. This property was demonstrated in Exercises 2-2 and 2-3, in which it was shown that $a + bX$ is Gaussian if X is and that $aX_1 + bX_2$ is Gaussian if both X_1 and X_2 are.

The second important property of a Gaussian random variable is the simple relation between the moments of various orders. Let U be a unit Gaussian random variable; then the nth moment of U is

$$E[U^n] = \int_{-\infty}^{\infty} u^n \frac{1}{\sqrt{2\pi}} \exp\left(\frac{-u^2}{2}\right) du \tag{4-20}$$

It is seen that

$$E[U^n] = 0 \qquad \text{for odd } n \tag{4-21}$$

since the integrand in (4-20) is then an odd function. For even n, (4-20) can be evaluated by successive integrations by parts, resulting in

$$E[U^n] = 1 \cdot 3 \cdot 5 \cdots (n-1) = 2^{n/2} \pi^{-\frac{1}{2}} \Gamma\left(\frac{n+1}{2}\right) \qquad \text{for even } n \tag{4-22}$$

‡ A physical counterpart of Lyapunov's condition.

A Gaussian random variable X with a mean μ and a standard deviation σ can be constructed from the linear relation

$$X = \sigma U + \mu$$

The central moments of X are simply

$$
\begin{aligned}
E[(X - \mu)^n] &= E[(\sigma U)^n] \\
&= \sigma^n E[U^n] \\
&= \begin{cases} 0 & n = \text{odd} \\ 2^{n/2}\pi^{-\frac{1}{2}}\sigma^n\Gamma\left(\dfrac{n+1}{2}\right) & n = \text{even} \end{cases}
\end{aligned}
\qquad (4\text{-}23)
$$

If $(X - \mu)^n$ is expanded and its expectation is taken, we have

$$E[(X - \mu)^n] = E[X^n] - n\mu E[X^{n-1}]$$
$$+ \frac{n(n-1)}{2!}\,\mu^2 E[X^{n-2}] + \cdots + (-1)^n\mu \qquad (4\text{-}24)$$

Equating (4-23) and (4-24) for $n = 1, 2, \ldots$, we obtain successive equations from which $E[X^n]$ may be determined. However, this method of obtaining $E[X^n]$ is not the most efficient. A more direct way is to differentiate the characteristic function successively and let $\theta = 0$. The result of such a procedure is

$$E[X^n] = \mu E[X^{n-1}] + (n-1)\sigma^2 E[X^{n-2}] \qquad (4\text{-}25)$$

The verification of Eq. (4-25) is left as an exercise at the end of this chapter. From Eq. (4-23) or Eq. (4-25) we see that a Gaussian random variable is completely defined by its mean and its variance. Such a conclusion also can be reached from the fact that the probability density function, or the characteristic function, or the log-characteristic function of a Gaussian random variable depends on μ and σ only.

Besides Eqs. (4-1), (4-2), and (4-2a), other alternative ways are possible by which a Gaussian random variable can be defined because of the remarkable fact that the characteristic function of a random variable can be expanded in terms of the moments of various orders and that the log-characteristic function can be expanded in terms of the cumulants of various orders if such expansions converge. A Gaussian random variable may also be defined as one whose central moments are related according to Eq. (4-23), as one whose moments are related according to Eq. (4-25), or as one whose cumulants of an order higher than 2 are zero. The last alternative definition, which may be made clear by a comparison of Eq. (2-74) and Eq. (4-2a), is especially concise.

4.3 / JOINTLY DISTRIBUTED GAUSSIAN RANDOM VARIABLES

Two random variables X and Y are said to be jointly Gaussian distributed if they are defined by the joint probability density function

$$p_{XY}(x, y) = \frac{1}{2\pi\sigma_X\sigma_Y \sqrt{1 - \rho_{XY}^2}}$$
$$\exp\left[-\frac{\sigma_Y^2(x - \mu_X)^2 - 2\sigma_X\sigma_Y\rho_{XY}(x - \mu_X)(y - \mu_Y) + \sigma_X^2(y - \mu_Y)}{2\sigma_X^2\sigma_Y^2(1 - \rho_{XY}^2)} \right]$$
$$-\infty < x, y < \infty \quad (4\text{-}26)$$

This joint density function is illustrated in Fig. 4.2. Straightforward integrations will show that

$$E[X] = \mu_X$$
$$E[Y] = \mu_Y$$
$$E[(X - \mu_X)^2] = \sigma_X^2 \qquad\qquad (4\text{-}27)$$
$$E[(Y - \mu_Y)^2] = \sigma_Y^2$$
$$E[(X - \mu_X)(Y - \mu_Y)] = \sigma_X\sigma_Y\rho_{XY}$$

Thus the five parameters involved in the joint density function (4-26) are the expected values given by (4-27). More generally, consider n random

Fig. 4.2 Probability density function of two jointly distributed Gaussian random variables.

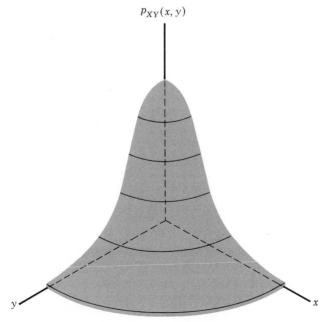

$p_{XY}(x, y)$

y

x

variables X_1, X_2, . . . , X_n with the expected values $E[X_j] = \mu_{X_j}$, where $j = 1, 2, . . . , n$, and the covariances $E[(X_j - \mu_{X_j})(X_k - \mu_{X_k})] = \kappa_{X_j X_k}$, where $j, k = 1, 2, . . . , n$. These random variables are said to be jointly Gaussian distributed if their joint probability density function is given by

$$p_{X_1 X_2 \cdots X_n}(x_1, x_2, . . . , x_n)$$

$$= \frac{1}{(2\pi)^{n/2}|S|^{\frac{1}{2}}} \exp\left[-\frac{1}{2|S|} \sum_{j=1}^{n} \sum_{k=1}^{n} |S|_{jk}(x_j - \mu_{X_j})(x_k - \mu_{X_k}) \right] \quad (4\text{-}28)$$

where $|S|$ is the determinant of the matrix of covariances and variances, i.e.,

$$S = \begin{bmatrix} \sigma_{X_1}^2 & \kappa_{X_1 X_2} & \cdots & \kappa_{X_1 X_n} \\ \kappa_{X_2 X_1} & \sigma_{X_2}^2 & \cdots & \kappa_{X_2 X_n} \\ \cdot \cdot \cdot \cdot \cdot \cdot \cdot \cdot \cdot \cdot \cdot \cdot \cdot \\ \kappa_{X_n X_1} & \kappa_{X_n X_2} & \cdots & \sigma_{X_n}^2 \end{bmatrix} \quad (4\text{-}29)$$

and $|S|_{jk}$ is the cofactor of the element in the jth row and the kth column of **S**. Here we have tacitly assumed that $|S| \neq 0$. It is seen that Eq. (4-28) reduces to (4-26) for $n = 2$.

Equation (4-28) may be also written

$$p_\mathbf{X}(\mathbf{x}) = \frac{1}{(2\pi)^{n/2}|S|^{\frac{1}{2}}} \exp\left[-\tfrac{1}{2}\{\mathbf{x} - \mathbf{\mu_X}\}'S^{-1}\{\mathbf{x} - \mu_\mathbf{X}\}\right] \quad (4\text{-}28a)$$

where $\{\mathbf{x} - \mathbf{\mu_X}\}$ is the column matrix with the elements $x_j - \mu_{X_j}$, $j = 1$, $2, . . . , n$; and the prime indicates transposition. Note also that $S = E[\{\mathbf{X} - \mathbf{\mu_X}\}\{\mathbf{X} - \mathbf{\mu_X}\}']$. In this notation, we regard X_1, X_2, . . . , X_n as the components of an n-dimensional random vector **X**, with a mathematical expectation $\mathbf{\mu_X}$. The argument of the multidimensional probability density function (4-28a) is the state vector **x**.

Consider another n-dimensional random vector **Y** which is derived from **X** through the following linear transformation:

$$\mathbf{Y} = \mathbf{AX} \quad (4\text{-}30)$$

For the moment we shall assume that the square matrix **A** is nonsingular; therefore $\mathbf{A}^{-1}$ exists, and

$$\mathbf{X} = \mathbf{A}^{-1}\mathbf{Y} \quad (4\text{-}31)$$

The state vectors **x** and **y** are related in the same way; i.e.,

$$\mathbf{y} = \mathbf{Ax} \qquad \mathbf{x} = \mathbf{A}^{-1}\mathbf{y} \quad (4\text{-}32)$$

Since $\mathbf{A}^{-1}$ is a matrix of constants, by taking the expectation on both sides of (4-31) we have

$$\pmb{\mu}_{\mathbf{X}} = \mathbf{A}^{-1}\pmb{\mu}_{\mathbf{Y}} \tag{4-33}$$

where $\pmb{\mu}_{\mathbf{Y}}$ is the mathematical expectation of $\mathbf{Y}$. The n-dimensional probability density function of $\mathbf{Y}$ can now be obtained by using Eq. (2-46) and the relations (4-32) and (4-33):

$$p_{\mathbf{Y}}(\mathbf{y}) = \frac{1}{(2\pi)^{n/2}|S|^{\frac{1}{2}}} \exp\left[-\tfrac{1}{2}\{\mathbf{y} - \pmb{\mu}_{\mathbf{Y}}\}'(\mathbf{A}^{-1})'\mathbf{S}^{-1}\mathbf{A}^{-1}\{\mathbf{y} - \pmb{\mu}_{\mathbf{Y}}\}\right]|J_n| \tag{4-34}$$

It is easily seen that the Jacobian of the transformation, J_n, is the determinant of the matrix $\mathbf{A}^{-1}$; that is,

$$J_n = |A^{-1}| \tag{4-35}$$

Furthermore, since the covariance matrix $\mathbf{S}$ is symmetrical for real random variables, it is always possible to find a square matrix $\mathbf{C}$ such that

$$\begin{aligned}\mathbf{CSC}' &= \mathbf{\Lambda} \\ \mathbf{C}' &= \mathbf{C}^{-1}\end{aligned} \tag{4-36}$$

where $\mathbf{\Lambda}$ is the diagonal matrix of the latent roots of $\mathbf{S}$. A matrix $\mathbf{C}$ which satisfies the conditions given in (4-36) is called an *orthogonal matrix*. These conditions are met by the normalized modal matrix of $\mathbf{S}$, that is,

$$\mathbf{C} = \mathbf{K}_r \tag{4-37}$$

where the rows in $\mathbf{K}_r$ are the modal rows of $\mathbf{S}$ each of which is normalized to have a unit amplitude. The first equation in (4-36) may be inverted to give

$$\mathbf{CS}^{-1}\mathbf{C}' = \mathbf{\Lambda}^{-1} \tag{4-38}$$

Furthermore, since $\mathbf{C}$ is an orthogonal matrix,

$$|C| = |C'| = |C^{-1}| = 1 \tag{4-39}$$

If the transformation matrix $\mathbf{A}$ is chosen to be $\mathbf{C}$, then the probability density function for $\mathbf{Y}$, Eq. (4-34), reduces to

$$p_{\mathbf{Y}}(\mathbf{y}) = \frac{1}{(2\pi)^{n/2}|\Lambda|^{\frac{1}{2}}} \exp\left[-\tfrac{1}{2}\{\mathbf{y} - \pmb{\mu}_{\mathbf{Y}}\}'\mathbf{\Lambda}^{-1}\{\mathbf{y} - \pmb{\mu}_{\mathbf{Y}}\}\right] \tag{4-40}$$

where use is made of the relation $|\mathbf{CSC}'| = |C|\,|S|\,|C'| = |\Lambda|$, or simply $|S| = |\Lambda|$. It may be noted that $\mathbf{\Lambda}^{-1}$ is also a diagonal matrix and that the diagonal elements of $\mathbf{\Lambda}^{-1}$ are the reciprocals of those in $\mathbf{\Lambda}$. If matrix notation is not used, Eq. (4-40) may be written as

$$p_{Y_1Y_2\cdots Y_n}(y_1, y_2, \ldots, y_n)$$

$$= \frac{1}{(2\pi)^{n/2}\sqrt{\lambda_1\lambda_2\cdots\lambda_n}} \exp\left[-\frac{1}{2}\sum_{j=1}^{n}\frac{1}{\lambda_j}(y_j - \mu_{Y_j})^2\right]$$

$$= \prod_{j=1}^{n}\frac{1}{\sqrt{2\pi\lambda_j}}\exp\left[-\frac{(y_j - \mu_{Y_j})^2}{2\lambda_j}\right]$$

$$= \prod_{j=1}^{n} p_{Y_j}(y_j) \qquad\qquad (4\text{-}40a)$$

where λ_j are the diagonal elements in $\boldsymbol{\Lambda}$, that is, the corresponding latent roots of $\mathbf{S}$. Equation (4-40a) shows that $Y_1, Y_2, \ldots, Y_n$ are independent random variables, each of which is Gaussian distributed. The foregoing derivation has shown that *mutually dependent random variables which are jointly Gaussian distributed can be linearly transformed to independent Gaussian random variables* provided that the covariance matrix is nonsingular, that is, $|S| \neq 0$. We shall take up the case where $|S| = 0$ later in this section. In passing we observe the remarkable fact that the joint probability density of Gaussian random variables always has the same form when expressed in a matrix notation, Eq. (4-28a) or Eq. (4-40), regardless of whether the random variables are independent or not.

The characteristic function of an n-dimensional Gaussian random vector can be easily obtained if the components of the random vector are independent, i.e., if the joint density function is given by Eq. (4-40a). The n-dimensional Fourier transfer of (4-40a) is

$$M_{Y_1Y_2\cdots Y_n}(\theta_1, \theta_2, \ldots, \theta_n) = \exp\left[\sum_{j=1}^{n}\left(i\mu_{Y_j}\theta_j - \frac{\lambda_j\theta_j^2}{2}\right)\right] \qquad (4\text{-}41)$$

or, vectorially,

$$M_{\mathbf{Y}}(\boldsymbol{\theta}) = \exp\left(i\boldsymbol{\mu}_Y'\boldsymbol{\theta} - \tfrac{1}{2}\boldsymbol{\theta}'\boldsymbol{\Lambda}\boldsymbol{\theta}\right) \qquad (4\text{-}41a)$$

The characteristic function of $\mathbf{X}$ which has dependent random components can be obtained in a few simple steps as follows. Substitute $\boldsymbol{\mu}_Y = \mathbf{C}\boldsymbol{\mu}_X$ into Eq. (4-41a) and let $\boldsymbol{\theta} = \mathbf{C}\boldsymbol{\psi}$:

$$M_{\mathbf{Y}}(\boldsymbol{\theta}) = M_{\mathbf{X}}(\boldsymbol{\psi}) = \exp\left(i\boldsymbol{\mu}_X'\boldsymbol{\psi} - \tfrac{1}{2}\boldsymbol{\psi}'\mathbf{C}'\boldsymbol{\Lambda}\mathbf{C}\boldsymbol{\psi}\right) \qquad (4\text{-}42)$$

Using the first equation in (4-36),

$$M_{\mathbf{X}}(\boldsymbol{\psi}) = \exp\left(i\boldsymbol{\mu}_X'\boldsymbol{\psi} - \tfrac{1}{2}\boldsymbol{\psi}'\mathbf{S}\boldsymbol{\psi}\right) \qquad (4\text{-}43)$$

or, in nonmatrix notation,

$$M_{X_1 X_2 \ldots X_n}(\psi_1, \psi_2, \ldots, \psi_n)$$

$$= \exp\left(i \sum_{j=1}^{n} \mu_{X_j}\psi_j - \frac{1}{2} \sum_{j=1}^{n} \sum_{k=1}^{n} \kappa_{X_j X_k}\psi_j\psi_k \right) \qquad (4\text{-}43a)$$

We observe also that the joint characteristic functions, Eqs. (4-41a) and (4-43), for independent and dependent Gaussian random variables, respectively, have the same form in matrix notation. The apparent similarity is lost in a nonmatrix notation, Eq. (4-41) or Eq. (4-43a).

The special form of the joint characteristic function, Eq. (4-43), or the natural logarithm of this function, can be used as an alternative definition for jointly distributed Gaussian random variables. In fact, this alternative definition is more general than the definition by the joint probability density since it applies even when **S** is singular. If **S** is singular and of a rank $r < n$, then there are exactly r nonzero latent roots and $n - r$ zero latent roots. Such a singular matrix may be considered as the limit of a sequence of nonsingular matrices $\mathbf{S}_k$ in which $n - r$ latent roots tend to zero as k approaches infinity. An examination of Eq. (4-40a) reveals that each latent root represents the variance of a random variable after a linear transformation; and in view of Chebyshev's inequality, a sequence of variances approaching to zero implies that the corresponding sequence of random variables approaches to a constant in probability. Therefore, when $n - r$ latent roots of a covariance matrix are zero, the probability measure is distributed within an r-dimensional subspace of the n-dimensional space. The same conclusion is reached if the Fourier transformation is taken of Eq. (4-41) with

$$\lambda_1 = \lambda_2 = \cdots = \lambda_{n-r} = 0$$

and with the use of a special form of the Dirac delta function, Eq. (V-7), Appendix V. Then

$$p_{Y_1 Y_2 \ldots Y_n}(y_1, y_2, \ldots, y_n)$$

$$= \prod_{j=1}^{n-r} \delta(y_j - \mu_{Y_j}) \prod_{k=n-r+1}^{n} \frac{1}{\sqrt{2\pi\lambda_k}} \exp\left[-\frac{(y_k - \mu_{Y_k})^2}{2\lambda_k} \right] \qquad (4\text{-}44)$$

The interesting properties of the Gaussian random variables discussed in Sec. 4.2 can be generalized to the case of Gaussian random vectors. That the class of Gaussian random vectors is closed under linear operations has, in fact, been shown in the above treatment of probability densities and characteristic functions when the mapping is n-dimensional on n-dimensional. The validity of this statement in linear operations involving different sample-space dimensions is left as an exercise at the end of this chapter.

The joint moment of a higher order of the components of a Gaussian random vector can also be expressed in terms of the joint moments of lower orders. Consider the nth joint moment $E[X_1 X_2 \cdots X_n]$, which may be computed by differentiating the characteristic function $M_{\mathbf{X}}(\psi)$. For simplicity we assume that $E[X_j] = 0$, $j = 1, 2, \ldots, n$. Thus the joint moment is the same as the joint central moment, and the characteristic function simplifies to

$$M_{\mathbf{X}}(\psi) = \exp [Q] \tag{4-45}$$

where

$$Q = \frac{-1}{2} \sum_{j=1}^{n} \sum_{k=1}^{n} E[X_j X_k] \psi_j \psi_k \tag{4-46}$$

Note that

$$\frac{\partial Q}{\partial \psi_j} = - \sum_{k=1}^{n} E[X_j X_k] \psi_k$$

$$\frac{\partial^2 Q}{\partial \psi_k \, \partial \psi_j} = - E[X_j X_k] \tag{4-47}$$

$$\frac{\partial^3 Q}{\partial \psi_l \, \partial \psi_k \, \partial \psi_j} = 0$$

Successive differentiations of (4-45) yield

$$\frac{\partial}{\partial \psi_j} M_{\mathbf{X}} = M_{\mathbf{X}} \frac{\partial Q}{\partial \psi_j}$$

$$\frac{\partial^2}{\partial \psi_k \, \partial \psi_j} M_{\mathbf{X}} = \frac{\partial M_{\mathbf{X}}}{\partial \psi_k} \frac{\partial Q}{\partial \psi_j} + M_{\mathbf{X}} \frac{\partial^2 Q}{\partial \psi_k \, \partial \psi_j}$$

$$\frac{\partial^3}{\partial \psi_l \, \partial \psi_k \, \partial \psi_j} M_{\mathbf{X}} = \frac{\partial^2 M_{\mathbf{X}}}{\partial \psi_l \, \partial \psi_k} \frac{\partial Q}{\partial \psi_j} + \frac{\partial M_{\mathbf{X}}}{\partial \psi_k} \frac{\partial^2 Q}{\partial \psi_l \, \partial \psi_j} + \frac{\partial M_{\mathbf{X}}}{\partial \psi_l} \frac{\partial^2 Q}{\partial \psi_k \, \partial \psi_j} \tag{4-48}$$

$$\cdots \cdots \cdots \cdots \cdots \cdots \cdots \cdots \cdots \cdots$$

$$\frac{\partial^n}{\partial \psi_1 \, \partial \psi_2 \cdots \partial \psi_n} M_{\mathbf{X}} = \frac{\partial^{n-1} M_{\mathbf{X}}}{\partial \psi_1 \partial \psi_2 \cdots \partial \psi_{j-1} \, \partial \psi_{j+1} \cdots \partial \psi_n} \frac{\partial Q}{\partial \psi_j}$$

$$+ \sum_k \frac{\partial^{n-2} M_{\mathbf{X}}}{\partial \psi_{r_1} \, \partial \psi_{r_2} \cdots \partial \psi_{r_{n-2}}} \frac{\partial^2 Q}{\partial \psi_k \, \partial \psi_j}$$

In the last of Eqs. (4-48), the sequence $r_1, r_2, \ldots, r_{n-2}$ does not include the two numbers k and j; and the summation over k does not include $k = j$.

The moments of various orders are obtained by letting

$$\psi_1 = \psi_2 = \cdots = \psi_n = 0$$

in (4-48). It suffices to investigate the last equation of (4-48) since it can be specialized to $n = 1, 2, 3, \ldots$. From (4-47), by noting that

$$\left(\frac{\partial Q}{\partial \psi_j}\right)_{\psi = 0} = 0$$

the last equation in (4-48) leads to

$$E[X_1 X_2 \cdots X_n] = \sum_k E[X_{r_1} X_{r_2} \cdots X_{r_{n-2}}] E[X_k X_j] \qquad (4\text{-}49)$$

Beyond the trivial cases $n = 1$ and $n = 2$, by letting $n = 3, 4, \ldots$, we have

$$E[X_1 X_2 X_3] = E[X_3] E[X_2 X_1] = 0$$
$$E[X_1 X_2 X_3 X_4] = \sum_{k = 2,3,4} E[X_{r_1} X_{r_2}] E[X_k X_1] = E[X_1 X_2] E[X_3 X_4]$$
$$+ E[X_1 X_3] E[X_2 X_4] + E[X_1 X_4] E[X_2 X_3]$$

$\cdot\ \cdot$

In general,

$$E[X_1 X_2 \cdots X_{2m+1}] = 0$$
$$E[X_1 X_2 \cdots X_{2m}] = \Sigma E[X_j X_k] E[X_r X_s] \cdots \qquad (4\text{-}50)$$

where the sum in the second equation of (4-50) is to be taken over all different ways by which we can group $2m$ elements into m pairs. Equations (4-50) have been derived under the assumption that the expected value of each of the jointly distributed random variables is zero; otherwise they apply to central joint moments.

The number of terms N included in the summation in the second equation of (4-50) may be determined in the following way. We note first that the total permutations of the $2m$ numbers are $(2m)!$ and $N < (2m)!$ since the sum does not include identical terms. Secondly, for each term in the sum, permutations of the m factors result in identical ways of breaking up the $2m$ elements. Thirdly, since $E[X_j X_k] = E[X_k X_j]$, an interchange of the order in such a pair does not yield a new pair. Thus

$$N(m!)(2^m) = (2m)!$$

or

$$N = (2m)!/m!2^m \qquad (4\text{-}51)$$

We remark that Eqs. (4-50) may be used to compute the joint moments of the type $E[X_j^n X_k^m \cdots X_l^r]$. For example,

$$E[X_1 X_2 X_3^2] = E[X_1 X_2]E[X_3^2] + 2E[X_1 X_3]E[X_2 X_3]$$

where the substitution is made for $X_4 = X_3$.

Relations (4-50) are unique Gaussian properties. Instead, a statement of these relations is an alternative definition for jointly distributed Gaussian random variables. Still another alternative definition is based on the fact that cumulants and joint cumulants of an order higher than 2 are equal to zero if and only if the random variables in question are jointly Gaussian distributed. This is evident from a comparison of the log-characteristic function of jointly distributed Gaussian random variables, viz.,

$$\ln M_{\mathbf{X}}(\boldsymbol{\psi}) = i\boldsymbol{\mu}_{\mathbf{X}}'\boldsymbol{\psi} - \tfrac{1}{2}\boldsymbol{\psi}'\mathbf{S}\boldsymbol{\psi}$$

$$= i\sum_{j=1}^{n} \mu_{X_j}\psi_j - \tfrac{1}{2}\sum_{j=1}^{n}\sum_{k=1}^{n} \kappa_{X_j X_k}\psi_j\psi_k \qquad (4\text{-}52)$$

and the expansion Eq. (2-80). If, in addition, all the second-order joint cumulants are also zero, i.e., if the Gaussian random variables are uncorrelated, then the double sum in Eq. (4-52) becomes a single sum, which, in turn, implies that the random variables are independent. Therefore the relations among Gaussian random variables are completely described in the covariance matrix, and being uncorrelated is both necessary and sufficient for being independent for Gaussian random variables.

The last statement can be further developed by rewriting Eq. (4-28) as follows:

$$p_{X_1 \cdots X_n}(x_1, \ldots, x_n) = \frac{1}{(2\pi)^{n/2}|S|^{\frac{1}{2}}} \exp\left[-\tfrac{1}{2}\sum_{j=1}^{n} \alpha_{jj}(x_j - \mu_{X_j})^2\right]$$

$$\exp\left[-\tfrac{1}{2}\sum_{\substack{j,k=1 \\ j \neq k}}^{n} \alpha_{jk}(x_j - \mu_{X_j})(x_k - \mu_{X_k})\right] \qquad (4\text{-}28b)$$

where $\alpha_{jk} = |S|^{-1}|S|_{jk}$ is the (j,k) element of the matrix $\mathbf{S}^{-1}$. The second exponential function in Eq. (4-28b) may be considered as a correction factor converting an independent distribution to a dependent distribution. It is entirely feasible that this exponential function can be expanded into a convergent series, and each partial sum of the series gives an approximation of such a correction factor. However, since it is desirable for an expansion to be orthogonal we shall indirectly pursue this matter from a consideration of the characteristic function. For convenience, let

$E[X_j] = 0$ for all j, and rewrite Eq. (4-43a) as follows:

$$M_{X_1 \cdots X_n}(\psi_1, \ldots, \psi_n) = \exp\left(-\tfrac{1}{2} \sum_{j=1}^{n} \sigma_{X_j}^2 \psi_j^2\right)$$

$$\exp\left(-\tfrac{1}{2} \sum_{\substack{j,k=1 \\ j \neq k}}^{n} \kappa_{X_j X_k} \psi_j \psi_k\right) \qquad (4\text{-}43b)$$

Before Eq. (4-43b) is Fourier-transformed to obtain the joint probability density, the second exponential function is first expanded as

$$\exp\left(-\tfrac{1}{2} \sum_{\substack{j,k=1 \\ j \neq k}}^{n} \kappa_{X_j X_k} \psi_j \psi_k\right) = \sum_{r=0}^{\infty} \frac{(-1)^r}{2^r r!} \left(\sum_{\substack{j,k=1 \\ j \neq k}}^{n} \kappa_{X_j X_k} \psi_j \psi_k\right)^r \qquad (4\text{-}53)$$

This procedure permits separate integrations on each of the ψ_j. Then the result of the Fourier transformation of Eq. (4-43b) can be expressed as a series of products of Hermite polynomials which satisfy the orthogonality condition

$$\int_{-\infty}^{\infty} \exp\left[-\left(\frac{z^2}{2}\right)\right] H_r(z) H_s(z)\, dz = \begin{cases} \sqrt{2\pi}\, r! & r = s \\ 0 & r \neq s \end{cases}$$

To show this we note that the Hermite polynomial $H_r(z)$ can be defined in terms of the rth derivative of the probability density of a unit Gaussian random variable as follows:

$$H_r(z) = (-1)^r (2\pi)^{\frac{1}{2}} \exp\left(\tfrac{1}{2} z^2\right) p_U^{(r)}(z) \qquad (4\text{-}54)$$

where

$$p_U(z) = \frac{1}{\sqrt{2\pi}} \exp\left(-\tfrac{1}{2} z^2\right)$$

Recall that the characteristic function of a unit Gaussian random variable is $\exp\left(-\tfrac{1}{2}\theta^2\right)$. We therefore have

$$p_U(z) = \frac{1}{2\pi} \int_{-\infty}^{\infty} \exp\left(-i\theta z - \tfrac{1}{2}\theta^2\right) d\theta \qquad (4\text{-}55)$$

Differentiating of Eq. (4-55) r times gives

$$p_U^{(r)}(z) = (-i)^r (2\pi)^{-1} \int_{-\infty}^{\infty} \theta^r \exp\left(-i\theta z - \tfrac{1}{2}\theta^2\right) d\theta \qquad (4\text{-}56)$$

Equations (4-54) and (4-56) are useful formulas when the Fourier transformation of Eq. (4-43b) is taken.

As an example, consider the characteristic function of a two-dimensional distribution:

$$M_{X_1 X_2}(\psi_1, \psi_2) = \exp\left(-\tfrac{1}{2}\sigma_{X_1}{}^2\psi_1{}^2 - \tfrac{1}{2}\sigma_{X_2}{}^2\psi_2{}^2 - \kappa_{X_1 X_2}\psi_1\psi_2\right)$$

$$= \exp\left(-\tfrac{1}{2}\sigma_{X_1}{}^2\psi_1{}^2\right)\exp\left(-\tfrac{1}{2}\sigma_{X_2}{}^2\psi_2{}^2\right)\sum_{r=0}^{\infty}\frac{(-1)^r}{r!}\left(\kappa_{X_1 X_2}\psi_1\psi_2\right)^r \quad (4\text{-}57)$$

The Fourier transform of Eq. (4-57) is

$$p_{X_1 X_2}(x_1, x_2) = \frac{1}{\sigma_{X_1}\sigma_{X_2}}\sum_{r=0}^{\infty}\frac{1}{r!}\left(\frac{\kappa_{X_1 X_2}}{\sigma_{X_1}\sigma_{X_2}}\right)^r p_U{}^{(r)}\left(\frac{x_1}{\sigma_{X_1}}\right)p_U{}^{(r)}\left(\frac{x_2}{\sigma_{X_2}}\right) \quad (4\text{-}58)$$

Then the application of Eq. (4-56) leads to

$$p_{X_1 X_2}(x_1, x_2) = \frac{1}{(2\pi)\sigma_{X_1}\sigma_{X_2}}\exp\left\{-\frac{1}{2}\left[\left(\frac{x_1}{\sigma_{X_1}}\right)^2 + \left(\frac{x_2}{\sigma_{X_2}}\right)^2\right]\right\}$$

$$\sum_{r=0}^{\infty}\frac{1}{r!}\left(\frac{\kappa_{X_1 X_2}}{\sigma_{X_1}\sigma_{X_2}}\right)^r H_r\left(\frac{x_1}{\sigma_{X_1}}\right)H_r\left(\frac{x_2}{\sigma_{X_2}}\right) \quad (4\text{-}59)$$

Expansions of the higher-order Gaussian probability densities can be obtained in an analogous way. Such expansions are useful in the study of certain nonlinear transformation problems.

4.4 / GAUSSIAN RANDOM PROCESSES

A random process $X(t)$, $t \in T$, is said to be Gaussian distributed if its characteristic functional is of the form

$$M_{\{X\}}[\theta(t)] = \exp\left[i\int_T \mu_X(t)\theta(t)\,dt\right.$$

$$\left. - \tfrac{1}{2}\iint_T \kappa_{XX}(t_1, t_2)\theta(t_1)\theta(t_2)\,dt_1\,dt_2\right] \quad (4\text{-}60)$$

where $\mu_X(t)$ and $\kappa_{XX}(t_1, t_2)$ are the mean and covariance functions of $X(t)$. An equivalent definition can be stated using the log-characteristic functional. For the case

$$\theta(t) = \sum_{j=1}^{n}\theta_j\,\delta(t - t_j)$$

the right-hand side of Eq. (4-60) becomes the joint characteristic function of jointly distributed Gaussian random variables $X(t_1)$, $X(t_2)$, . . . , $X(t_n)$:

$$\exp\left[i\sum_{j=1}^{n}\theta_j\mu_X(t_j) - \tfrac{1}{2}\sum_{j,k=1}^{n}\kappa_{XX}(t_j, t_k)\theta_j\theta_k\right]$$

Therefore, the assignment of different parametric values to a Gaussian random process always results in Gaussian random variables. Conversely, if for any n, $X(t_1)$, . . . , $X(t_n)$ are Gaussian random variables, then $X(t)$ must be a Gaussian random process.‡ The converse statement, which is often expressed in terms of the joint probability density, has also been used as a definition for Gaussian random processes.

It is clear from Eq. (4-60) that a Gaussian random process is completely defined by its mean function $\mu_X(t)$ and its covariance function $\kappa_{XX}(t_1, t_2)$. For an arbitrary weakly stationary random process, $\mu_X(t)$ is a constant and $\kappa_{XX}(t_1, t_2)$ is a function of $t_1 - t_2$; but for a Gaussian process, no distinction need be made between the weakly and the strongly stationary cases since one implies the other.

A comparison of Eq. (3-12) and the natural logarithm¶ of Eq. (4-60) shows that a Gaussian random process can be defined as one whose cumulant functions higher than the second order are equal to zero or as one whose moment functions are related as follows:

$$E\{[X(t_1) - \mu_X(t_1)][X(t_2) - \mu_X(t_2)] \cdot \cdot \cdot [X(t_{2m+1}) - \mu_X(t_{2m+1})]\} = 0$$

$$\begin{aligned} E\{[X(t_1) - \mu_X(t_1)][X(t_2) - \mu_X(t_2)] \cdot \cdot \cdot [X(t_{2m}) - \mu_X(t_{2m})]\} \\ = \Sigma E\{[X(t_j) - \mu_X(t_j)][X(t_k) - \mu_X(t_k)]\} \\ E\{[X(t_q) - \mu_X(t_q)][X(t_s) - \mu_X(t_s)]\} \cdot \cdot \cdot \end{aligned} \quad (4\text{-}61)$$

where the summation involves $(2m)!/(2^m m!)$ terms corresponding to different ways by which $2m$ elements can be broken up into m pairs. Equations (4-61) are analogous to Eqs. (4-50).

It has been demonstrated that a linear transformation of a set of Gaussian random variables gives rise to a new set of Gaussian random variables. Similarly, a linear operation on a Gaussian process results in another Gaussian process, provided that the resulting random process exists in a certain sense.§ The most important linear operations are differentiation and integration. An example‡‡ of the differentiation of a Gaussian random process has been given in Sec. 3.6. To show that the integral

$$Z(\tau) = \int_a^b X(t) h(t, \tau) \, dt$$

yields a Gaussian random process if $X(t)$ is a Gaussian random process,

---

‡ To prove the converse statement rigorously, we should require the consistency theorem of probability. For this theorem, see, for example, M. Loéve, "Probability Theory," 3rd ed., p. 93, D. Van Nostrand, Princeton, N.J., 1963.

¶ The principal value is always implied.

§ Refer to Sec. 3.5.

‡‡ See Eqs. (3-57) and (3-61).

it is only necessary to examine the relation

$$\kappa_n[Z(\tau_1) \cdots Z(\tau_n)] = \int_a^b \cdots \int_a^b \kappa_n[X(t_1) \cdots X(t_n)]h(t_1, \tau_1)$$
$$\cdots h(t_n, \tau_n) \, dt_1 \cdots dt_n \quad (3\text{-}73)$$

and note that $\kappa_n[X(t_1) \cdots X(t_n)] = 0$ for $n > 2$.

4.5 / POISSON PROCESSES

Poisson processes belong to the general class of *counting processes* which arise in problems concerning counting the natural numbers. For example, the number of telephone calls to be handled through a switchboard, the number of electrons emitted from the cathode of a vacuum tube, the number of customers arriving at a service station, the number of airplanes taking off at an airport, etc., are counting random processes. Let $N(t)$ denote the random number of counts in the semiclosed interval $(0, t]$. If there exist probability functions $P_{\{N\}}(n, t)$, $P_{\{N\}}(n_1, t_1; n_2, t_2)$, ... which give the probabilities of the events $\{N(t) = n\}$, $\{N(t_1) = n_1$ and $N(t_2) = n_2\}$, ... , then $N(t)$ is a counting process. The choice of a semiclosed interval $(0, t]$ rather than a closed interval $[0, t]$ or an open interval $(0, t)$ is basically arbitrary; however, it will become apparent in the following development that this choice simplifies somewhat the expression of certain results. The deletion of the initial point in the time interval implies that if the first count occurs at $t = 0$, it is treated as an affair prior to the commencement of the counting process.‡

A counting process is a *Poisson process with stationary increments* if the following conditions are satisfied:

1. Independent arrivals—the arrivals in the future are independent of the arrivals in the past.
2. Stationary arrival rate—the probability of one arrival in $(t, t + dt]$ is equal to the probability of one arrival in $(t + h, t + h + dt]$, and both are equal to $\lambda \, dt$, where λ is a positive constant.
3. Negligible probability for simultaneous arrivals—within an infinitesimal interval $(t, t + dt]$, the probability of one arrival is $\lambda \, dt$, and the probability of two or more arrivals is negligible compared with $\lambda \, dt$.

If the conditions 1 to 3 are satisfied, it will be shown that

$$P_{\{N\}}(n, t) = e^{-\lambda t} \frac{(\lambda t)^n}{n!} \qquad (4\text{-}62)$$

‡ For the sake of convenience we shall call, hereafter, the first count the first arrival, the second count the second arrival, etc., although it is conceivable that the parameter may not be time; for example, it may be the space coordinate.

If the substitution $\mu = \lambda t$ is made, Eq. (4-62) is seen to coincide with the probability function of a Poisson random variable given in Appendix I.

If only conditions 1 and 3 are satisfied, the counting process is called a *Poisson process with nonstationary increments*. In this case λ becomes a nonnegative function of the parameter t. If the probability for simultaneous arrivals is not negligible compared with that for single arrival, the counting process is called a *generalized Poisson process*.

To prove (4-62), we first note that the event $N(t + dt) = n$ is the union of the following two mutually exclusive events: either $N(t) = n$ with no arrival in $(t, t + dt]$, or $N(t) = n - 1$ with one arrival in $(t, t + dt]$. Since the arrivals are independent,

$$P_{\{N\}}(n, t + dt) = P_{\{N\}}(n, t)P_{\{N\}}(0, dt) + P_{\{N\}}(n - 1, t)P_{\{N\}}(1, dt) \qquad (4\text{-}63)$$

and since the counting process $N(t)$ has a stationary arrival rate,

$$\begin{aligned} P_{\{N\}}(1, dt) &= \lambda \, dt \\ P_{\{N\}}(0, dt) &= 1 - P_{\{N\}}(1, dt) = 1 - \lambda \, dt \end{aligned} \qquad (4\text{-}64)$$

Substituting (4-64) into (4-63) and rearranging,

$$\frac{P_{\{N\}}(n, t + dt) - P_{\{N\}}(n, t)}{dt} = \lambda[P_{\{N\}}(n - 1, t) - P_{\{N\}}(n, t)] \qquad (4\text{-}65)$$

By taking the limit as $dt \to 0$ we obtain a differential equation for $P_{\{N\}}(n, t)$ as follows:

$$\frac{d}{dt} P_{\{N\}}(n, t) + \lambda P_{\{N\}}(n, t) = \lambda P_{\{N\}}(n - 1, t) \qquad (4\text{-}66)$$

from which we can determine $P_{\{N\}}(n, t)$ if $P_{\{N\}}(n - 1, t)$ is known. The general solution of (4-66) may be written as follows:

$$P_{\{N\}}(n, t)e^{\lambda t} = \int \lambda P_{\{N\}}(n - 1, t)e^{\lambda t} \, dt + C_n \qquad (4\text{-}67)$$

where C_n is the constant of integration. Equation (4-67) can now be used recursively to determine $P_{\{N\}}(n, t)$ for different n. For $n = 0$, Eq. (4-67) gives

$$P_{\{N\}}(0, t)e^{\lambda t} = \int \lambda P_{\{N\}}(-1, t)e^{\lambda t} \, dt + C_0 \qquad (4\text{-}68)$$

Obviously $P_{\{N\}}(-1, t) = 0$ since the state variable n admits only nonnegative integers; that is, it is impossible to have a negative count. Thus

$$P_{\{N\}}(0, t) = C_0 e^{-\lambda t} \qquad (4\text{-}69)$$

Now the assumption that counting commences immediately *after* $t = 0$ enables us to write

$$P_{\{N\}}(0, 0) = 1 \qquad (4\text{-}70)$$

corresponding to the fact that a zero count is a certain event at $t = 0$. When (4-70) is used to determine the constant C_0, Eq. (4-69) is reduced to

$$P_{\{N\}}(0, t) = e^{-\lambda t} \tag{4-71}$$

For $n = 1$, we obtain from Eq. (4-67)

$$P_{\{N\}}(1, t)e^{\lambda t} = \lambda t + C_1 \tag{4-72}$$

The constant of integration $C_1 = 0$ since $P_{\{N\}}(1, 0) = 0$. Thus

$$P_{\{N\}}(1, t) = e^{-\lambda t}(\lambda t) \tag{4-73}$$

From a similar procedure, we find that

$$P_{\{N\}}(2, t) = e^{-\lambda t} \frac{(\lambda t)^2}{2!} \tag{4-74}$$

etc. It can easily be shown that the general expression is

$$P_{\{N\}}(n, t) = e^{-\lambda t} \frac{(\lambda t)^n}{n!} \tag{4-62}$$

Figure 4.3 shows the variation of the probability function with respect to time for a Poisson random process with stationary increments. It can easily be shown by use of Eq. (4-62) that $E[N(t)] = \lambda t$. Therefore, the constant λ is equal to the expected arrival rate.

For a Poisson process with nonstationary increments, an analogous

Fig. 4.3 The variation of the probability function with respect to dimensionless time λt for a Poisson random process with stationary increments.

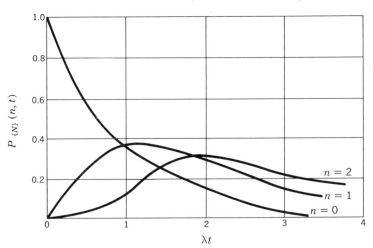

development leads to

$$P_{\{N\}}(n, t) = \exp\left[-\int_0^t \lambda(\tau)\, d\tau\right] \int_0^t \int_0^{\tau_n} \cdots \int_0^{\tau_2} \lambda(\tau_n)$$
$$\lambda(\tau_{n-1}) \cdots \lambda(\tau_1)\, d\tau_n\, d\tau_{n-1} \cdots d\tau_1$$
$$= \frac{1}{n!}\left[\int_0^t \lambda(\tau)\, d\tau\right]^n \exp\left[-\int_0^t \lambda(\tau)\, d\tau\right] \qquad (4\text{-}75)$$

where $\lambda(t)$ is again the expected arrival rate, which is now a function of t. Equation (4-75) includes Eq. (4-62) as a special case. The derivation of (4-75) is left as an exercise at the end of this chapter.

4.6 / RANDOM PULSES

A useful class of random processes may be constructed from superposition of random pulses arriving at random times. This class has the general form

$$X(t) = \sum_{k=1}^{N(t)} W_k(t, \tau_k) \qquad (4\text{-}76)$$

where $N(t)$ is a counting process and each $W_k(t, \tau_k)$ represents a random pulse which commences at a random time τ_k. For most practical applications, it is sufficient to consider a subclass

$$X(t) = \sum_{k=1}^{N(t)} Y_k w(t, \tau_k) \qquad (4\text{-}77)$$

Here the Y_k are identically distributed random variables which are mutually independent and independent of the distribution of τ_k, and $w(t, \tau_k)$ is a deterministic function describing the shape of a pulse. In this more restrictive form of random process [Eq. (4-77)], all pulses are of the same form but with random amplitudes. Since physically the pulse-shape function $w(t, \tau)$ must satisfy the condition

$$w(t, \tau) = 0 \qquad t < \tau \qquad (4\text{-}78)$$

Eq. (4-77) can be replaced by

$$X(t) = \sum_{k=1}^{N(T)} Y_k w(t, \tau_k) \qquad T > t \qquad (4\text{-}77a)$$

The random process $X(t)$ will be considered as defined in the time domain $(0, T]$.

The probabilistic structure of $X(t)$ may be revealed by computing the characteristic functional defined in Eq. (3-6):

$$M_{\{X\}}[\theta(t)] = E\left\{\exp\left[i\int_0^T \theta(t)X(t)\, dt\right]\right\} \qquad (3\text{-}6)$$

Substituting (4-77a) into (3-6),

$$M_{\{X\}}[\theta(t)] = E\left\{\exp\left[i\int_0^T \theta(t)\sum_{k=1}^{N(T)} Y_k w(t, \tau_k)\, dt\right]\right\}$$

$$= E\left[E\left\{\exp\left[i\int_0^T \theta(t)\sum_{k=1}^{N(T)} Y_k w(t, \tau_k)\, dt\right]\,\Big|\, N(T)\right\}\right]$$

$$= \sum_{n=0}^{\infty} P_{\{N\}}(n, T)E\left\{\exp\left[i\int_0^T \theta(t)\sum_{k=1}^{n} Y_k w(t, \tau_k)\, dt\right]\right\} \quad (4\text{-}79)$$

If the counting process $N(t)$ is Poisson, i.e., if the pulse arrival times τ_k are independent, then

$$E\left\{\exp\left[i\int_0^T \theta(t)\sum_{k=1}^{n} Y_k w(t, \tau_k)\, dt\right]\right\}$$

$$= E\left\{\prod_{k=1}^{n}\exp\left[i\int_0^T \theta(t) Y_k w(t, \tau_k)\, dt\right]\right\}$$

$$= \prod_{k} E\left\{\exp\left[i\int_0^T \theta(t) Y_k w(t, \tau_k)\, dt\right]\right\} \quad (4\text{-}80)$$

The last line in Eq. (4-80) follows from the commutability of the operations of expectation and multiplication for independent random variables. Write

$$E\left\{\exp\left[i\int_0^T \theta(t) Y_k w(t, \tau_k)\, dt\right]\right\}$$

$$= 1 + E\left\{\sum_{m=1}^{\infty} \frac{i^m}{m!}\left[\int_0^T \theta(t) Y_k w(t, \tau_k)\, dt\right]^m\right\}$$

$$= 1 + \alpha \quad (4\text{-}81)$$

Since the arrival of τ_k is a Poisson event,

$$\alpha = \sum_{m=1}^{\infty} \frac{i^m}{m!}\int_{-\infty}^{\infty} y^m p_Y(y)\, dy \int_0^T \cdots \int_0^T \theta(t_1) \cdots \theta(t_m)$$

$$\frac{\int_0^T w(t_1, \tau) \cdots w(t_m, \tau)\lambda(\tau)\, d\tau}{\int_0^T \lambda(\tau)\, d\tau} dt_1 \cdots dt_m \quad (4\text{-}82)$$

where $\lambda(\tau)$ is the expected nonstationary arrival rate and $p_Y(y)$ is the common probability density of Y_k. We note that α is independent of k.

Using (4-81) in (4-80) and substituting the result into (4-79), we obtain

$$
\begin{aligned}
M_{\{x\}}[\theta(t)] &= \sum_{n=0}^{\infty} P_{\{N\}}(n, T)(1 + \alpha)^n \\
&= \sum_{n=0}^{\infty} \frac{1}{n!} \exp\left[-\int_0^T \lambda(\tau)\, d\tau\right]\left[\int_0^T \lambda(\tau)\, d\tau\right]^n (1 + \alpha)^n \\
&= \exp\left[\alpha \int_0^T \lambda(\tau)\, d\tau\right]
\end{aligned}
\tag{4-83}
$$

The log-characteristic functional of $X(t)$ is

$$
\ln M_{\{x\}}[\theta(t)] = \alpha \int_0^T \lambda(\tau)\, d\tau = \sum_{m=1}^{\infty} \frac{i^m}{m!} E[Y^m] \int_0^T \cdots \int_0^T \theta(t_1) \cdots \theta(t_m)
$$
$$
\left[\int_0^T w(t_1, \tau) \cdots w(t_m, \tau)\lambda(\tau)\, d\tau\right] dt_1 \cdots dt_m \tag{4-84}
$$

If this equation is compared with Eq. (3-12), it is clear that the cumulant functions of $X(t)$ are given by

$$
\kappa_m[X(t_1) \cdots X(t_m)] = E[Y^m] \int_0^{\min(t_1, \ldots, t_m)} w(t_1, \tau) \cdots w(t_m, \tau)\lambda(\tau)\, d\tau
\tag{4-85}
$$

where $\min(t_1, \ldots, t_m)$ denotes the smallest value among $t_1, \ldots, t_m$. The upper limit of the integral on the right-hand side of (4-85) is changed to $\min(t_1, \ldots, t_m)$ in view of the condition (4-78). For $m = 1$ and $m = 2$, Eq. (4-85) gives, respectively, the mean function and the covariance function of $X(t)$, that is,

$$
\begin{aligned}
\mu_X(t) &= \mu_Y \int_0^t w(t, \tau)\lambda(\tau)\, d\tau \\
\kappa_{XX}(t_1, t_2) &= E[Y^2] \int_0^{\min(t_1, t_2)} w(t_1, \tau)w(t_2, \tau)\lambda(\tau)\, d\tau
\end{aligned}
\tag{4-86}
$$

The variance function is obtained by letting $t_1 = t_2 = t$ in the second equation in (4-86), that is,

$$
\sigma_X{}^2(t) = E[Y^2] \int_0^t w^2(t, \tau)\lambda(\tau)\, d\tau \tag{4-87}
$$

Let us digress for a moment to examine the consequence if the constituent pulses in $X(t)$ arrive infinitely frequently, that is, if $\lambda(t)$ becomes unbounded. Write $\lambda(t) = \lambda_0\nu(t)$, where $\nu(t)$ is a bounded function but the factor λ_0 approaches infinity in the limit. In view of the central limit theorem, we expect that $X(t)$ tends to be Gaussian distributed if it exists. For simplicity, assume $E[Y] = 0$. In order for $X(t)$ to remain a second-order random process we replace Y_k in Eq. (4-77) by

$Z_k/\sqrt{\lambda_0}$, where Z_k are identically distributed as a random variable Z. Then Equations (4-86) become

$$\mu_X(t) = 0$$
$$\kappa_{XX}(t_1, t_2) = E[Z^2] \int_0^{\min (t_1, t_2)} w(t_1, \tau)w(t_2, \tau)\nu(\tau) \, d\tau \qquad (4\text{-}86a)$$

The higher cumulant functions of $X(t)$ vanish if $E[Y^m]\lambda_0 = E[Z^m]\lambda_0^{1-m/2}$ vanishes for all $m > 2$. Therefore, $X(t)$ becomes Gaussian distributed in the limit with the mean and the covariance function in $(4\text{-}86a)$.

Return now to Eq. (4-85) and consider a special case in which the pulse-shape function w is a function of the difference $t - \tau$, and the arrival rate of the pulses is stationary, i.e., λ is a constant. Then Eq. (4-85) becomes

$$\kappa_m[X(t_1) \; \cdots \; X(t_m)] = \lambda E[Y^m] \int_0^{\min (t_1, \ldots, t_m)} w(t_1 - \tau) \; \cdots \; w(t_m - \tau) \, d\tau$$
$$(4\text{-}85a)$$

If we further assume that $w(t - \tau)$ is essentially zero except for small $t - \tau$, then we may expect that $X(t)$ tends to be stationary at large t, that is, after the arrival of a large number of pulses. To show this we replace the lower limit and the upper limit of the integral in Eq. (4-85a) by $-\infty$ and ∞, respectively. With a change of variable $u = t_1 - \tau$, we obtain

$$\kappa_m[X(t_1) \; \cdots \; X(t_m)] = \lambda E[Y^m] \int_{-\infty}^{\infty} w(u) \; \cdots \; w(t_m - t_1 + u) \, du \qquad (4\text{-}88)$$

Then Eqs. (4-86) and (4-87) reduce to

$$\mu_X = \lambda\mu_Y \int_{-\infty}^{\infty} w(u) \, du$$
$$\kappa_{XX}(t_1, t_2) = \Gamma_{XX}(t_2 - t_1)$$
$$\qquad = \lambda E[Y^2] \int_{-\infty}^{\infty} w(u)w(t_2 - t_1 + u) \, du \qquad (4\text{-}89)$$
$$\sigma_X^2 = \lambda E[Y^2] \int_{-\infty}^{\infty} w^2(u) \, du$$

Equations (4-89) are a statement of the well-known Campbell's theorem.‡

The situation becomes more complicated with the removal of the restriction that the underlying counting mechanism $N(t)$ be Poisson. One way to specify a general counting process $N(t)$ is to regard the arrivals as random points on the time axis. Such random points can be

‡ See, for example, S. O. Rice, Mathematical Analysis of Random Noise, Bell System Tech. J., **23**:282–332 (1944); **24**:46–156 (1945). Reprinted in N. Wax (ed.), "Selected Papers on Noise and Stochastic Processes," p. 147, Dover, New York, 1954.

characterized by their distribution functions‡

$f_1(t), f_2(t_1, t_2), f_3(t_1, t_2, t_3), \ldots$

Stratonovich has shown that for a system of random points with continuous statistical properties these distribution functions are related to a generating functional by the following expansion:

$$L_T[v(t)] = 1 + \sum_{m=1}^{\infty} \frac{1}{m!} \int \cdots \int_T f_m(t_1, \ldots, t_m)$$
$$v(t_1) \cdots v(t_m) \, dt_1 \cdots dt_m \quad (4\text{-}90)$$

where the generating functional is defined as

$$L_T[v(t)] = E \left\{ \prod_{k=1}^{N(T)} [1 + v(t_k)] \right\} \quad (4\text{-}91)$$

The function $v(t)$ belongs to a class for which the generating functional exists. A comparison of Eqs. (4-90) and (3-11) reveals that the distribution functions of a sequence of random points are analogous to the moment functions of a random process. Then it is logical to define a log-generating functional which has the expansion

$$\ln L_T[v(t)] = \sum_{m=1}^{\infty} \frac{1}{m!} \int \cdots \int_T g_m(t_1, \ldots, t_m)$$
$$v(t_1) \cdots v(t_m) \, dt_1 \cdots dt_m \quad (4\text{-}92)$$

where g_m may be called the mth cumulant function of the random points. Clearly, a complete set of such cumulant functions also characterizes a sequence of random points. The first three cumulant functions of a sequence of random points are analogous to the central moment functions; thus

$$g_1(t) = f_1(t)$$
$$g_2(t_1, t_2) = f_2(t_1, t_2) - f_1(t_1)f_2(t_2)$$
$$g_3(t_1, t_2, t_3) = f_3(t_1, t_2, t_3) - f_2(t_1, t_2)f_1(t_3)$$
$$- f_2(t_1, t_3)f_1(t_2) - f_2(t_2, t_3)f_1(t_1) + 2f_1(t_1)f_1(t_2)f_1(t_3)$$
$$(4\text{-}93)$$

In the special case where $N(t)$ is Poisson,

$$f_m(t_1, t_2, \ldots, t_m) = \lambda(t_1)\lambda(t_2) \cdots \lambda(t_m) \quad (4\text{-}94)$$

‡ They should not be confused with the probability distribution functions. See R. L. Stratonovich, "Topics in the Theory of Random Noise," p. 144, English translation by R. A. Silverman, Gordon and Breach, Science Publishers, New York, 1963.

or, equivalently,

$$g_1(t) = \lambda(t)$$
$$g_2 = g_3 = \cdots = 0 \tag{4-94a}$$

Equation (4-79) remains valid for a random process $X(t)$ which is constructed from random pulses arriving at correlated random times. However, in this case it is expedient to rewrite this equation as

$$M_{\{X\}}[\theta(t)] = E\left\{ \prod_{k=1}^{N(T)} \exp\left[i \int_T \theta(t)\, Y_k w(t, \tau_k)\, dt \right] \right\}$$
$$= L_T\left[v(\tau) \right] \tag{4-95}$$

where

$$v(\tau) = \sum_{l=1}^{\infty} \frac{i^l}{l!} E[Y^l] \int \cdots \int_T \theta(t_1)\, \cdots\, \theta(t_l) w(t_1, \tau)$$
$$\cdots w(t_l, \tau)\, dt_1 \cdots dt_l$$

If logarithms are taken on both sides of Eq. (4-95) and use is made of the expansions (3-10) and (4-92), we obtain the expressions for the cumulant functions of $X(t)$ by comparing the same number of integrations on the t's on both sides of the equation. In particular, the mean and covariance functions of $X(t)$ are now given by

$$\kappa_1[X(t)] = E[X(t)] = E[Y] \int_T g_1(\tau)w(t, \tau)\, d\tau$$
$$\kappa_2[X(t_1)X(t_2)] = \kappa_{XX}(t_1, t_2) \tag{4-96}$$
$$= E[Y^2] \int_T g_1(\tau)w(t_1, \tau)w(t_2, \tau)\, d\tau$$
$$+ E^2[Y] \iint_T g_2(\tau_1, \tau_2)w(t_1, \tau_1)w(t_2, \tau_2)\, d\tau_1\, d\tau_2$$

When the pulse shape w is a function of $t - \tau$, it is sometimes convenient to deal with the generalized spectral density of $X(t)$. Using Eq. (3-75b),

$$\hat{\Phi}_{XX}(\omega_1, \omega_2) = \frac{E[Y^2]}{(2\pi)^2} \iint_{-\infty}^{\infty} \left[\int_T g_1(\tau)w(t_1 - \tau)w(t_2 - \tau)\, d\tau \right]$$

$$\exp\left[-i(\omega_1 t_1 - \omega_2 t_2) \right]\, dt_1\, dt_2$$

$$+ \frac{E^2[Y]}{(2\pi)^2} \iint_{-\infty}^{\infty} \left[\iint_T g_2(\tau_1, \tau_2)w(t_1 - \tau_1)w(t_2 - \tau_2)\, d\tau_1\, d\tau_2 \right]$$

$$\exp\left[-i(\omega_1 t_1 - \omega_2 t_2) \right]\, dt_1\, dt_2 \tag{4-97}$$

Interchanging the order of the integrations,

$$\hat{\Phi}_{XX}(\omega_1, \omega_2) = (2\pi)^2 W(\omega_1) W^*(\omega_2) \left\{ E[Y^2] \frac{G_1(\omega_1 - \omega_2)}{2\pi} + E^2[Y] \hat{G}_2(\omega_1, \omega_2) \right\}$$

$$(4\text{-}98)$$

where

$$W(\omega) = \frac{1}{2\pi} \int_{-\infty}^{\infty} w(t) \exp(-i\omega t) \, dt$$

$$G_1(\omega) = \frac{1}{2\pi} \int_{T} g_1(t) \exp(-i\omega t) \, dt \qquad\qquad (4\text{-}99)$$

$$\hat{G}_2(\omega_1, \omega_2) = \frac{1}{(2\pi)^2} \iint_{T} g_2(t_1, t_2) \exp[-i(\omega_1 t_1 - \omega_2 t_2)] \, dt_1 \, dt_2$$

When proving Campbell's theorem, Eqs. (4-89), we noted that under certain conditions the random process obtained by the superposition of independently arriving random pulses tends to be stationary. Similar conclusions may be deduced for the superposition of random pulses with correlated arrival times. An examination of Eqs. (4-96) shows that, in particular, $X(t)$ tends to be weakly stationary if the following conditions are met. Firstly, the function $g_1(t)$, which is the expected pulse arrival rate, must be a constant; and the function $g_2(t_1, t_2)$, which is the correlation between the arrival rates at two times, must be a function of the time difference $t_2 - t_1$. Secondly, the pulse shape $w(t, \tau)$ must be a function of $t - \tau$. Thirdly, both g_2 and w must diminish when $|t_2 - t_1|$ and $t - \tau$ become large, respectively. Under these conditions,

$$\kappa_1[X(t)] = E[X(t)] = E[Y]g_1 \int_{-\infty}^{\infty} w(u) \, du$$

$$\kappa_2[X(t_1)X(t_2)] = \Gamma_{XX}(t_2 - t_1)$$

$$= E[Y^2] \, g_1 \int_{-\infty}^{\infty} w(u)w(t_2 - t_1 + u) \, du \qquad (4\text{-}96a)$$

$$+ E^2[Y] \int_{-\infty}^{\infty} \int_{-\infty}^{\infty} g_2(t_2 - t_1 + u - v)w(u)w(v) \, du \, dv$$

The spectral density of $X(t)$ is obtained from the Fourier transformation of the following correlation function:

$$R_{XX}(t_2 - t_1) = \Gamma_{XX}(t_2 - t_1) + E^2[X(t)]$$

$$= E[Y^2] \, g_1 \int_{-\infty}^{\infty} w(u)w(t_2 - t_1 + u) \, du$$

$$+ E^2[Y] \left\{ \int_{-\infty}^{\infty} \int_{-\infty}^{\infty} g_2(t_2 - t_1 + u - v)w(u)w(v) \, du \, dv \right.$$

$$\left. + \left[g_1 \int_{-\infty}^{\infty} w(u) \, du \right]^2 \right\} \qquad (4\text{-}100)$$

The result is

$$\Phi_{XX}(\omega) = (2\pi)^2 \left\{ E[Y^2]\frac{g_1}{2\pi} + E^2[Y]G_2(\omega) \right\} |W(\omega)|^2$$

$$+ \left\{ E[Y]g_1 \int_{-\infty}^{\infty} w(u) \, du \right\}^2 \delta(\omega) \qquad (4\text{-}101)$$

where $W(\omega)$ has been defined in (4-99) and

$$G_2(\omega) = \frac{1}{2\pi} \int_{-\infty}^{\infty} g_2(\tau) \exp\left(-i\omega\tau\right) d\tau \qquad \tau = t_2 - t_1 \qquad (4\text{-}102)$$

The term involving the Dirac delta function $\delta(\omega)$ drops out if $X(t)$ has a zero expectation.

4.7 / SHOT NOISE AND WHITE NOISE

A random process $S(t)$ is called a *shot noise* if its mean and the covariance functions are given by

$$\begin{aligned} \mu_S(t) &= 0 \\ \kappa_{SS}(t_1, t_2) &= I(t_1)\,\delta(t_2 - t_1) \end{aligned} \qquad (4\text{-}103)$$

where function $I(t)$ is called the *intensity function* of a shot noise. One shot noise belongs to the class of random pulse sequences considered in Sec. 4.6. Such a shot noise is represented by

$$S(t) = \sum_{k=1}^{N(t)} Y_k\,\delta(t - \tau_k) \qquad (4\text{-}104)$$

where $N(t)$ is a Poisson process with either stationary or nonstationary increments, and the Y_k are independent random variables with zero expectations, identically distributed as a random variable Y, and are independent of the distribution of the τ_k. Equation (4-104) is obtained from Eq. (4-77) by specifying the pulse-shape function to be

$$w(t, \tau) = \delta(t - \tau)$$

It is easy to see that Eqs. (4-103) are reducible from Eqs. (4-86) if we set

$$\mu_Y = 0 \qquad I(t) = E[Y^2]\lambda(t)$$

If a shot noise is weakly stationary, then its covariance function becomes

$$\Gamma_{SS}(\tau) = I\,\delta(\tau) \qquad \tau = t_1 - t_2 \qquad (4\text{-}105)$$

We see that the intensity function of a weakly stationary shot noise is just a constant. Since the expectation of a shot noise is zero, its covariance function is the same as its correlation function. Thus the spectral density of a weakly stationary shot noise is the Fourier transform of Eq. (4-105), which is

$$\Phi_{SS}(\omega) = \frac{I}{2\pi} = \text{const}$$

A weakly stationary random process having a constant spectral density is called a *white noise*, to be denoted by $W(t)$. That is, a white noise is defined by either one of the following equivalent properties:

$$\Phi_{WW}(\omega) = K$$
$$R_{WW}(\tau) = 2\pi K \, \delta(\tau) \qquad \tau = t_2 - t_1 \qquad (4\text{-}106)$$

Therefore, a weakly stationary shot noise is a white noise. The physical interpretation of a constant spectral density is that the energy content in the random process is uniformly distributed over the entire frequency range. This property is the origin for the name *white noise*. One white noise has the representation of Eq. (4-104) with $N(t)$ specified to be a Poisson process with stationary increments. This white noise, however, is strongly stationary.

Analogously, the generalized spectral density of a nonstationary shot noise, when it exists, is a function of the frequency difference $\omega_1 - \omega_2$; that is,

$$\hat{\Phi}_{SS}(\omega_1, \omega_2)$$
$$= \frac{1}{(2\pi)^2} \int_{-\infty}^{\infty} \int I(t_1) \, \delta(t_2 - t_1) \exp\left[-i(\omega_1 t_1 - \omega_2 t_2)\right] dt_1 \, dt_2$$
$$= \Omega_{SS}(\omega_1 - \omega_2) \qquad (4\text{-}107)$$

The mean-square value of a white noise or, more generally, a shot noise, is unbounded, as can be seen by setting $\tau = 0$ in the second equation of (4-106) or by setting $t_2 = t_1$ in the second equation of (4-103). Since a physically realizable random process cannot have an infinite average energy, both the shot-noise process and the white-noise process are simply mathematical idealizations. However, analyses in which physical phenomena are modeled as shot-noise or white-noise processes may lead to meaningful results. Justifications of such analyses will be discussed in Chap. 5.

4.8 / MARKOV RANDOM PROCESSES

A discrete random process $X(t)$ is said to be Markovian if the following relation exists between the conditional probability functions:

$$P_{\{X\}}(x_n, t_n | x_{n-1}, t_{n-1}; \ldots ; x_2, t_2; x_1, t_1) = P_{\{X\}}(x_n, t_n | x_{n-1}, t_{n-1})$$
$$t_n > t_{n-1} > \cdots > t_2 > t_1 \qquad (4\text{-}108)$$

Equation (4-108) states that the probability for the random process $X(t)$ to take on a value x_n at the time $t = t_n$, under the condition that its values at some earlier times are known, depends only on the knowledge of its most recent value, $X(t) = x_{n-1}$ at $t = t_{n-1}$. This relation gives rise to the nickname "one-step-memory random process."

The conditional probability function appearing on the right-hand side of (4-108) is especially known as *the transition probability function* of the Markov process $X(t)$. A discrete Markov process is completely defined by its first probability function $P_{\{X\}}(x, t)$ and the transition probability function. For example, the second probability function may be obtained from

$$P_{\{X\}}(x_1, t_1; x_2, t_2) = P_{\{X\}}(x_1, t_1)P_{\{X\}}(x_2, t_2|x_1, t_1) \qquad t_2 > t_1 \qquad (4\text{-}109)$$

and the third probability function from

$$
\begin{aligned}
P_{\{X\}}&(x_1, t_1; x_2, t_2; x_3, t_3) \\
&= P_{\{X\}}(x_1, t_1)P_{\{X\}}(x_2, t_2|x_1, t_1)P_{\{X\}}(x_3, t_3|x_2, t_2; x_1, t_1) \\
&= P_{\{X\}}(x_1, t_1)P_{\{X\}}(x_2, t_2|x_1,t_1)P_{\{X\}}(x_3, t_3|x_2, t_2) \qquad t_3 > t_2 > t_1 \qquad (4\text{-}110)
\end{aligned}
$$

etc. The physical implication of Eqs. (4-109) and (4-110) is that if the probabilistic information of the random process is known at time t, and if the evolution mechanism (represented by the transition probability) is also given, then the complete probabilistic structure of the random process beyond t can be deduced.

Alternatively, we may say that a discrete Markov process is completely defined by its second probability function. The statement becomes clear by noting that

$$
\begin{aligned}
P_{\{X\}}(x_1, t_1) &= \sum_{\substack{\text{range} \\ \text{for } x_2}} P_{\{X\}}(x_1, t_1; x_2, t_2) \\
P_{\{X\}}(x_2, t_2|x_1, t_1) &= \frac{P_{\{X\}}(x_1, t_1; x_2, t_2)}{P_{\{X\}}(x_1, t_1)}
\end{aligned}
\qquad (4\text{-}111)
$$

However, if the initial value, say $X(0) = x_0$, of a discrete Markov process is known precisely or, at least, with probability 1, then the transition probability *alone* adequately specifies the process. This is physically clear, since complete probability structure can be deduced from the knowledge of the initial state and the evolution mechanism. In this case the first probability function $P_{\{X\}}(x_1, t_1)$ appearing in Eqs. (4-109), (4-110), etc., is replaced by the probability function conditional on $X(0) = x_0$; that is, $P_{\{X\}}(x_1, t_1)$ is replaced by $P_{\{X\}}(x_1, t_1|x_0, 0)$.

Although the discrete Markov processes find many applications in social and physical sciences,‡ most problems in structural dynamics concern random processes which are continuously valued. Therefore, we shall focus our attention henceforth on continuous Markov random

‡ For such applications, see A. T. Bharucha-Reid, "Elements of the Theory of Markov Processes and Their Applications," McGraw-Hill, New York, 1960.

processes with the foregoing brief discussion serving as an introductory exposition.

Analogously, a continuously valued random process $X(t)$ is said to be Markovian if the following relation exists between the conditional probability density functions;

$$p_{\{X\}}(x_n, t_n | x_{n-1}, t_{n-1}; \ldots ; x_2, t_2; x_1, t_1)$$
$$= p_{\{X\}}(x_n, t_n | x_{n-1}, t_{n-1}) \qquad t_n > t_{n-1} > \cdots > t_1 \qquad (4\text{-}112)$$

The notion of a conditional probability density has been introduced in Sec. 2.8, and Eq. (4-112) should be interpreted accordingly. The conditional probability density appearing on the right-hand side of (4-112) is called *the transition probability density*. Analogous to the discrete case, a continuous Markov process is specified in any one of three equivalent ways: (1) by the first probability density $p_{\{X\}}(x, t)$ and the transition probability density $p_{\{X\}}(x_2, t_2 | x_1, t_1)$; (2) by the second probability density $p_{\{X\}}(x_1, t_1; x_2, t_2)$; or (3) by the transition probability density, if the initial value of the random process is known at least with probability 1. These three different ways are equivalent in view of the following relations:

$$p_{\{X\}}(x_1, t_1; x_2, t_2) = p_{\{X\}}(x_1, t_1)p_{\{X\}}(x_2, t_2 | x_1, t_1) \qquad t_2 > t_1 \qquad (4\text{-}109a)$$

$$p_{\{X\}}(x_1, t_1; x_2, t_2; x_3, t_3)$$
$$= p_{\{X\}}(x_1, t_1)p_{\{X\}}(x_2, t_2 | x_1, t_1)p_{\{X\}}(x_3, t_3 | x_2, t_2) \qquad t_3 > t_2 > t_1 \qquad (4\text{-}110a)$$
$$\cdots \cdots \cdots \cdots \cdots \cdots \cdots \cdots \cdots \cdots \cdots \cdots \cdots$$

$$p_{\{X\}}(x_1, t_1) = \int p_{\{X\}}(x_1, t_1; x_2, t_2) \, dx_2$$
$$p_{\{X\}}(x_2, t_2 | x_1, t_1) = \frac{p_{\{X\}}(x_1, t_1; x_2, t_2)}{p_{\{X\}}(x_1, t_1)} \qquad\qquad (4\text{-}111a)$$

If $X(0) = x_0$ is known at least with probability 1, then $p_{\{X\}}(x_1, t_1)$ in the above relations is replaced by $p_{\{X\}}(x_1, t_1 | x_0, 0)$. These relations are analogous to Eqs. (4-109) through (4-111) for discrete Markov processes. Since the transition probability density occupies the central role in the theory of the continuous Markov process, it will be denoted hereafter by a special symbol $q_{\{X\}}(x_2, t_2 | x_1, t_1)$.

4.9 / THE CHAPMAN-KOLMOGOROV-SMOLUCHOWSKI EQUATION

Since Eq. (4-112) is valid for any set of parametric values $t_1, t_2, \ldots, t_n$ as long as the inequality $t_1 < t_2 < \cdots < t_n$ holds, there exists a certain restriction which a Markov random process must satisfy so that no inconsistencies may arise. For an arbitrary continuous random process

$$p_{\{X\}}(x_2, t_2 | x_1, t_1) = \int p_{\{X\}}(x_2, t_2; x, t | x_1, t_1) \, dx$$
$$= \int p_{\{X\}}(x, t | x_1, t_1)p_{\{X\}}(x_2, t_2 | x, t; x_1, t_1) \, dx \qquad (4\text{-}113)$$

However, if $X(t)$ is Markovian, Eq. (4-113) reduces to

$$q_{\{X\}}(x_2, t_2|x_1, t_1) = \int q_{\{X\}}(x, t|x_1, t_1)q_{\{X\}}(x_2, t_2|x, t)\, dx \qquad t_2 > t > t_1 \qquad (4\text{-}114)$$

Let $\tau = t - t_1$ and $\Delta\tau = t_2 - t$; then Eq. (4-114) may be written alternatively as follows:

$$\begin{aligned}
q_{\{X\}}&(x_2, t_1 + \tau + \Delta\tau|x_1, t_1) \\
&= \int q_{\{X\}}(x, t_1 + \tau|x_1, t_1)q_{\{X\}}(x_2, t_1 + \tau + \Delta\tau|x, t_1 + \tau)\, dx \qquad (4\text{-}114a)
\end{aligned}$$

Equation (4-114) or (4-114a) is known as the *Chapman-Kolmogorov-Smoluchowski equation*, which may well be called the compatibility equation for a Markov process. The latter form of the equation is more descriptive in that the time intervals for transition from state x_1 to state x and then from state x to state x_2 are clearly indicated. Figure 4.4 gives a schematic representation of the Chapman-Kolmogorov-Smoluchowski equation.

If the transition probability density is invariant with respect to a shift of the time origin, that is, if for any τ,

$$q_{\{X\}}(x_2, t_2|x_1, t_2) = q_{\{X\}}(x_2, t_2 + \tau|x_1, t_1 + \tau) \qquad (4\text{-}115)$$

the Markov process is said to have *stationary increments*. For this special

Fig. 4.4 A schematic representation of the Chapman-Kolmogorov-Smoluchowski equation.

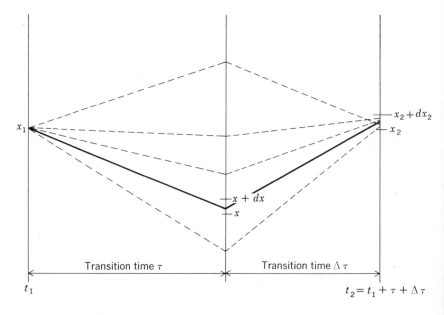

case the Chapman-Kolmogorov-Smoluchowski equation reduces to

$$q_{\{x\}}(x_2, \tau + \Delta\tau | x_1) = \int q_{\{x\}}(x, \tau | x_1) q_{\{x\}}(x_2, \Delta\tau | x) \, dx \qquad (4\text{-}116)$$

where only the transition time intervals need be given in the arguments of the transition probability density functions. It should be noted that a stationary Markov process must be one with stationary increments, but the reverse is not necessarily true.

The first probability density of a *stationary* Markov process may be obtained from the transition probability density, necessarily of a stationary-increment type, by letting the transition time interval approach to infinity, i.e.,

$$p_{\{x\}}(x) = \lim_{\tau \to \infty} q_{\{x\}}(x, \tau | x_1) \qquad (4\text{-}117)$$

If the transition time interval is infinitely long, then the condition of the initial state $X(0) = x_1$ becomes immaterial. It follows that a stationary Markov process is sufficiently defined by its transition probability density function alone.

Equations (4-113) to (4-117) were written for a scalar (one-dimensional) random process. The extension to vectorially valued (multidimensional) random processes is obvious. For example, the generalization of Eq. (4-114a) would read

$$q_{\{\mathbf{x}\}}(\mathbf{x}_2, t_1 + \tau + \Delta\tau | \mathbf{x}_1, t_1)$$
$$= \int \cdots \int q_{\{\mathbf{x}\}}(\mathbf{y}, t_1 + \tau | \mathbf{x}_1, t_1) q_{\{\mathbf{x}\}}(\mathbf{x}_2, t_1 + \tau + \Delta\tau | \mathbf{y}, t_1 + \tau) \, dy_1 \, dy_2$$
$$\cdots dy_n \qquad (4\text{-}114b)$$

where the vector $\mathbf{y} = (y_1, y_2, \ldots, y_n)$.

4.10 / FOKKER-PLANCK EQUATION

The Chapman-Kolmogorov-Smoluchowski equation (4-114) or (4-114b) is an integral equation which governs the transition probability density of a Markov process. Solutions to this integral equation are frequently obtained by solving an equivalent differential equation, called the *Fokker-Planck* equation. We shall derive the Fokker-Planck equation by following the general procedure given by Wang and Uhlenbeck.‡

Let $X(t)$ be a one-dimensional Markov process, and consider the integral

$$I = \int_{-\infty}^{\infty} R(y) \frac{\partial}{\partial t} q_{\{x\}}(y, t | x_0, t_0) \, dy \qquad t > t_0 \qquad (4\text{-}118)$$

‡ M. C. Wang and G. E. Uhlenbeck, On The Theory of the Brownian Motion II, *Rev. Mod. Phys.*, **17**(2, 3): 323–342 (1945). Collected in N. Wax (ed.), "Selected Papers on Noise and Stochastic Processes," Dover, New York, 1954.

where $R(y)$ is an arbitrary function of y which goes to zero sufficiently fast as y approaches $+\infty$ or $-\infty$. Specifically, we assume that for any n,

$$\lim_{y \to \pm\infty} \frac{d^n}{dy^n} R(y) = 0 \qquad (4\text{-}119)$$

Now the integral (4-118) may be written as

$$I = \int_{-\infty}^{\infty} R(y) \lim_{\Delta t \to 0} \frac{1}{\Delta t} [q_{\{x\}}(y, t + \Delta t | x_0, t_0) - q_{\{x\}}(y, t | x_0, t_0)] \, dy$$

$$= \lim_{\Delta t \to 0} \frac{1}{\Delta t} \int_{-\infty}^{\infty} R(y)[q_{\{x\}}(y, t + \Delta t | x_0, t_0) - q_{\{x\}}(y, t | x_0, t_0)] \, dy \qquad (4\text{-}120)$$

The order of the integration and the limit operation is interchangeable as long as the improper integral converges uniformly in a neighborhood of t. Using the Chapman-Kolmogorov-Smoluchowski equation,

$$I = \lim_{\Delta t \to 0} \frac{1}{\Delta t} \left\{ \int_{-\infty}^{\infty} R(y) \left[\int_{-\infty}^{\infty} q_{\{x\}}(x, t | x_0, t_0) q_{\{x\}}(y, t + \Delta t | x, t) \, dx \right] dy \right.$$

$$\left. - \int_{-\infty}^{\infty} R(y) q_{\{x\}}(y, t | x_0, t_0) \, dy \right\} \qquad (4\text{-}121)$$

Further assume that the arbitrary function $R(y)$ can be developed in a Taylor's series about the point x,

$$R(y) = R(x) + (y - x)R'(x) + \frac{(y - x)^2}{2!} R''(x) + \frac{(y - x)^3}{3!} R'''(x)$$

$$+ \cdots \qquad (4\text{-}122)$$

Substituting (4-122) into (4-121) and integrating first on y,

$$I = \int_{-\infty}^{\infty} \left[R'(x)A(x, t) + \frac{1}{2!} R''(x)B(x, t) \right.$$

$$\left. + \frac{1}{3!} R'''(x)C(x, t) + \cdots \right] q_{\{x\}}(x, t | x_0, t_0) \, dx \qquad (4\text{-}123)$$

where

$$A(x, t) = \lim_{\Delta t \to 0} \frac{1}{\Delta t} \int_{-\infty}^{\infty} (y - x) q_{\{x\}}(y, t + \Delta t | x, t) \, dy$$

$$B(x, t) = \lim_{\Delta t \to 0} \frac{1}{\Delta t} \int_{-\infty}^{\infty} (y - x)^2 q_{\{x\}}(y, t + \Delta t | x, t) \, dy \qquad (4\text{-}124)$$

$$C(x, t) = \lim_{\Delta t \to 0} \frac{1}{\Delta t} \int_{-\infty}^{\infty} (y - x)^3 q_{\{x\}}(y, t + \Delta t | x, t) \, dt$$

. . . .

In obtaining (4-123), use has been made of the normalization condition that for any x, t and Δt

$$\int_{-\infty}^{\infty} q_{\{x\}}(y, t + \Delta t | x, t)\, dy = 1$$

The functions defined in Eqs. (4-124) give the rates of various moments of the increment in $X(t)$ conditional on $X(t) = x$. They are called the *derivate moments*.‡ It is sometimes more indicative to write

$$A(x, t) = \lim_{\Delta t \to 0} \frac{1}{\Delta t} E[X(t + \Delta t) - X(t)|X(t) = x]$$

$$B(x, t) = \lim_{\Delta t \to 0} \frac{1}{\Delta t} E\{[X(t + \Delta t) - X(t)]^2|X(t) = x\} \qquad (4\text{-}124a)$$

$$C(x, t) = \lim_{\Delta t \to 0} \frac{1}{\Delta t} E\{[X(t + \Delta t) - X(t)]^3|X(t) = x\}$$

. . . .

The integration in (4-123) can now be carried out by parts for each term. By use of the assumption (4-119), the integration leads to

$$I = \int_{-\infty}^{\infty} R(x) \left[-\frac{\partial}{\partial x}(A q_{\{x\}}) + \frac{1}{2}\frac{\partial^2}{\partial x^2}(B q_{\{x\}}) \right.$$
$$\left. - \frac{1}{3!}\frac{\partial^3}{\partial x^3}(C q_{\{x\}}) + \cdots \right] dx \qquad (4\text{-}125)$$

where for brevity the arguments of $q_{\{x\}}(x, t|x_0, t_0)$, $A(x, t)$, $B(x, t)$, $C(x, t)$, . . . have been omitted. It follows from a combination of (4-118) and (4-125) that

$$\int_{-\infty}^{\infty} R(x) \left[\frac{\partial}{\partial t} q_{\{x\}} + \frac{\partial}{\partial x}(A q_{\{x\}}) - \frac{1}{2}\frac{\partial^2}{\partial x^2}(B q_{\{x\}}) \right.$$
$$\left. + \frac{1}{3!}\frac{\partial^3}{\partial x^3}(C q_{\{x\}}) - \cdots \right] dx = 0 \qquad (4\text{-}126)$$

Since Eq. (4-126) must be valid for any choice of $R(x)$ which satisfies the rather general restriction (4-119) and which can be expanded in a Taylor series, it is necessary that

$$\frac{\partial}{\partial t} q_{\{x\}} + \frac{\partial}{\partial x}(A q_{\{x\}}) - \frac{1}{2}\frac{\partial^2}{\partial x^2}(B q_{\{x\}})$$
$$+ \frac{1}{3!}\frac{\partial^3}{\partial x^3}(C q_{\{x\}}) - \cdots = 0 \qquad (4\text{-}127)$$

‡ The names were used by Moyal. See J. E. Moyal, Stochastic Processes and Statistical Physics, *J. Roy. Statist. Soc. (London)*, **B11**:150–210 (1949).

Equation (4-127) is the Fokker-Planck equation for the transition probability density $q_{\{X\}}(x, t|x_0, t_0)$ for a one-dimensional Markov process. This equation is also known as the Kolmogorov *forward* equation. The adjective *forward* refers to the fact that $(\partial/\partial t) q_{\{X\}}$ is a derivative with respect to the later time.

In passing we remark that the Kolmogorov *backward* equation reads

$$\frac{\partial}{\partial t_0} q_{\{X\}} + A \frac{\partial}{\partial x_0} q_{\{X\}} + \frac{1}{2} B \frac{\partial^2}{\partial x_0{}^2} q_{\{X\}} + \frac{1}{3!} C \frac{\partial^3}{\partial x_0{}^3} q_{\{X\}} + \cdots = 0 \quad (4\text{-}128)$$

which is the adjoint of Eq. (4-127). Here, the coefficients A, B, C, $\ldots$ should be expressed as functions of t_0 and x_0; that is, they are given by Eqs. (4-124) with t and x replaced by t_0 and x_0, respectively. The adjective *backward*, of course, refers to the fact that $(\partial/\partial t_0)q_{\{X\}}$ is a derivative with respect to the earlier time. The existence and uniqueness of the solutions to the Kolmogorov forward and backward equations in which only the coefficients A and B are nonzero were studied by Feller.[‡] In particular, if the boundary conditions are natural,[¶] then both equations yield the same unique solution subject to the condition

$$q_{\{X\}}(x, t_0|x_0, t_0) = \delta(x - x_0) \qquad (4\text{-}129)$$

Equation (4-129) states that no change of state may occur if the transition time is zero. It is interesting to note that besides the transition probability density $q_{\{X\}}(x, t|x_0, t)$, Eqs. (4-127) and (4-128) are satisfied by other functions corresponding to initial conditions other than Eq. (4-129). In particular, the backward equation (4-128) is also satisfied by the transition distribution function

$$F_{\{X\}}(x, t|x_0, t_0) = \int_{-\infty}^{x+} q_{\{X\}}(u, t|x_0, t_0) \, du \qquad (4\text{-}130)$$

This is easily seen since the independent variables in Eq. (4-128) are t_0 and x_0, and integration of this equation on x does not change the form of the equation. However, here we require the initial condition

$$F_{\{X\}}(x, t_0|x_0, t_0) = \begin{cases} 1 & x \geq x_0 \\ 0 & x < x_0 \end{cases} \qquad (4\text{-}131)$$

Similarly, the solution to the forward equation (4-127) is the uncondi-

---

[‡] W. Feller, The Parabolic Differential Equations and the Associated Semigroups of Transformations, *Ann. Math.*, **55**:468–519 (1952).

[¶] A natural boundary condition is one which is automatically satisfied by the fundamental solution of a differential equation. Such cases usually occur when a boundary is inaccessible; for example, a random process $X(t)$ can never take on the value ∞ or $-\infty$.

tional probability density

$$p_{\{x\}}(x, t) = \int_{-\infty}^{\infty} q_{\{x\}}(x, t|x_0, t_0)f(x_0)\,dx_0 \qquad (4\text{-}132)$$

if the following condition is imposed:

$$p_{\{x\}}(x, t_0) = f(x) \qquad (4\text{-}133)$$

From here onward our discussion will be limited to the forward equation. The procedure to obtain a solution to this equation can be discussed only when the specific functional forms of the coefficients A, B, etc., are known. This matter will be considered in Chaps. 5, 6, and 8 in connection with different structural dynamics problems.

The Fokker-Planck equation for the transition probability density of a Markov vector process can be derived in a similar way. We begin with the Chapman-Kolmogorov-Smoluchowski equation for a multidimensional Markov process (4-114b) and treat the multifold integral

$$J = \int_{-\infty}^{\infty} \cdots \int_{-\infty}^{\infty} R(\mathbf{y}) \frac{\partial}{\partial t} q_{\{x\}}(\mathbf{y}, t|\mathbf{z}, t_0)\,dy_1\,dy_2 \cdots dy_n \qquad (4\text{-}134)$$

where $R(\mathbf{y})$ is an arbitrary function of y_j, $j = 1, 2, \ldots, n$, which goes to zero sufficiently fast as any y_j approaches $+\infty$ or $-\infty$. Specifically, we assume that for any j and $m = l + r + \cdots + s$, as $y_j \to \pm\infty$,

$$\frac{\partial^m}{\partial y_1{}^l\,\partial y_2{}^r \cdots \partial y_n{}^s} R(\mathbf{y}) \to 0 \qquad (4\text{-}135)$$

We also assume that $R(\mathbf{y})$ can be expanded in the form of a Taylor series about a point $\mathbf{x}$, that is,

$$\begin{aligned}
R(\mathbf{y}) = R(\mathbf{x}) &+ (y_j - x_j)\frac{\partial R(\mathbf{x})}{\partial x_j} \\
&+ \frac{1}{2!}(y_j - x_j)(y_k - x_k)\frac{\partial^2 R(\mathbf{x})}{\partial x_j\,\partial x_k} \\
&+ \frac{1}{3!}(y_j - x_j)(y_k - x_k)(y_l - x_l)\frac{\partial^3 R(\mathbf{x})}{\partial x_j\,\partial x_k\,\partial x_l} + \cdots \quad (4\text{-}136)
\end{aligned}$$

where a repeated index represents the summation over $1, 2, \ldots, n$. Thus, the second term on the right-hand side of (4-136) indicates a single summation, the third term a double summation, etc. Following a procedure similar to that used in the derivation of the Fokker-Planck equation for a one-dimensional Markov process, we are led to

$$\begin{aligned}
\frac{\partial}{\partial t} q_{\{x\}} &+ \frac{\partial}{\partial x_j}(A_j q_{\{x\}}) - \frac{1}{2!}\frac{\partial^2}{\partial x_j\,\partial x_k}(B_{jk}q_{\{x\}}) \\
&+ \frac{1}{3!}\frac{\partial^3}{\partial x_j\,\partial x_k\,\partial x_l}(C_{jkl}q_{\{x\}}) \cdots = 0 \quad (4\text{-}137)
\end{aligned}$$

where $q_{\{x\}}$ and A_j, B_{jk}, C_{jkl}, $\cdots$ are abbreviations for $q_{\{x\}}(\mathbf{x}, t | \mathbf{z}, t_0)$

$$A_j(\mathbf{x}, t) = \lim_{\Delta t \to 0} \frac{1}{\Delta t} \int \cdots \int (y_j - x_j) q_{\{x\}}(\mathbf{y}, t + \Delta t | \mathbf{x}, t) dy_1 \, dy_2$$
$$\cdots dy_n$$

$$B_{jk}(\mathbf{x}, t) = \lim_{\Delta t \to 0} \frac{1}{\Delta t} \int \cdots \int (y_j - x_j)(y_k - x_k)$$
$$q_{\{x\}}(\mathbf{y}, t + \Delta t | \mathbf{x}, t) \, dy_1 \, dy_2 \cdots dy_n \quad (4\text{-}138)$$

$$C_{jkl}(\mathbf{x}, t) = \lim_{\Delta t \to 0} \frac{1}{\Delta t} \int \cdots \int (y_j - x_j)(y_k - x_k)(y_l - x_l)$$
$$q_{\{x\}}(\mathbf{y}, t + \Delta t | \mathbf{x}, t) \, dy_1 \, dy_2 \cdots dy_n$$

. . . .

The functions A_j, B_{jk}, C_{jkl}, etc., may be expressed more indicatively as follows:

$$A_j(\mathbf{x}, t) = \lim_{\Delta t \to 0} \frac{1}{\Delta t} E[\Delta X_j | \mathbf{X}(t) = \mathbf{x}]$$

$$B_{jk}(\mathbf{x}, t) = \lim_{\Delta t \to 0} \frac{1}{\Delta t} E[(\Delta X_j)(\Delta X_k) | \mathbf{X}(t) = \mathbf{x}] \qquad (4\text{-}138a)$$

$$C_{jkl}(\mathbf{x}, t) = \lim_{\Delta t \to 0} \frac{1}{\Delta t} E[(\Delta X_j)(\Delta X_k)(\Delta X_l) | \mathbf{X}(t) = \mathbf{x}]$$

. . . .

where ΔX_j is an abbreviation for $X_j(t + \Delta t) - X_j(t)$, etc. The solution of Eq. (4-137) is the transition probability density if it is required to satisfy the condition

$$q_{\{x\}}(\mathbf{x}, t_0 | \mathbf{z}, t_0) = \prod_{j=1}^{n} \delta(x_j - z_j) \qquad (4\text{-}139)$$

4.11 / MARKOV PROCESSES IN THE WIDE SENSE

The definition of a *wide-sense* Markov process is based on a special property possessed by its variance and covariance functions. A second-order random process $X(t)$ is said to be Markovian in the wide sense if and only if its correlation-coefficient function $\rho_{XX}(x, u)$ satisfies the functional equation‡

$$\rho_{XX}(s, u) = \rho_{XX}(s, t)\rho_{XX}(t, u) \qquad s \leq t \leq u \qquad (4\text{-}140)$$

‡ In advanced probability theory a wide-sense Markov process is defined by

$$\hat{E}[X(t_n) | X(t_{n-1}), \ldots, X(t_1)] = \hat{E}[X(t_n) | X(t_{n-1})] \qquad t_n > t_{n-1} > \cdots > t_1$$

with probability 1, where $\hat{E}[\ ]$ denotes the best mean-square estimate. Then Eq. (4-140) is a necessary and sufficient condition. Since the best mean-square estimates have not been discussed in this book, we use Eq. (4-140) as a definition. See J. L. Doob, "Stochastic Processes," p. 233, Wiley, New York, 1953.

A theorem attributed to Doob‡ states that if $X(t)$ is Gaussian, then being wide-sense Markovian is both necessary and sufficient for it to be strictly Markovian. Recall that the adjective *wide-sense* has been used to describe a weaker property for a stationary random process, and that for a Gaussian process wide-sense (weak) stationarity coincides with strict-sense (strong) stationarity. Therefore, the relation between wide-sense and strict-sense Markov processes is similar to that between weakly and strongly stationary processes in this regard. However, a dissimilar aspect between these two cases should be noted. While strong stationarity implies weak stationarity, it is not always true that a strict-sense Markov non-Gaussian process must be one in the wide sense.

If a random process $X(t)$ is both wide-sense Markovian and weakly stationary, then

$$\rho_{XX}(t_3 - t_1) = \rho_{XX}(t_2 - t_1)\rho_{XX}(t_3 - t_2) \qquad t_1 \leq t_2 \leq t_3 \qquad (4\text{-}140a)$$

The nontrivial solution to (4-140a) is

$$\rho_{XX}(\tau) = \exp\left(-\beta|\tau|\right) \tag{4-141}$$

where $\beta = -\ln \rho_{XX}(1)$ is a positive constant, and $\tau = t_k - t_j$. A generalization¶ of Eq. (4-141) for an n-dimensional weakly stationary and wide-sense Markov vector $\mathbf{X}(t) = \{X_1(t), X_2(t), \ldots, X_n(t)\}$ is

$$\varrho(\tau) = \begin{cases} \exp\left(-\mathbf{Q}\tau\right) & \tau > 0 \\ \exp\left(\mathbf{Q}'\tau\right) & \tau < 0 \end{cases} \tag{4-141a}$$

where

$$\varrho(\tau) = \begin{bmatrix} \rho_{X_1X_1}(t, t+\tau) & \rho_{X_1X_2}(t, t+\tau) & \cdots & \rho_{X_1X_n}(t, t+\tau) \\ \rho_{X_2X_1}(t, t+\tau) & \rho_{X_2X_2}(t, t+\tau) & \cdots & \rho_{X_2X_n}(t, t+\tau) \\ \cdots\cdots\cdots\cdots\cdots\cdots\cdots\cdots\cdots\cdots\cdots\cdots\cdots\cdots \\ \rho_{X_nX_1}(t, t+\tau) & \rho_{X_nX_2}(t, t+\tau) & \cdots & \rho_{X_nX_n}(t, t+\tau) \end{bmatrix}$$

is an $n \times n$ matrix of correlation-coefficient functions, which, by definition, satisfies§

$$\varrho(\tau) = \varrho'(-\tau) \tag{4-142}$$

and $\mathbf{Q}$ is a constant matrix. Equation (4-141a) is the solution to the matrix functional relation

$$\varrho(t_3 - t_1) = \varrho(t_2 - t_1)\varrho(t_3 - t_2) \tag{4-140b}$$

Equation (4-141) or Eq. (4-141a) becomes the necessary and sufficient condition for the random process $X(t)$ or the random vector $\mathbf{X}(t)$ to be

‡ *Ibid.*, p. 90.

¶ Wang and Uhlenbeck, *loc. cit.*

§ A prime on a matrix symbol indicates transposition rather than a differentiation.

strictly Markovian if $X(t)$ or $\mathbf{X}(t)$ is also Gaussian. It is clear that matrix $\mathbf{Q}$ can be computed from

$$\mathbf{Q} = - \left[\frac{d}{d\tau} \boldsymbol{\varrho}(\tau) \right] \boldsymbol{\varrho}^{-1}(\tau) \qquad (4\text{-}143)$$

Note that $\boldsymbol{\varrho}^{-1}(\tau)$ always exists since $\exp(-\mathbf{Q}\tau)$ is never singular. In fact, $\boldsymbol{\varrho}^{-1}(\tau) = \exp(\mathbf{Q}\tau)$. Since the matrix $\mathbf{Q}$ is independent of τ, the computation of this matrix may be simplified by evaluating the right-hand side of Eq. (4-143) at a chosen τ value, say $\tau = 0$.

Let us explore some implications that are a result of a weakly stationary random process $X(t)$ being Markovian in the wide sense. For simplicity assume $E[X(t)] = 0$ and denote $E[X^2(t)]$ by $\sigma_X{}^2$. Then the correlation function is the same as the covariance function, which is

$$R_{XX}(\tau) = \Gamma_{XX}(\tau) = \sigma_X{}^2 \exp(-\beta|\tau|) \qquad (4\text{-}144)$$

and the spectral density is obtained as

$$
\begin{aligned}
\Phi_{XX}(\omega) &= \frac{1}{2\pi} \int_{-\infty}^{\infty} \sigma_X{}^2 \exp(-\beta|\tau| - i\omega\tau)\, d\tau \\
&= \frac{\sigma_X{}^2}{2\pi} \left\{ \int_{-\infty}^{0} \exp[(\beta - i\omega)\tau]\, d\tau + \int_{0}^{\infty} \exp[-(\beta + i\omega)\tau]\, d\tau \right\} \\
&= \frac{\sigma_X{}^2}{2\pi} \left(\frac{1}{\beta - i\omega} + \frac{1}{\beta + i\omega} \right) = \frac{\sigma_X{}^2 \beta}{\pi(\beta^2 + \omega^2)} \qquad (4\text{-}145)
\end{aligned}
$$

Equations (4-144) and (4-145) are plotted in Figs. 4.5 and 4.6, respectively, for different β values.

Fig. 4.5 Autocorrelation functions, Eq. (4-144), of weakly stationary and wide-sense Markovian random processes.

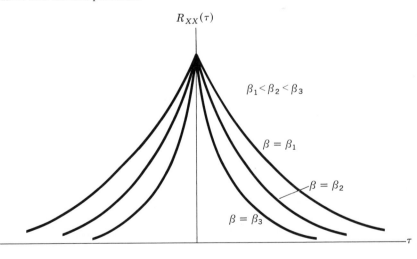

$R_{XX}(\tau)$

$\beta_1 < \beta_2 < \beta_3$

$\beta = \beta_1$

$\beta = \beta_2$

$\beta = \beta_3$

Two important observations can be made from the graphs in Figs. 4.5 and 4.6. Firstly, the second derivative of an autocorrelation function of a weakly stationary and wide-sense Markovian random process does not exist at $\tau = 0$; therefore, such a random process is not mean-square differentiable.‡ Secondly, the greater the parameter β the faster an autocorrelation function falls off (exponentially) from the origin $\tau = 0$, and on the spectral density plot, the greater is the interval about $\omega = 0$ that the spectral density function remains nearly flat. A rough estimate is that $R_{XX}(\tau)$ falls off to negligible magnitude for $\tau > 3\beta^{-1}$ and that $\Phi_{XX}(\omega)$ is practically constant for $\omega < 0.2\beta$.

It is interesting to note that one white noise is a limiting case of a weakly stationary and wide-sense Markov process. To see this we rewrite Eq. (4-145) as follows:

$$\Phi_{XX}(\omega) = \frac{\sigma_X^2}{\pi\beta}\left(1 + \frac{\omega^2}{\beta^2}\right)^{-1} \tag{4-145a}$$

If both σ_X^2 and β increase without limit while the ratio σ_X^2/β remains a constant, say $I/2$, then

$$\lim_{\beta\to\infty}\Phi_{XX}(\omega) = \frac{I}{2\pi}\lim_{\beta\to\infty}\left(1 + \frac{\omega^2}{\beta^2}\right)^{-1}$$

$$= \frac{I}{2\pi} \tag{4-146}$$

‡ See Sec. 3.6.

Fig. 4.6 Spectral density functions, Eq. (4-145), of weakly stationary and wide-sense Markovian random processes.

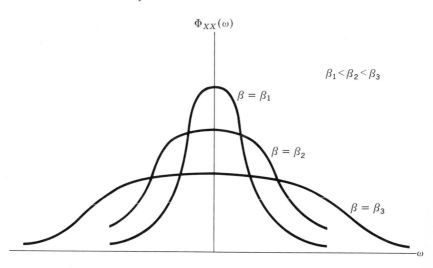

EXERCISES

4-1. Let $X_1, X_2, \ldots, X_n$ be a sequence of independent and identically distributed random variables. Let μ and σ^2, which are both finite, be their common mean and variance. Show that the sum

$$S_n = \sum_{k=1}^{n} X_n$$

when centralized and normalized to a zero mean and a unit standard deviation, tends to the unit Gaussian random variable as n tends to infinity. This statement is known as the central limit theorem for independent identically distributed random variables.

4-2. Let X be a Gaussian random variable with a characteristic function

$$M_X(\theta) = \exp\left(i\mu\theta - \frac{\sigma^2\theta^2}{2}\right)$$

Show that

$$E[X^n] = \mu E[X^{n-1}] + (n - 1)\sigma^2 E[X^{n-2}]$$

4-3. Let X and Y be jointly distributed Gaussian random variables with a joint probability density given in Eq. (4-26). Find two new random variables U and V by a linear transformation such that U and V are independent. Determine the means and variances of the new random variables.

4-4. Let $\mathbf{Y}$ be an n-dimensional Gaussian random vector and let $\mathbf{X} = \mathbf{AY}$, where $\mathbf{A}$ is an $m \times n$ matrix of transformation. Show that the characteristic function of $\mathbf{X}$ has the form of Eq. (4-43) and therefore is an m-dimensional Gaussian random vector.

4-5. Let $X(t)$ be a random process and $Y(t) = (d/dt) X(t)$ be the mean-square derivative of $X(t)$. Give the general condition so that $E[Y(t_1)Y(t_2) \cdots Y(t_n)]$ exists. Show that if $X(t)$ is Gaussian, then the condition reduces to the existence of the mixed second derivative of $E[X(t_j)X(t_k)]$.

4-6. Let N be a Poisson-distributed random variable having a probability function

$$P_N(n) = e^{-\mu} \frac{\mu^n}{(n!)} \qquad n = 0, 1, \cdots$$

Show that $X = (N - \mu)\mu^{-\frac{1}{2}}$ approaches a Gaussian random variable as μ approaches infinity.

4-7. Show that the probability function of a Poisson random process with nonstationary increments is

$$P_{\{N\}}(n, t) = \frac{1}{n!} \left[\int_0^t \lambda(\tau)\, d\tau\right]^n \exp\left[-\int_0^t \lambda(\tau)\, d\tau\right]$$

where $\lambda(t)$ is the expected arrival rate at time t.

4-8. Determine the autocorrelation function of the random process

$$X(t) = \sum_{k=1}^{N(t)} Y_k \mathbb{1}(t - \tau_k)$$

where $N(t)$ is a Poisson process with stationary increments, $\mathbb{1}(t - \tau_k)$ is Heaviside's step function, and Y_k are independent random variables identically distributed and having a finite mean and a finite variance.

4-9. Determine the autocorrelation function of the random process

$$X(t) = \sum_{k=1}^{N(t)} Y_k\, w(t - \tau_k)$$

where $N(t)$ is a Poisson process with stationary increments, Y_k are independent random variables identically distributed as a random variable Y with $E[Y] = 0$ and $E[Y^2] < \infty$, and

$$w(t - \tau_k) = \begin{cases} \dfrac{1}{\Delta} & t \geq \tau_k \geq t - \Delta \\ 0 & \text{otherwise} \end{cases}$$

Show that $X(t)$ approaches to a white noise as Δ tends to zero.

4-10. Show that the following random process approaches a stationary wide-sense Markov process at large t:

$$X(t) = \sum_{k=1}^{N(t)} Y_k \exp\left[-a(t - \tau_k)\right]\mathbb{1}(t - \tau_k)$$

where $N(t)$ is a Poisson process with stationary increments, $\mathbb{1}(t - \tau_k)$ is Heaviside's step function, $a > 0$, and Y_k are independent random variables identically distributed as Y with $E[Y] = 0$ and $E[Y^2] < \infty$.

4-11. Give a complete derivation of the Fokker-Planck equation for the transition probability density of an n-dimensional Markov-vector process.

4-12.‡ Show that if $\mathbf{X}(t) = \{X_1(t),\ X_2(t),\ \ldots,\ X_n(t)\}$ is a stationary Markov vector which is also Gaussian, then the matrix of correlation-coefficient functions $\varrho(t_k - t_j)$ satisfies the functional relation

$$\varrho(t_3 - t_1) = \varrho(t_2 - t_1)\varrho(t_3 - t_2)$$

‡ See Wang and Uhlenbeck, *loc. cit.*

5 | LINEAR STRUCTURES WITH SINGLE DEGREE OF FREEDOM

Having discussed the fundamentals of a theory of random variables and random processes, we now turn to the application of this theory to structural dynamics problems. The problems of linear structures will be considered in three consecutive chapters, beginning with the present one devoted to systems with a single degree of freedom. It is, of course, natural to gain an insight into the basic physical relationships of linear structures by first confining oneself to the simplest configuration and postponing the consideration of structural complexities until the following two chapters. The importance of a thorough understanding of this simplest case cannot be overemphasized, since in it analogies can usually be found to the results to be expected from more complicated cases.

5.1 / A REVIEW OF THE DETERMINISTIC THEORY

It is assumed that the reader is familiar with the deterministic theory of mechanical vibrations. However, a brief review of certain basic relations of the deterministic theory is in order to facilitate the later discussion of the probabilistic theory.

Consider the differential equation governing the motion of a typical mass-spring-dashpot system

$$m\ddot{x} + c\dot{x} + kx = f(t) \qquad (5\text{-}1)$$

or

$$m\ddot{x} + c(\dot{x} - \dot{x}_0) + k(x - x_0) = 0 \qquad (5\text{-}2)$$

In the first case the system is excited by the external force $f(t)$. This situation has been represented schematically in Fig. 1.1. In the second case, the excitation is the motion of the foundation $x_0 = x_0(t)$. However, Eq. (5-2) can be converted to the same form as Eq. (5-1) by letting $y = x - x_0$. Then

$$m\ddot{y} + c\dot{y} + ky = -m\ddot{x}_0 \qquad (5\text{-}3)$$

Therefore, imposing a certain motion at the foundation is equivalent to applying an inertia force $f(t) = -m\ddot{x}_0$ to the system, and the study of both types of excitations can be combined into one. For convenience, we shall use Eq. (5-1) as the basis of our discussions. When there is no need for distinction, an excitation to a mechanical system will be nondiscriminatively called an input, which may be either an external force or an imposed motion at the foundation, or both. Correspondingly, the induced response of the system, either an absolute displacement such as x

in Eq. (5-1), or a relative displacement such as y in Eq. (5-3), or even a function of x or y, may be nondiscriminatively called an output.

By introducing $\omega_0^2 = k/m$, $\zeta = c/2\omega_0 m = c/2\sqrt{km}$, Eq. (5-1) is changed to the so-called standard form

$$\ddot{x} + 2\zeta\omega_0\dot{x} + \omega_0^2 x = \frac{f(t)}{m} \tag{5-4}$$

Thus a single-degree-of-freedom linear system is characterized by the mass m and the two constants ω_0 and ζ appearing on the left-hand side of (5-4). The first constant ω_0 is the undamped natural frequency, and the second constant ζ is the ratio of the actual damping to the critical damping.

For our purposes it is more convenient to characterize a linear system by its response to specific inputs, in particular, the sinusoidal input and the impulsive input.

For a sinusoidal input,

$$f(t) = A \exp(i\omega t) \tag{5-5}$$

where A is a complex constant, the solution to (5-4) may be written as follows:

$$x = B \exp[(-\zeta + i\sqrt{1 - \zeta^2})\omega_0 t] + \frac{A \exp(i\omega t)}{Z(\omega)} \tag{5-6}$$

In this solution, B is a complex constant of integration to be determined from the initial conditions, and $Z(\omega) = m(\omega_0^2 - \omega^2 + 2i\zeta\omega_0\omega)$ is a complex function of the exciting frequency ω. The function $Z(\omega)$ is called the *mechanical impedance* of the system. The reciprocal of the mechanical impedance,

$$H(\omega) = \frac{1}{Z(\omega)} = \frac{1}{m(\omega_0^2 - \omega^2 + 2i\zeta\omega_0\omega)}$$

is called the *frequency response function* or the *transfer function* of the system. Usually, the real part of Eq. (5-5) is taken to represent the exciting force. Then only the real part of Eq. (5-6) represents the actual response of the system. The first term on the right-hand side of (5-6) is the complementary function of the differential equation representing the free vibration of the system, and the second term is the particular solution representing the forced vibration of the system. Note that the separation of these two terms is not unique, but the sum always results in a unique solution after the imposition of the initial conditions.

For an impulsive input,

$$f(t) = C \delta(t) \tag{5-7}$$

where $\delta(t)$ is the Dirac delta function, and C is a real constant. The solution for Eq. (5-4) now may be expressed as the following sum of a complementary function and a particular solution:

$$x = D \exp\left[(-\zeta + i\sqrt{1 - \zeta^2})\omega_0 t\right] + Ch(t) \tag{5-8}$$

In passing, we note that although the complementary functions in Eqs. (5-6) and (5-8) are of the same form, we purposely use different symbols for the arbitrary constants. The significance of such a distinction will be pointed out later.

Since the separation of the two terms on the right-hand side of (5-8) is not unique, we are free to choose any suitable particular solution $Ch(t)$ which satisfies Eq. (5-4) with the forcing function specified in (5-7). The form to be chosen is one which renders the arbitrary constant of the complementary function equal to zero if the system is at rest immediately prior to the impulse excitation. Immediately after the impulse excitation the mass gains a momentum of magnitude C; but there is still no time for a displacement, and thereafter the system is left without excitation. The above reasoning leads us to write the particular solution in the *same* form as the free vibration, but satisfying the conditions

$$Ch(0) = 0 \quad \text{and} \quad C\dot{h}(0) = \frac{C}{m} \tag{5-9}$$

The imposition of (5-9) gives

$$h(t) = \begin{cases} \dfrac{-i}{\sqrt{1 - \zeta^2}\,\omega_0 m} \exp\left[(-\zeta + i\sqrt{1 - \zeta^2})\omega_0 t\right] & t \geq 0 \\ 0 & t < 0 \end{cases} \tag{5-10}$$

with the understanding that only the real part represents the actual motion. If the real form is preferred,

$$h(t) = \begin{cases} \dfrac{1}{\omega_d m} \exp\left(-\zeta\omega_0 t\right) \sin \omega_d t & t \geq 0 \\ 0 & t < 0 \end{cases} \tag{5-10a}$$

where ω_d, the damped natural frequency of the system, has been written for $\sqrt{1 - \zeta^2}\,\omega_0$. The function $h(t)$ is called the *impulse response function* of the system. It is to be noted that although the particular solution $Ch(t)$ in (5-8) is obtained by considering the special case where the system is originally at rest immediately prior to the impulse excitation, Eq. (5-8) with the special form of $h(t)$ given in Eq. (5-10) is applicable to other initial conditions, and for these cases the constant D is no longer zero.

With the knowledge of the system's response to a sinusoidal input or to an impulsive input, we can compute the response to any arbitrary input. For example, an arbitrary forcing function can be synthesized from an aggregate of infinitesimal sinusoidal forces. Assuming that the excitation begins at $t = 0$, that is, $f(t) = 0$ for $t < 0$, we may write

$$f(t) = \int_{-\infty}^{\infty} \bar{f}(\omega) \exp (i\omega t) \, d\omega \qquad (5\text{-}11)$$

where

$$\bar{f}(\omega) = \frac{1}{2\pi} \int_{0}^{\infty} f(t) \exp (-i\omega t) \, dt \qquad (5\text{-}12)$$

is the Fourier transform of $f(t)$ and where it has been tacitly assumed that such a transform exists. Since the principle of superposition holds for a linear system, we have for the response of the system to an arbitrary forcing function $f(t)$ the solution

$$x = B \exp [(-\zeta + i \sqrt{1 - \zeta^2})\omega_0 t] + \int_{-\infty}^{\infty} H(\omega)\bar{f}(\omega) \exp (i\omega t) \, d\omega \qquad (5\text{-}13)$$

Alternatively, the same forcing function $f(t)$ can be constructed from a sequence of impulses,

$$f(t) = \int_{0}^{\infty} f(\tau) \, \delta(t - \tau) \, d\tau \qquad (5\text{-}14)$$

Application of Eq. (5-8) leads to

$$x = D \exp [(-\zeta + i \sqrt{1 - \zeta^2})\omega_0 t] + \int_{0}^{\infty} f(\tau)h(t - \tau) \, d\tau \qquad (5\text{-}15)$$

Since $h(t - \tau) = 0$ for $\tau > t$, the upper limit of the integral in (5-15) may be changed to t:

$$x = D \exp [(-\zeta + i \sqrt{1 - \zeta^2})\omega_0 t] + \int_{0}^{t} f(\tau)h(t - \tau) \, d\tau \qquad (5\text{-}15a)$$

The integral on the right-hand side of (5-15a) is known as the *Duhamel integral.*

The need for a distinction between the arbitrary constants B and D can now be appreciated by comparing Eqs. (5-13) and (5-15a) at $t = 0$. The comparison shows that if $f(t) = 0$ for $t < 0$, then

$$\text{Re} \, [D] = \text{Re} \left[B + \int_{-\infty}^{\infty} H(\omega)\bar{f}(\omega) \, d\omega \right]$$

That B is different from D here in spite of the same form taken by the first term in (5-13) and the first term in (5-15a) substantiates our earlier statement that the separation of the complementary function and the particular solution is not unique.

A linear system is said to be *stable* if, without excitation and for any initial conditions, the motion tends to diminish. Then the response of a stable linear system to an arbitrary excitation is practically independent of the initial conditions after the excitation has been acting for a time much greater than its natural period. When the influence of the initial conditions on the overall motion becomes negligible, the response is said to have reached the *steady-state* condition. If only the steady-state motion is of interest, it is convenient to regard the excitation as having begun from the infinite past. Then by use of either the frequency response function or the impulse response function, the steady-state motion can be computed as follows:

$$x_{\text{steady}} = \int_{-\infty}^{\infty} H(\omega)\tilde{f}(\omega) \exp{(i\omega t)} \, d\omega = \int_{-\infty}^{\infty} f(\tau)h(t - \tau) \, d\tau \qquad (5\text{-}16)$$

Here, of course,

$$\tilde{f}(\omega) = \frac{1}{2\pi} \int_{-\infty}^{\infty} f(t) \exp{(-i\omega t)} \, dt \qquad (5\text{-}12a)$$

Equation (5-16) suggests that the functions $H(\omega)$ and $h(t)$ are related. Indeed, if we rewrite this equation as

$$\int_{-\infty}^{\infty} H(\omega) \left[\frac{1}{2\pi} \int_{-\infty}^{\infty} f(\tau) \exp{(- i\omega\tau)} \, d\tau \right] \exp{(i\omega t)} \, d\omega = \int_{-\infty}^{\infty} f(\tau)h(t - \tau) \, d\tau$$

then it becomes obvious that by letting $u = t - \tau$

$$h(u) = \frac{1}{2\pi} \int_{-\infty}^{\infty} H(\omega) \exp{(i\omega u)} \, d\omega$$

and, therefore, $\qquad\qquad\qquad\qquad\qquad\qquad\qquad\qquad\qquad (5\text{-}17)$

$$H(\omega) = \int_{-\infty}^{\infty} h(t) \exp{(-i\omega t)} \, dt$$

Except for the fact that the coefficient $1/(2\pi)$ has been interchanged, the functions $h(t)$ and $H(\omega)$ are seen to be Fourier transform pairs. That Eq. (5-16) implies Eqs. (5-12a) and (5-17), and conversely, is of course true for any two pairs of Fourier transforms such as $f(t)$ and $\tilde{f}(\omega)$, $h(t)$ and $(2\pi)^{-1}H(\omega)$. This relation is known as the *convolution theorem* of Fourier transformations.

The results concerning the frequency response function and the impulse response function of a linear system governed by a second-order differential equation can be generalized. If the governing equation is

$$\sum_{k=0}^{n} a_k \frac{d^k x}{dt^k} = f(t) \tag{5-18}$$

where the a_k are real constants and $a_n \neq 0$, then the frequency response function of the system is given by

$$H(\omega) = \Big[\sum_{k=0}^{n} a_k (i\omega)^k \Big]^{-1} \tag{5-19}$$

The impulse response function $h(t)$ satisfies the homogeneous equation

$$\sum_{k=0}^{n} a_k \frac{d^k h}{dt^k} = 0 \tag{5-20}$$

and the initial conditions that, at $t = 0$,

$$\frac{d^{n-1} h}{dt^{n-1}} = \frac{1}{a_k} \qquad \frac{d^{n-2} h}{dt^{n-2}} = \cdots = \frac{dh}{dt} = h = 0 \tag{5-21}$$

Equations (5-17) remain valid in the more general case.

5.2 / SYSTEM RESPONSE TO RANDOM EXCITATIONS

In the deterministic theory of a linear single-degree-of-freedom dynamic system as reviewed in Sec. 5.1, we assume that except for the motion x, every item in the governing equation is precisely known. Then the motion can be precisely computed for a given set of initial conditions. If any of the given items is random, the motion will also be random. In almost all problems encountered by structural dynamicists only random excitations are of major concern, while the other parameters of the system and the initial conditions can be reasonably assumed to be deterministic. In what follows we shall limit our attention to such problems. In particular, we shall consider the second-order stochastic differential equation

$$\ddot{X}(t) + 2\zeta\omega_0\dot{X}(t) + \omega_0^2 X(t) = \frac{1}{m} F(t) \tag{5-22}$$

obtained from replacing the forcing function $f(t)$ in Eq. (5-4) by a random process $F(t)$ and denoting the random motion of the system by $X(t)$. We shall assume that the random excitation begins at $t = 0$. Strictly speaking, Eq. (5-22) is meaningful only if the derivatives of $X(t)$ in this equation exist in one of the senses discussed in Sec. 3.5. Mean-square differentiation, which was considered in Sec. 3.6, will be implied at all times in the following discussion since the existence of such derivatives can be most simply verified.

The solution to Eq. (5-22), expressed in terms of the impulse response function, is

$$X(t) = D \exp\left[(-\zeta + i\sqrt{1 - \zeta^2})\omega_0 t\right] + \int_0^t F(\tau)h(t - \tau)\, d\tau \qquad (5\text{-}23)$$

analogous to Eq. (5-15a). The first term depends only on the initial conditions; therefore it is deterministic. Since the principle of superposition holds for a linear system, we can, for convenience, set aside the deterministic term of the solution. We then write

$$X(t) = \int_0^t F(\tau)h(t - \tau)\, d\tau \qquad (5\text{-}23a)$$

We repeat that this expression gives the total displacement if the system was originally at rest prior to exposure to the excitation (at $t = 0$), but it gives the random deviation from the course of the free vibration if the system was not originally at rest. Equation (5-23a) is a special case of the second equation in (3-67). Therefore, Eqs. (3-72) and (3-73) can be used to find the nth moment function and the nth cumulant function of $X(t)$.

$$E[X(t_1)X(t_2) \cdots X(t_n)] = \int_0^{t_1} \cdots \int_0^{t_n} E[F(\tau_1)F(\tau_2) \cdots F(\tau_n)]$$
$$h(t_1 - \tau_1)h(t_2 - \tau_2) \cdots h(t_n - \tau_n)\, d\tau_1\, d\tau_2 \cdots d\tau_n \qquad (5\text{-}24)$$

and

$$\kappa_n[X(t_1)X(t_2) \cdots X(t_n)] = \int_0^{t_1} \cdots \int_0^{t_n} \kappa_n[F(\tau_1)F(\tau_2) \cdots F(\tau_n)]$$
$$h(t_1 - \tau_1)h(t_2 - \tau_2) \cdots h(t_n - \tau_n)\, d\tau_1\, d\tau_2 \cdots d\tau_n \qquad (5\text{-}25)$$

where use has been made of the fact that $h(t - \tau) = 0$ for $t < \tau$. A moment function or a cumulant function of the response process exists provided the indicated integral, Eq. (5-24) or Eq. (5-25), exists. It is to be recalled, however, that the stochastic integral (5-23a) is well defined in mean square if the correlation function of $X(t)$ computed from (5-24) is finite [cf. condition (3-68)], or, equivalently, if the first two cumulant functions computed from (5-25) are finite. We remark that although the stochastic integral (5-23a) is obtained from the stochastic differential equation (5-22) which involves its derivatives, the existence of the stochastic integral need not imply the existence of its derivatives. This point will be further noted later.

Either Eq. (5-24) or Eq. (5-25) shows how a knowledge of the probabilistic response process, in the form of the moment functions or the cumulant functions of ascending order, can be obtained from the knowledge of the excitation process. The use of Eq. (5-25) is especially desirable if the higher cumulant functions of the excitation process are zero. In particular, if $F(t)$ is Gaussian, then $X(t)$ is also Gaussian (cf. Sec. 4.4), and the only nonzero cumulants are those of the first and second orders which are the same as the mean and covariance functions.

$$
E[X(t)] = \int_0^t E[F(\tau)]h(t - \tau)\, d\tau
$$

$$
\kappa_{XX}(t_1, t_2) = \int_0^{t_1} \int_0^{t_2} \kappa_{FF}(\tau_1, \tau_2)h(t_1 - \tau_1)h(t_2 - \tau_2)\, d\tau_1\, d\tau_2
$$

$$(5\text{-}26)$$

These two functions completely specify a Gaussian response process.

As was mentioned before (page 39), even in a non-Gaussian case, the first- and second-order statistical properties of the response process still provide the most important information about this process, and they are useful in judging the reliability of the system when subjected to random excitations (cf. Sec. 9.5). In Secs. 5.3 and 5.4 we shall further elaborate upon the computation of these statistical properties in the case of weakly stationary excitations and the case of nonstationary excitations. It will be assumed in both cases that we have sufficient knowledge about the excitations to carry out the computations. In practical applications, however, either these statistical properties of the excitation must be estimated by taking averages of the experimental data, or the basic random mechanism in the excitation must be postulated and certain parameters estimated from experimental records.

5.3 / WEAKLY STATIONARY EXCITATIONS

A large number of practical problems involve excitations which may be reasonably assumed to be weakly stationary. For example, an automobile traveling at a constant speed on a superhighway having a weakly homogeneous random roughness senses a weakly stationary excitation. In an actual situation, the automobile may have to slow down or speed up temporarily when following or passing; but if only a small percentage of the total time is spent traveling at varying speeds, then it is permissible to neglect the nonstationary portion of the excitation in assessing, say, the fatigue damage of a structural part on the automobile. Another example of a weakly stationary excitation may be found in the vibrations of aircraft panels induced by jet noise. It is known that the major damage to the panels occurs during takeoff, when the jet engines are operated at maximum power. Clearly, the engine power must be gradually built up to the maximum level and, as the airplane gains speed, gradually reduced to the level required for cruising flight. Therefore, strictly speaking, the generated acoustic pressure is not stationary. However, during the maximum engine power run, which lasts from 1 to 2 min, the generated acoustic pressure measured at a given point on the fuselage or wing surface exhibits a weakly stationary pattern. Therefore, if the purpose of the analysis is to assess the fatigue damage of the panels, it is justifiable to disregard the nonstationary portion of the excitation, which causes only negligible damage.

When the forcing process is weakly stationary, the autocorrelation of the forcing process is a function of the difference in the parametric values,

$$E[F(\tau_1)F(\tau_2)] = R_{FF}(\tau_1 - \tau_2)$$

This autocorrelation function can be written as the inverse Fourier transform of the spectral density,

$$R_{FF}(\tau_1 - \tau_2) = \int_{-\infty}^{\infty} \Phi_{FF}(\omega) \exp\left[i\omega(\tau_1 - \tau_2)\right] d\omega \qquad (5\text{-}27)$$

If this relationship is used to compute the correlation function of the response, we have

$$\phi_{XX}(t_1, t_2) = \int_0^{t_1} d\tau_1 \int_0^{t_2} d\tau_2 \int_{-\infty}^{\infty} d\omega$$
$$\Phi_{FF}(\omega) \exp\left[i\omega(\tau_1 - \tau_2)\right]h(t_1 - \tau_1)h(t_2 - \tau_2) \qquad (5\text{-}28)$$

Integrate first on τ_1 and τ_2; then

$$\phi_{XX}(t_1, t_2) = \int_{-\infty}^{\infty} \Phi_{FF}(\omega)\mathcal{H}(\omega, t_1)\mathcal{H}^*(\omega, t_2) \exp\left[i\omega(t_1 - t_2)\right] d\omega \qquad (5\text{-}29)$$

where we have used the notation

$$\mathcal{H}(\omega, t) = \int_0^t h(u) \exp\left(-i\omega u\right) du \qquad (5\text{-}30)$$

The interchange of the order of integration in Eq. (5-28) is permissible provided that the function $\mathcal{H}(\omega, t)$ is uniformly bounded in ω. This condition is always satisfied for systems with positive damping. For such cases, the impulse response function is absolutely integrable;‡ therefore, the integral in (5-30) always exists in view of the following inequalities:

$$\left| \int_0^t h(u) \exp\left(-i\omega u\right) du \right| \leq \int_0^t |h(u) \exp\left(-i\omega u\right)| \, du$$
$$= \int_0^t |h(u)| \, du < \int_{-\infty}^{\infty} |h(u)| \, du < \infty$$

Note that the lower limit of the integral in (5-30) can be extended to $-\infty$, since $h(u)$ vanishes for negative u. If the expression for the impulse response function, Eq. (5-10a), is substituted into Eq. (5-30) and the

---

‡ Recall that the impulse response function has the same form as the free vibration term with a zero initial displacement but a nonzero initial velocity.

result from the integration is simplified, we obtain

$$\mathfrak{IC}(\omega, t) = H(\omega) \left\{ 1 - (\cos \omega_d t + \frac{\zeta \omega_0 + i\omega}{\omega_d} \sin \omega_d t) \exp\left[-(\zeta \omega_0 + i\omega)t\right] \right\}$$

$$(5\text{-}31)$$

It is seen that $\mathfrak{IC}(\omega, t)$ tends to the frequency response function $H(\omega)$ as t approaches infinity, as expected. Using Eq. (5-31) in Eq. (5-29), we find that

$$\phi_{XX}(t_1, t_2) = \int_{-\infty}^{\infty} \Phi_{FF}(\omega) |H(\omega)|^2 \{ \exp\left[i\omega(t_1 - t_2)\right]$$

$$- \exp\left(-\zeta \omega_0 t_1\right) \left[\left(\cos \omega_d t_1 + \frac{\zeta \omega_0}{\omega_d} \sin \omega_d t_1 \right) \cos \omega t_2 + \frac{\omega}{\omega_d} \sin \omega_d t_1 \sin \omega t_2 \right]$$

$$- \exp\left(-\zeta \omega_0 t_2\right) \left[\left(\cos \omega_d t_2 + \frac{\zeta \omega_0}{\omega_d} \sin \omega_d t_2 \right) \cos \omega t_1 + \frac{\omega}{\omega_d} \sin \omega_d t_2 \sin \omega t_1 \right]$$

$$+ \exp\left[-\zeta \omega_0 (t_1 + t_2)\right] \left[\cos \omega_d t_1 \cos \omega_d t_2 + \frac{\zeta^2 \omega_0^2 + \omega^2}{\omega_d^2} \sin \omega_d t_1 \sin \omega_d t_2 \right.$$

$$\left. \left. + \frac{\zeta \omega_0}{\omega_d} \sin \omega_d (t_1 + t_2) \right] \right\} d\omega \qquad (5\text{-}29a)$$

The mean-square response is obtained by letting $t_1 = t_2 = t$:

$$E[X^2(t)] = \int_{-\infty}^{\infty} \Phi_{FF}(\omega) |H(\omega)|^2 \{ 1$$

$$+ \exp\left(-2\omega_0 \zeta t\right) \left[1 + \frac{2\omega_0 \zeta}{\omega_d} \sin \omega_d t \cos \omega_d t \right.$$

$$- \exp\left(\omega_0 \zeta t\right) \left(2 \cos \omega_d t + \frac{2\omega_0 \zeta}{\omega_d} \sin \omega_d t \right) \cos \omega t$$

$$- \exp\left(\omega_0 \zeta t\right) \left(\frac{2\omega}{\omega_d} \right) \sin \omega_d t \sin \omega t$$

$$\left. \left. + \frac{(\omega_0 \zeta)^2 - \omega_d^2 + \omega^2}{\omega_d^2} \sin^2 \omega_d t \right] \right\} d\omega \qquad (5\text{-}32)$$

Some important conclusions‡ can be drawn from Eqs. (5-29a) and (5-32):

1. In the beginning the system response to a weakly stationary excitation is nonstationary, as $\phi_{XX}(t_1, t_2)$ is not just a function of $t_2 - t_1$ for small t_1 and t_2, and $E[X^2(t)]$ is a function of t for small t.

2. For large t_1 and t_2

$$\phi_{XX}(t_1, t_2) \to R_{XX}(t_1 - t_2) = \int_{-\infty}^{\infty} |H(\omega)|^2 \Phi_{FF}(\omega) \exp\left[i\omega(t_1 - t_2)\right] d\omega$$

$$(5\text{-}33)$$

‡ See T. K. Caughey and H. J. Stumpf, Transient Response of a Dynamic System under Random Excitation, *J. Appl. Mech.*, **28**:563–566 (1961).

and for large t

$$E[X^2(t)] \rightarrow R_{XX}(0) = \int_{-\infty}^{\infty} |H(\omega)|^2 \Phi_{FF}(\omega) \, d\omega \qquad (5\text{-}34)$$

Therefore the motion becomes weakly stationary‡ after the system has been exposed to a weakly stationary excitation for a sufficiently long time.

3. At $t = 0$, $E[X^2(t)] = 0$, as would be expected since the system is assumed to be initially at rest.

The limiting form (5-33) can also be obtained by considering that the weakly stationary excitation has acted since the infinite past. Then

$$\phi_{XX}(t_1, t_2) = \int_{-\infty}^{t_1} \int_{-\infty}^{t_2} \int_{-\infty}^{\infty}$$
$$\Phi_{FF}(\omega) \exp[i\omega(\tau_1 - \tau_2)]h(t_1 - \tau_1) \, h(t_2 - \tau_2) \, d\omega \, d\tau_1 \, d\tau_2$$
$$= \int_{-\infty}^{\infty} \int_{-\infty}^{\infty} \int_{-\infty}^{\infty} \Phi_{FF}(\omega) \exp[i\omega(\tau_1 - \tau_2)]$$
$$h(t_1 - \tau_1)h(t_2 - \tau_2) \, d\omega \, d\tau_1 \, d\tau_2 \qquad (5\text{-}35)$$

where use has been made of the fact that the impulse response function $h(t - \tau)$ vanishes for negative arguments. Let $u = t_1 - \tau_1$ and $v = t_2 - \tau_2$; Eq. (5-35) is transformed into

$$\phi_{XX}(t_1, t_2) = \int_{-\infty}^{\infty} \int_{-\infty}^{\infty} \int_{-\infty}^{\infty} \Phi_{FF}(\omega) \exp[i\omega(t_1 - t_2 - u + v)]$$
$$h(u)h(v) \, d\omega \, du \, dv \qquad (5\text{-}35a)$$

Equation (5-33) follows upon integration on u and v:

$$\phi_{XX}(t_1, t_2) = \int_{-\infty}^{\infty} |H(\omega)|^2 \Phi_{FF}(\omega) \exp[i\omega(t_1 - t_2)] \, d\omega$$
$$= R_{XX}(t_1 - t_2) \qquad (5\text{-}33)$$

A comparison of Eq. (5-33) and Eq. (3-81) reveals that

$$\Phi_{XX}(\omega) = \Phi_{FF}(\omega)|H(\omega)|^2 \qquad (5\text{-}36)$$

This relation states that when both the excitation and the response are weakly stationary, the response spectral density is the product of the excitation spectral density and the function $|H(\omega)|^2$. Figure 5.1 illustrates this simple relationship. The function $|H(\omega)|^2$ is called the *transmittancy function* or the *system function*, which prescribes the fraction of energy to be transmitted through the system at various frequencies. For this reason a linear system is sometimes called a *linear filter*.

‡ This is true regardless of whether or not the system is originally at rest, since the influence of the initial conditions diminishes as time increases, a fact characterized by the vanishing of the first term in Eq. (5-23) at large t.

The time required for the response to become dominantly weakly stationary depends on the magnitude of the damping in the system. For practical purposes, Eqs. (5-33), (5-34), and (5-36) are considered sufficiently accurate after the system has been exposed to a weakly stationary excitation for a time, for example, of about four natural periods if $\zeta = 0.1$ or about twenty natural periods if $\zeta = 0.02$. This time is required for the transient response and the effect of the initial state of motion to be damped out. The weakly stationary response is analogous to the steady-state response in the deterministic vibration theory. It may be called the steady state in the *probabilistic* sense.

The integrations in (5-29a) and (5-32), and their weakly stationary forms (5-33) and (5-34), can be carried out once the spectral density

Fig. 5.1   Relation between the input spectral density $\Phi_{FF}(\omega)$ and the output spectral density $\Phi_{XX}(\omega)$ for a weakly stationary excitation and response.

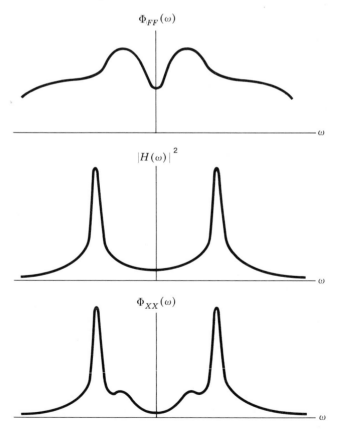

of the excitation is given. We shall consider various cases in the order of increasing complexity, and we shall begin by evaluating the mean-square response in the weakly stationary state, i.e., Eq. (5-34). The simplest situation is one in which the excitation is a white noise. For this case, the spectral density of the excitation is a constant, say K. Then

$$R_{XX}(0) = K \int_{-\infty}^{\infty} |H(\omega)|^2 \, d\omega = KI \qquad (5\text{-}37)$$

The integral

$$I = \int_{-\infty}^{\infty} |H(\omega)|^2 \, d\omega = \int_{-\infty}^{\infty} \frac{d\omega}{m^2[(\omega_0^2 - \omega^2)^2 + (2\zeta\omega\omega_0)^2]} \qquad (5\text{-}38)$$

can be evaluated by the *method of residues*. The integrand, a function of the real variable ω, is treated as a function of the complex variable z; that is,

$$f(z) = \frac{1}{m^2[(\omega_0^2 - z^2)^2 + (2\zeta\omega_0 z)^2]} \qquad (5\text{-}39)$$

This function has two simple poles in the upper half complex plane, namely,

$$\begin{aligned} z_1 &= \sqrt{1 - \zeta^2}\, \omega_0 + i\zeta\omega_0 \\ z_2 &= -\sqrt{1 - \zeta^2}\, \omega_0 + i\zeta\omega_0 \end{aligned} \qquad (5\text{-}40)$$

It follows that

$$\begin{aligned} I &= 2\pi i \{\Sigma \text{ residues of } f(z) \text{ in the upper complex plane}\} \\ &= 2\pi i \{[(z - z_1)f(z)]_{z=z_1} + [(z - z_2)f(z)]_{z=z_2}\} \\ &= \frac{\pi}{2\zeta\omega_0^3 m^2} \end{aligned} \qquad (5\text{-}41)$$

Therefore,

$$R_{XX}(0) = \frac{\pi K}{2\zeta\omega_0^3 m^2} \qquad (5\text{-}42)$$

It has been mentioned that an ideal white noise is physically impossible since it corresponds to an infinite mean-square value of the random process. However, Eq. (5-42) shows that as long as there exists some damping in the system, that is, $\zeta > 0$, the mean-square output is finite even when the mean-square input is infinite. Some insight into this matter can be gained by reviewing the stochastic differential equation (5-22), the starting point of our analysis. Recall that one case of a white noise is a stationary shot noise which is a sequence of independent random impulses arriving at Poisson distributed times; then $F(t)$ is an impulse if there is an arrival at t; otherwise it is zero. Consequently, the acceleration process $\ddot{X}(t)$ is either zero or nonexistent, and strictly speaking Eq. (5-22) is meaningless. If each impulse is replaced by a square pulse with a finite duration Δ (cf. Exercise 4-9), then the excitation is not a white noise and the foregoing analysis is legitimate. The mean-square value of the weakly stationary response is still given by (5-34) with a varying $\Phi_{FF}(\omega)$. It can easily be shown (by taking the Fourier transform of the correlation function obtained in Exercise 4-9) that $\Phi_{FF}(\omega)$ varies as $\sin^2(\omega\Delta/2)/(\omega\Delta/2)^2$. As can be seen from Fig. 5.2, the shorter the duration Δ of each square pulse in the excitation process, the slower the function $\Phi_{FF}(\omega)$ varies with ω. In the limit when the

Fig. 5.2 Excitation process idealized as random square pulses. (a) A typical sample function; (b) spectral density.

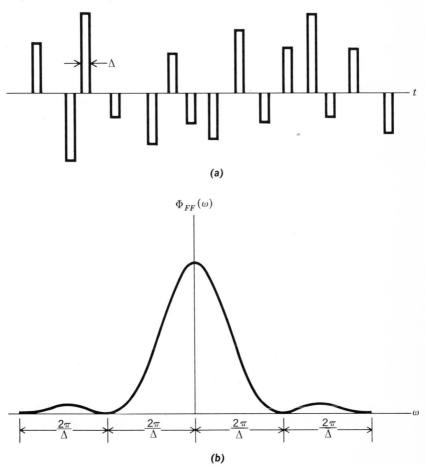

(a)

$\Phi_{FF}(\omega)$

(b)

duration of each square pulse becomes infinitesimally short accompanied by an inversely proportional increase in the pulse magnitude, the mean-square response approaches to that given in Eq. (5-42). The mean-square response of a system to such a white-noise excitation may then be interpreted as the limit of a sequence of mean-square responses, as outlined above. This limit exists for a damped system in the sense that the result computed from Eq. (5-42) is finite.

Since different sequences may approach the same limit, other interpretations of the system response to a white-noise excitation may also be devised. One of the many alternatives‡ is a sequence of excitation processes F_n characterized by the spectral densities

$$\Phi_{F_n F_n}(\omega) = \begin{cases} K & -\Omega_n < \omega < \Omega_n \\ \tfrac{1}{2}K & |\omega| = \Omega_n \\ 0 & |\omega| > \Omega_n \end{cases} \qquad (5\text{-}43)$$

or, equivalently, by the correlation function

$$R_{F_n F_n}(\tau) = \frac{2K}{\tau} \sin \Omega_n \tau \qquad (5\text{-}44)$$

Then the mean-square system response to a white-noise excitation can be interpreted as the limit of the sequence of mean-square responses corresponding to the sequence of excitations F_n as n, $\Omega_n \rightarrow \infty$.

The question that remains is whether or not the mean-square output $R_{XX}(0)$ computed by approximating a suitable actual excitation spectral density by a white-noise spectral density is physically meaningful in the sense of being a good approximation to the actual mean-square output. The answer to this question is affirmative, and an explanation can be obtained by referring again to Fig. 5.1 and recalling that the mean-square value of a random process is just the area under its spectral density curve [cf. Eq. (3-82)]. Now the output spectral density $\Phi_{XX}(\omega)$ is the product of the input spectral density $\Phi_{FF}(\omega)$ and the system transmittancy function $|H(\omega)|^2$. Since $|H(\omega)|^2$ decreases as ω^{-4} for large absolute values of ω, there is a large class of excitation spectral densities such that for $|\omega| > \omega_c$, a suitable value of ω, the product $\Phi_{FF}(\omega)|H(\omega)|^2$ also decreases very rapidly, i.e., sufficiently rapidly that

$$\int_{-\infty}^{-\omega_c} \Phi_{FF}(\omega)|H(\omega)|^2 \, d\omega + \int_{+\omega_c}^{+\infty} \Phi_{FF}(\omega)|H(\omega)|^2 \, d\omega \ll \int_{-\omega_c}^{\omega_c} \Phi_{FF}(\omega)|H(\omega)|^2 \, d\omega$$

The white-noise spectral density is obviously such a spectral density. (Since the mean-square value of an actual excitation process must be finite, every actual spectral density must also belong to this class.) Thus

‡ See Eq. (4-146) for another example of white noise.

an excitation spectral density in this class, which is also near to being constant in the interval $[-\omega_c, \omega_c]$, can conveniently and realistically be approximated by a white-noise spectral density regardless of its functional form for $|\omega| > \omega_c$.

When the damping in the system is small (that is, $\zeta \ll 1$), the range of the applicability of the white-noise idealization can be extended. In this case the transmittancy function $|H(\omega)|^2$ is very sharply peaked at approximately plus and minus the undamped natural frequency ω_0. A detailed shape of this function for a lightly damped system is shown in Fig. 5.3. Note that the magnitude of this function reduces to only half the peak value at the short distance of $\zeta\omega_0$ from either side of a peak. For such a transmittancy function, the major contribution to the integral (5-34) is often obtained in the vicinities of $\pm\omega_0$ on the abscissa. When most of the value of the integral (5-34) does indeed come from the vicinities of $\pm\omega_0$ and, in addition, the actual spectral density is slowly

Fig. 5.3   The transmittancy function $|H(\omega)|^2$ of a lightly damped (that is, $\zeta \ll 1$) system. k = spring rate.

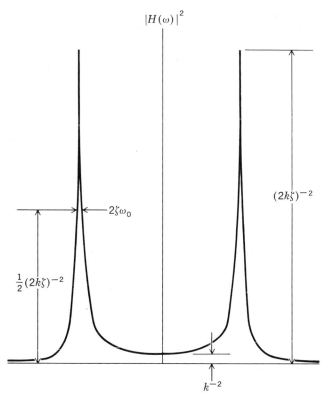

varying in these vicinities, then the value of the spectral density function outside these vicinities is unimportant. Therefore the white-noise idealization is again acceptable. Some sketches of spectral densities that could reasonably be replaced by a white-noise spectral density, and a sketch of a spectral density that could not be replaced by a white-noise spectral density, all relative to a transmittancy function with $\zeta \ll 1$, are shown in Fig. 5.4. For those cases where the replacement is permissible,

Fig. 5.4 Sketches of actual excitation spectral densities either suitable or unsuitable for white-noise idealization. The transmittancy function of the lightly damped system is shown by the dashed line.

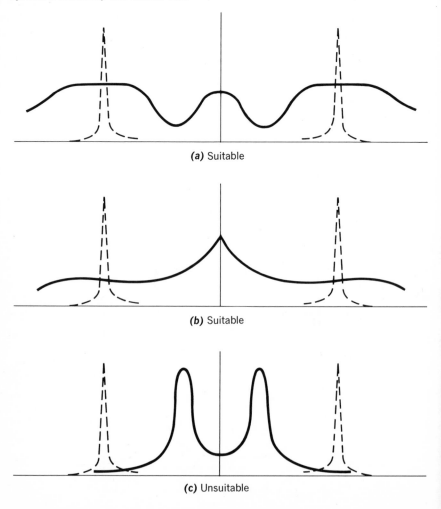

(a) Suitable

(b) Suitable

(c) Unsuitable

we may write

$$R_{XX}(0) = \int_{-\infty}^{\infty} |H(\omega)|^2 \Phi_{FF}(\omega) \, d\omega \approx \Phi_{FF}(\omega_0) \int_{-\infty}^{\infty} |H(\omega)|^2 \, d\omega$$

$$= \frac{\pi \Phi_{FF}(\omega_0)}{2\zeta\omega_0{}^3 m^2} \qquad (5\text{-}42a)$$

A lightly damped system is often called a *narrow-band filter*, and the distance $2\zeta\omega_0$ is called its *bandwidth*, since a rough estimate is that only the excitation "energy" contained in the frequency bands $[\omega_0 - \zeta\omega_0,$ $\omega_0 + \zeta\omega_0]$ and $[-\omega_0 - \zeta\omega_0, -\omega_0 + \zeta\omega_0]$ is transmitted by the filter. It is interesting to note that this rough estimate results in an $R_{XX}(0) \approx$ $\Phi_{FF}(\omega_0)/(\zeta\omega_0{}^3 m^2)$, which is lower than that obtained from Eq. (5-42a).

The mean-square response in the transient state, Eq. (5-32), may be evaluated in a similar way. If the excitation is a white noise with a constant spectral density K, then an application of the method of residues yields

$$E[X^2(t)] = \frac{\pi K}{2\zeta\omega_0{}^3 m^2} \left\{ 1 - \frac{\exp(-2\zeta\omega_0 t)}{\omega_d{}^2} \left[\omega_d{}^2 + 2(\zeta\omega_0 \sin \omega_d t)^2 \right. \right.$$
$$\left. \left. + \zeta\omega_0\omega_d \sin 2\omega_d t \right] \right\} \qquad (5\text{-}45)$$

When the excitation is not a white noise but the system is lightly damped and $\Phi_{FF}(\omega)$ varies slowly near the natural frequency of the system, etc., Eq. (5-32) may be evaluated approximately as

$$E[X^2(t)] \approx \frac{\pi \Phi_{FF}(\omega_0)}{2\zeta\omega_0{}^3 m^2} \left\{ 1 - \frac{\exp(-2\zeta\omega_0 t)}{\omega_d{}^2} \right.$$
$$\left. \left[\omega_d{}^2 + 2(\zeta\omega_0 \sin \omega_d t)^2 + \zeta\omega_0\omega_d \sin 2\omega_d t \right] \right\} \qquad (5\text{-}45a)$$

Equation (5-45) is plotted in Fig. 5.5 for several values of the damping ratio. It is seen that each mean-square response shows a general trend to increase with time; however, small fluctuations are superposed on the increasing trend. The mean-square response approaches the stationary value in a shorter time for a larger damping ratio than for a small one. The transient response is of interest if the time during which a system is exposed to an excitation is not long in comparison with the natural period of the system. Also included in Fig. 5.5 is the case of an undamped system. For this case, the expression for the mean-square response is obtained by expanding the exponential function in Eq. (5-45) into a series prior to taking the limit $\zeta \to 0$, so that

$$\lim_{\zeta \to 0} E[X^2(t)] = \frac{\pi K}{2\omega_0{}^3} (2\omega_0 t - \sin 2\omega_0 t) \qquad (5\text{-}46)$$

This expression is unbounded as t increases.

The evaluation of the correlation function of the response in the weakly stationary state, Eq. (5-33), and in the transient state, Eq. (5-29a), can also be effected by the method of residues. The results are theoretically exact for an ideal white-noise excitation, and they are good approximations for a lightly damped system subject to an excitation whose spectral density is slowly varying at and near the natural frequency of the system, etc. The integrations are left as exercises for the reader. Since a large number of practical structures are lightly damped, white noise occupies an important role in the analyses that are useful in practical applications. For example, the damping ratio ζ in most flight-vehicle structural members ranges from 0.005 to 0.04, which is certainly sufficiently small for such structures to be considered lightly damped.

In passing we reiterate that if the excitation is Gaussian, then the response is also Gaussian; and then the statements in this section concerning weak stationarity can be changed to strong-stationary statements.

Fig. 5.5 Mean-square value of the transient response of a single-degree-of-freedom system under white-noise excitation. [*Taken from T. K. Caughey and H. J. Stumpf, Transient Response of a Dynamic System under Random Excitation, J. Appl. Mech.,* **28**(4): 563 (1961).]

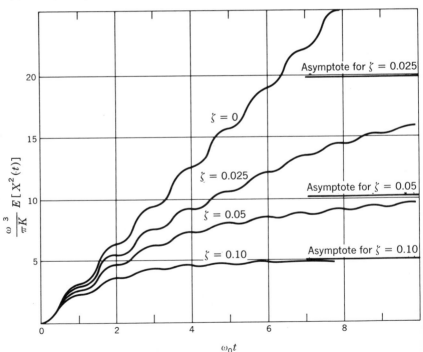

5.4 / NONSTATIONARY EXCITATIONS

There are practical problems in structural dynamics which involve non-stationary excitations, although there are relatively few analyses or experimental studies dealing with such problems in the literature. Fung‡ appears to be the first to have suggested an interesting application when he considered the landing of an aircraft as a nonstationary random excitation. More recently, Amin¶ has shown that nonstationary models are suitable for representing strong motion earthquakes.

Nonstationary excitations must, of course, lead to nonstationary responses. The general solution for the response of a linear system in terms of the various moment functions or the cumulant functions, Eqs. (5-24) and (5-25), is applicable in the case of nonstationary excitations. If for the moment we confine our attention to either Gaussian processes or to processes that are not Gaussian, but where our immediate concern is limited to the first- and second-order properties of such processes, then the task is reduced to only that of evaluating Eqs. (5-26). The information required in the analysis is then the expectation and covariance functions of the excitation process, $E[F(\tau)]$ and $\kappa_{FF}(\tau_1, \tau_2)$. We shall assume that these functions are known. In practical applications these functions are commonly estimated by averaging over a large number of sample records. This procedure was used by Fung§ in the landing analysis of a B-24D airplane, and his plots of the estimated mean and correlation functions are reproduced in Figs. 5.6 through 5.8 for illustration. In these figures the "first wheel" denotes the one that first touched the ground or, if both wheels contacted the ground at apparently the same time, the one that gave the larger impact load. It is clear that to obtain meaningful estimates of the statistical properties of a nonstationary random process many more records are needed than would be required if the process were stationary. Unfortunately, field measurements are usually expensive, and therefore available records are often limited. (Perhaps the scarcity of experimental data has been the major reason for lesser attention that has been paid to nonstationary excitations in structural problems.) However, if there is sufficient physical insight into the underlying random mechanism of an excitation, then the general forms of the mean and covariance functions can be determined and the values of certain key parameters can be adequately estimated by use of a smaller number of field records.

‡ Y. C. Fung, The Analysis of Dynamic Stresses in Aircraft Structures during Landing as Nonstationary Random Processes, *J. Appl. Mech.*, **22**:449–457 (1955).
¶ M. Amin, "Nonstationary Stochastic Model for Strong Motion Earthquakes," Ph.D. thesis, University of Illinois, 1966.
§ *Loc. cit.*

Nonstationary excitations are generally short in duration. Excluding the case of unstable systems (that is, $\zeta \leq 0$) for which the effect of an earlier excitation continues or is amplified in the evolution of time, the response of a system to a nonstationary excitation dies out soon after the excitation is terminated. For such cases the generalized spectral densities of both the excitation and the response processes generally exist, and it is often convenient to work with the generalized spectral densities. Recall that the second equation of (5-26) implies $F(t) = 0$ for $t < 0$ and that the impulse response function vanishes for negative arguments. Then this equation may be rewritten as follows:

$$\kappa_{XX}(t_1, t_2) = \int_{-\infty}^{\infty} \int_{-\infty}^{\infty} \kappa_{FF}(\tau_1, \tau_2) h(t_1 - \tau_1) h(t_2 - \tau_2) \, d\tau_1 \, d\tau_2 \qquad (5\text{-}47)$$

with the understanding that $\kappa_{FF}(\tau_1, \tau_2) = 0$ when τ_1 or $\tau_2 < 0$. Application of Eq. (3-75b) yields

$$\hat{\Phi}_{XX}(\omega_1, \omega_2) = \frac{1}{(2\pi)^2} \int_{-\infty}^{\infty} \int_{-\infty}^{\infty} \kappa_{XX}(t_1, t_2) \exp\left[-i(\omega_1 t_1 - \omega_2 t_2)\right] dt_1 \, dt_2$$

$$= \frac{1}{(2\pi)^2} \int_{-\infty}^{\infty} \int_{-\infty}^{\infty} \int_{-\infty}^{\infty} \int_{-\infty}^{\infty} \kappa_{FF}(\tau_1, \tau_2) h(t_1 - \tau_1) h(t_2 - \tau_2)$$

$$\exp\left[-i(\omega_1 t_1 - \omega_2 t_2)\right] d\tau_1 \, d\tau_2 \, dt_1 \, dt_2 \qquad (5\text{-}48)$$

Fig. 5.6 Estimated expectation of landing impact of B-24D airplane (gross weight 48,900 to 50,000 lb). [*After Y. C. Fung, The Analysis of Dynamic Stresses in Aircraft Structures during Landing as Nonstationary Random Processes, J. Appl. Mech.,* **22**: 449–457 (1955).]

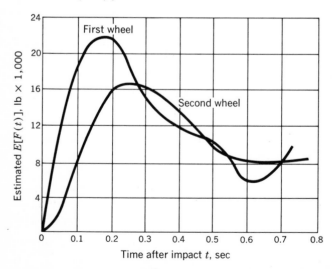

By interchanging the order of integration, we arrive at

$$\hat{\Phi}_{XX}(\omega_1, \omega_2) = \hat{\Phi}_{FF}(\omega_1, \omega_2)H(\omega_1)H^*(\omega_2) \tag{5-49}$$

This relation is an analogue of Eq. (5-36) for the weakly stationary case and shows how the generalized spectral density of the nonstationary response can be computed from that of the nonstationary excitation. If desired, Eq. (5-49) can be inverted to find the covariance function of the response.

Equation (5-49) provides an alternative means by which the second-order property of the response process can be determined. The application of this equation requires the knowledge of the generalized spectral density of the nonstationary excitation, which is just the twofold Fourier

Fig. 5.7 Estimated correlation function of landing impact of B-24D airplane (first wheel). [*After Y. C. Fung, The Analysis of Dynamic Stresses in Aircraft Structures during Landing as Nonstationary Random Processes, J. Appl. Mech.*, **22**: 449–457 (1955).]

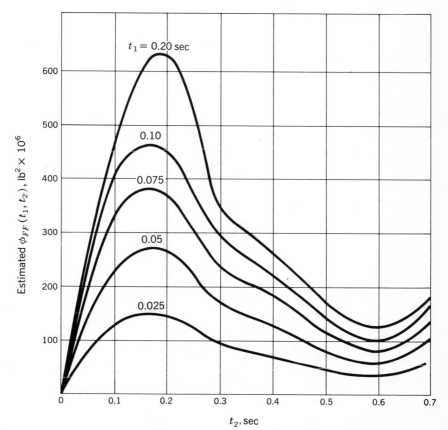

transform of the excitation covariance function needed for an application of Eq. (5-47). As was pointed out before, available field records are always very limited, especially in a nonstationary case, but sufficient physical insight into the underlying random mechanism may be a basis of assuming suitable forms for the moment functions or the cumulant functions with a number of unknown parameters in these functions. Then the limited field measurements can be used to estimate the values of the unknown parameters. Partly for the development of insights of this kind and partly for illustration, we propose a study of some special cases below.

Perhaps one of the simplest nonstationary excitations is a nonstationary shot noise (discussed in Sec. 4.7), which has a covariance function

$$\kappa_{SS}(\tau_1, \tau_2) = \lambda(\tau_1)E[Y^2]\,\delta(\tau_2 - \tau_1) \qquad (4\text{-}103)$$

It has been pointed out before (cf. page 95) that a nonstationary shot noise is a mathematical idealization and, strictly speaking, it is physically impossible. However, from the experience we gained in idealizing weakly stationary excitations as white noise we expect that the response of a linear system computed for a nonstationary shot-noise excitation may be a good approximation to reality under certain conditions. We shall first present such a solution and then discuss the conditions under which the assumption of nonstationary shot-noise excitation is acceptable. By

Fig. 5.8 Estimated correlation function of landing impact of B-24D airplane (second wheel). [*After Y. C. Fung, The Analysis of Dynamic Stresses in Aircraft Structure during Landing as Nonstationary Random Processes, J. Appl. Mech.*, **22**: 449–457 (1955).]

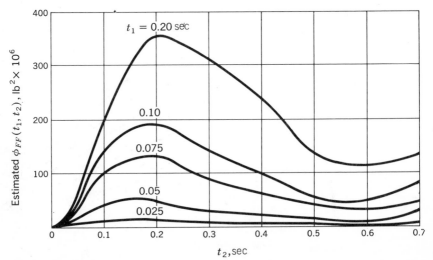

substituting Eq. (4-103) for $\kappa_{FF}(\tau_1, \tau_2)$ into Eq. (5-47), we obtain

$$\kappa_{XX}(t_1, t_2) = E[Y^2]\int_0^{t_1} \lambda(\tau_1)h(t_1 - \tau_1)h(t_2 - \tau_1)\,d\tau_1$$

$$= \frac{E[Y^2]}{2m^2\omega_d^2}\exp\left[-\zeta\omega_0(t_1 + t_2)\right]$$

$$\left[\cos \omega_d(t_1 - t_2)\int_0^{t_1} \lambda(\tau_1)\exp(2\zeta\omega_0\tau_1)\,d\tau_1\right.$$

$$\left. - \int_0^{t_1} \lambda(\tau_1)\exp(2\zeta\omega_0\tau_1)\cos\omega_d(t_1 + t_2 - 2\tau_1)\,d\tau_1\right] \qquad t_2 \geq t_1 \quad (5\text{-}50)$$

The variance function follows by letting $t_1 = t_2 = t$:

$$\sigma_X{}^2(t) = \frac{E[Y^2]}{4m^2\omega_d^2}\exp(-2\zeta\omega_0 t)\int_0^t \lambda(\tau)\exp(2\zeta\omega_0\tau)\sin^2\omega_d(t - \tau)\,d\tau \qquad (5\text{-}51)$$

The integrations in Eqs. (5-50) and (5-51) can be carried out when the expected nonstationary arrival rate $\lambda(t)$ is given.

As an example, let

$$\lambda(t) = \begin{cases} \lambda_0 \sin\dfrac{\pi t}{b} & 0 \leq t \leq b \\ 0 & \text{otherwise} \end{cases} \qquad (5\text{-}52)$$

indicating that the expected arrival rate of the random impulses increases from zero to a maximum value λ_0 and then decreases to zero. The variation is idealized as a half sine wave. By substituting (5-52) into (5-50) and (5-51), straightforward integrations yield

$$\kappa_{XX}(t_1, t_2) = \frac{\lambda_0 E[Y^2]}{2m^2\omega_d^2}\exp\left[-\zeta\omega_0(t_1 + t_2)\right]\left(\frac{\cos\omega_d(t_1 - t_2)}{(2\zeta\omega_0)^2 + (\pi/b)^2}\right.$$

$$\left[\exp(2\zeta\omega_0 t_1)\left(2\zeta\omega_0\sin\frac{\pi t_1}{b} - \frac{\pi}{b}\cos\frac{\pi t_1}{b}\right) + \frac{\pi}{b}\right]$$

$$- \left\{\frac{\exp(2\zeta\omega_0 t_1)}{(2\zeta\omega_0)^2 + (\pi/b + 2\omega_d)^2}\left[\zeta\omega_0\sin\left(\frac{\pi t_1}{b} - \omega_d t_2 + \omega_d t_1\right)\right.\right.$$

$$\left. - \frac{\pi/b + 2\omega_d}{2}\cos\left(\frac{\pi t_1}{b} - \omega_d t_2 + \omega_d t_1\right)\right]$$

$$+ \frac{\exp(2\zeta\omega_0 t_1)}{(2\zeta\omega_0)^2 + (\pi/b - 2\omega_d)^2}\left[\zeta\omega_0\sin\left(\frac{\pi t_1}{b} + \omega_d t_2 - \omega_d t_1\right)\right.$$

$$\left. - \frac{\pi/b - 2\omega_d}{2}\cos\left(\frac{\pi t_1}{b} + \omega_d t_2 - \omega_d t_1\right)\right]$$

$$+ \frac{1}{(2\zeta\omega_0)^2 + (\pi/b + 2\omega_d)^2}\left[\zeta\omega_0\sin\omega_d(t_1 + t_2)\right.$$

$$\left. + \frac{\pi/b + 2\omega_d}{2}\cos\omega_d(t_1 + t_2)\right]$$

$$- \frac{1}{(2\zeta\omega_0)^2 + (\pi/b - 2\omega_d)^2}\left[\zeta\omega_0\sin\omega_d(t_1 + t_2)\right.$$

$$\left.\left.\left. - \frac{\pi/b - 2\omega_d}{2}\cos\omega_d(t_1 + t_2)\right]\right\}\right) \qquad t_2 \geq t_1, 0 \leq t_1 \leq b \quad (5\text{-}53a)$$

$$\kappa_{XX}(t_1, t_2) = \frac{\lambda_0 E[Y^2]}{2m^2\omega_d^2} \exp\left[-\zeta\omega_0(t_1 + t_2)\right]$$

$$\left(\frac{\pi/b \cos \omega_d(t_1 - t_2)}{(2\zeta\omega_0)^2 + (\pi/b)^2}[\exp(2\zeta\omega_0 b) + 1]\right.$$

$$-\left\{\frac{\exp(2\zeta\omega_0 b)}{(2\zeta\omega_0)^2 + (\pi/b + 2\omega_d)^2}\left[-\zeta\omega_0 \sin(2\omega_d b - \omega_d t_1 - \omega_d t_2)\right.\right.$$

$$\left.+ \frac{\pi/b + 2\omega_d}{2}\cos(2\omega_d b - \omega_d t_1 - \omega_d t_2)\right]$$

$$+ \frac{\exp(2\zeta\omega_0 b)}{(2\zeta\omega_0)^2 + (\pi/b - 2\omega_d)^2}\left[-\zeta\omega_0 \sin(-2\omega_d b + \omega_d t_1 + \omega_d t_2)\right.$$

$$\left.+ \frac{\pi/b - 2\omega_d}{2}\cos(-2\omega_d b + \omega_d t_1 + \omega_d t_2)\right]$$

$$+ \frac{1}{(2\zeta\omega_0)^2 + (\pi/b + 2\omega_d)^2}\left[\zeta\omega_0 \sin \omega_d(t_1 + t_2)\right.$$

$$\left.+ \frac{\pi/b + 2\omega_d}{2}\cos \omega_d(t_1 + t_2)\right]$$

$$- \frac{1}{(2\zeta\omega_0)^2 + (\pi/b - 2\omega_d)^2}\left[\zeta\omega_0 \sin \omega_d(t_1 + t_2)\right.$$

$$\left.\left.\left.- \frac{\pi/b - 2\omega_d}{2}\cos \omega_d(t_1 + t_2)\right]\right\}\right) \qquad t_2 \geq t_1 > b \quad (5\text{-}53b)$$

$$\sigma_X^2(t) = \frac{\lambda_0 E[Y^2]\exp(-2\zeta\omega_0 t)}{2m^2\omega_d^2}\left\{\frac{1}{(2\zeta\omega_0)^2 + (\pi/b)^2}\right.$$

$$\left[\exp(2\zeta\omega_0 t)\left(2\zeta\omega_0 \sin \frac{\pi t}{b} - \frac{\pi}{b}\cos \frac{\pi t}{b}\right) + \frac{\pi}{b}\right]$$

$$- \frac{\exp(2\zeta\omega_0 t)}{(2\zeta\omega_0)^2 + (\pi/b + 2\omega_d)^2}\left(\zeta\omega_0 \sin \frac{\pi t}{b} - \frac{\pi/b + 2\omega_d}{2}\cos \frac{\pi t}{b}\right)$$

$$+ \frac{\exp(2\zeta\omega_0 t)}{(2\zeta\omega_0)^2 + (\pi/b - 2\omega_d)^2}\left(\zeta\omega_0 \sin \frac{\pi t}{b} - \frac{\pi/b - 2\omega_d}{2}\cos \frac{\pi t}{b}\right)$$

$$+ \frac{1}{(2\zeta\omega_0)^2 + (\pi/b + 2\omega_d)^2}\left(\zeta\omega_0 \sin 2\omega_d t + \frac{\pi/b + 2\omega_d}{2}\cos 2\omega_d t\right)$$

$$- \frac{1}{(2\zeta\omega_0)^2 + (\pi/b - 2\omega_d)^2}\left(\zeta\omega_0 \sin 2\omega_d t - \frac{\pi/b - 2\omega_d}{2}\cos 2\omega_d t\right)\right\}$$

$$t \leq b \quad (5\text{-}54a)$$

$$\sigma_X^2(t) = \frac{\lambda_0 E[Y^2]\exp(-2\zeta\omega_0 t)}{2m^2\omega_d^2}\left\{\frac{\pi/b}{(2\zeta\omega_0)^2 + (\pi/b)^2}[\exp(2\zeta\omega_0 b) + 1]\right.$$

$$- \frac{\exp(2\zeta\omega_0 b)}{(2\zeta\omega_0)^2 + (\pi/b + 2\omega_d)^2}\left[-\zeta\omega_0 \sin 2\omega_d(b - t)\right.$$

$$\left.+ \frac{\pi/b + 2\omega_d}{2}\cos 2\omega_d(b - t)\right]$$

$$+ \frac{\exp{(2\zeta\omega_0 b)}}{(2\zeta\omega_0)^2 + (\pi/b - 2\omega_d)^2}$$

$$\left[\zeta\omega_0 \sin 2\omega_d(b - t) + \frac{\pi/b - 2\omega_d}{2} \cos 2\omega_d(b - t) \right]$$

$$+ \frac{1}{(2\zeta\omega_0)^2 + (\pi/b + 2\omega_d)^2} \left(\zeta\omega_0 \sin 2\omega_d t + \frac{\pi/b + 2\omega_d}{2} \cos 2\omega_d t \right)$$

$$- \frac{1}{(2\zeta\omega_0)^2 + (\pi/b - 2\omega_d)^2} \left(\zeta\omega_0 \sin 2\omega_d t \right.$$

$$\left. \left. - \frac{\pi/b - 2\omega_d}{2} \cos 2\omega_d t \right) \right\} \qquad t > b \qquad (5\text{-}54b)$$

The variance function $\sigma_X{}^2(t)$ is illustrated in Fig. 5.9 for the case $\omega_0 > \pi/b$.

The generalized spectral density of a nonstationary shot noise has the special form

$$\hat{\Phi}_{SS}(\omega_1, \omega_2) = \Omega_{SS}(\omega_1 - \omega_2) = (2\pi)^{-1} E[Y^2]\Lambda(\omega_1 - \omega_2) \qquad (5\text{-}55)$$

where $\Lambda(\omega)$ is the Fourier transform of $\lambda(t)$. In the present example

$$\Lambda(\omega) = \frac{\lambda_0}{2\pi} \int_0^b \sin\frac{\pi t}{b} \exp{(-i\omega t)}\, dt$$

$$= \frac{\lambda_0}{2} \frac{b}{\pi^2 - (b\omega)^2} [1 + \exp{(-i\omega b)}] \qquad (5\text{-}56)$$

Then the generalized spectral density of the response is obtained from Eq. (5-49) with $\hat{\Phi}_{FF}(\omega_1, \omega_2)$ replaced by $\Omega_{SS}(\omega_1 - \omega_2)$:

$$\hat{\Phi}_{XX}(\omega_1, \omega_2) = \frac{(4\pi)^{-1}\lambda_0 E[Y^2]b}{\pi^2 - b^2(\omega_1 - \omega_2)^2} \{1 + \exp{[-i(\omega_1 - \omega_2)b]}\}H(\omega_1)H^*(\omega_2)$$

$$(5\text{-}57)$$

The inversion of the generalized spectral density of $X(t)$, that is,

$$\int_{-\infty}^{\infty} \int_{-\infty}^{\infty} \hat{\Phi}_{XX}(\omega_1, \omega_2) \exp{[i(\omega_1 t_1 - \omega_2 t_2)]}\, d\omega_1\, d\omega_2$$

Fig. 5.9 (*a*) Expected nonstationary arrival rate of impulses in a shot-noise excitation process; (*b*) variance of the response of a linear system to such a nonstationary shot-noise excitation. (ω_0 = undamped natural frequency of the linear system.)

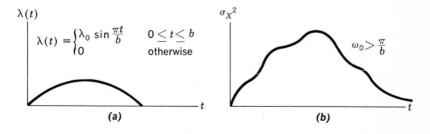

$\lambda(t)$

$$\lambda(t) = \begin{cases} \lambda_0 \sin\frac{\pi t}{b} & 0 \le t \le b \\ 0 & \text{otherwise} \end{cases}$$

$\sigma_X{}^2$

$\omega_0 > \frac{\pi}{b}$

(a)

(b)

should produce Eq. (5-53), although the actual integration appears to be difficult.

It has been pointed out that a nonstationary shot noise is a mathematical idealization which is not physically realizable. We now turn to investigate the conditions under which the assumption of a nonstationary shot-noise excitation is acceptable for practical calculations. Unfortunately, it is not possible to state such conditions in mathematical terms as was partially true in the case of the white-noise idealization. Therefore we shall approach this matter from a physical standpoint. One type of shot noise is a sequence of independent random impulses which arrive independently. If we confine our attention to this type of shot noise, then the question is: What constitutes valid reasons for replacing an actual input by an input consisting of independent and independently arriving impulses? The answer best can be given with reference to a practical example. In Fig. 5.10 there is shown a typical record of an earthquake. The record represents the more intense ground acceleration in a horizontal direction‡ at a certain station as it was picked up by a seismometer. Two main features of this record are clearly observable. Firstly, within the total record length of about 7 sec, the ground accelera-

‡ An earthquake is usually recorded in three directions, that is, in the east-west, north-south, and up-down directions.

Fig. 5.10 A typical earthquake record.

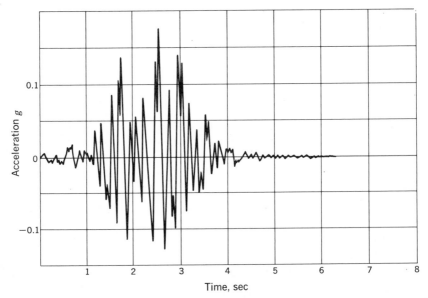

Time, sec

tion shows a general trend of first increasing and then decreasing with time. Secondly, very little correlation in the ground motion is noticeable for two time instants about $\frac{1}{2}$ sec or longer apart. So, from this sample function, we can say that nonstationarity is quite evident. However, whether or not independent and independently arriving impulses, when playing the role of a random excitation to a structure, would have the same effect as that of such earthquakes depends also on the characteristics of the structure. The effect would be approximately the same if the average time spacing between independent impulses substituting for the actual excitation is "short" as it is sensed by the structure. For the present example this average time spacing should be about $\frac{1}{2}$ sec. Recall that the response of a single-degree-of-freedom system to each impulse has the form of a damped free vibration which has an apparent natural period‡ of $T = 2\pi/[\omega_0(1 - \zeta^2)^{\frac{1}{2}}]$. So, a suitable measure of the shortness of the average time spacing between independent impulses is to compare this time spacing with T. Thus for a system having an apparent natural period equal to, say, about 5 sec or longer and subjected to a random earthquake excitation having a typical sample function as shown in Fig. 5.10, the assumption of such a nonstationary shot-noise excitation is suitable.

Since a shot noise can be other than a sequence of independent and independently arriving impulses, it is conceivable that the shot-noise idealization may have a wider range of applicability than the situation described above. However, it is not clear what this wider range may be. Before further understanding of the shot-noise process can be gained, we are certain only that it is a suitable model for practical problems such as the one just illustrated.

When the apparent natural period of a structure is not much longer than the time separation for which the excitation process is essentially uncorrelated, a model more general than nonstationary shot noise is required. One such model is obtained by a superposition of random pulses; that is, the excitation process is assumed to be representable as

$$F(t) = \sum_{k=1}^{N(t)} Y_k w(t, \tau_k) \qquad (5\text{-}58)$$

where $w(t, \tau_k)$ describes the shape of a pulse commencing at time τ_k, Y_k is the random amplitude of the pulse, and $N(t)$ is a counting process. The general theory of random pulses discussed in Sec. 4.6 can then be conveniently applied. Equation (5-58) includes shot noise as a special case, the case when $w(t, \tau_k) = \delta(t - \tau_k)$. It is interesting to note that Eq. (5-58) has been used by a number of authors to simulate earthquake

‡ We use the term *apparent period* since damped free vibration is not truly periodic.

processes.‡   The original idea is generally attributed to Housner, who suggested a full-sine wave as a possible pulse shape.

When the excitation is represented as a sum of random pulses, the response can also be written as a similar sum,

$$X(t) = \sum_{k=1}^{N(t)} Y_k h_c(t, \tau_k) \tag{5-59}$$

where

$$h_c(t, \tau_k) = \int_{t_k}^{t} h(t - \tau)w(\tau, \tau_k) \, d\tau \tag{5-60}$$

Then the moment or cumulant functions of any arbitrary order of the response can be computed by use of the general theory discussed in Sec. 4.6.

In order to gain additional insights let us consider an excitation having the general form of Eq. (5-58) with the pulse-shape function given by

$$w(t, \tau) = \begin{cases} \sin \dfrac{\pi(t - \tau)}{a} & 0 \leq t - \tau \leq a \\ 0 & \text{otherwise} \end{cases} \tag{5-61}$$

The random amplitudes Y_k are assumed to be identically distributed as a random variable Y and to be mutually independent and independent of the distribution of τ_k.   Let it be required to compute the variance function $\sigma_F^2(t)$ and the generalized spectral density $\hat{\Phi}_{FF}(\omega_1, \omega_2)$ under two different assumptions: (1) $N(t)$ is a Poisson process with an expected nonstationary arrival rate

$$\lambda(t) = \begin{cases} \lambda_0 \sin \dfrac{\pi t}{b} & 0 \leq t \leq b, \, b > a, \, \lambda_0 > 0 \\ 0 & \text{otherwise} \end{cases} \tag{5-62}$$

(2) $N(t)$ is a general counting process which gives the number of counts of random points in the interval $(0, t]$, and the first two cumulant functions of the random points are given by

$$g_1(t) = \begin{cases} \lambda_0 \sin \dfrac{\pi t}{b} & 0 \leq t \leq b, \, b > a, \, \lambda_0 > 0 \\ 0 & \text{otherwise} \end{cases} \tag{5-63}$$

$$g_2(t_1, t_2) = \begin{cases} \lambda_0^2 \exp\left[-c|t_1 - t_2|\right] & 0 \leq t_1, t_2 \leq b, \, b > a, \, c > 0 \\ 0 & \text{otherwise} \end{cases} \tag{5-64}$$

‡ For a review and discussion of earthquake simulation by independently arriving random pulses see C. A. Cornell, Stochastic Process Models in Structural Engineering, *Stanford Univ. Civil Eng. Dept. Tech. Rept. 34*, May, 1964.

Under the first assumption, that is, $N(t)$ is Poisson, the variance function is computed from Eq. (4-87). Let $E[Y^2] = A$; we obtain, upon substitution of Eqs. (5-61) and (5-62),

$$
\sigma_F{}^2(t) = \begin{cases}
A\lambda_0 \int_0^t \sin^2 \dfrac{\pi(t-\tau)}{a} \sin \dfrac{\pi\tau}{b}\, d\tau & 0 \le t \le a \\[2ex]
A\lambda_0 \int_{t-a}^t \sin^2 \dfrac{\pi(t-\tau)}{a} \sin \dfrac{\pi\tau}{b}\, d\tau & a \le t \le b \\[2ex]
A\lambda_0 \int_{t-a}^b \sin^2 \dfrac{\pi(t-\tau)}{a} \sin \dfrac{\pi\tau}{b}\, d\tau & b \le t \le a+b \\[2ex]
0 & t < 0 \text{ or } t > a+b
\end{cases}
\tag{5-65}
$$

Under the second assumption, i.e., the arrival times for $N(t)$ are characterized by Eqs. (5-63) and (5-64), the variance function of $F(t)$ is computed from the second equation in (4-96) by letting $t_1 = t_2 = t$:

$$
\sigma_F{}^2(t) = A \int_0^t w^2(t-\tau) g_1(\tau)\, d\tau
$$
$$
+ B^2 \int_0^t \int_0^t w(t-\tau_1) w(t-\tau_2) g_2(\tau_1, \tau_2)\, d\tau_1\, d\tau_2
\tag{5-66}
$$

where $B = E[Y]$. Using Eqs. (5-61), (5-63), and (5-64) and noting that for the present example the integrand in the double integral in Eq. (5-66) is symmetrical in τ_1 and τ_2, we have

$$
\sigma_F{}^2(t) = \begin{cases}
\begin{aligned}
& A\lambda_0 \int_0^t \sin^2 \frac{\pi(t-\tau)}{a} \sin \frac{\pi\tau}{b}\, d\tau + B^2\lambda_0{}^2 \int_0^t \sin \frac{\pi(t-\tau_2)}{a} \\
& \left\{ 2 \int_0^{\tau_2} \sin \frac{\pi(t-\tau_1)}{a} \exp\left[-c(\tau_2 - \tau_1)\right] d\tau_1 \right\} d\tau_2 \\
& \hspace{6cm} 0 \le t \le a
\end{aligned} \\[6ex]
\begin{aligned}
& A\lambda_0 \int_{t-a}^t \sin^2 \frac{\pi(t-\tau)}{a} \sin \frac{\pi\tau}{b}\, d\tau \\
& + B^2\lambda_0{}^2 \int_{t-a}^t \sin \frac{\pi(t-\tau_2)}{a} \\
& \left\{ 2 \int_{t-a}^{\tau_2} \sin \frac{\pi(t-\tau_1)}{a} \exp\left[-c(\tau_2 - \tau_1)\right] d\tau_1 \right\} d\tau_2 \\
& \hspace{6cm} a \le t \le b
\end{aligned} \\[6ex]
\begin{aligned}
& A\lambda_0 \int_{t-a}^b \sin^2 \frac{\pi(t-\tau)}{a} \sin \frac{\pi\tau}{b}\, d\tau \\
& + B^2\lambda_0{}^2 \int_{t-a}^b \sin \frac{\pi(t-\tau_2)}{a} \\
& \left\{ 2 \int_{t-a}^{\tau_2} \sin \frac{\pi(t-\tau_1)}{a} \exp\left[-c(\tau_2 - \tau_1)\right] d\tau_1 \right\} d\tau_2 \\
& \hspace{6cm} b \le t \le a+b
\end{aligned} \\[6ex]
0 \qquad t < 0 \text{ or } t > a+b
\end{cases}
\tag{5-67}
$$

Fig. 5.11 (a) Variance functions of nonstationary random processes obtained from the superposition of independently (Poisson) arriving half-sine random pulses; (b) variance functions of nonstationary random processes obtained from the superposition of correlatedly arriving half-sine random pulses.

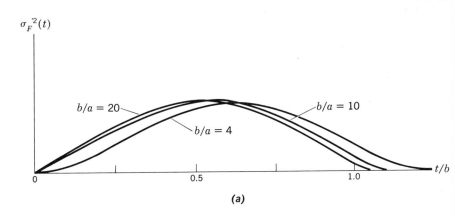

$\sigma_F^{\cdot 2}(t)$

$b/a = 20$

$b/a = 4$

$b/a = 10$

0   0.5   1.0 t/b

(a)

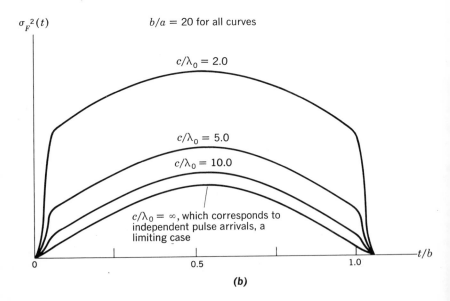

$\sigma_F^2(t)$ $b/a = 20$ for all curves

$c/\lambda_0 = 2.0$

$c/\lambda_0 = 5.0$

$c/\lambda_0 = 10.0$

$c/\lambda_0 = \infty$, which corresponds to independent pulse arrivals, a limiting case

0   0.5   1.0 t/b

(b)

The variance functions corresponding to Eqs. (5-65) and (5-67) are plotted in Fig. 5.11. In Fig. 5.11b the case $c \to \infty$, corresponding to independent (Poisson-type) pulse arrivals, is also included for comparison. Each of these curves shows that the average energy in the simulated excitation increases with time to a maximum and then decreases with time to zero. The same tendency is demonstrated in the typical earthquake record, Fig. 5.10. Solely from the evidence of the computed variance functions, it appears that earthquakes can be simulated by such random pulse trains.

The generalized spectral density follows from Eq. (4-98), namely,

$$\hat{\Phi}_{FF}(\omega_1, \omega_2) = (2\pi)^2 W(\omega_1) W^*(\omega_2) \left[A \frac{G_1(\omega_1 - \omega_2)}{2\pi} + B^2 \hat{G}_2(\omega_1, \omega_2) \right] \quad (5\text{-}68)$$

where

$$W(\omega) = \frac{1}{2\pi} \int_0^a \sin \frac{\pi t}{a} \exp(-i\omega t) \, dt$$

$$= \frac{a}{2(\pi^2 - a^2\omega^2)} \left[\exp(-i\omega a) + 1 \right] \quad (5\text{-}69)$$

$$G_1(\omega) = \frac{1}{2\pi} \int_0^b \lambda_0 \sin \frac{\pi t}{b} \exp(-i\omega t) \, dt$$

$$= \frac{\lambda_0}{2} \frac{b}{\pi^2 - b^2\omega^2} \left[\exp(-i\omega b) + 1 \right] \quad (5\text{-}70)$$

and, if $N(t)$ is non-Poisson,

$$\hat{G}_2(\omega_1, \omega_2) = \frac{1}{(2\pi)^2} \int_0^b \int_0^b \lambda_0{}^2 \exp(-c|t_1 - t_2|)$$

$$\exp\left[-i(\omega_1 t_1 - \omega_2 t_2)\right] \, dt_1 \, dt_2$$

$$= \frac{\lambda_0{}^2}{(2\pi)^2} \left(\frac{1}{c - i\omega_1} \left\{ \frac{\exp\left[i(\omega_2 - \omega_1)b\right] - 1}{i(\omega_2 - \omega_1)} \right. \right.$$

$$\left. + \frac{\exp\left[(-c + i\omega_2)b\right] - 1}{c - i\omega_2} \right\} + \frac{1}{c + i\omega_2}$$

$$\left. \left\{ \frac{\exp\left[i(\omega_2 - \omega_1)b\right] - 1}{i(\omega_2 - \omega_1)} + \frac{\exp\left[(-c - i\omega_1)b\right] - 1}{c + i\omega_1} \right\} \right) \quad (5\text{-}71)$$

In obtaining Eq. (5-71) use has been made of the fact that the integrand in the double integration is hermitian in ω_1 and ω_2. Furthermore, $\hat{G}_2(\omega_1, \omega_2) = 0$ if $N(t)$ is Poisson. The covariance function of $F(t)$ can be obtained either by inverting the generalized spectral density or directly by using the second equation in (4-86) or in (4-96), depending upon whether $N(t)$ is Poisson or non-Poisson.

Equation (5-68) can be used conveniently to find the generalized spectral density of the response, whence

$$\hat{\Phi}_{XX}(\omega_1, \omega_2) = (2\pi)^2 A H(\omega_1) W(\omega_1) H^*(\omega_2) W^*(\omega_2)$$
$$\left[\frac{G_1(\omega_1 - \omega_2)}{2\pi} + \hat{G}_2(\omega_1, \omega_2) \right] \quad (5\text{-}72)$$

It is interesting to note that if the excitation is a sequence of independent and independently arriving impulses than $W(\omega) = W^*(\omega) = 1/(2\pi)$ and $\hat{G}_2(\omega_1, \omega_2) = 0$; then Eq. (5-72) is seen to agree with Eq. (5-57).

5.5 / JOINT BEHAVIOR OF THE RESPONSE AND THE TIME DERIVATIVE OF THE RESPONSE

So far, we have been concerned only with certain statistical properties of the response $X(t)$, namely, its moment or cumulant functions. Since the state of motion at a time instant is characterized by both $X(t)$ and $d/dt\, X(t) = \dot{X}(t)$, it would appear that a more complete analysis should deal with a random vector process in a phase plane, with $X(t)$ and $\dot{X}(t)$ as the two random components. The joint behavior of these two components may be specified, for example, by their joint moment functions of various orders.

Let $\dot{X}(t)$ be a mean-square derivative. Since mean-square differentiation and expectation commute, the joint moments of $X(t)$ and $\dot{X}(t)$ can be obtained from those of $X(t)$. Specifically,

$$E[X(t_1) \cdots X(t_m)\dot{X}(t_{m+1}) \cdots \dot{X}(t_{m+n})]$$
$$= \frac{\partial^n}{\partial t_{m+1} \cdots \partial t_{m+n}} E[X(t_1) \cdots X(t_{m+n})] \quad (5\text{-}73)$$

where $r > s$ does not necessarily imply $t_r > t_s$. Equation (5-73) shows that an analysis of $X(t)$ alone is entirely sufficient. However, it is worthwhile to note the following known results. If $X(t)$ is weakly stationary, then $X(t)$ and $\dot{X}(t)$ are orthogonal when evaluated at the same time instant (cf. page 50). If, in addition, $X(t)$ is Gaussian with a zero expectation, then they are also independent. Therefore, for a Gaussian process $X(t)$,

$$p_{\{X\}\{\dot{X}\}}(x, t; \dot{x}, t) = -\frac{1}{2\pi\sigma_X\sigma_{\dot{X}}} \exp\left[-\frac{1}{2}\left(\frac{x^2}{\sigma_X^2} + \frac{\dot{x}^2}{\sigma_{\dot{X}}^2} \right) \right] \quad (5\text{-}74)$$

where σ_X^2 and $\sigma_{\dot{X}}^2$ are the variances of $X(t)$ and $\dot{X}(t)$, respectively, which are obtainable from the spectral density of $X(t)$ as follows:

$$\sigma_X^2 = \int_{-\infty}^{\infty} \Phi_{XX}(\omega)\, d\omega$$
$$\sigma_{\dot{X}}^2 = \int_{-\infty}^{\infty} \omega^2 \Phi_{XX}(\omega)\, d\omega \quad (5\text{-}75)$$

The joint probability density of $X(t)$ and $\dot{X}(t)$, such as the one given in

Eq. (5-74), is useful in computing the expected number of times per unit time that the random process $X(t)$ crosses a certain threshold, either from below or from above. This problem will be considered in Chap. 9. Also to be considered in that chapter is the number of peaks per unit time in the random process $X(t)$, for which the joint probability density of $X(t)$, $\dot{X}(t)$, and $\ddot{X}(t)$ will be required.

5.6 / THE RESPONSE AND ITS TIME DERIVATIVES TREATED AS COMPONENTS OF A MARKOV VECTOR

If the excitation is a sequence of independent and independently arriving random impulses (one type of shot noise), we should expect the state of the motion of the system represented by a random vector process on the phase plane to be one with independent increments. This is so since the cause for the change of state, the excitation, is independent at any two different times. If, in addition, the state at time $t = 0$ is known at least with probability 1, then the random vector process is a Markov vector.‡ For brevity the name *shot noise* in the present section will refer to that special type of excitation which is a sequence of independent and independently arriving impulses. The nonstationary case will be considered for generality.

The theory of Markov processes also applies if the excitation is a *filtered shot noise*, by which we refer to an excitation $F(t)$ satisfying the stochastic differential equation

$$Q[F(t)] = \sum_{k=0}^{N} a_n \frac{d^n}{dt_n{}^n} F(t) = S(t) \qquad a_N \neq 0 \qquad (5\text{-}76)$$

and a set of initial conditions, where $S(t)$ is a shot noise and the a_n are constants. A filtered shot noise can also be constructed from random pulses; in particular, if at $t = 0$

$$\frac{d^{n-1}}{dt^{n-1}} F(t) = \frac{1}{a_n} \qquad \text{and} \qquad \frac{d^{n-2}}{dt^{n-2}} F(t) = \cdots = F(t) = 0$$

then the shape of the random pulses may be obtained from (cf. Sec. 5.1)

$$h_Q(t - \tau) = \frac{1}{2\pi} \int_{-\infty}^{\infty} \Big[\sum_{n=0}^{N} (i\omega)^n a_n \Big]^{-1} \exp\left[i\omega(t - \tau)\right] d\omega \qquad (5\text{-}77)$$

Under the excitation of a filtered shot noise, the equation of motion can be written as

$$Q[\ddot{X}(t) + 2\zeta\omega_0\dot{X}(t) + \omega_0{}^2 X(t)] = S(t) \qquad (5\text{-}78)$$

---

‡ See J. L. Doob, "Stochastic Processes," p. 96, Wiley, New York, 1953. We remark however, that it is not necessary for a Markov process to have independent increments.

or

$$P[X(t)] = \sum_{m=0}^{M} b_m \frac{d^m}{dt^m} X(t) = S(t) \tag{5-78a}$$

where $M = N + 2$, the b_m are constants, and $b_M \neq 0$. Clearly, the M-dimensional random vector process with the components $X(t)$, $d/dt\, X(t), \ldots, (d^{M-1}/dt^{M-1})X(t)$ is a Markov vector. Equation (5-78a) includes the special case of a shot-noise excitation, the case where $M = 2$. Therefore, it is sufficient to consider the general form Eq. (5-78a). Denote $d^m/dt^m X(t)$ by $Y_{m+1}(t)$, $m = 0, 1, 2, \ldots, M - 1$. The Fokker-Planck equation for the Markov vector $\mathbf{Y} = \{Y_1, Y_2, \ldots, Y_M\}$ has the general form

$$\frac{\partial}{\partial t} q + \frac{\partial}{\partial y_i} (A_i q) - \frac{1}{2!} \frac{\partial^2}{\partial y_i \, \partial y_j} (B_{ij} q)$$
$$+ \frac{1}{3!} \frac{\partial^3}{\partial y_i \, \partial y_j \, \partial y_l} (C_{ijl} q) - \cdots = 0 \tag{4-137}$$

where $q = q_{\{\mathbf{Y}\}}(\mathbf{y}, t | \mathbf{y}_0, t_0)$ is the transition probability density of $\mathbf{Y}$. The transition is from a state $\mathbf{y}_0$ at an earlier time t_0 to a state in $[\mathbf{y}, \mathbf{y} + d\mathbf{y}]$ at a later time t. At the present time, Eq. (4-137) can be solved only when the excitation $S(t)$ is a Gaussian shot noise. We shall assume that this is the case. The essential elements constituting Eq. (4-137) are the derivate moments A_i, B_{ij}, C_{ijl}, etc., defined in Eqs. (4-138). However, Eqs. (4-138) contain the transition probability density, which is still unknown. Therefore, these derivate moments must be determined by other means. A logical place to search for such information is Eq. (5-78a), which governs the behavior of the system.

Corresponding to the components of the random vector process $\mathbf{Y} = \{Y_1, Y_2, \ldots, Y_M\}$, Eq. (5-78a) may be replaced by M simultaneous stochastic differential equations of the first order,

$$\dot{Y}_i = Y_{i+1} \quad i = 1, 2, \ldots, M - 1$$
$$\dot{Y}_M = -\sum_{m=0}^{M-1} b_m Y_{m+1} + S(t) \tag{5-79}$$

where, without loss of generality, b_M has been taken to be unity. Recall that the alternative representation of the derivate moments A_i, B_{ij}, C_{ijl}, etc., is

$$A_i = \lim_{\Delta t \to 0} \frac{E[\Delta Y_i | \mathbf{Y}(t) = \mathbf{y}]}{\Delta t}$$
$$B_{ij} = \lim_{\Delta t \to 0} \frac{E[(\Delta Y_i)(\Delta Y_j) | \mathbf{Y}(t) = \mathbf{y}]}{\Delta t} \tag{4-138a}$$
$$C_{ijl} = \lim_{\Delta t \to 0} \frac{E[(\Delta Y_i)(\Delta Y_j)(\Delta Y_l) | \mathbf{Y}(t) = \mathbf{y}]}{\Delta t}$$

where $\Delta Y_i = Y_i(t + \Delta t) - Y_i(t)$, etc. Assuming that the change of state is continuous, we deduce from integrating Eqs. (5-79) that, for a sufficiently small time interval Δt,

$$[\Delta Y_i | \mathbf{Y}(t) = \mathbf{y}] = y_{i+1}(\Delta t) + O(\overline{\Delta t^2}) \qquad i = 1, 2, \ldots, M - 1$$

$$[\Delta Y_M | \mathbf{Y}(t) = \mathbf{y}] = -\sum_{m=0}^{M-1} b_m y_{m+1}(\Delta t) + \int_t^{t+\Delta t} S(\tau)\,d\tau + O(\overline{\Delta t^2}) \qquad (5\text{-}80)$$

The symbol $O(\overline{\Delta t^2})$ denotes a remainder which is of an order of $(\Delta t)^2$. By substituting (5-80) into Eqs. (4-138a) and using the Gaussian property Eq. (4-61), we find that the derivate moments of an order equal to or higher than 3 vanish. The first and second derivate moments are summarized as follows:

$$A_i = g_{ij} y_j \qquad i, j = 1, 2, \ldots, M \qquad (5\text{-}81)$$

with

$$g_{ij} = \begin{cases} 1 & \text{for } i = 1, 2, \ldots, M - 1 \text{ and } j = i + 1 \\ 0 & \text{for } i = 1, 2, \ldots, M - 1 \text{ and } j \neq i + 1 \end{cases} \qquad (5\text{-}82)$$

$$g_{Mj} = -b_{j-1} \qquad \text{for } j = 1, 2, \ldots, M$$

and

$$B_{ij} = \begin{cases} I(t) & \text{for } i = j = M \\ 0 & \text{otherwise} \end{cases} \qquad (5\text{-}83)$$

where $I(t)$ is the intensity function of the shot noise. Thus the Fokker-Planck equation reduces to

$$\frac{\partial}{\partial t} q_{\{\mathbf{Y}\}} = -\frac{\partial}{\partial y_i} (A_i q_{\{\mathbf{Y}\}}) + \frac{1}{2} \frac{\partial^2}{\partial y_i \, \partial y_j} (B_{ij} q_{\{\mathbf{Y}\}}) \qquad (5\text{-}84)$$

The solution of Eq. (5-84) may be obtained as follows.‡ The state variables y_i are first linearly transformed to z_i through the relationship

$$z_i = c_{ij} y_j \qquad (5\text{-}85)$$

where the c_{ij} are related to the g_{ij} of Eq. (5-82) by

$$c_{ij} g_{jl} = \lambda_i c_{il} \qquad \text{no summation on } i \qquad (5\text{-}86)$$

Equation (5-86) implies that the λ_i are the roots of the characteristic equation of the matrix $\mathbf{g}$. We assume that these roots are distinct.

‡ See Y. K. Lin, On Nonstationary Shot Noise, *J. Acoust. Soc. Am.*, **36**:82–84 (1964). This solution is a generalization of the one given by M. C. Wang and G. E. Uhlenbeck, On the Theory of the Brownian Motion II, *Rev. Mod. Phys.*, **17**(2, 3): 323–342 (1945); collected in N. Wax (ed.), "Selected Papers on Noise and Stochastic Processes," Dover, New York, 1954.

Then the matrix **c** can, in fact, be obtained by inverting a square matrix whose columns are modal columns of **g**. It can easily be shown that for each λ_i the corresponding modal column is $\{1, \lambda_i, \lambda_i^2, \ldots, \lambda_i^{M-1}\}$. Thus

$$
\mathbf{c}^{-1} = \begin{bmatrix}
1 & 1 & \cdots & 1 \\
\lambda_1 & \lambda_2 & \cdots & \lambda_M \\
\lambda_1^2 & \lambda_2^2 & \cdots & \lambda_M^2 \\
\cdots\cdots\cdots\cdots\cdots\cdots\cdots \\
\lambda_1^{M-1} & \lambda_2^{M-1} & \cdots & \lambda_M^{M-1}
\end{bmatrix} \tag{5-87}
$$

A matrix of the form of (5-87) is called a Vandermonde matrix. Since all the latent roots λ_i are assumed to be distinct, it can be shown‡ that this matrix is nonsingular, and therefore **c** exists. Substituting (5-85) into (5-84),

$$
\frac{\partial}{\partial t} q_{\{z\}} = -\lambda_l \frac{\partial}{\partial z_l} (z_l q_{\{z\}}) + \frac{1}{2} \gamma_{lm} \frac{\partial^2}{\partial z_l \, \partial z_m} q_{\{z\}} \tag{5-88}
$$

where

$$
\gamma_{lm} = c_{li} B_{ij} c_{mj} \tag{5-89}
$$

and is obviously a function of t. The new dependent variable $q_{\{z\}}$ is the same as $q_{\{y\}}$ but is expressed in terms of the new state vector **z**. Equation (5-88) is solved with the condition

$$
q_{\{z\}}(z; t_0|z_0; t_0) = \delta(z_1 - z_{1,0}) \, \delta(z_2 - z_{2,0}) \, \cdots \, \delta(z_M - z_{M,0}) \tag{5-90}
$$

where $z_0 = \{z_{1,0}, z_{2,0}, \ldots, z_{M,0}\} = \mathbf{c}y_0$.

Equation (5-88) is a partial differential equation of the second order with $M + 1$ independent variables. It can be reduced to one of the first order by a multidimensional Fourier transformation. In particular, we shall convert Eq. (5-88) for $q_{\{z\}}$ into an equation for the characteristic function of **Z**,

$$
M_{\{Z\}} = \underbrace{\int \cdots \int}_{M\text{-fold}} q_{\{z\}} \exp\left(i \sum \theta_l z_l \right) dz_1 \, dz_2 \, \cdots \, dz_M \tag{5-91}
$$

This transformation leads to

$$
\frac{\partial}{\partial t} M_{\{Z\}} = \lambda_l \theta_l \frac{\partial}{\partial \theta_l} M_{\{Z\}} - \frac{1}{2} \gamma_{lm} \theta_l \theta_m M_{\{Z\}} \tag{5-92}
$$

As was true with Eq. (5-86), the first member on the right-hand side of (5-92) involves only a single summation on l; that is, the index for λ when repeated does not imply a summation.

‡ R. Bellman, "Introduction to Matrix Analysis," p. 186, McGraw-Hill, New York, 1960.

The solution for (5-92) can be obtained by first solving the following $M + 1$ independent subsidiary equations:‡

$$\frac{dt}{1} = -\frac{d\theta_1}{\lambda_1\theta_1} = -\frac{d\theta_2}{\lambda_2\theta_2} = \cdots = -\frac{d\theta_M}{\lambda_M\theta_M}$$

$$= -\frac{dM_{\{Z\}}}{\frac{1}{2}M_{\{Z\}}\Sigma\Sigma\gamma_{lm}\theta_l\theta_m} \tag{5-93}$$

The solutions for the subsidiary equations

$$\frac{dt}{1} = -\frac{d\theta_j}{\lambda_j\theta_j} \qquad j = 1, 2, \ldots, M \tag{5-94}$$

are given by

$$\theta_j \exp(\lambda_j t) = C_j \qquad j = 1, 2, \ldots, M \tag{5-95}$$

For the combination

$$\frac{dt}{1} = -\frac{dM_{\{Z\}}}{\frac{1}{2}M_{\{Z\}}\Sigma\Sigma\gamma_{lm}\theta_l\theta_m} \tag{5-96}$$

the double sum $\Sigma\Sigma\gamma_{lm}\theta_l\theta_m$ may be expressed as a function of t, that is,

$$\Sigma\Sigma\gamma_{lm}\theta_l\theta_m = \Sigma\Sigma\gamma_{lm}C_lC_m \exp\left[-(\lambda_l + \lambda_m)t\right] \tag{5-97}$$

By substituting (5-97) into (5-96) and integrating, we obtain

$$\ln CM_{\{Z\}} = -\tfrac{1}{2}\Sigma\Sigma C_lC_m\int\gamma_{lm}\exp\left[-(\lambda_l + \lambda_m)t\right]dt$$

$$= -\tfrac{1}{2}\Sigma\Sigma\theta_l\theta_m\exp\left[(\lambda_l + \lambda_m)t\right]\int\gamma_{lm}\exp\left[-(\lambda_l + \lambda_m)t\right]dt \tag{5-98}$$

or

$$M_{\{Z\}}\exp\left\{\tfrac{1}{2}\Sigma\Sigma\theta_l\theta_m\exp\left[(\lambda_l + \lambda_m)t\right]\int\gamma_{lm}\exp\left[-(\lambda_l + \lambda_m)t\right]dt\right\} = C_{M+1} \tag{5-98a}$$

The general solution to (5-92) now can be written as follows:

$$M_{\{Z\}} = \psi[\theta_1\exp(\lambda_1 t), \theta_2\exp(\lambda_2 t), \ldots, \theta_M\exp(\lambda_M t)]$$

$$\exp\left\{-\tfrac{1}{2}\Sigma\Sigma\theta_l\theta_m[\exp(\lambda_l + \lambda_m)t]\int\gamma_{lm}\exp\left[-(\lambda_l + \lambda_m)t\right]dt\right\} \tag{5-99}$$

where ψ represents an arbitrary functional form. This general solution must satisfy the condition

$$[M_{\{Z\}}]_{t=t_0} = \int\cdots\int_{M\text{-fold}}[\Pi\,\delta(z_j - z_{j,0})]\exp\left(i\sum\theta_j z_j\right)dz_1\,dz_2\cdots dz_M$$

$$= \exp\left(i\sum\theta_j z_{j,0}\right) \tag{5-100}$$

Thus

$$M_{\{Z\}} = \exp\left\{i\sum\theta_j z_{j,0}\exp\left[\lambda_j(t - t_0)\right] - \tfrac{1}{2}\sum\sum\theta_j\theta_l\int_{t_0}^{t}\gamma_{jl}(\tau)\exp\left[(\lambda_j + \lambda_l)(t - \tau)\right]d\tau\right\} \tag{5-101}$$

‡ See, for example, F. H. Miller, "Partial Differential Equations," p. 95, Wiley, New York, 1941.

This expression is readily recognized to be the characteristic function of an M-dimensional Gaussian distribution with a mean vector

$$E[\mathbf{Z}] = \exp\left[\lambda(t - t_0)\right]\mathbf{z}_0 = \exp\left[\lambda(t - t_0)\right]\mathbf{c}\mathbf{y}_0 \qquad (5\text{-}102)$$

and a covariance matrix $\mathbf{S}$ whose element in the jth row and the lth column is

$$\kappa_{jl} = \int_{t_0}^{t} \gamma_{jl}(\tau) \exp\left[(\lambda_j + \lambda_l)(t - \tau)\right] d\tau \qquad (5\text{-}103)$$

In Eq. (5-102), $\exp\left[\lambda(t - t_0)\right]$ is a diagonal matrix with diagonal elements $\exp\left[\lambda_j(t - t_0)\right]$, $j = 1, 2, \ldots, M$. Note also that $\kappa_{jl} = 0$ at $t = t_0$, which refers to the fact that the covariances are computed for a prescribed condition $\mathbf{Y}(t_0) = \mathbf{y}_0$.

In the special case when $S(t)$ is stationary (a white noise), γ_{jl} is independent of time. Equation (5-103) then reduces to

$$\kappa_{jl} = -\frac{\gamma_{jl}}{\lambda_j + \lambda_l}\left\{1 - \exp\left[(\lambda_j + \lambda_l)(t - t_0)\right]\right\} \qquad (5\text{-}104)$$

which is of the same form as that given by Wang and Uhlenbeck.‡

Since the random vector process $\mathbf{Y}$ is a linear function of $\mathbf{Z}$, it follows that $\mathbf{Y}$ is also Gaussian. It suffices to find the mean vector and the covariance matrix for $\mathbf{Y}$. The mean vector of $\mathbf{Y}$ is

$$E[\mathbf{Y}] = \mathbf{c}^{-1}E[\mathbf{Z}] = \mathbf{c}^{-1} \exp\left[\lambda(t - t_0)\right]\mathbf{c}\mathbf{y}_0 \qquad (5\text{-}105)$$

From the series expansion

$$\begin{aligned}
\exp\left[\lambda(t - t_0)\right] &= \lim_{n \to \infty} \left(\mathbf{I} + \lambda\frac{t - t_0}{n}\right)^n \\
&= \sum_{n=0}^{\infty} \frac{(t - t_0)^n}{n!}\lambda^n
\end{aligned} \qquad (5\text{-}106)$$

we have

$$E[\mathbf{Y}] = \mathbf{c}^{-1} \sum_{n=0}^{\infty} \frac{(t - t_0)^n}{n!}\lambda^n\mathbf{c}\mathbf{y}_0 \qquad (5\text{-}107)$$

From the relation (5-86) we have

$$\lambda^n = \mathbf{c}\mathbf{g}^n\mathbf{c}^{-1} \qquad (5\text{-}108)$$

Substituting (5-108) into (5-107),

$$E[\mathbf{Y}] = \sum_{n=0}^{\infty} \frac{(t - t_0)^n}{n!}\mathbf{g}^n\mathbf{y}_0 = \exp\left[\mathbf{g}(t - t_0)\right]\mathbf{y}_0 \qquad (5\text{-}109)$$

‡ *Loc. cit.*

Note that this matrix is, in general, different from the one whose elements are exp $[g_{ij}(t - t_0)]$ except when $\mathbf{g}$ is a diagonal matrix. In passing, we remark that in view of the Cayley-Hamilton theorem,[‡] the matrix exp $[\mathbf{g}(t - t_0)]$ can be expanded as follows:

$$\exp [\mathbf{g}(t - t_0)] = a_{M-1}[\mathbf{g}(t - t_0)]^{M-1} + a_{M-2}[\mathbf{g}(t - t_0)]^{M-2} \\ + \cdots + a_1[\mathbf{g}(t - t_0)] + a_0\mathbf{I} \quad (5\text{-}110)$$

The coefficients $a_{M-1}, a_{M-2}, \ldots, a_0$ can be determined if the latent roots of $\mathbf{g}$ are known.

The covariance matrix for $\mathbf{Y}$ is

$$\hat{\mathbf{S}} = E[\{\mathbf{Y} - E(\mathbf{Y})\}\{\mathbf{Y} - E(\mathbf{Y})\}'] \quad (5\text{-}111)$$

where the prime indicates transposition. The application of (5-85) leads to

$$\hat{\mathbf{S}} = E[\mathbf{c}^{-1}\{\mathbf{Z} - E(\mathbf{Z})\}\{\mathbf{Z} - E(\mathbf{Z})\}'\mathbf{c}^{-1'}] \\ = \mathbf{c}^{-1}\mathbf{S}\mathbf{c}^{-1'} \quad (5\text{-}112)$$

The covariance matrix $\mathbf{S}$ of $\mathbf{Z}$, whose elements are given in Eq. (5-103), may be expressed more concisely as follows:

$$\mathbf{S} = \int_{t_0}^t \exp [\lambda(t - \tau)]\boldsymbol{\gamma}(\tau) \exp [\lambda(t - \tau)] \, d\tau \quad (5\text{-}103a)$$

Note that exp $[\lambda(t - \tau)]$ is a diagonal matrix; hence it is equal to its transpose. If (5-103a) is substituted into (5-112), and use is made of the relations

$$\boldsymbol{\gamma} = \mathbf{c}\mathbf{B}\mathbf{c}'$$

and

$$\exp [\mathbf{g}(t - \tau)] = \mathbf{c}^{-1} \exp [\lambda(t - \tau)]\mathbf{c}$$

we obtain

$$\hat{\mathbf{S}} = \int_{t_0}^t \exp [\mathbf{g}(t - \tau)]\mathbf{B}(\tau) \exp [\mathbf{g}'(t - \tau)] \, d\tau \quad (5\text{-}113)$$

where the elements in $\mathbf{B}$ are specified in (5-83). Note that

$$\exp [\mathbf{g}'(t - \tau)] = \Big[\exp [\mathbf{g}(t - \tau)] \Big]'$$

It is seen from Eqs. (5-109) and (5-113) that while the statistical mean of $\mathbf{Y}$ is related to the conditional state $\mathbf{y}_0$, this is not the case for the covariance matrix. The transition probability density for the random

---

[‡] See Bellman, *op. cit.*, p. 200. Refer also to page 162.

vector $\mathbf{Y}$ is thus given by

$$q_{\{\mathbf{Y}\}}(\mathbf{y}, t|\mathbf{y}_0, t_0) = \frac{1}{(2\pi)^{M/2}|\hat{S}|^{\frac{1}{2}}} \exp\left(-\tfrac{1}{2}\{\mathbf{y} - \exp\left[\mathbf{g}(t - t_0)\right]\mathbf{y}_0\}'\hat{S}^{-1}\right.$$
$$\left.\{\mathbf{y} - \exp\left[\mathbf{g}(t - t_0)\right]\mathbf{y}_0\}\right) \quad (5\text{-}114)$$

where the matrices $\mathbf{g}$ and $\hat{S}$ are given in (5-82) and (5-113), respectively. It is interesting to note that $\mathbf{g}$ represents merely the characteristics of the linear system (including, if any, the filter Q). On the other hand, $\hat{S}$ depends not only on the linear system but also on the nonstationary intensity of the shot noise, and each element in $\hat{S}$ is a function of t_0 and t.

Equation (5-114) becomes the first probability density of $\mathbf{Y}$ if t_0 is replaced by the initial time (that is, $t_0 = 0$) and if the initial state of the random vector is known with probability 1. This probability density governs the joint behavior of the components $X(t)$, $\dot{X}(t)$, etc., of a Markov vector. It was mentioned earlier that such information is required to compute the expected rates of threshold crossings or maxima in a random process (cf. page 143). Furthermore, if the initial state is known with probability 1, then the transition probability density Eq. (5-114) can be used to compute the autocorrelation functions and the crosscorrelation functions of $X(t)$ and its time derivatives. For example, the autocorrelation function of $X(t)$, which is the same as that of $Y_1(t)$, is computed from

$$\phi_{XX}(t_0, t) = \phi_{Y_1 Y_1}(t_0, t) = \int \cdots \int_{2M\text{-fold}} y_1 u_1 q_{\{\mathbf{Y}\}}(\mathbf{y}, t|\mathbf{u}, t_0)$$
$$q_{\{\mathbf{Y}\}}(\mathbf{u}, t_0|\mathbf{u}_0, 0)\, dy_1\, dy_2\, \cdots\, dy_M\, du_1\, du_2\, \cdots\, du_M \quad (5\text{-}115)$$

More generally, the crosscorrelation function of $Y_j(t)$ and $Y_k(t)$ is given by

$$\phi_{Y_j Y_k}(t_0, t) = \int \cdots \int_{2M\text{-fold}} y_k u_j q_{\{\mathbf{Y}\}}(\mathbf{y}, t|\mathbf{u}, t_0)$$
$$q_{\{\mathbf{Y}\}}(\mathbf{u}, t_0|\mathbf{u}_0, 0)\, dy_1\, dy_2\, \cdots\, dy_M\, du_1\, du_2\, \cdots\, du_M \quad (5\text{-}116)$$

5.7 / DIRECT DETERMINATION OF THE CONDITIONAL MEANS AND COVARIANCES

The central result obtained in Sec. 5.6 is that the mean vector and the covariance matrix of a Markov vector $\mathbf{Y} = \{X, \dot{X}, \ldots\}$, computed on the condition $\mathbf{Y}(t_0) = \mathbf{y}_0$, are

$$E[\mathbf{Y}] = \exp\left[\mathbf{g}(t - t_0)\right]\mathbf{y}_0 \quad (5\text{-}109)$$

and

$$\hat{S} = \int_{t_0}^{t} \exp\left[\mathbf{g}(t - \tau)\right]B(\tau) \exp\left[\mathbf{g}'(t - \tau)\right] d\tau \quad (5\text{-}113)$$

The classical method of Fokker-Planck was used to obtain this result. With the assumption that the excitation is a filtered Gaussian shot noise (the special type as implied throughout Sec. 5.6), the required transition probability density for **Y** is found to be of a Gaussian type;‡ therefore, it is completely specified by the mean vector and the covariance matrix. However, the simple forms exhibited in Eqs. (5-109) and (5-113) suggest that a more direct procedure to derive these equations is possible. This more direct procedure will be given below, and it will be shown that Eqs. (5-109) and (5-113) are valid even without the assumptions that the shot noise is a sequence of independent and independently arriving impulses and is Gaussian.

We begin with the system of stochastic differential equations (5-79), which may be written more concisely as follows:

$$\frac{d}{dt} \mathbf{Y} = \mathbf{gY} + \mathbf{F} \qquad (5\text{-}79a)$$

where **F** is the column matrix of the forcing functions, and in the present case $\mathbf{F} = \{0, \ldots, 0, S(t)\}$. Since the operations of mean-square differentiation and expectation commute, we obtain, upon taking the expectations on both sides of Eq. (5-79a),

$$\frac{d}{dt} E[\mathbf{Y}] = \mathbf{g}E[\mathbf{Y}] \qquad (5\text{-}117)$$

The solution to this matrix differential equation under the initial condition $E[\mathbf{Y}(t_0)] = \mathbf{y}_0$ is Eq. (5-109), as can be easily verified by substitution.

To find a matrix differential equation for the covariance matrix, we subtract Eq. (5-117) from Eq. (5-79a) to obtain

$$\frac{d}{dt} \{\mathbf{Y} - E[\mathbf{Y}]\} = \mathbf{g}\{\mathbf{Y} - E[\mathbf{Y}]\} + \mathbf{F} \qquad (5\text{-}118)$$

or, with $\mathbf{Z} = \mathbf{Y} - E[\mathbf{Y}]$,

$$\frac{d}{dt} \mathbf{Z} = \mathbf{gZ} + \mathbf{F} \qquad (5\text{-}118a)$$

Post-multiply both sides of (5-118a) by the row **Z′**:

$$\left(\frac{d}{dt} \mathbf{Z}\right) \mathbf{Z'} = \mathbf{gZZ'} + \mathbf{FZ'} \qquad (5\text{-}119)$$

If we apply matrix transposition on Eq. (5-119) and the result is added to

‡ This was accomplished without using the argument that linear functions of a Gaussian random process are jointly Gaussian distributed.

Eq. (5-119), we obtain

$$\left(\frac{d}{dt}\mathbf{Z}\right)\mathbf{Z}' + \mathbf{Z}\frac{d}{dt}\mathbf{Z}' = \frac{d}{dt}(\mathbf{Z}\mathbf{Z}')$$

$$= \mathbf{g}(\mathbf{Z}\mathbf{Z}') + (\mathbf{Z}\mathbf{Z}')\mathbf{g}' + \mathbf{F}\mathbf{Z}' + \mathbf{Z}\mathbf{F}' \quad (5\text{-}120)$$

The expectation of (5-120) is

$$\frac{d}{dt}\hat{\mathbf{S}} = \mathbf{g}\hat{\mathbf{S}} + \hat{\mathbf{S}}\mathbf{g}' + E[\mathbf{F}\mathbf{Z}'] + E[\mathbf{Z}\mathbf{F}'] \quad (5\text{-}121)$$

To evaluate the matrices $E[\mathbf{F}\mathbf{Z}']$ and $E[\mathbf{Z}\mathbf{F}']$, we note that since a shot noise is uncorrelated‡ with its own past, and since $Y_j(t), j = 1, 2, \ldots,$ $M - 1$ result from the past shot noise up to time t,

$$E[S(t)Z_j(t)] = E[S(t)Y_j(t)] - E[S(t)]E[Y_j(t)]$$
$$= E[S(t)Y_j(t)] = 0 \quad j < M \quad (5\text{-}122)$$

Furthermore, if, in a shot noise, an impulse arrives at time t, this impulse is solely responsible for a jump $Y_M(t + \epsilon) - Y_M(t - \epsilon)$ equal to the strength of the impulse, where ϵ is an arbitrarily small positive number. Thus,

$$E[S(t)Y_M(t)] = \int_{t-\epsilon}^{t} I(\tau)\,\delta(t - \tau)\,d\tau = \tfrac{1}{2}I(t) \quad (5\text{-}123)$$

Here we have used the usual assumption that the probability for the simultaneous arrival of two or more impulses is zero. We see, then, that

$$E[\mathbf{F}\mathbf{Y}'] = E[\mathbf{Y}\mathbf{F}'] = E[\mathbf{F}\mathbf{Z}'] = E[\mathbf{Z}\mathbf{F}'] = \tfrac{1}{2}\mathbf{B} \quad (5\text{-}124)$$

where $\mathbf{B}$ is specified in Eq. (5-83). Thus the matrix equation for the covariance matrix results when Eq. (5-124) is substituted into Eq. (5-121):

$$\frac{d}{dt}\hat{\mathbf{S}} = \mathbf{g}\hat{\mathbf{S}} + \hat{\mathbf{S}}\mathbf{g}' + \mathbf{B} \quad (5\text{-}125)$$

It can be seen that with the initial condition $\hat{\mathbf{S}}(t_0) = 0$, Eq. (5-113) is the unique solution to Eq. (5-125).

Since only the assumption of uncorrelated impulses in the shot noise is used in the derivation of Eqs. (5-117) and (5-125), it is clear that the expressions for the conditional mean vector and the conditional covariance matrix are valid for the case of a general shot noise $S(t)$. Of course, in the general case, the knowledge of the conditional mean vector and conditional covariance is insufficient to determine the transition probability density.

---

‡ Note that we do not require the assumption of independence here. Therefore this shot noise is a general type having a correlation function $\phi_{SS}(t_1, t_2) = I(t_1)\,\delta(t_2 - t_1)$.

EXERCISES

5-1. Using the method of residues, show that the integration of Eq. (5-32) results in Eq. (5-45) if the excitation is a white noise.

5-2. Evaluate approximately the integral in Eq. (5-29a), assuming that $\zeta \ll 1$ and that $\Phi_{FF}(\omega)$ is slowly varying, especially in the neighborhood of $\omega = \omega_0$.

5-3.‡ The motion of a lifting surface deviating from a steady flight path because of atmospheric turbulence is idealized as being governed by Eq. (5-22). At a constant forward speed u, the lifting surface is assumed to sense a weakly stationary upward air flow (upwash) having a velocity spectral density

$$\Phi_{TT}(\omega) = A^2 \frac{1 + 3(L\omega/u)^2}{[1 + (L\omega/u)^2]^2}$$

where L is called the scale of turbulence. The air turbulence gives rise to a random lift $F(t)$ which, based on a two-dimensional airfoil theory, has a spectral density

$$\Phi_{FF}(\omega) = \left(1 + \frac{\pi\omega c}{u}\right)^{-1} \Phi_{TT}(\omega)$$

where c is the chord length of the airfoil. Determine the mean-square response of the lifting surface in the steady state.

5-4.‡ For a tail surface of an aircraft situated near the edge of the wake of a stalled wing, the flow at the tail may be idealized as a random downwash which changes direction (a negative downwash is an upwash) at random times distributed according to a Poisson process with stationary increments. Such a random downwash is characterized by its spectral density

$$\Phi_{TT}(\omega) = \frac{B^2}{1 + (\omega/2\lambda)^2}$$

where λ is the average rate of sign changes. Assuming that the motion of the tail is governed by Eq. (5-22) and that a two-dimensional airfoil theory (as used in Exercise 5-3) is adequate, determine the mean-square motion of the tail.

5-5. An earthquake-response analysis is to be made for a building which is idealized to be a single-degree-of-freedom linear system. Assuming that the excitation process can be treated as a shot noise having a nonstationary intensity function

$$I(t) = I_0 e^{-at} \sin^2 kt \qquad a > 0, \ I_0 > 0$$

find the covariance functions of the excitation and of the response.

5-6. If the excitation process in Exercise 5-5 is changed to random pulses with

$$g_1(t) = \lambda_0 e^{-at} \sin^2 kt \qquad a > 0, \ \lambda_0 > 0$$
$$g_2(t_1, t_2) = \lambda_0^2 \exp\left(-c|t_1 - t_2|\right) \qquad c > 0$$

determine the generalized spectral densities for the excitation and the response.

5-7. For a second-order stochastic differential equation

$$\ddot{X} + 2\zeta\omega_0\dot{X} + \omega_0^2 X = S(t)$$

where $S(t)$ is a Gaussian shot noise which is a sequence of independent and independently arriving random impulses, show that the associated Fokker-Planck equa-

‡ See H. W. Liepmann, On the Application of Statistical Concepts to the Buffeting Problem, *J. Aeron. Sci*, **19**(12):793–800, 822 (1952).

tion is

$$\frac{\partial q}{\partial t} = - y_2 \frac{\partial q}{\partial y_1} + \frac{\partial}{\partial y_2} \left[(2\zeta\omega_0 y_2 + \omega_0^2 y_1)q \right] + I \frac{\partial^2 q}{\partial y_2^2}$$

where y_1 and y_2 are the state variables for X and $\dot{X}$, respectively, and I is the intensity function of the shot noise.

5-8. Compute the conditional mean vector and the conditional covariance matrix of the Gaussian Markov vector $\mathbf{Y} = \{X, \dot{X}\}$, where X is governed by the stochastic differential equation given in Exercise 5-7. Check the result by showing that the transition probability density so constructed satisfies the Fokker-Planck equation.

5-9. Find the autocorrelation function $\phi_{XX}(t_0, t)$ using the transition probability density obtained in Exercise 5-8.

6 | LINEAR STRUCTURES WITH FINITELY MANY DEGREES OF FREEDOM

6.1 / A GENERAL ANALYTICAL FRAMEWORK In dealing with a linear structure idealized as a system with n degrees of freedom it is convenient to use matrix notation. In this notation a general set of equations for the description of the response of such a structure under random excitations may be written analogous to those of a single-degree-of-freedom structure. The response may be described either by use of statistical properties or by use of probability distributions. Here, the term *response* means a displacement‡ or a linear function of a displacement, such as a bending moment, a stress, or a strain. As was mentioned in the beginning of Sec. 5.2, the randomness of the system response may be due to reasons other than or in addition to the randomness of the excitations, but again we act on the fact that for most structural dynamics problems, only random excitations are of interest; i.e., throughout our discussions we shall assume that the system characteristics and the initial conditions are precisely known.

Since our immediate concern in this chapter is the response, it is convenient to specify the dynamic characteristics of a linear finite-degrees-of-freedom structure by a matrix of frequency response functions, $\mathbf{H}(\omega)$, or a matrix of impulse response functions, $\mathbf{h}(t)$. To explain the physical meaning of a typical element $H_{jk}(\omega)$, a frequency response function, in the matrix $\mathbf{H}(\omega)$, let us refer to Fig. 6.1. In this figure there is shown an arbitrary structure of standard arbitrary shape supported against rigid-body motion. We assume that dissipation (damping) mechanisms are present such that, without excitations, the motion of the structure will

‡ As is commonplace in structural mechanics, a displacement may be a generalized displacement, and a force may be a generalized force.

Fig. 6.1

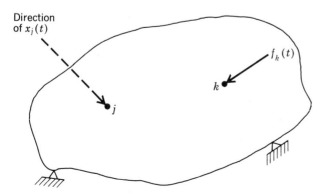

Direction
of $x_j(t)$

$f_k(t)$

k

j

tend to diminish for any initial state of motion. We shall call such a structure a *stable* structure. With excitations, the motion of a stable structure becomes less and less dependent upon the initial state as the duration of the excitations is prolonged. When the effect of the initial state becomes negligible, the motion is called the *steady-state response* to the given excitations.

Let us now consider a single sinusoidal excitation acting upon our arbitrary structure. Let the excitation act at a given point k and in a specified direction so that we may describe the excitation as $f_k(t) = A \exp (i\omega t)$, where A is a complex constant. (We shall again follow the usual practice of taking the real part of a complex function as representing the physically real quantity.) We may then express the steady-state response at point j, which has the same frequency ω as the excitation, as $x_j(t) = AH_{jk}(\omega) \exp (i\omega t)$. Therefore the frequency response function $H_{jk}(\omega)$ is the ratio of the steady-state response at point j to the sinusoidal excitation at point k. In general, this function is complex. The absolute value of this function is the ratio of the amplitudes, and the negative value of the phase angle of this function is the time lag between the excitation and the trailing response times the frequency ω. Similarly, a typical element $h_{jk}(t)$, an impulse response function, in the matrix $\mathbf{h}(t)$ describes the motion at j due to a unit impulse excitation at k applied at time $t = 0$, assuming that the structure is at rest prior to the excitation. Naturally, $h_{jk}(t) = 0$ for $t < 0$.

The matrices $\mathbf{H}(\omega)$ and $\mathbf{h}(t)$ are related as follows:

$$\mathbf{h}(t) = \frac{1}{2\pi} \int_{-\infty}^{\infty} \mathbf{H}(\omega) \exp (i\omega t) \, d\omega$$

$$\mathbf{H}(\omega) = \int_{-\infty}^{\infty} \mathbf{h}(t) \exp (-i\omega t) \, dt$$

$$(6\text{-}1)$$

which are perfect analogies to Eqs. (5-17). The determination of these matrices pertaining to different structural models of practical interest will be considered in Secs. 6.2 through 6.5.

If the matrix of impulse response functions, $\mathbf{h}(t)$, is known, the random response $\mathbf{X}(t) = \{X_1(t), X_2(t), \ldots, X_n(t)\}$ due to the random excitation $\mathbf{F}(t) = \{F_1(t), F_2(t), \ldots, F_m(t)\}$ is given by

$$\mathbf{X}(t) = \int_0^t \mathbf{h}(t - \tau)\mathbf{F}(\tau) \, d\tau \tag{6-2}$$

where the integration is interpreted in the sense of mean-square convergence, and the structure is considered to be at rest prior to the commencement of the excitation.‡ In this equation the matrix $\mathbf{h}(t)$ is, of course,

---

‡ If the structure is not originally at rest, then $\mathbf{X}(t)$ represents the random deviation from the course of the unexcited free motion.

$n \times m$. Component-wise, Eq. (6-2) may also be written as

$$X_j(t) = \int_0^t h_{jk}(t - \tau)F_k(\tau) \, d\tau \tag{6-2a}$$

where, again, the repeated index k signifies a summation over the range 1 to m. Equation (6-2a) can be used conveniently to find the joint moment functions or the joint cumulant functions of $X_j(t)$. For example, the third joint moment function and the third joint cumulant function are, respectively,

$$E[X_j(t_1)X_k(t_2)X_l(t_3)]$$
$$= \int_0^{t_1} \int_0^{t_2} \int_0^{t_3} h_{jp}(t_1 - \tau_1)h_{kq}(t_2 - \tau_2)h_{ls}(t_3 - \tau_3)$$
$$E[F_p(\tau_1)F_q(\tau_2)F_s(\tau_3)] \, d\tau_1 \, d\tau_2 \, d\tau_3 \tag{6-3}$$
$$\kappa_3[X_j(t_1)X_k(t_2)X_l(t_3)]$$
$$= \int_0^{t_1} \int_0^{t_2} \int_0^{t_3} h_{jp}(t_1 - \tau_1)h_{kq}(t_2 - \tau_2)h_{ls}(t_3 - \tau_3)$$
$$\kappa_3[F_p(\tau_1)F_q(\tau_2)F_s(\tau_3)] \, d\tau_1 \, d\tau_2 \, d\tau_3$$

For the first- and second-order statistical properties of the response vector, advantage can again be taken of concise matrix notation. For example,

$$\kappa_1\{\mathbf{X}(t)\} = E\{\mathbf{X}(t)\} = \int_0^t \mathbf{h}(t - \tau)E\{\mathbf{F}(\tau)\} \, d\tau$$
$$\kappa_2[\mathbf{X}(t_1)\mathbf{X}'(t_2)] = \int_0^{t_1} \int_0^{t_2} \mathbf{h}(t_1 - \tau_1)\kappa_2[\mathbf{F}(\tau_1)\mathbf{F}'(\tau_2)]\mathbf{h}'(t_2 - \tau_2) \, d\tau_1 \, d\tau_2 \tag{6-4}$$

where $\kappa_2[\mathbf{X}(t_1)\mathbf{X}'(t_2)]$ and $\kappa_2[\mathbf{F}(\tau_1)\mathbf{F}'(\tau_2)]$ are the covariance matrices for the response and excitation vectors, respectively. The upper limits of the integrals in Eqs. (6-4) may be extended to infinity since $\mathbf{h}$ is a null matrix for negative arguments. Since Eqs. (6-4) also imply that the excitation starts at $t = 0$ and that prior to the excitation the structure is at rest, the lower limits of the integrals in Eqs. (6-4) can be extended to minus infinity. Then by an application of a twofold Fourier transform to the second equation in (6-4), we obtain

$$\hat{\mathbf{\Phi}}_{\mathbf{X}}(\omega_1, \omega_2) = \mathbf{H}(\omega_1)\hat{\mathbf{\Phi}}_{\mathbf{F}}(\omega_1, \omega_2)\mathbf{H}'^*(\omega_2) \tag{6-5}$$

where $\hat{\mathbf{\Phi}}_{\mathbf{X}}$ and $\hat{\mathbf{\Phi}}_{\mathbf{F}}$ are the matrices of the generalized cross spectral densities of the response and the excitation vectors, respectively. A typical element in the matrix $\mathbf{\Phi}_{\mathbf{X}}(\omega_1, \omega_2)$ is

$$\hat{\Phi}_{X_j X_k}(\omega_1, \omega_2) = \frac{1}{(2\pi)^2} \int_{-\infty}^{\infty} \int_{-\infty}^{\infty} \kappa_2[X_j(t_1)X_k(t_2)] \exp\left[-i(\omega_1 t_1 - \omega_2 t_2)\right] dt_1 \, dt_2 \tag{6-6}$$

Similar elements are contained in the matrix $\hat{\mathbf{\Phi}}_{\mathbf{F}}(\omega_1, \omega_2)$. Of course, Eq. (6-5) is valid only if the generalized cross spectral densities involved exist. In particular, Eq. (6-5) does not apply if the components of the excitation vector are jointly weakly stationary (we say that the vector is weakly stationary for simplicity) and if the weakly stationary response is considered.

The relation between the correlation matrices of the excitation and the response is similar to the second equation of (6-4); i.e.,

$$E[\mathbf{X}(t_1)\mathbf{X}'(t_2)] = \int_0^{t_1} \int_0^{t_2} \mathbf{h}(t_1 - \tau_1) E[\mathbf{F}(\tau_1)\mathbf{F}'(\tau_2)]\mathbf{h}'(t_2 - \tau_2) \, d\tau_1 \, d\tau_2 \qquad (6\text{-}7)$$

For a weakly stationary excitation the correlation matrix (and the covariance matrix) of the excitation vector depends only on the time difference for which the correlations are evaluated. Denote this matrix by

$$\mathbf{R_F}(\tau_1 - \tau_2) = E[\mathbf{F}(\tau_1)\mathbf{F}'(\tau_2)] \qquad (6\text{-}8)$$

and assume that every element in $\mathbf{R_F}$ is continuous, absolutely integrable, and of bounded variation in the entire domain of its argument. Then

$$\mathbf{R_F}(\tau_1 - \tau_2) = \int_{-\infty}^{\infty} \mathbf{\Phi_F}(\omega) \exp[i\omega(\tau_1 - \tau_2)] \, d\omega$$

$$\mathbf{\Phi_F}(\omega) = \frac{1}{2\pi} \int_{-\infty}^{\infty} \mathbf{R_F}(u) \exp(-i\omega u) \, du \qquad (6\text{-}9)$$

where $\mathbf{\Phi_F}(\omega)$ is the matrix of the cross spectral densities of the excitations. Substituting the first equation in (6-9) into Eq. (6-7) and interchanging the order of integration, we obtain

$$E[\mathbf{X}(t_1)\mathbf{X}'(t_2)] = \int_{-\infty}^{\infty} \mathfrak{K}(\omega, t_1)\mathbf{\Phi_F}(\omega)\mathfrak{K}'^*(\omega_2, t_2) \exp[i\omega(t_1 - t_2)] \, d\omega \qquad (6\text{-}10)$$

where

$$\mathfrak{K}(\omega, t) = \int_0^t \mathbf{h}(u) \exp(-i\omega u) \, du$$

$$= \int_{-\infty}^t \mathbf{h}(u) \exp(-i\omega u) \, du \qquad (6\text{-}11)$$

Note that $\mathfrak{K}(\omega, \infty) = \mathbf{H}(\omega)$. Equation (6-10) is useful for computing the *transient nonstationary* response under *weakly stationary* excitations. As t_1 and t_2 approach infinity, but the difference $t_1 - t_2$ is kept finite, Eq. (6-10) yields the correlation matrix of the weakly stationary response; i.e.,

$$\mathbf{R_X}(t_1 - t_2) = \int_{-\infty}^{\infty} \mathbf{H}(\omega)\mathbf{\Phi_F}(\omega)\mathbf{H}'^*(\omega) \exp[i\omega(t_1 - t_2)] \, d\omega \qquad (6\text{-}12)$$

From the relation in the weakly stationary state between $\mathbf{R_X}(t_1 - t_2)$ and the matrix of the cross spectral densities of the response, $\mathbf{\Phi_X}(\omega)$, which is of the same form as that given in Eqs. (6-9), we see that

$$\mathbf{\Phi_X}(\omega) = \mathbf{H}(\omega)\mathbf{\Phi_F}(\omega)\mathbf{H}'^*(\omega) \qquad (6\text{-}13)$$

The general framework developed in the foregoing permits consideration of either stationary or nonstationary excitations and of either stationary or nonstationary responses for a linear structure with multiple degrees of freedom. Most of the results have been obtained for second-order statistical properties. By use of the matrix notation these results can be expressed concisely, and each has a perfect analogy to the case of a single degree of freedom. Higher-order relations, such as Eqs. (6-3), can also be written if needed, but computations of higher-order properties are increasingly laborious. However, as was noted in Sec. 3.2, the second-order statistical properties are particularly important from a practical point of view.

6.2 / THE STIFFNESS-COEFFICIENT REPRESENTATION

In a *stiffness-coefficient* representation of a linear structure the elastic behavior of the structure is represented by a matrix‡ of stiffness coefficients, k. Correspondingly, the inertial properties are represented by a matrix of concentrated masses and mass moments of inertia, $\bar{m}$. Then the potential¶ and kinetic energies of the system, V and T, are given by

$$V = \tfrac{1}{2}x'kx$$
$$T = \tfrac{1}{2}\dot{x}'\bar{m}\dot{x}$$

$$(6-14)$$

where $x = \{x_1(t), x_2(t), \ldots, x_n(t)\}$ is the column of the generalized displacements. Here, matrix $\bar{m}$ is positive definite while matrix k is at least nonnegative definite.§ Application of the Lagrange equation yields

$$\tfrac{1}{2}(\bar{m} + \bar{m}')\ddot{x} + \tfrac{1}{2}(k + k')x = 0 \qquad (6-15)$$

From the Maxwell reciprocity theorem we know that k is symmetrical; therefore, $\tfrac{1}{2}(k + k') = k$. We shall write $m = \tfrac{1}{2}(\bar{m} + \bar{m}')$, which is also symmetrical,‡‡ and rewrite Eq. (6-15) as

$$m\ddot{x} + kx = 0 \qquad (6-15a)$$

---

‡ The matrix of stiffness coefficients, k, is the inverse of the matrix of flexibility influence coefficients, say a. The typical element a_{ij} in a gives the generalized displacement at i due to a static unit generalized force at j.

¶ The potential energy is usually evaluated by using the static-equilibrium configuration as a datum.

§ A square matrix A is said to be positive (nonnegative) definite if, for an arbitrary column matrix q whose elements are not all zero, $q'Aq$ is positive (nonnegative). Matrix k is also positive definite if no rigid-body motion is permitted.

‡‡ Quite frequently $\bar{m}$ is symmetrical; then $\bar{m} = m$. However, a valid equation of motion of the same matrix form as Eq. (6-15a) may be derived by use of a method (say d'Alembert's principle) other than application of the Lagrange equation. Then the matrix m is not necessarily symmetrical.

This is the matrix equation for the undamped free vibrations of the system. When excitations and viscous damping are present, the motion is governed by

$$m\ddot{x} + c\dot{x} + kx = f \tag{6-16}$$

In one method the column of the generalized forces

$$f = \{f_1(t), f_2(t), \ldots, f_n(t)\}$$

and the matrix of the damping coefficients can be obtained from

$$\frac{\partial W}{\partial x_j} = \lim_{\Delta x_j \to 0} \frac{\Delta W}{\Delta x_j} = f_j - c_{jl}\dot{x}_l \tag{6-17}$$

where ΔW is the *virtual work* done by the exciting and damping forces through a virtual displacement Δx_j. In many cases the matrix c is also symmetrical, but we need not restrict ourselves to this case at the present time. We wish to limit our consideration, however, to stable systems, that is, systems whose motions gradually diminish after the applied excitations are terminated. Therefore, the matrix c is positive definite.

To illustrate the matrices appearing in Eq. (6-16) we choose a simple two-degrees-of-freedom system, as shown in Fig. 6.2. Only one exciting force, $g(t)$, is acting on the first mass m_1. The generalized displacements are chosen to be the absolute displacements x_1 and x_2 of the two masses, respectively, measured from the static equilibrium configuration. Fol-

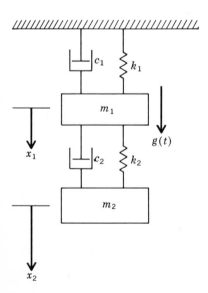

Fig. 6.2 Illustrative two-degrees-of-freedom mechanical system.

lowing the procedure outlined above, it can be shown that

$$\mathbf{m} = \begin{bmatrix} m_1 & 0 \\ 0 & m_2 \end{bmatrix} \quad \mathbf{c} = \begin{bmatrix} c_1 + c_2 & -c_2 \\ -c_2 & c_2 \end{bmatrix}$$

$$\mathbf{k} = \begin{bmatrix} k_1 + k_2 & -k_2 \\ -k_2 & k_2 \end{bmatrix} \quad \mathbf{x} = \begin{Bmatrix} x_1 \\ x_2 \end{Bmatrix} \quad \mathbf{f} = \begin{Bmatrix} g(t) \\ 0 \end{Bmatrix}$$

The matrix of the frequency response functions, $\mathbf{H}(\omega)$, can be obtained by letting the excitation column be $\mathbf{f} = \mathbf{f}_0 \exp (i\omega t)$, where $\mathbf{f}_0$ is a column of constants, and letting the response column be $\mathbf{x} = \mathbf{H}(\omega)\mathbf{f}$. Thus

$$\mathbf{H}(\omega) = [-\omega^2 \mathbf{m} + i\omega \mathbf{c} + \mathbf{k}]^{-1} \qquad (6\text{-}18)$$

Here, the matrix $\mathbf{H}(\omega)$ is, of course, $n \times n$. It has been common practice to account separately for structural damping, when it is important, by adding an imaginary part to the stiffness matrix in Eq. (6-18), because structural damping is often hypothesized to be proportional to the magnitude of the displacement but opposite in direction to the velocity.

The matrix of the impulse reponse functions, $\mathbf{h}(t)$, may be obtained from $\mathbf{H}(\omega)$ by use of the transformation specified in the first equation of (6-1); however, it can also be determined directly. To show this, let

$$\begin{Bmatrix} y_1 \\ y_2 \\ \cdot \\ \cdot \\ \cdot \\ y_n \end{Bmatrix} = \begin{Bmatrix} \dot{x}_1 \\ \dot{x}_2 \\ \cdot \\ \cdot \\ \cdot \\ \dot{x}_n \end{Bmatrix} \qquad \begin{Bmatrix} y_{n+1} \\ y_{n+2} \\ \cdot \\ \cdot \\ \cdot \\ y_{2n} \end{Bmatrix} = \begin{Bmatrix} x_1 \\ x_2 \\ \cdot \\ \cdot \\ \cdot \\ x_n \end{Bmatrix} \qquad (6\text{-}19)$$

Then Eq. (6-16) may be replaced by a first-order matrix equation for $\mathbf{y} = \{y_1(t), y_2(t), \ldots, y_{2n}(t)\}$,

$$\mathbf{r}\dot{\mathbf{y}} + \mathbf{s}\mathbf{y} = \begin{Bmatrix} 0 \\ \text{---} \\ \mathbf{f} \end{Bmatrix} \qquad (6\text{-}20)$$

where

$$\mathbf{r} = \begin{bmatrix} 0 & \vdots & \mathbf{m} \\ \cdots & \vdots & \cdots \\ \mathbf{m} & \vdots & \mathbf{c} \end{bmatrix} \quad \mathbf{s} = \begin{bmatrix} -\mathbf{m} & \vdots & 0 \\ \cdots & \vdots & \cdots \\ 0 & \vdots & \mathbf{k} \end{bmatrix}$$

and the partitioning of the matrices is indicated by the dashed lines. Equation (6-20) is readily transformed into

$$\dot{\mathbf{y}} + \mathbf{g}\mathbf{y} = \begin{Bmatrix} \mathbf{m}^{-1}\mathbf{f} \\ \text{------} \\ 0 \end{Bmatrix} \qquad (6\text{-}20a)$$

where

$$
\mathbf{g} = \begin{bmatrix} \mathbf{m}^{-1}\mathbf{c} & \vdots & \mathbf{m}^{-1}\mathbf{k} \\ \hline -\mathbf{I} & \vdots & \mathbf{0} \end{bmatrix}
$$

The inverse matrix $\mathbf{m}^{-1}$ exists since $\mathbf{m} = \frac{1}{2}(\overline{\mathbf{m}} + \overline{\mathbf{m}}')$ must be also positive definite. Note that $\mathbf{g}$ is generally unsymmetrical. The solution to Eq. (6-20a) may be written as

$$
\mathbf{y} = \exp\left(-\mathbf{g}t\right)\mathbf{y}_0 + \int_0^t \exp\left[-\mathbf{g}(t - \tau)\right] \begin{bmatrix} \mathbf{m}^{-1} \\ \hline \mathbf{0} \end{bmatrix} \mathbf{f}(\tau)\, d\tau \tag{6-21}
$$

It is clear that the $2n \times n$ matrix

$$
\exp\left(-\mathbf{g}t\right) \begin{bmatrix} \mathbf{m}^{-1} \\ \hline \mathbf{0} \end{bmatrix}
$$

gives the impulse response functions for $\mathbf{y}$, the last n components of which are the impulse response functions for $x_1, x_2, \ldots, x_n$. By retaining only the impulse response functions for $\mathbf{x}$, we have

$$
\mathbf{h}(t) = \begin{cases} [\mathbf{0} \vdots \mathbf{I}] \exp\left(-\mathbf{g}t\right) \begin{bmatrix} \mathbf{m}^{-1} \\ \hline \mathbf{0} \end{bmatrix} & t \geq 0 \\ \\ \mathbf{0} & t < 0 \end{cases} \tag{6-22}
$$

To evaluate the matrix $\exp\left(-\mathbf{g}t\right)$, we note that if $\mathbf{T}$ is a $2n \times 2n$ matrix whose columns are the modal columns of $\mathbf{g}$, then[‡]

$$
\exp\left(-\mathbf{g}t\right) = \mathbf{T} \exp\left(-\mathbf{b}t\right)\mathbf{T}^{-1}
$$

where $\mathbf{b} = \mathbf{T}^{-1}\mathbf{g}\mathbf{T}$ is a diagonal matrix of the latent roots of $\mathbf{g}$. The matrix $\exp\left(-\mathbf{b}t\right)$ is also a diagonal matrix having the diagonal elements $\exp\left(-b_{jj}t\right)$. The main task in the application of Eq. (6-22) is to find the latent roots and the corresponding modal columns of $\mathbf{g}$. Since $\mathbf{g}$ is unsymmetrical, the latent roots are either real or complex conjugate pairs. An iterative procedure for determining the complex latent roots is outlined by Frazer, Duncan, and Collar.[¶]

When the damping matrix $\mathbf{c}$ is symmetrical, an alternative method to be discussed below is sometimes more convenient. It has been mentioned before that this is frequently the case. Now, the matrices $\mathbf{r}$ and $\mathbf{s}$ on the left-hand side of Eq. (6-20) are symmetrical. Assume that there

‡ Compare with the derivation from Eqs. (5-105) to (5-109).

¶ R. A. Frazer, W. J. Duncan, and A. R. Collar, "Elementary Matrices," p. 327, Cambridge, London, 1946.

exists a matrix of transformation $U = GD$, where the columns in G are the modal columns of r, each of which is normalized to have a unit modulus, and D is a diagonal matrix constructed from the latent roots λ_j of r as follows:

$$
D = \begin{bmatrix}
\dfrac{1}{\sqrt{\lambda_1}} & 0 & \cdots & 0 \\
0 & \dfrac{1}{\sqrt{\lambda_2}} & \cdots & 0 \\
\cdots\cdots\cdots\cdots\cdots\cdots\cdots \\
0 & 0 & \cdots & \dfrac{1}{\sqrt{\lambda_{2n}}}
\end{bmatrix}
$$

Since r is symmetrical and G is normalized, $G' = G^{-1}$. Therefore,

$$
\begin{aligned}
U'rU &= D'G'rGD \\
&= DG^{-1}rGD = I
\end{aligned} \tag{6-23}
$$

If $y = Uv$ is substituted into Eq. (6-20) and the result is premultiplied by U', we obtain

$$
\dot{v} + U'sUv = U' \left\{ \begin{array}{c} 0 \\ \hline f \end{array} \right\} = U' \begin{bmatrix} 0 \\ \hline I \end{bmatrix} f \tag{6-24}
$$

The solution to this equation is

$$
v = \exp\left(-U'sUt\right)\{v(0)\} + \int_0^t \exp\left[-U'sU(t-\tau)\right]U' \begin{bmatrix} 0 \\ \hline I \end{bmatrix} f(\tau)\, d\tau \tag{6-25}
$$

The required matrix of the impulse response functions, $h(t)$, is thus given by

$$
h(t) = \begin{cases} [0 \mid I]U \exp\left[-U'sUt\right]U' \begin{bmatrix} 0 \\ \hline I \end{bmatrix} & t \geq 0 \\[2ex] 0 & t < 0 \end{cases} \tag{6-26}
$$

An application of Eq. (6-26) requires a knowledge of the latent roots and the modal columns of the matrices r and $U'sU$, but both these matrices are symmetrical. The latent roots of r are real, and the iterative process for finding them and the associated modal columns is simpler than the one used for the complex latent roots. However, we cannot always make the same claim for the matrix $U'sU$ since it may contain imaginary elements.

It is interesting to note that the matrix of impulse response functions, $\mathbf{h}(t)$, as given by Eq. (6-26) is symmetrical. This is also evident from Eq. (6-18) since if the mass, damping, and stiffness matrices are all symmetrical, then the matrix of frequency response functions, $\mathbf{H}(\omega)$, is symmetrical, and so must be its Fourier transform $\mathbf{h}(t)$. The symmetry in the matrices $\mathbf{H}(\omega)$ and $\mathbf{h}(t)$ may be regarded as a statement of a reciprocity theorem in structural dynamics.

As an example, consider a massless uniform cantilevered beam supporting a heavy rigid block, as shown in Fig. 6.3. The structural model is a two-degrees-of-freedom system since the configuration of the system is specified by the deflection and the rotation at the right end of the beam, $x_1(t)$ and $x_2(t)$, which will be chosen as the generalized displacements. It can be shown by use of the elementary techniques of strength of

Fig. 6.3 A structure with two degrees of freedom. (*a*) Physical arrangement; (*b*) selected generalized coordinates.

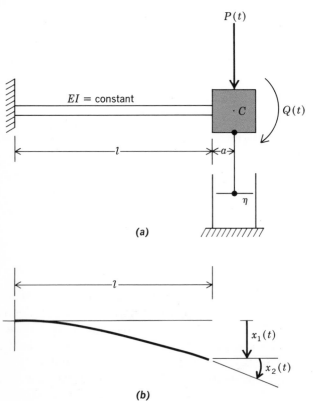

materials that the strain energy is given by

$$V = \frac{6EI}{l^3} x_1{}^2 - \frac{6EI}{l^2} x_1 x_2 + \frac{2EI}{l} x_2{}^2 \qquad (6\text{-}27)$$

The kinetic energy can be expressed most simply in terms of the translational and rotational velocities $\dot{x}_C$ and $\dot{\alpha}$ of the centroid C of the heavy block; i.e.,

$$T = \tfrac{1}{2} m \dot{x}_C{}^2 + \tfrac{1}{2} I_C \dot{\alpha}^2 \qquad (6\text{-}28)$$

where m and I_C are the mass and the mass polar moment of inertia about C of the block. Now $\alpha = x_2$, and, within the scope of a small deflection theory, $x_C = x_1 + a x_2$. Then, in terms of the generalized velocities,

$$T = \tfrac{1}{2} m \dot{x}_1{}^2 + m a \dot{x}_1 \dot{x}_2 + \tfrac{1}{2}(I_C + m a^2) \dot{x}_2{}^2 \qquad (6\text{-}29)$$

With virtual displacements Δx_1 and Δx_2 the virtual work‡ done by the excitation and the damping force is

$$\Delta W = (\Delta x_1 + a \, \Delta x_2) P + \Delta x_2 \, Q - \eta(\dot{x}_1 + a \dot{x}_2)(\Delta x_1 + a \, \Delta x_2)$$

Therefore

$$\frac{\partial W}{\partial x_1} = P - \eta \dot{x}_1 - a \eta \dot{x}_2$$

$$\frac{\partial W}{\partial x_2} = aP + Q - a \eta \dot{x}_1 - a^2 \eta \dot{x}_2 \qquad (6\text{-}30)$$

Application of the Lagrange equation

$$\frac{d}{dt}\left(\frac{\partial T}{\partial \dot{x}_j}\right) + \frac{\partial V}{\partial x_j} = \frac{\partial W}{\partial x_j} \qquad j = 1, 2$$

leads to

$$\begin{bmatrix} m & ma \\ ma & I_C + ma^2 \end{bmatrix} \begin{Bmatrix} \ddot{x}_1 \\ \ddot{x}_2 \end{Bmatrix} + \begin{bmatrix} \eta & a\eta \\ a\eta & a^2\eta \end{bmatrix} \begin{Bmatrix} \dot{x}_1 \\ \dot{x}_2 \end{Bmatrix}$$

$$+ \begin{bmatrix} \dfrac{12EI}{l^3} & -\dfrac{6EI}{l^2} \\ -\dfrac{6EI}{l^2} & \dfrac{4EI}{l} \end{bmatrix} \begin{Bmatrix} x_1 \\ x_2 \end{Bmatrix} = \begin{Bmatrix} P \\ aP + Q \end{Bmatrix} \qquad (6\text{-}31)$$

‡ The virtual work is computed by assuming that the forces remain unchanged through the virtual displacements.

where the matrices $\mathbf{m}$, $\mathbf{c}$, $\mathbf{k}$, and $\mathbf{f}$ are explicitly indicated. Substituting these matrices into Eq. (6-18), we find

$$
\mathbf{H}(\omega) = \begin{bmatrix} \dfrac{12EI}{l^3} - \omega^2 m + i\omega\eta & -\dfrac{6EI}{l^2} - \omega^2 ma + i\omega a\eta \\[2mm] -\dfrac{6EI}{l^2} - \omega^2 ma + i\omega a\eta & \dfrac{4EI}{l} - \omega^2(I_C + ma^2) + i\omega a^2\eta \end{bmatrix}^{-1}
$$

$$
= \frac{1}{\Delta} \begin{bmatrix} \dfrac{4EI}{l} - \omega^2(I_C + ma^2) + i\omega a^2\eta & \dfrac{6EI}{l^2} + \omega^2 ma - i\omega a\eta \\[2mm] \dfrac{6EI}{l^2} + \omega^2 ma - i\omega a\eta & \dfrac{12EI}{l^3} - \omega^2 m + i\omega\eta \end{bmatrix}
$$

$$(6\text{-}32)$$

where

$$
\Delta = mI_C\omega^4 - \frac{4EI\omega^2}{l}\left[m + \frac{3}{l}ma + \frac{3}{l^2}(I_C + ma^2) \right]
$$
$$
+ \frac{12(EI)^2}{l^4} + i\omega\eta\left(-I_C\omega^2 + \frac{12EIa^2}{l^3} + \frac{12EIa}{l^2} + \frac{4EI}{l} \right) \quad (6\text{-}33)
$$

To determine the matrix of the impulse response functions, $\mathbf{h}(t)$, for this structure by the direct method, we should have to work with numerical data. However, for illustration purposes we shall consider a special case of the present example so that we may continue further with a symbolic representation. Let $a = 0$ in Eq. (6-31); then the generalized displacements are coupled only through the stiffness matrix. When this equation is changed to the form of Eq. (6-20), we find

$$
\mathbf{r} = \begin{bmatrix} 0 & 0 & m & 0 \\ 0 & 0 & 0 & I_C \\ m & 0 & \eta & 0 \\ 0 & I_C & 0 & 0 \end{bmatrix} \qquad \mathbf{s} = \begin{bmatrix} -m & 0 & 0 & 0 \\ 0 & -I_C & 0 & 0 \\ 0 & 0 & \dfrac{12EI}{l^3} & -\dfrac{6EI}{l^2} \\ 0 & 0 & -\dfrac{6EI}{l^2} & \dfrac{4EI}{l} \end{bmatrix} \qquad (6\text{-}34)
$$

The latent roots of $\mathbf{r}$ are found to be

$$
\lambda_{1,2} = \pm I_C \qquad \lambda_{3,4} = \frac{\eta}{2} \pm \sqrt{\left(\frac{\eta}{2}\right)^2 + m^2} \qquad (6\text{-}35)
$$

and the normalized modal columns are

$$
\begin{Bmatrix} 0 \\ \dfrac{1}{\sqrt{2}} \\ 0 \\ \dfrac{1}{\sqrt{2}} \end{Bmatrix} \quad \begin{Bmatrix} 0 \\ \dfrac{1}{\sqrt{2}} \\ 0 \\ \dfrac{-1}{\sqrt{2}} \end{Bmatrix} \quad \begin{Bmatrix} \dfrac{m}{\sqrt{m^2 + \lambda_3{}^2}} \\ 0 \\ \dfrac{\lambda_3}{\sqrt{m^2 + \lambda_3{}^2}} \\ 0 \end{Bmatrix} \quad \begin{Bmatrix} \dfrac{m}{\sqrt{m^2 + \lambda_4{}^2}} \\ 0 \\ \dfrac{\lambda_4}{\sqrt{m^2 + \lambda_4{}^2}} \\ 0 \end{Bmatrix} \qquad (6\text{-}36)
$$

The required matrix of transformation $\mathbf{U}$ for the application of Eq. (6-26) is therefore

$$
\mathbf{U} =
\begin{bmatrix}
0 & 0 & \dfrac{m}{\sqrt{\lambda_3}\sqrt{m^2 + \lambda_3{}^2}} & \dfrac{m}{\sqrt{\lambda_4}\sqrt{m^2 + \lambda_4{}^2}} \\[2ex]
\dfrac{1}{\sqrt{2I_c}} & \dfrac{1}{i\sqrt{2I_c}} & 0 & 0 \\[2ex]
0 & 0 & \dfrac{\sqrt{\lambda_3}}{\sqrt{m^2 + \lambda_3{}^2}} & \dfrac{\sqrt{\lambda_4}}{\sqrt{m^2 + \lambda_4{}^2}} \\[2ex]
\dfrac{1}{\sqrt{2I_c}} & \dfrac{i}{\sqrt{2I_c}} & 0 & 0
\end{bmatrix}
\qquad (6\text{-}37)
$$

Let $\mathbf{E} = \mathbf{U}'\mathbf{s}\mathbf{U}$; the elements of $\mathbf{E}$ are readily computed to be

$$e_{11} = -\frac{1}{2} + \frac{2EI}{I_c l}$$

$$e_{22} = \frac{1}{2} - \frac{2EI}{I_c l}$$

$$e_{33} = -\frac{m^3}{\lambda_3(m^2 + \lambda_3{}^2)} + \frac{12EI\lambda_3}{l^3(m^2 + \lambda_3{}^2)}$$

$$e_{44} = -\frac{m^3}{\lambda_4(m^2 + \lambda_4{}^2)} + \frac{12EI\lambda_4}{l^3(m^2 + \lambda_4{}^2)}$$

$$e_{12} = e_{21} = \frac{i}{2} + \frac{2iEI}{I_c l}$$

$$e_{13} = e_{31} = -\frac{6EI\sqrt{\lambda_3}}{\sqrt{2I_c}\sqrt{m^2 + \lambda_3{}^2}\,l^2} \qquad (6\text{-}38)$$

$$e_{14} = e_{41} = -\frac{6EI\sqrt{\lambda_4}}{\sqrt{2I_c}\sqrt{m^2 + \lambda_4{}^2}\,l^2}$$

$$e_{23} = e_{32} = \frac{6EI\sqrt{\lambda_3}}{\sqrt{-2I_c}\sqrt{m^2 + \lambda_3{}^2}\,l^2}$$

$$e_{24} = e_{42} = \frac{6EI\sqrt{\lambda_4}}{\sqrt{-2I_c}\sqrt{m^2 + \lambda_4{}^2}\,l^2}$$

$$e_{34} = e_{43} = -\frac{m^3}{\sqrt{\lambda_3\lambda_4}\sqrt{m^2 + \lambda_3{}^2}\sqrt{m^2 + \lambda_4{}^2}}$$
$$+ \frac{12EI\sqrt{\lambda_3\lambda_4}}{\sqrt{m^2 + \lambda_3{}^2}\sqrt{m^2 + \lambda_4{}^2}\,l^3}$$

The next step is to find the latent roots and the modal columns of $\mathbf{E}$. Using these modal columns as the columns of a matrix $\mathbf{L}$,

$$
\exp(-\mathbf{E}t) = \exp[-\mathbf{U}'\mathbf{s}\mathbf{U}t] = \mathbf{L}
\begin{bmatrix}
e^{-\lambda_1 t} & 0 & 0 & 0 \\
0 & e^{-\lambda_2 t} & 0 & 0 \\
0 & 0 & e^{-\lambda_3 t} & 0 \\
0 & 0 & 0 & e^{-\lambda_4 t}
\end{bmatrix}
\mathbf{L}^{-1} \qquad (6\text{-}39)
$$

We now have all the constituents necessary to construct the matrix $\mathbf{h}(t)$ according to Eq. (6-26).

A method of attack well known to structural engineers is the *method of normal modes*. In this method a linear transformation is employed to change Eq. (6-16) to an uncoupled system. Substitute $\mathbf{x} = \mathbf{bz}$ into Eq. (6-16), where $\mathbf{b}$ is the desired matrix of transformation, and premultiply the result by $(\mathbf{mb})^{-1} = \mathbf{b}^{-1}\mathbf{m}^{-1}$,

$$\ddot{\mathbf{z}} + \mathbf{b}^{-1}\mathbf{m}^{-1}\mathbf{cb}\dot{\mathbf{z}} + \mathbf{b}^{-1}\mathbf{m}^{-1}\mathbf{kbz} = \mathbf{b}^{-1}\mathbf{m}^{-1}\mathbf{f} \qquad (6\text{-}40)$$

For Eq. (6-40) to be uncoupled in the components of $\mathbf{z}$, it is necessary that both $(\mathbf{b}^{-1}\mathbf{m}^{-1}\mathbf{cb})$ and $(\mathbf{b}^{-1}\mathbf{m}^{-1}\mathbf{kb})$ be diagonal matrices. Mathematically, this is a very restrictive condition, and a sufficient condition for it to be true is that $\mathbf{m}^{-1}\mathbf{c}$ is expressible as a function of $\mathbf{m}^{-1}\mathbf{k}$, or vice versa.‡ This is clear since a function of an $n \times n$ matrix can be expanded¶ as a polynomial of the $(n-1)$st order in this matrix; i.e.,

$$\theta(\mathbf{B}) = a_{n-1}\mathbf{B}^{n-1} + a_{n-2}\mathbf{B}^{n-2} + \cdots + a_1\mathbf{B} + a_0\mathbf{I} \qquad (6\text{-}41)$$

provided that $\theta(\lambda)$ exists§ for every latent root λ of $\mathbf{B}$; and if $\mathbf{b}^{-1}\mathbf{Bb}$ is diagonal, so are $\mathbf{b}^{-1}\mathbf{B}^2\mathbf{b}$, $\mathbf{b}^{-1}\mathbf{B}^3\mathbf{b}$, etc. In general, the previous restrictive condition is not satisfied, but in common practice $\mathbf{b}$ is chosen to diagonalize $\mathbf{m}^{-1}\mathbf{k}$, and the nondiagonal elements in the matrix $\mathbf{b}^{-1}\mathbf{m}^{-1}\mathbf{cb}$ are neglected. This is usually permissible when the structure is lightly damped. The resulting Eq. (6-40) can now be solved for each component in $\mathbf{z}$ separately by the same method used for systems with a single degree of freedom. Denote

$$\mathbf{b}^{-1}\mathbf{m}^{-1}\mathbf{kb} = \Omega^2 \qquad \mathbf{b}^{-1}\mathbf{m}^{-1}\mathbf{cb} = 2\zeta\Omega \qquad (6\text{-}42)$$

where Ω and ζ are diagonal matrices. Then the matrix of the impulse response function for $\mathbf{z}$ is

$$\mathbf{h}_{\mathbf{Z}}(t) = \begin{cases} \mathbf{D}^{-1} \exp\left[(-\zeta\Omega + i\mathbf{D})t\right]\mathbf{b}^{-1}\mathbf{m}^{-1} & t \geq 0 \\ 0 & t < 0 \end{cases} \qquad (6\text{-}43)$$

where $\mathbf{D}$ is another diagonal matrix with its diagonal elements given by

$$D_{jj} = \Omega_{jj}\sqrt{1 - \zeta_{jj}^2} \qquad (6\text{-}44)$$

---

‡ For a detailed study, see T. K. Caughey and M. E. J. O'Kelly, Classical Normal Modes in Damped Linear Dynamic Systems, *J. Appl. Mech.*, **32**:583 (1965) and the discussion of this paper by Y. K. Lin, *J. Appl. Mech.*, **33**:471 (1966).

¶ A consequence of the Cayley-Hamilton theorem; cf. footnote on page 149.

§ If the latent roots of $\mathbf{B}$ are not all distinct, then for each latent root λ_s with a multiplicity m we also require the existence of $\theta'(\lambda)$ $\theta''(\lambda)$ ... $\theta^{(m-1)}(\lambda)$ at $\lambda = \lambda_s$.

It follows that the matrix of the impulse response functions for $\mathbf{x}$ is

$$\mathbf{h}(t) = \begin{cases} \mathbf{b}\mathbf{D}^{-1} \exp\left[(-\zeta\Omega + i\mathbf{D})t\right]\mathbf{b}^{-1}\mathbf{m}^{-1} & t \geq 0 \\ 0 & t < 0 \end{cases} \qquad (6\text{-}45)$$

6.3 / THE HOLZER-MYKLESTAD REPRESENTATION

For a beam or a beam like structure, it is often convenient to use an approximate representation which was originated by Holzer‡ for torsional vibration analyses and later adapted by Myklestad¶ to bending vibration analyses. Recently the scope and potential of this method of representing beamlike structures has been greatly expanded by the use of matrix notation.

Consider a multispanned beam supported at discrete points by deflectional and torsional springs and excited by a random pressure, as shown in Fig. 6.4. To any degree of accuracy the beam can be approximated by a discrete system, as depicted in Fig. 6.5a. The distributed mass of the beam is now lumped at discrete points . . . , $j - 1$, j, $j + 1$, ... The inertial properties of the beam are represented by

‡ H. Holzer, "Die Berechnung der Drehschwingungen," Springer, Berlin, 1921.
¶ N. O. Myklestad, A New Method of Calculating Natural Modes of Uncoupled Bending Vibration of Airplane Wings and Other Types of Beams, *J. Aeron. Sci.*, **11**:153–162 (1944).

Fig. 6.4 Elastically supported beam under random load $P(x, t)$.

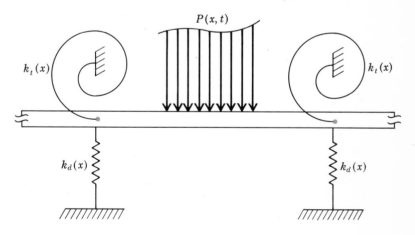

the discrete masses . . . , μ_{j-1}, μ_j, μ_{j+1}, . . . and by the discrete rotational moments of inertia . . . , J_{j-1}, J_j, J_{j+1}, ... The discrete masses are connected by massless elastic bars. For an accuracy consistent with the beam representation, the distributed random pressure $P(x, t)$ also can be approximated by a series of concentrated random forces . . . , $P_{j-1}(t)$, $P_j(t)$, $P_{j+1}(t)$ . . . plus a series of concentrated random moments . . . , $Q_{j-1}(t)$, $Q_j(t)$, $Q_{j+1}(t)$, . . . acting at the stations indicated by the subscripts, as shown in Fig. 6.5b. These random forces and moments are now random processes with a single parameter t. Our immediate concern is to find the matrix of the frequency response functions corresponding to both the force-type excitation and the moment-type excitation.

One advantage of the present approach is the ease of considering simultaneously several types of response at the same station. Let the deflection δ, the slope θ, the bending moment M, and the shear V be the responses of interest. These can be treated as components of a state vector $\mathbf{Z} = \{\delta, \theta, M, V\}$. If we view the output at one station as being "propagated" from another nearby station, the propagation device is represented by a square matrix, called the *transfer* matrix. Write

$$\mathbf{Z}_{j+1}^l = \mathbf{F}_{j+1}\mathbf{Z}_j^r \qquad (6\text{-}46)$$

Fig. 6.5 (a) Approximate representation of a beam by a discrete system; (b) corresponding discrete random excitation.

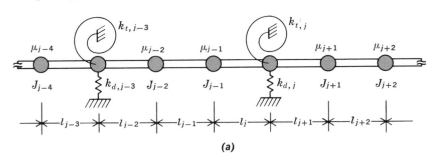

(a)

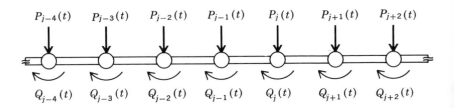

(b)

where the superscript and the subscript associated with each vector **Z** indicate respectively on which side, left or right, of which station the vector is evaluated. The matrix $\mathbf{F}_{j+1}$ is the transfer matrix associated with the elastic segment $j + 1$ which connects station j and station $j + 1$. The elements of matrix $\mathbf{F}_{j+1}$ can be determined by use of the elementary techniques described in any standard book on the strength of materials. If the segment has a uniform bending stiffness EI, and if the deflections due to shear are negligible, then[‡]

$$\mathbf{F}_{j+1} = \begin{bmatrix} 1 & l & \dfrac{l^2}{2EI} & \dfrac{l^3}{6EI} \\ 0 & 1 & \dfrac{l}{EI} & \dfrac{l^2}{2EI} \\ 0 & 0 & 1 & l \\ 0 & 0 & 0 & 1 \end{bmatrix}_{j+1} \qquad (6\text{-}47)$$

where the subscript $j + 1$ signifies that the physical constants of the segment $j + 1$ should be used in computing this matrix; i.e., in the present case, it implies that $l = l_{j+1}$ and $EI = (EI)_{j+1}$. The signs associated with the elements in a matrix **F** are chosen to agree with the positive directions specified in Fig. 6.6. With suitable sign conventions and with the order of the components in the related state vectors properly arranged, a transfer matrix can usually be made to be symmetrical about its *cross diagonal*, as in Eq. (6-47). The physical reason for this is that

[‡] It may be desirable in some cases to consider a nonuniform elastic segment.

Fig. 6.6 Deformed and undeformed elastic segment.

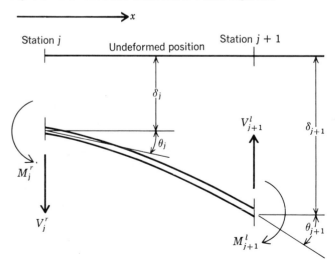

the same relation exists whether the state is transferred from left to right or from right to left.

As is implied in Eq. (6-46), the matrix $\mathbf{F}_{j+1}$ accounts for the mechanism furnished by segment $j + 1$ to propagate the vector $\mathbf{Z}$ from one end of the segment to the other. For this reason it is called a *field transfer matrix*. The fact that all the elements in $\mathbf{F}_{j+1}$ are real indicates a spontaneous propagation without a time delay. This is to be expected since, firstly, the segment is considered massless and, secondly, no provision has been made for the damping effect. In the case of a single frequency oscillation, which is implied in the determination of the frequency response functions, the usual way to allow for the structural damping is to introduce an imaginary part into the modulus of elasticity, that is, to replace E by $E(1 + i\alpha)$; therefore,

$$
\mathbf{F}_{j+1} =
\begin{bmatrix}
1 & l & \dfrac{l^2}{2EI(1 + i\alpha)} & \dfrac{l^3}{6EI(1 + i\alpha)} \\
0 & 1 & \dfrac{l}{EI(1 + i\alpha)} & \dfrac{l^2}{2EI(1 + i\alpha)} \\
0 & 0 & 1 & l \\
0 & 0 & 0 & 1
\end{bmatrix}_{j+1}
\tag{6-48}
$$

The structural damping parameter α is often assumed to be a constant, but in the present formulation it is permissible for α to vary with the frequency.

The relation between the state vectors on the two sides of a station may be obtained from the equations of motion for this station. These equations involve an inertia force passing through the mass center and an inertia torque about the mass center. Consider station j. For a simple harmonic motion with a frequency ω, the inertia force and torque are $\mu_j \ddot{\delta}_j = -\omega^2 \mu_j \delta_j$ and $J_j \ddot{\theta} = -\omega^2 J_j \theta$, respectively. If the beam is elastically supported at this station, then the restraining forces from the springs must also enter into the equations of motion. It is convenient to write these equations in the following matrix form:

$$
\mathbf{Z}_j{}^r = \mathbf{S}_j \mathbf{Z}_j{}^l + \mathbf{L}_j
\tag{6-49}
$$

where $\mathbf{L}_j$ is a column of the sinusoidal inputs at station j and

$$
\mathbf{S}_j =
\begin{bmatrix}
1 & 0 & 0 & 0 \\
0 & 1 & 0 & 0 \\
0 & k_t(1 + i\beta_t) - \omega^2 J & 1 & 0 \\
-[k_d(1 + i\beta_d) - \omega^2\mu] & 0 & 0 & 1
\end{bmatrix}_j
\tag{6-50}
$$

where the subscript j signifies that the physical constants of station j should be used to compute this matrix. This square matrix is called a *point transfer matrix* since it relates the state vectors on two sides of one station if the external excitation is absent. Added to the torsional and displacement spring constants k_t and k_d appearing in matrix $\mathbf{S}_j$ are the imaginary parts $i\beta_t k_t$ and $i\beta_d k_d$ which account for the structural damping at the support. It is generally believed that structural damping is an important consideration at the joints. The ease of taking this local structural damping into consideration is a significant advantage of the present approach. For a station at which the beam is not supported, it is only necessary to set $k_t = k_d = 0$ in the construction of the $\mathbf{S}$ matrix. Note that $\mathbf{S}_j$ is also cross symmetrical.

With the two basic types of transfer matrices, $\mathbf{F}$ and $\mathbf{S}$, just described, it is now a simple matter to relate two state vectors at any two stations on a beam, especially when no input is present between these stations. However, Eq. (6-49) shows that an input at a station merely causes an additional jump in the value of a state vector across this station. Such a jump will also be propagated through the mechanism represented by the $\mathbf{F}$- and $\mathbf{S}$- type matrices. It is, therefore, clear that the required information about the frequency response functions can be extracted from these matrices. In what follows we shall show how the $\mathbf{F}$- and $\mathbf{S}$-type matrices can be used to compute a frequency response function $H_{qp}(\omega)$. The case $q < p$ will be chosen for discussion.‡

Let $\mathbf{T}$, with proper subscripts and superscripts, denote a general transfer matrix relating the state vectors at any two stations on a beam. For example, $_k^l\mathbf{T}_j^r$ is the matrix transferring a state vector at the right side of station j to that at the left-hand side of station k, etc. In terms of the more basic $\mathbf{F}$- and $\mathbf{S}$-type matrices:

$$
\begin{aligned}
_k^r\mathbf{T}_j^l &= \mathbf{S}_k\mathbf{F}_k \cdots \mathbf{F}_{j+2}\mathbf{S}_{j+1}\mathbf{F}_{j+1}\mathbf{S}_j \\
_k^l\mathbf{T}_j^l &= \mathbf{F}_k\mathbf{S}_{k-1} \cdots \mathbf{F}_{j+2}\mathbf{S}_{j+1}\mathbf{F}_{j+1}\mathbf{S}_j \\
_k^l\mathbf{T}_j^r &= \mathbf{F}_k\mathbf{S}_{k-1} \cdots \mathbf{F}_{j+2}\mathbf{S}_{j+1}\mathbf{F}_{j+1}
\end{aligned}
\tag{6-51}
$$

For the purpose of discussion, it will be assumed that the two extreme ends, stations 0 and N, are simply supported, although the general scheme to be presented below applies to any other boundary conditions.

To determine the frequency response functions $H_{qp}(\omega)$, only station p is assumed to be excited. For the sign convention used herein

$$
\mathbf{L}_p = \begin{Bmatrix} 0 \\ 0 \\ -\bar{Q} \\ \bar{P} \end{Bmatrix} \exp{(i\omega t)}
\tag{6-52}
$$

Let the response vector at a station be $\{\bar{\delta},\ \bar{\theta},\ \bar{M},\ \bar{V}\} \exp{(i\omega t)}$. Then

‡ Note that the transfer-matrix approach does not guarantee $H_{pq} = H_{qp}$.

there is the relation

$$
\begin{Bmatrix} 0 \\ \bar{\theta} \\ 0 \\ \bar{V} \end{Bmatrix}_N^l = {}_N\mathbf{T}_0^r \begin{Bmatrix} 0 \\ \bar{\theta} \\ 0 \\ \bar{V} \end{Bmatrix}_0^r + {}_N\mathbf{T}_p^r \begin{Bmatrix} 0 \\ 0 \\ -\bar{Q} \\ \bar{P} \end{Bmatrix}_p \tag{6-53}
$$

where the boundary conditions for the simple supports,

$\bar{\delta}_N = \bar{M}_N = \bar{\delta}_0 = \bar{M}_0 = 0,$

have been incorporated. Now

$$
\begin{Bmatrix} 0 \\ 0 \end{Bmatrix} = {}_N\begin{bmatrix} t_{12} & t_{14} \\ t_{32} & t_{34} \end{bmatrix}_0^r \begin{Bmatrix} \bar{\theta} \\ \bar{V} \end{Bmatrix}_0^r + {}_N\begin{bmatrix} -t_{13} & t_{14} \\ -t_{33} & t_{34} \end{bmatrix}_p^r \begin{Bmatrix} \bar{Q} \\ \bar{P} \end{Bmatrix}_p \tag{6-54}
$$

can be extracted from Eq. (6-53), where t_{jk} represents the (j, k) element taken from the indicated $\mathbf{T}$ matrix. Solving for $\{\bar{\theta}, \bar{V}\}_0^r$,

$$
\begin{Bmatrix} \bar{\theta} \\ \bar{V} \end{Bmatrix}_0^r = - \left({}_N\begin{bmatrix} t_{12} & t_{14} \\ t_{32} & t_{34} \end{bmatrix}_0^r \right)^{-1} {}_N\begin{bmatrix} -t_{13} & t_{14} \\ -t_{33} & t_{34} \end{bmatrix}_p^r \begin{Bmatrix} \bar{Q} \\ \bar{P} \end{Bmatrix}_p \tag{6-55}
$$

The state vector at the left-hand side of station q is given by

$$
\begin{Bmatrix} \bar{\delta} \\ \bar{\theta} \\ \bar{M} \\ \bar{V} \end{Bmatrix}_q^l = {}_q\mathbf{T}_0^r \begin{Bmatrix} 0 \\ \bar{\theta} \\ 0 \\ \bar{V} \end{Bmatrix}_0^r \tag{6-56}
$$

for $p > q$. Equation (6-56) can be reduced to

$$
\begin{Bmatrix} \bar{\delta} \\ \bar{\theta} \\ \bar{M} \\ \bar{V} \end{Bmatrix}_q^l = {}_q\begin{bmatrix} t_{12} & t_{14} \\ t_{22} & t_{24} \\ t_{32} & t_{34} \\ t_{42} & t_{44} \end{bmatrix}_0^r \begin{Bmatrix} \bar{\theta} \\ \bar{V} \end{Bmatrix}_0^r \tag{6-57}
$$

Substitution of Eq. (6-55) into Eq. (6-57) results in

$$
\begin{Bmatrix} \bar{\delta} \\ \bar{\theta} \\ \bar{M} \\ \bar{V} \end{Bmatrix}_q^l = - {}_q\begin{bmatrix} t_{12} & t_{14} \\ t_{22} & t_{24} \\ t_{32} & t_{34} \\ t_{42} & t_{44} \end{bmatrix}_0^r \left({}_N\begin{bmatrix} t_{12} & t_{14} \\ t_{32} & t_{34} \end{bmatrix}_0^r \right)^{-1} {}_N\begin{bmatrix} -t_{13} & t_{14} \\ -t_{33} & t_{34} \end{bmatrix}_p^r \begin{Bmatrix} \bar{Q} \\ \bar{P} \end{Bmatrix}_p \tag{6-58}
$$

Equation (6-58) contains the information for eight frequency response functions corresponding to four types of response on the left-hand side of station q and two types of excitation at station p. It is convenient to include all the eight frequency response functions in a matrix denoted by $\mathbf{H}_{qp}(\omega)$. Then

$$
\mathbf{H}_{qp}(\omega) = - {}_{q}^{l}\begin{bmatrix} t_{12} & t_{14} \\ t_{22} & t_{24} \\ t_{32} & t_{34} \\ t_{42} & t_{44} \end{bmatrix}_{0}^{r} \left({}_{N}^{l}\begin{bmatrix} t_{12} & t_{14} \\ t_{32} & t_{34} \end{bmatrix}_{0}^{r} \right)^{-1} {}_{N}^{l}\begin{bmatrix} -t_{13} & t_{14} \\ -t_{33} & t_{34} \end{bmatrix}_{p}^{r} \qquad p > q
$$

$$(6\text{-}59)$$

This matrix is 4×2, since the input vector is two-dimensional whereas the output vector is four-dimensional. If the output vector is to be evaluated on the right-hand side of station q, it is necessary only to replace in Eq. (6-59)

$$
{}_{q}^{l}\begin{bmatrix} t_{12} & t_{14} \\ t_{22} & t_{24} \\ t_{32} & t_{34} \\ t_{42} & t_{44} \end{bmatrix}_{0}^{r} \qquad \text{by} \qquad {}_{q}^{r}\begin{bmatrix} t_{12} & t_{14} \\ t_{22} & t_{24} \\ t_{32} & t_{34} \\ t_{42} & t_{44} \end{bmatrix}_{0}^{r}
$$

In the present case if Eq. (6-13) or Eq. (6-5) is used to compute the matrix of cross spectral densities or generalized cross spectral densities for all the four types of outputs, the matrix $\mathbf{H}(\omega)$ in these equations must contain all the eight types of elements computed from Eq. (6-59). Since the number of outputs and the number of inputs are different, the matrix $\mathbf{H}(\omega)$ is not square. It may be more convenient to consider, at each time, the outputs at two stations only, say stations q and s. Thus Eq. (6-13) may be replaced by

$$
[\Phi_{qs}(\omega)]_O = \sum_{p} \sum_{r} \mathbf{H}_{qp}(\omega)[\Phi_{pr}(\omega)]_I \mathbf{H}_{sr}'^{*}(\omega) \tag{6-60}
$$

and Eq. (6-5) may be replaced by

$$
[\hat{\Phi}_{qs}(\omega_1, \omega_2)]_O = \sum_{p} \sum_{r} \mathbf{H}_{qp}(\omega_1)[\hat{\Phi}_{pr}(\omega_1, \omega_2)]_I \mathbf{H}_{sr}'^{*}(\omega_2) \tag{6-61}
$$

where the subscripts O and I associated with the square brackets signify the outputs and the inputs, respectively.

The spectral densities and the cross spectral densities of the inputs contained in $[\Phi_{pr}(\omega)]_I$, or the generalized versions contained in $[\hat{\Phi}_{pr}(\omega_1, \omega_2)]_I$, are referred to $P_j(t)$ and $Q_j(t)$, the discrete approximations of the random pressure $P(x, t)$ (cf. Figs. 6.4 and 6.5). A simple calculation will show that

$$
P_j(t) = \frac{l_{j+1} + l_j}{2} [P(x, t)]_{x=x_j} + \frac{1}{8}(l_{j+1}^2 - l_j^2)\left[\frac{\partial}{\partial x} P(x, t) \right]_{x=x_j} \tag{6-62}
$$

$$
Q_j(t) = \tfrac{1}{24}(l_{j+1}^3 - l_j^3)\left[\frac{\partial}{\partial x} P(x, t) \right]_{x=x_j} + \frac{l_{j+1}^2 - l_j^2}{8} [P(x, t)]_{x=x_j} \tag{6-63}
$$

Since $P(x, t)$ is a random process, the derivatives in Eqs. (6-62) and (6-63) are mean-square derivatives. The statistical properties of the discrete excitations $P_j(t)$ and $Q_j(t)$ follow from the commutability of mean-square differentiation and expectation. In particular, the expectations and the correlation functions of these concentrated random forces and moments are given by

$$E[P_j(t)] = \left[\frac{l_{j+1} + l_j}{2} + \frac{1}{8} (l_{j+1}^2 - l_j^2) \frac{\partial}{\partial x_j} \right] E[P(x_j, t)] \qquad (6\text{-}64)$$

$$E[Q_j(t)] = \left[\tfrac{1}{24}(l_{j+1}^3 + l_j^3) \frac{\partial}{\partial x_j} + \frac{1}{8} (l_{j+1}^2 - l_j^2) \right] E[P(x_j, t)] \qquad (6\text{-}65)$$

$$E[P_j(t_1)P_k(t_2)] = \phi_{P_j P_k}(t_1, t_2)$$

$$= \frac{(l_{j+1} + l_j)(l_{k+1} + l_k)}{4} \left[1 + \tfrac{1}{4}(l_{j+1} - l_j) \frac{\partial}{\partial x_j} \right.$$

$$\left. + \frac{1}{4} (l_{k+1} - l_k) \frac{\partial}{\partial x_k} + \frac{1}{16} (l_{j+1} - l_j)(l_{k+1} - l_k) \frac{\partial^2}{\partial x_j\, \partial x_k} \right] \phi_{PP}(x_j, t_1; x_k, t_2)$$

$$(6\text{-}66)$$

$$E[P_j(t_1)Q_k(t_2)] = \phi_{P_j Q_k}(t_1, t_2) = \left[\tfrac{1}{16}(l_{j+1} + l_j)(l_{k+1}^2 - l_k^2) \right.$$

$$+ \tfrac{1}{32}(l_{j+1} - l_j)(l_{k+1}^2 - l_k^2) \frac{\partial}{\partial x_j} + \tfrac{1}{48}(l_{j+1} + l_j)(l_{k+1}^3 + l_k^3) \frac{\partial}{\partial x_k}$$

$$\left. + \tfrac{1}{96}(l_{j+1} - l_j)(l_{k+1}^3 + l_k^3) \frac{\partial^2}{\partial x_j\, \partial x_k} \right] \phi_{PP}(x_j, t_1; x_k, t_2) \qquad (6\text{-}67)$$

$$E[Q_j(t_1)Q_k(t_2)] = \phi_{Q_j Q_k}(t_1, t_2) = \left\{ \tfrac{1}{64}(l_{j+1}^2 - l_j^2)(l_{k+1}^2 - l_k^2) \right.$$

$$+ \tfrac{1}{192} \left[(l_{j+1}^2 - l_j^2)(l_{k+1}^3 + l_k^3) \frac{\partial}{\partial x_k} + (l_{k+1}^2 - l_k^2)(l_{j+1}^3 + l_j^3) \frac{\partial}{\partial x_j} \right]$$

$$\left. + \tfrac{1}{576}(l_{j+1}^3 + l_j^3)(l_{k+1}^3 + l_k^3) \frac{\partial^2}{\partial x_j\, \partial x_k} \right\} \phi_{PP}(x_j, t_1; x_k, t_2) \qquad (6\text{-}68)$$

where $\phi_{PP}(x_j, t_1; x_k, t_2) = E[P(x_j, t_1)P(x_k, t_2)]$, and the differentiation of an expectation, such as

$$\frac{\partial^2}{\partial x_j\, \partial x_k} \phi_{PP}(x_j, t_1; x_k, t_2)$$

must be interpreted as an abbreviation for

$$\left[\frac{\partial^2}{\partial x_1\, \partial x_2} \phi_{PP}(x_1, t_1; x_2, t_2) \right]_{x_1 = x_j,\ x_2 = x_k}$$

Thus the first- and second-order statistical properties of $P_j(t)$ and $Q_j(t)$ can be computed from the expectation and the correlation function of the random pressure $P(x, t)$, and they are well defined provided that the left-hand sides of Eqs. (6-64) through (6-68) exist in the usual sense. The cross spectral densities or the generalized cross spectral densities of the discrete excitations required for the application of Eq. (6-60) or Eq. (6-61) can be obtained from Eqs. (6-66) through (6-68). For example, in the weakly stationary case

$$
\Phi_{P_j Q_k}(\omega) = \left[\tfrac{1}{16}(l_{j+1} + l_j)(l_{k+1}^2 - l_k^2) + \tfrac{1}{32}(l_{j+1} - l_j)(l_{k+1}^2 - l_k^2) \frac{\partial}{\partial x_j} \right.
$$
$$
+ \tfrac{1}{48}(l_{j+1} + l_j)(l_{k+1}^3 + l_k^3) \frac{\partial}{\partial x_k}
$$
$$
\left. + \tfrac{1}{96}(l_{j+1} - l_j)(l_{k+1}^3 + l_k^3) \frac{\partial^2}{\partial x_j \, \partial x_k} \right] \Phi_{PP}(x_j, x_k; \omega) \qquad (6\text{-}69)
$$

where $\Phi_{PP}(x_j, x_k; \omega)$ is the cross spectral density of $P(x_j, t)$ and $P(x_k, t)$. Again, the differentiation of a cross spectral density, such as

$$
\frac{\partial^2}{\partial x_j \, \partial x_k} \Phi_{PP}(x_j, x_k; \omega)
$$

must be interpreted as an abbreviation for

$$
\left[\frac{\partial^2}{\partial x_1 \, \partial x_2} \Phi_{PP}(x_1, x_2; \omega) \right]_{x_1 = x_j, \ x_2 = x_k}
$$

In the nonstationary case, it is only necessary to replace $\Phi_{P_j Q_k}(\omega)$ by $\hat{\Phi}_{P_j Q_k}(\omega_1, \omega_2)$ and $\Phi_{PP}(x_j, x_k; \omega)$ by $\hat{\Phi}_{PP}(x_j, x_k; \omega_1, \omega_2)$ in Eq. (6-69).

As an example, consider a massless uniform beam simply supported at both ends and with a concentrated mass attached to the center of the span. The physical arrangement is depicted in Fig. 6.7. The model is a two-degrees-of-freedom system. The beam is exposed to a random

Fig. 6.7 An example.

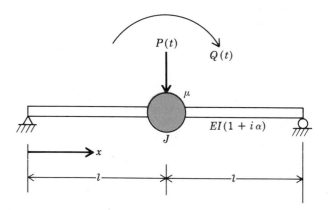

pressure field having a mean $E[P(x, t)] = 0$ and a correlation function $\phi_{PP}(x_1, t_1; x_2, t_2) = 2\pi K\,\delta(\xi - v\tau)$, where $\xi = x_2 - x_1$ and $\tau = t_2 - t_1$. This correlation function corresponds to an uncorrelated "frozen" random pattern which moves at a velocity v relative to the beam in the positive direction of the x axis. When this random pressure is approximated by a concentrated force $P(t)$ and a concentrated moment $Q(t)$ using Eqs. (6-62) and (6-63), the matrix of the spectral densities and the cross spectral densities of $P(t)$ and $Q(t)$ can be shown to be

$$
\begin{bmatrix} \Phi_{PP} & \Phi_{PQ} \\ \Phi_{QP} & \Phi_{QQ} \end{bmatrix} = \begin{bmatrix} \dfrac{l^2 K}{v} & -i\,\dfrac{l^4 K}{12v}\,\dfrac{\omega}{v} \\[4mm] i\,\dfrac{l^4 K}{12v}\left(\dfrac{\omega}{v}\right) & \dfrac{l^6 K}{144v}\left(\dfrac{\omega}{v}\right)^2 \end{bmatrix}
$$

Suppose that we are interested in the spectral density of the random bending moment $M(t)$ at the left side of the mass. We then require. the third-row elements of the matrix of frequency response functions, Eq. (6-59). To be more specific, we denote these elements by $H_{MQ}(\omega)$ and $H_{MP}(\omega)$, which are the frequency response functions for the moment $M(t)$ due to $Q(t)$ and $P(t)$, respectively. A straight forward application

Fig. 6.8 Frequency response function H_{MP}.

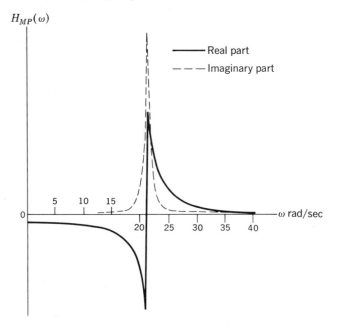

$H_{MP}(\omega)$

of Eq. (6-59) yields

$$H_{MQ}(\omega) = \frac{l^2}{\Delta}\left[2 - \frac{l^3\mu\omega^2}{3EI(1 + i\alpha)}\right]$$

$$H_{MP}(\omega) = \frac{l^3}{\Delta}\left[-2 + \frac{lJ\omega^2}{3EI(1 + i\alpha)}\right]$$

where

$$\Delta = 4l^2 - \frac{2\omega^2 l^3}{3EI(1 + i\alpha)}(\mu l^2 + J) + \frac{\omega^4 l^6 \mu J}{9E^2 I^2(1 + i\alpha)^2}$$

The spectral density of the response $M(t)$ can be computed from

$$\Phi_{MM}(\omega) = \Phi_{PP}|H_{MP}|^2 + \Phi_{QQ}|H_{MQ}|^2 + \Phi_{PQ}H_{MP}H_{MQ}^* + \Phi_{QP}H_{MQ}H_{MP}^*$$

This expression is the (3, 3) element of the matrix in Eq. (6-13). Recall that $\Phi_{QP} = \Phi_{PQ}^*$. The spectral density of the response computed from the above is seen to be purely real, as it should be. In Figs. 6.8 and 6.9 we show the real and imaginary parts of the two frequency response

Fig. 6.9 Frequency response function H_{MQ}.

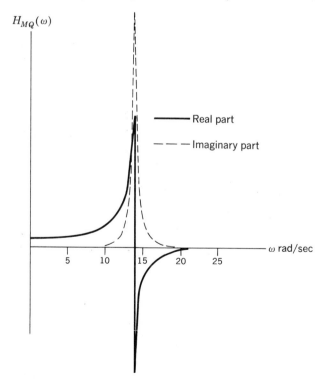

functions which are possible for the present example. The associated response spectral density $\Phi_{MM}(\omega)$ is plotted in Fig. 6.10. It is seen that the higher frequency peak of a response spectral density sometimes can be more important than the lower frequency peak. This is true, for example, when the rotary inertia J of the concentrated mass is relatively large but the translatory inertia μ is relatively small, and when the bending moment is the required response. This example shows that we must be very careful not to associate the predominant mode with the lowest natural frequency without sufficient justification.

6.4 / RESPONSE OF A FLEXIBLE AIRPLANE
TO ATMOSPHERIC TURBULENCE

With certain modifications the method described in Sec. 6.3 can be used to determine the response of a flexible airplane to atmospheric turbulence (random gusts). Figure 6.11 shows a Holzer-Myklestad model of such an airplane with a variably swept slender wing and a slender fuselage. The configuration represents a possible design of a high subsonic or a low supersonic transport. For simplicity, it is assumed that the axes of the connected elastic bars and the mass centers lie in a horizontal plane. However, from the following formulation it will be clear that the analysis can easily be modified to account for dihedrals or a more general type of distribution of mass centers. It will also be assumed that the airplane response can be determined with sufficient accuracy by considering the effect of the vertical component of the gust alone.

Fig. 6.10 Spectral density of a response random moment.

$\Phi_{MM}(\omega)$

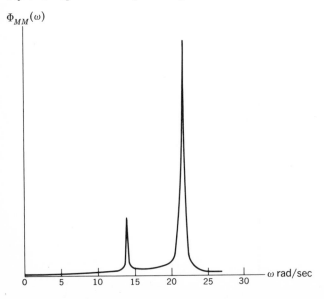

Consider a typical straight segment of an elastic bar representing one portion of the wing, as shown in Fig. 6.12. The elastic bar is assumed to be uniform‡ from station to station. Since the airplane response to just the vertical component of gust is of interest, it is necessary to consider only the vertical deflection and the torsional deformation of the elastic bar. The forces in and the deformations of the elastic bar at a given location can be represented by a state vector $Z = \{\psi, \delta, \theta, M, V, Q\}$. The components of this vector are, in the order indicated, the angle of twist about the elastic axis, the vertical displacement, the slope in the vertical plane, the bending moment, the shear force, and the torsional moment. For a single frequency oscillation we write $Z = \bar{Z} \exp (i\omega t)$, where $\bar{Z}$ is a column of complex constants, the complex amplitudes of the

‡ See footnote on page 171.

Fig. 6.11 Structural model for a large flexible airplane with variably swept wings.

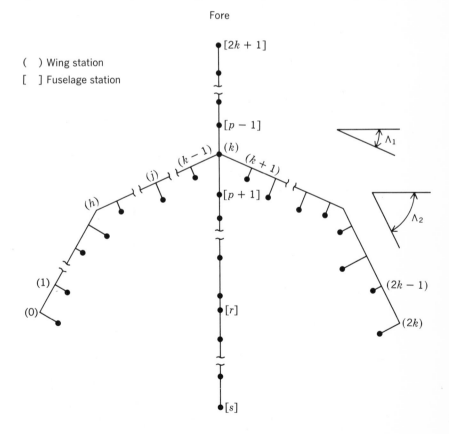

Fore

( ) Wing station
[ ] Fuselage station

Aft

components in the state vector **Z**. Given the length l_j, the bending rigidity $(EI)_j$, the torsional rigidity $(GJ)_j$, and the shear rigidity $(\eta GA)_j$ of this segment,‡ the column of complex amplitudes of the state vector

‡ η is a coefficient depending on the shape of cross section; for example, $\eta = 1.2$ for a solid beam of rectangular cross section.

Fig. 6.12 Structural model of a typical segment of the wing: (*a*) plan view from beneath the airplane; (*b*) positive directions for bending moment *M*, shear *V*, and torsional moment *Q*; (*c*) positive directions for slope θ, vertical displacement δ, and angle of twist ψ.

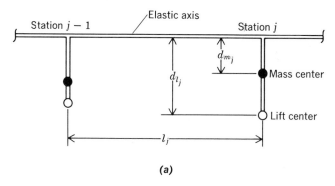

(a)

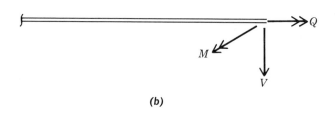

(b)

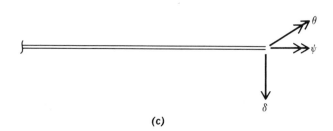

(c)

on the left of station j can be computed from that on the right of station $j - 1$ by writing

$$\bar{\mathbf{Z}}_j{}^l = \mathbf{F}_j \bar{\mathbf{Z}}_{j-1}^r \tag{6-70}$$

The transfer matrix $\mathbf{F}_j$ is given by

$$\begin{bmatrix} 1 & 0 & 0 & 0 & 0 & \dfrac{l}{GJ(1 + i\beta)} \\[2mm] 0 & 1 & l & \dfrac{-l^2}{2EI(1 + i\alpha)} & \dfrac{-l^3}{6EI(1 + i\alpha)} + \dfrac{l}{\eta GA(1 + i\beta)} & 0 \\[2mm] 0 & 0 & 1 & \dfrac{-l}{EI(1 + i\alpha)} & \dfrac{-l^2}{2EI(1 + i\alpha)} & 0 \\[2mm] 0 & 0 & 0 & 1 & l & 0 \\[1mm] 0 & 0 & 0 & 0 & 1 & 0 \\[1mm] 0 & 0 & 0 & 0 & 0 & 1 \end{bmatrix}_j \tag{6-71}$$

where the subscript j again indicates that the physical constants of the segment j should be used to compute this matrix. Note that if $G \to \infty$ the central four rows and four columns of this matrix are the same as those in Eq. (6-47), except for some changes in sign. The changes are, of course, due to the opposite sign convention used here for the components M and V.

To relate the state vectors $\mathbf{Z}_j{}^r$ and $\mathbf{Z}_j{}^l$ the unsteady aerodynamic forces must be taken into consideration. Let the relation be expressed as

$$\bar{\mathbf{Z}}_j{}^r = \mathbf{G}_j \bar{\mathbf{Z}}_j{}^l + \bar{\mathbf{K}}_j + \bar{\mathbf{L}}_j \tag{6-72}$$

where $\bar{\mathbf{L}}_j$ is associated with the lift resulting from the airplane's penetrating a sinusoidal gust but not departing from its steady flight, $\bar{\mathbf{K}}_j$ is associated with the additional unsteady lift that results from the deviation of the airplane motion from steady flight, and

$$\mathbf{G}_j = \begin{bmatrix} 1 & 0 & 0 & 0 & 0 & 0 \\[1mm] 0 & 1 & 0 & 0 & 0 & 0 \\[1mm] 0 & 0 & 1 & 0 & 0 & 0 \\[1mm] 0 & 0 & J_q\omega^2 & 1 & 0 & 0 \\[1mm] -\mu d_m\omega^2 & -\mu\omega^2 & 0 & 0 & 1 & 0 \\[1mm] -(J_p + \mu d_m{}^2)\omega^2 & -\mu d_m{}^2\omega^2 & 0 & 0 & 0 & 1 \end{bmatrix}_j \tag{6-73}$$

The subscript j in Eq. (6-73) signifies that the mass μ, the mass eccentricity d_m, the mass moments of inertia J_p and J_q are those associated with station j.

Equation (6-72) implies that the gust-penetration effect $\bar{\mathbf{L}}$ and the unsteady-motion effect $\bar{\mathbf{K}}$ are independent of each other. This is true when the unsteady motion of the airplane is small in comparison with the forward flight speed, and the linearized aerodynamic theory is valid. Let $\bar{W}$ be the complex amplitude of the velocity of a vertical sinusoidal gust. The column $\bar{L}_j$ is dependent on $\bar{W}$:

$$\bar{L}_j = \left\{ \begin{array}{c} 0 \\ 0 \\ 0 \\ 0 \\ -1 \\ -d_l \end{array} \right\} \bar{W} g_j(\omega) \qquad (6\text{-}74)$$

where $g_j(\omega)$ is a scalar function converting the complex amplitude of the gust velocity to the complex amplitude of the penetration lift. Here, the penetration lift is considered as a concentrated sinusoidally varying force which is transmitted through a rigid arm to station j. Thus $g_j(\omega)$ is proportional to the contributing area assigned to this station. In general, this function g is, at least, a function of the frequency ω, the sweep angle Λ, and the local geometry of the lifting surface. The exact expression of this function in the most general case‡ remains unknown; in some cases it may be approximated by modifying the Sears function.

The column $\bar{K}_j$ may be written as follows:

$$\bar{K}_j = \left\{ \begin{array}{c} 0 \\ 0 \\ 0 \\ 0 \\ \psi f_2(\omega) + \bar{\delta} f_1(\omega) \\ \psi f_3(\omega) + \bar{\delta} f_4(\omega) \end{array} \right\}_j \qquad (6\text{-}75)$$

The physical meanings of the functions $f_1(\omega)$ through $f_4(\omega)$ are clear. For example, $f_1(\omega)$ is the complex amplitude of the unsteady lift due to a unit sinusoidal vertical translation at the station considered, and $f_2(\omega)$ is the complex amplitude of the unsteady lift due to a unit sinusoidal angle of twist. From the reciprocal relation which exists in a linear theory, we expect that $f_2(\omega) = f_4(\omega)$. For a rigid wing with an infinite span, the f functions involve the Theordosen functions.¶ In the general case, how-

‡ In the special case of an infinitely long straight wing in an incompressible flow, the $g(\omega)$ function is proportional to the well-known Sears function, which is often expressed in terms of the reduced frequency $k = \omega b/u$, where b is the chord width of the wing and u is the forward flight speed. See H. W. Liepmann, On the Application of Statistical Concepts to the Buffeting Problem, *J. Aeron. Sci.*, **19**(12):793–800, 822 (1952). See also Y. C. Fung, Statistical Aspects of Dynamics Loads, *J. Aeron. Sci.*, **20**:317–330 (1953).

¶ See, for example, Y. C. Fung, "An Introduction to the Theory of Aeroelasticity," p. 214, Wiley, New York, 1955.

ever, these f functions are not available in the literature, although it is clear that they must be at least functions of the frequency, the sweep angle, and the local geometry of the lifting surface; and they may sometimes be approximated by modifying the Theordosen functions.

Since the column $\bar{\mathbf{K}}_j$ depends on the displacements δ and ψ, it is convenient to rewrite Eq. (6-72) in the following way:

$$\bar{\mathbf{Z}}_j{}^r = \mathbf{S}_j\bar{\mathbf{Z}}_j{}^l + \bar{\mathbf{L}}_j \tag{6-76}$$

where

$$\mathbf{S}_j = \begin{bmatrix} 1 & 0 & 0 & 0 & 0 & 0 \\ 0 & 1 & 0 & 0 & 0 & 0 \\ 0 & 0 & 1 & 0 & 0 & 0 \\ 0 & 0 & J_q\omega^2 & 1 & 0 & 0 \\ -\mu d_m\omega^2 + f_2(\omega) & -\mu\omega^2 + f_1(\omega) & 0 & 0 & 1 & 0 \\ -(J_p + \mu d_m{}^2)\omega^2 + f_3(\omega) & -\mu d_m\omega^2 + f_2(\omega) & 0 & 0 & 0 & 1 \end{bmatrix} \tag{6-77}$$

This square matrix is a point transfer matrix since it relates the state vectors on two sides of a station if active excitation is absent.

A different situation arises when the transfer of state involves a change in the coordinate system. An example is found at station h in Fig. 6.11, where the positive directions for Q and M and for ψ and θ are rotated by an angle $\gamma = \Lambda_2 - \Lambda_1$. For the sake of simplicity let us assume that no mass is attached and no lift is applied at this station. Then the change can be accomplished by introducing the point transfer matrix

$$\mathbf{S}_h = \begin{bmatrix} \cos\gamma & 0 & -\sin\gamma & 0 & 0 & 0 \\ 0 & 1 & 0 & 0 & 0 & 0 \\ \sin\gamma & 0 & \cos\gamma & 0 & 0 & 0 \\ 0 & 0 & 0 & \cos\gamma & 0 & -\sin\gamma \\ 0 & 0 & 0 & 0 & 1 & 0 \\ 0 & 0 & 0 & \sin\gamma & 0 & \cos\gamma \end{bmatrix} \tag{6-78}$$

This transfer matrix is also symmetrical about the cross diagonal.

A more complicated situation exists at the station where the wing joins with the fuselage. In Fig. 6.11 this station is k on the wings, but it is also p on the fuselage. Consider the transfer of state along the fuselage proceeding in the fore-to-aft direction:

$$\bar{\mathbf{Z}}_p{}^a = \mathbf{S}_p\bar{\mathbf{Z}}_p{}^f + \bar{\mathbf{L}}_p + \begin{Bmatrix} 0 \\ 0 \\ 0 \\ X \\ Y \\ Z \end{Bmatrix} \tag{6-79}$$

Equation (6-79) is essentially the same as Eq. (6-76) except for the last column, which accounts for the bending moment, the vertical shear, and the torsional moment transmitted from the wing. Here X, Y, Z are expressed in terms of the coordinate system of the fuselage. Since X, Y, Z must also be the reactions from the fuselage acting at station k on the wing, we have

$$
\bar{Z}_k{}^r = S_k \bar{Z}_k{}^l - \begin{bmatrix} 0 & & 0 & \\ \hline & \sin \Lambda_1 & 0 & \cos \Lambda_1 \\ 0 & 0 & 1 & 0 \\ & -\cos \Lambda_1 & 0 & \sin \Lambda_1 \end{bmatrix} \begin{Bmatrix} 0 \\ 0 \\ 0 \\ X \\ Y \\ Z \end{Bmatrix} \qquad (6\text{-}80)
$$

where S_k may be obtained from Eq. (6-78) by replacing γ by $2\Lambda_1$. The quantities X, Y, Z may be eliminated since they appear both in Eq. (6-79) and in Eq. (6-80). Furthermore, compatibility in displacements requires

$$
\begin{Bmatrix} \psi \\ \bar{\delta} \\ \bar{\theta} \end{Bmatrix}_k^l = \begin{bmatrix} -\sin \Lambda_1 & 0 & \cos \Lambda_1 \\ 0 & 1 & 0 \\ -\cos \Lambda_1 & 0 & -\sin \Lambda_1 \end{bmatrix} \begin{Bmatrix} \psi \\ \bar{\delta} \\ \bar{\theta} \end{Bmatrix}_p^f \qquad (6\text{-}81)
$$

The matrix of frequency response functions, $H_{rj}(\omega)$, is obtained by assuming that only station j is excited by a unit sinusoidal gust upwash (that is, $\bar{W} = 1$). The response of interest is $\bar{Z} = \{\psi, \bar{\delta}, \bar{\theta}, \bar{M}, \bar{V}, \bar{Q}\}$ at a point r. To illustrate, let j be a station on the left side of the wing and r be on the rear fuselage, as shown in Fig. 6.11. Using the same notation as that specified in Eqs. (6-51), we have

$$
\begin{Bmatrix} \psi \\ \bar{\delta} \\ \bar{\theta} \\ 0 \\ 0 \\ 0 \end{Bmatrix}_{2k}^r = {}_{2k}^r T_0^l \begin{Bmatrix} \psi \\ \bar{\delta} \\ \bar{\theta} \\ 0 \\ 0 \\ 0 \end{Bmatrix}_0 + {}_{2k}^r T_j^l \begin{Bmatrix} 0 \\ 0 \\ 0 \\ 0 \\ -1 \\ -d \end{Bmatrix}_j g_j(\omega)
$$

$$
- {}_{2k}^r T_k^l \begin{bmatrix} 0 & & 0 & \\ \hline & \sin \Lambda_1 & 0 & \cos \Lambda_1 \\ 0 & 0 & 1 & 0 \\ & -\cos \Lambda_1 & 0 & \sin \Lambda_1 \end{bmatrix} \begin{Bmatrix} 0 \\ 0 \\ 0 \\ X \\ Y \\ Z \end{Bmatrix} \qquad (6\text{-}82)
$$

where the boundary conditions $\{M, V, Q\}_0^l = \{M, V, Q\}_{2k}^r = \{0, 0, 0\}$ have been inserted in this equation. Consider the change of state from fore to aft along the fuselage:

$$
\begin{Bmatrix} \underline{\psi} \\ \bar{\delta} \\ \bar{\theta} \\ 0 \\ 0 \\ 0 \end{Bmatrix}_s = {}_s^a\mathbf{T}_{2k+1}^f \begin{Bmatrix} \underline{\psi} \\ \bar{\delta} \\ \bar{\theta} \\ 0 \\ 0 \\ 0 \end{Bmatrix}_{2k+1} + {}_s^a\mathbf{T}_p^f \begin{Bmatrix} 0 \\ 0 \\ 0 \\ X \\ Y \\ Z \end{Bmatrix}
\tag{6-83}
$$

where the general transfer matrix $\mathbf{T}$ is similarly defined as in Eqs. (6-51) with a (aft) replacing r (right) and f (fore) replacing l (left). Now

$$
\begin{Bmatrix} 0 \\ 0 \\ 0 \end{Bmatrix}_{2k} = {}^r\begin{bmatrix} t_{41} & t_{42} & t_{43} \\ t_{51} & t_{52} & t_{53} \\ t_{61} & t_{62} & t_{63} \end{bmatrix}_{2k}^l \begin{Bmatrix} \underline{\psi} \\ \bar{\delta} \\ \bar{\theta} \end{Bmatrix}_0 + {}^r\begin{bmatrix} t_{45} & t_{46} \\ t_{55} & t_{56} \\ t_{65} & t_{66} \end{bmatrix}_{2k}^l \begin{Bmatrix} -1 \\ -d_l \end{Bmatrix}_j g_j(\omega)
$$
$$
- {}^r\begin{bmatrix} t_{44} & t_{45} & t_{46} \\ t_{54} & t_{55} & t_{56} \\ t_{64} & t_{65} & t_{66} \end{bmatrix}_k^l \begin{bmatrix} \sin\Lambda_1 & 0 & \cos\Lambda_1 \\ 0 & 1 & 0 \\ -\cos\Lambda_1 & 0 & \sin\Lambda_1 \end{bmatrix} \begin{Bmatrix} X \\ Y \\ Z \end{Bmatrix}
\tag{6-84}
$$

can be extracted from Eq. (6-82), where each t_{lm} represents the (l, m) element taken from the indicated $\mathbf{T}$ matrix (the indices at the corners of the matrix signify which $\mathbf{T}$ matrix, constructed according to the chain rule). Similarly, from Eq. (6-83)

$$
\begin{Bmatrix} 0 \\ 0 \\ 0 \end{Bmatrix} = {}_s^a\begin{bmatrix} t_{41} & t_{42} & t_{43} \\ t_{51} & t_{52} & t_{53} \\ t_{61} & t_{62} & t_{63} \end{bmatrix}_{2k+1}^f \begin{Bmatrix} \underline{\psi} \\ \bar{\delta} \\ \bar{\theta} \end{Bmatrix}_{2k+1} + {}_s^a\begin{bmatrix} t_{44} & t_{45} & t_{46} \\ t_{54} & t_{55} & t_{56} \\ t_{64} & t_{65} & t_{66} \end{bmatrix}_p^f \begin{Bmatrix} X \\ Y \\ Z \end{Bmatrix}
\tag{6-85}
$$

Solving for $\{X, Y, Z\}$:

$$
\begin{Bmatrix} X \\ Y \\ Z \end{Bmatrix} = - \left({}_s^a\begin{bmatrix} t_{44} & t_{45} & t_{46} \\ t_{54} & t_{55} & t_{56} \\ t_{64} & t_{65} & t_{66} \end{bmatrix}_p^f \right)^{-1} {}_s^a\begin{bmatrix} t_{41} & t_{42} & t_{43} \\ t_{51} & t_{52} & t_{53} \\ t_{61} & t_{62} & t_{63} \end{bmatrix}_{2k+1}^f \begin{Bmatrix} \underline{\psi} \\ \bar{\delta} \\ \bar{\theta} \end{Bmatrix}_{2k+1}
\tag{6-85a}
$$

Substituting into Eq. (6-84) gives

$$
\begin{Bmatrix} 0 \\ 0 \\ 0 \end{Bmatrix} = {}^r\begin{bmatrix} t_{41} & t_{42} & t_{43} \\ t_{51} & t_{52} & t_{53} \\ t_{61} & t_{62} & t_{63} \end{bmatrix}_{2k}^l \begin{Bmatrix} \underline{\psi} \\ \bar{\delta} \\ \bar{\theta} \end{Bmatrix}_0 + {}^r\begin{bmatrix} t_{45} & t_{46} \\ t_{55} & t_{56} \\ t_{65} & t_{66} \end{bmatrix}_{2k}^l \begin{Bmatrix} -1 \\ -d_l \end{Bmatrix}_j g_j(\omega)
$$
$$
+ {}^r\begin{bmatrix} t_{44} & t_{45} & t_{46} \\ t_{54} & t_{55} & t_{56} \\ t_{64} & t_{65} & t_{66} \end{bmatrix}_k^l \begin{bmatrix} \sin\Lambda_1 & 0 & \cos\Lambda_1 \\ 0 & 1 & 0 \\ -\cos\Lambda_1 & 0 & \sin\Lambda_1 \end{bmatrix} \left({}_s^a\begin{bmatrix} t_{44} & t_{45} & t_{46} \\ t_{54} & t_{55} & t_{56} \\ t_{64} & t_{65} & t_{66} \end{bmatrix}_p^f \right)^{-1}
$$
$$
{}_s^a\begin{bmatrix} t_{41} & t_{42} & t_{43} \\ t_{51} & t_{52} & t_{53} \\ t_{61} & t_{62} & t_{63} \end{bmatrix}_{2k+1}^f \begin{Bmatrix} \underline{\psi} \\ \bar{\delta} \\ \bar{\theta} \end{Bmatrix}_{2k+1}
\tag{6-86}
$$

Obviously the vectors $\{\bar{\psi}, \bar{\delta}, \bar{\theta}\}_0$ and $\{\bar{\psi}, \bar{\delta}, \bar{\theta}\}_{2k+1}$ are not independent; and their relationship may be found as follows:

Write

$$
\begin{Bmatrix} \bar{\psi} \\ \bar{\delta} \\ \bar{\theta} \\ \bar{M} \\ \bar{V} \\ \bar{Q} \end{Bmatrix}_p^f = {}_p^f\mathbf{T}_{2k+1}^f \begin{Bmatrix} \bar{\psi} \\ \bar{\delta} \\ \bar{\theta} \\ 0 \\ 0 \\ 0 \end{Bmatrix}_{2k+1}^f
\tag{6-87}
$$

and

$$
\begin{Bmatrix} \bar{\psi} \\ \bar{\delta} \\ \bar{\theta} \\ \bar{M} \\ \bar{V} \\ \bar{Q} \end{Bmatrix}_k^l = {}_k^l\mathbf{T}_0^l \begin{Bmatrix} \bar{\psi} \\ \bar{\delta} \\ \bar{\theta} \\ 0 \\ 0 \\ 0 \end{Bmatrix}_0^l + {}_k^l\mathbf{T}_j^l \begin{Bmatrix} 0 \\ 0 \\ 0 \\ 0 \\ -1 \\ -d_l \end{Bmatrix}_j g_j(\omega)
\tag{6-88}
$$

These equations contain

$$
\begin{Bmatrix} \bar{\psi} \\ \bar{\delta} \\ \bar{\theta} \end{Bmatrix}_p^f = {}_p^f\begin{bmatrix} t_{11} & t_{12} & t_{13} \\ t_{21} & t_{22} & t_{23} \\ t_{31} & t_{32} & t_{33} \end{bmatrix}_{2k+1}^f \begin{Bmatrix} \bar{\psi} \\ \bar{\delta} \\ \bar{\theta} \end{Bmatrix}_{2k+1}
\tag{6-89}
$$

and

$$
\begin{Bmatrix} \bar{\psi} \\ \bar{\delta} \\ \bar{\theta} \end{Bmatrix}_k^l = {}_k^l\begin{bmatrix} t_{11} & t_{12} & t_{13} \\ t_{21} & t_{22} & t_{23} \\ t_{31} & t_{32} & t_{33} \end{bmatrix}_0^l \begin{Bmatrix} \bar{\psi} \\ \bar{\delta} \\ \bar{\theta} \end{Bmatrix}_0 + {}_k^l\begin{bmatrix} t_{15} & t_{16} \\ t_{25} & t_{26} \\ t_{35} & t_{36} \end{bmatrix}_j^l \begin{Bmatrix} -1 \\ -d_l \end{Bmatrix} g_j(\omega)
\tag{6-90}
$$

Thus

$$
\begin{Bmatrix} \bar{\psi} \\ \bar{\delta} \\ \bar{\theta} \end{Bmatrix}_0 = -\left({}_k^l\begin{bmatrix} t_{11} & t_{12} & t_{13} \\ t_{21} & t_{22} & t_{23} \\ t_{31} & t_{32} & t_{33} \end{bmatrix}_0^l \right)^{-1} {}_k^l\begin{bmatrix} t_{15} & t_{16} \\ t_{25} & t_{26} \\ t_{35} & t_{36} \end{bmatrix}_j^l \begin{Bmatrix} -1 \\ -d_l \end{Bmatrix} g_j(\omega)
$$
$$
+ \left({}_k^l\begin{bmatrix} t_{11} & t_{12} & t_{13} \\ t_{21} & t_{22} & t_{23} \\ t_{31} & t_{32} & t_{33} \end{bmatrix}_0^l \right)^{-1} \begin{bmatrix} -\sin\Lambda_1 & 0 & \cos\Lambda_1 \\ 0 & 1 & 0 \\ -\cos\Lambda_1 & 0 & +\sin\Lambda_1 \end{bmatrix}
$$
$$
{}_p^f\begin{bmatrix} t_{11} & t_{12} & t_{13} \\ t_{21} & t_{22} & t_{23} \\ t_{31} & t_{32} & t_{33} \end{bmatrix}_{2k+1}^f \begin{Bmatrix} \bar{\psi} \\ \bar{\delta} \\ \bar{\theta} \end{Bmatrix}_{2k+1}
\tag{6-91}
$$

where the relation (6-81) has been used. Let

$$
\mathbf{B} = {}_{2k}^{r}\begin{bmatrix} t_{45} & t_{46} \\ t_{55} & t_{56} \\ t_{65} & t_{66} \end{bmatrix}_{j}^{l} - {}_{2k}^{r}\begin{bmatrix} t_{41} & t_{42} & t_{43} \\ t_{51} & t_{52} & t_{53} \\ t_{61} & t_{62} & t_{63} \end{bmatrix}_{0}^{l}
$$
$$
\left({}_{k}^{l}\begin{bmatrix} t_{11} & t_{12} & t_{13} \\ t_{21} & t_{22} & t_{23} \\ t_{31} & t_{32} & t_{33} \end{bmatrix}_{0}^{l} \right)^{-1} {}_{k}^{l}\begin{bmatrix} t_{15} & t_{16} \\ t_{25} & t_{26} \\ t_{35} & t_{36} \end{bmatrix}_{j}^{l} \qquad (6\text{-}92)
$$

and

$$
\mathbf{C} = {}_{2k}^{r}\begin{bmatrix} t_{41} & t_{42} & t_{43} \\ t_{51} & t_{52} & t_{53} \\ t_{61} & t_{62} & t_{63} \end{bmatrix}_{0}^{l} \left({}_{k}^{l}\begin{bmatrix} t_{11} & t_{12} & t_{13} \\ t_{21} & t_{22} & t_{23} \\ t_{31} & t_{32} & t_{33} \end{bmatrix}_{0}^{l} \right)^{-1}
$$
$$
\begin{bmatrix} -\sin \Lambda_1 & 0 & \cos \Lambda_1 \\ 0 & 1 & 0 \\ -\cos \Lambda_1 & 0 & -\sin \Lambda_1 \end{bmatrix}_{p}^{f} {}_{2k+1}\begin{bmatrix} t_{11} & t_{12} & t_{13} \\ t_{21} & t_{22} & t_{23} \\ t_{31} & t_{32} & t_{33} \end{bmatrix}_{2k+1}
$$
$$
+ {}_{2k}^{r}\begin{bmatrix} t_{44} & t_{45} & t_{46} \\ t_{54} & t_{55} & t_{56} \\ t_{64} & t_{65} & t_{66} \end{bmatrix}_{k}^{l} \begin{bmatrix} \sin \Lambda_1 & 0 & \cos \Lambda_1 \\ 0 & 1 & 0 \\ -\cos \Lambda_1 & 0 & \sin \Lambda_1 \end{bmatrix}
$$
$$
\left({}_{s}^{a}\begin{bmatrix} t_{44} & t_{45} & t_{46} \\ t_{54} & t_{55} & t_{56} \\ t_{64} & t_{65} & t_{66} \end{bmatrix}_{r}^{f} \right)^{-1} {}_{s}^{a}\begin{bmatrix} t_{41} & t_{42} & t_{43} \\ t_{51} & t_{52} & t_{53} \\ t_{61} & t_{62} & t_{63} \end{bmatrix}_{2k+1}^{f} \qquad (6\text{-}93)
$$

Then Eq. (6-86) reduces to

$$
\begin{Bmatrix} 0 \\ 0 \\ 0 \end{Bmatrix} = \mathbf{B} \begin{Bmatrix} -1 \\ -d_l \end{Bmatrix}_j g_j(\omega) + \mathbf{C} \begin{Bmatrix} \psi \\ \bar{\delta} \\ \bar{\theta} \end{Bmatrix}_{2k+1} \qquad (6\text{-}86a)
$$

Rearranging:

$$
\begin{Bmatrix} \psi \\ \bar{\delta} \\ \bar{\theta} \end{Bmatrix}_{2k+1} = \mathbf{C}^{-1}\mathbf{B} \begin{Bmatrix} -1 \\ -d_l \end{Bmatrix} g_j(\omega) \qquad (6\text{-}86b)
$$

Now

$$
\begin{Bmatrix} \psi \\ \bar{\delta} \\ \bar{\theta} \\ \bar{M} \\ \bar{V} \\ \bar{Q} \end{Bmatrix}_r^a = {}_{r}^{a}\mathbf{T}_{2k+1}^{f} \begin{Bmatrix} \psi \\ \bar{\delta} \\ \bar{\theta} \\ 0 \\ 0 \\ 0 \end{Bmatrix}_{2k+1}^{f} + {}_{r}^{a}\mathbf{T}_p^{f} \begin{Bmatrix} 0 \\ 0 \\ 0 \\ X \\ Y \\ Z \end{Bmatrix}
$$
$$
= {}_{r}^{a}\begin{bmatrix} t_{11} & t_{12} & t_{13} \\ t_{21} & t_{22} & t_{23} \\ t_{31} & t_{32} & t_{33} \\ t_{41} & t_{42} & t_{43} \\ t_{51} & t_{52} & t_{53} \\ t_{61} & t_{62} & t_{63} \end{bmatrix}_{2k+1}^{f} \begin{Bmatrix} \psi \\ \bar{\delta} \\ \bar{\theta} \end{Bmatrix}_{2k+1} + {}_{r}^{a}\begin{bmatrix} t_{14} & t_{15} & t_{16} \\ t_{24} & t_{25} & t_{26} \\ t_{34} & t_{35} & t_{36} \\ t_{44} & t_{45} & t_{46} \\ t_{54} & t_{55} & t_{56} \\ t_{64} & t_{65} & t_{66} \end{bmatrix}_{p}^{f} \begin{Bmatrix} X \\ Y \\ Z \end{Bmatrix} \qquad (6\text{-}94)
$$

It follows from Eqs. (6-85a) and (6-86b) that

$$
\left\{\begin{array}{c} \bar{\psi} \\ \bar{\delta} \\ \bar{\theta} \\ \bar{M} \\ \bar{V} \\ \bar{Q} \end{array}\right\}_r^a = \left\langle {}^a\!\begin{bmatrix} t_{11} & t_{12} & t_{13} \\ t_{21} & t_{22} & t_{23} \\ t_{31} & t_{32} & t_{33} \\ t_{41} & t_{42} & t_{43} \\ t_{51} & t_{52} & t_{53} \\ t_{61} & t_{62} & t_{63} \end{bmatrix}_{2k+1}^f {}_r - {}^a\!\begin{bmatrix} t_{14} & t_{15} & t_{16} \\ t_{24} & t_{25} & t_{26} \\ t_{34} & t_{35} & t_{36} \\ t_{44} & t_{45} & t_{46} \\ t_{54} & t_{55} & t_{56} \\ t_{64} & t_{65} & t_{66} \end{bmatrix}_p^f {}_r \right.
$$

$$
\left. \left({}^a\!\begin{bmatrix} t_{44} & t_{45} & t_{46} \\ t_{54} & t_{55} & t_{56} \\ t_{64} & t_{65} & t_{66} \end{bmatrix}_p^f {}_s \right)^{-1} {}^a\!\begin{bmatrix} t_{41} & t_{42} & t_{43} \\ t_{51} & t_{52} & t_{53} \\ t_{61} & t_{62} & t_{63} \end{bmatrix}_{2k+1}^f {}_s \right\rangle \mathbf{C}^{-1}\mathbf{B} \left\{\begin{array}{c} -1 \\ -d_l \end{array}\right\} g_j(\omega) \quad (6\text{-}95)
$$

This equation gives the complex amplitudes of the angle of twist, deflection, slope, moment, shear, and torsional moment immediately aft of station r on the rear fuselage due to a unit sinusoidal gust upwash at station j on the left side of the wing. By definition, these are the H_{rj} functions, each of which corresponds to one type of response being considered. The frequency response functions corresponding to other pairs of stations can be found in an analogous manner.

In using Eq. (6-60) or Eq. (6-61) to compute the cross spectral densities or the generalized cross spectral densities of the response, we require the cross spectral densities or the generalized cross spectral densities of the gust velocity field as sensed by the moving airplane. Strictly speaking, the velocity of a gust is a random function of both time and space. In high-speed flights, however, it is generally permissible in the analysis of the airplane response to regard the gust velocity field to be random only in space. Thus the airplane is considered as flying through a random pattern of a gust which is "frozen" in space; and at a given location on the airplane it senses an input which is random in time. If the gust field is homogeneous, i.e., if the statistical properties of the gust velocity are invariant with respect to a change of the origin of the reference coordinate axes, then the airplane senses stationary inputs; otherwise, it senses nonstationary inputs.

Consider, for example, a homogeneous and isotropic‡ gust field. Let $O\text{-}x,y,z$ be the reference coordinates attached to the moving air plane, and let the xz plane be the plane of symmetry, as shown in Fig. 6.13. The airplane is assumed to be moving at a constant velocity u along the negative direction of the x axis. The crosscorrelation function for the inputs at locations j and l on the airplane is then

$$
\phi_{I_j I_l}(t_1, t_2) = E[W(x_j - ut_1, y_j) W(x_l - ut_2, y_l)] \quad (6\text{-}96)
$$

where W is the random gust vertical velocity. For a homogeneous gust,

‡ Isotropicity implies that the statistical properties of the gust field are invariant with respect to a change of coordinate orientation.

the right-hand side of Eq. (6-96) may be replaced by

$$\int_{-\infty}^{\infty} \int_{-\infty}^{\infty} \Phi_{WW}(k_1, k_2)$$
$$\exp\left(i\{k_1[(x_j - ut_1) - (x_l - ut_2)] + k_2(y_j - y_l)\}\right) dk_1 dk_2 \quad (6\text{-}97)$$

where $\Phi_{WW}(k_1, k_2)$ is the two-dimensional spectral density of the gust vertical velocity in the domain of the wave numbers k_1 and k_2. By further restricting the gust field to be isotropic,[‡]

$$\Phi_{WW}(k_1, k_2) = \frac{3}{4}\frac{\sigma^2 L^2}{\pi}\frac{L^2(k_1^2 + k_2^2)}{[1 + L^2(k_1^2 + k_2^2)]^{\frac{5}{2}}} \quad (6\text{-}98)$$

In this equation, L is called the *scale of turbulence* which is a measure of the average size of the eddies, and σ^2 is the variance of the gust vertical velocity. By writing $\xi = x_j - x_l$, $\eta = y_j - y_l$, and $\tau = t_1 - t_2$, Eqs. (6-96) through (6-98) may be combined as

$$\phi_{I_j I_l}(t_1, t_2) = R_{I_j I_l}(\tau) = \frac{3}{4}\frac{\sigma^2 L^2}{\pi}\int_{-\infty}^{\infty}\int_{-\infty}^{\infty}\frac{L^2(k_1^2 + k_2^2)}{[1 + L^2(k_1^2 + k_2^2)]^{\frac{5}{2}}}$$
$$\exp\left[i(k_1\xi - k_1 u\tau + k_2\eta)\right] dk_1 dk_2 \quad (6\text{-}99)$$

The cross spectral density of the inputs is the Fourier transform of (6-99):

$$\Phi_{I_j I_l}(\omega) = \frac{1}{2\pi}\int_{-\infty}^{\infty} R_{I_j I_l}(\tau) \exp(-i\omega\tau) d\tau$$
$$= \frac{3}{4}\frac{\sigma^2 L^2}{\pi}\exp\left(-i\frac{\omega}{u}\xi\right)$$
$$\int_{-\infty}^{\infty}\frac{L^2[(\omega/u)^2 + k_2^2]}{\{1 + L^2[(\omega/u)^2 + k_2^2]\}^{\frac{5}{2}}}\exp(ik_2\eta)\,dk_2 \quad (6\text{-}100)$$

[‡] See G. K. Batchelor, "Theory of Homogeneous Turbulence," Cambridge, London, 1953.

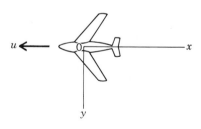

Fig. 6.13.

where use has been made of the relation‡

$$\frac{1}{2\pi} \int_{-\infty}^{\infty} \exp\left[-i(k_1 u + \omega)\tau\right] d\tau = \delta(k_1 u + \omega)$$

The integral in Eq. (6-100) can be evaluated with the aid of existing tables;¶ the result is

$$\Phi_{I_i I_i}(\omega) = \frac{2\sigma^2 L}{\pi} \exp\left(-i\frac{\omega}{u}\xi\right) \left\{ \left(\frac{\omega}{u}\right)^2 \left[\frac{\eta^2}{4a^2} K_2\left(a\frac{\eta}{L}\right)\right] \right.$$
$$\left. + \left(\frac{1}{2a}\right)^2 \frac{a\eta}{L}\left[3K_1\left(\frac{a\eta}{L}\right) - \frac{a\eta}{L}K_2\left(\frac{a\eta}{L}\right)\right]\right\} \qquad (6\text{-}101)$$

where the K_m are the modified Bessel functions of the second kind, and $a = [1 + (L\omega/u)^2]^{\frac{1}{2}}$.

The spectral density of the input (at one single location) is obtained by letting $\xi = \eta = 0$ in Eq. (6-101). Observing that as $z \to 0$,

$$zK_1(z) \to 1$$
$$z^2 K_2(z) \to 2$$

it follows that

$$\Phi_{I_i I_i}(\omega) = \frac{\sigma^2 L}{2\pi} \frac{1 + 3(\omega L/u)^2}{[1 + (\omega L/u)^2]^2} \qquad (6\text{-}102)$$

Equation (6-102) is a well-known result frequently used in the study of airplane response to a one-dimensional random gust.§

6.5 / STRUCTURES CONSTRUCTED FROM IDENTICAL INTERIOR COMPONENTS

Many a practical structure consists of an array of identical units in its interior. The simplified model of an N-story building‡‡ shown in Fig. 6.14 is an example. For such a structure the method of difference equations sometimes can be used with advantage. Suppose we are interested in the motion of each floor due to the excitation of a random earthquake. Since the excitation is fed in only at the ground, i.e., the zeroth floor, the required knowledge of the structure is the frequency response functions

‡ Compare with Eq. (V-7), Appendix V.

¶ A. Erdélyi (ed.), "Tables of Integral Transforms," vol. 1, p. 11, McGraw-Hill, New York, 1954.

§ B. Etkin, "Dynamics of Flight," p. 318, Wiley, New York, 1959. See also Exercise 5-3.

‡‡ This model was considered by A. C. Eringen in Response of Tall Buildings to Random Earthquakes, *Proc. 3rd U.S. Natl. Congr. Appl. Mech.*, p. 141, ASME, June, 1958. In this paper, however, the mass and the viscous damping constant of the roof floor, m_N and c_N, were assumed to be the same as those of an interior floor.

$H_{j,0}(\omega)$ or the impulse response functions $h_{j,0}(t)$, $j = 1, 2, \ldots, N$. It is assumed that the masses are concentrated at the floor levels and that each floor, except the roof, has the same mass. Both structural and viscous damping will be considered. The equations of motion for this N-degrees-of-freedom system may be written as

$$m_N \ddot{Y}_N + c_N \dot{Y}_N + k(Y_N - Y_{N-1}) = 0$$
$$m \ddot{Y}_j + c \dot{Y}_j + k(2Y_j - Y_{j+1} - Y_{j-1}) = 0$$
$$j = 1, 2, \ldots, N - 1 \quad (6\text{-}103)$$
$$Y_0 = G(t)$$

where the last equation $Y_0 = G(t)$ specifies the ground displacement. To compute the frequency response functions, we change $G(t)$ to a deterministic sinusoidal motion with a unit amplitude, that is, exp $(i\omega t)$, and

Fig. 6.14 Model of a tall building.

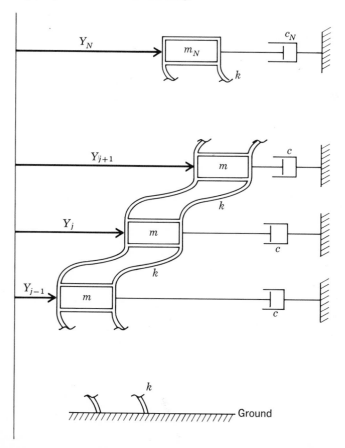

Y_j to $H_{j,0}(\omega) \exp{(i\omega t)}$. Then Eqs. (6-103) reduce to a set of algebraic equations‡

$$
\begin{aligned}
&(k + i\omega c_N - \omega^2 m_N)H_{N,0} - kH_{(N-1),0} = 0 \\
&kH_{(j+1),0} - (2k + i\omega c - \omega^2 m)H_{j,0} \\
&\qquad\qquad + kH_{(j-1),0} = 0 \qquad j = 1, 2, \ldots, N-1 \qquad (6\text{-}104) \\
&H_{0,0} = 1
\end{aligned}
$$

In order to account specifically for structural damping, the spring constant k in Eqs. (6-104) may be replaced by $k(1 + i\alpha)$; that is,

$$
\begin{aligned}
&[k(1 + i\alpha) + i\omega c_N - \omega^2 m_N]H_{N,0} - k(1 + i\alpha)H_{(N-1),0} = 0 \\
&k(1 + i\alpha)H_{(j+1),0} - [2k(1 + i\alpha) + i\omega c - \omega^2 m]H_{j,0} \\
&\qquad\qquad + k(1 + i\alpha)H_{(j-1),0} = 0 \qquad j = 1, 2, \ldots, N-1 \qquad (6\text{-}104a) \\
&H_{0,0} = 1
\end{aligned}
$$

These equations are the second-order difference equations of the recurrence type for the $H_{j,0}$, and they may be expressed in the convenient form

$$
\begin{aligned}
&-2H_N \cosh \psi_N + H_{N-1} = 0 \\
&H_{j+1} - 2H_j \cosh \psi + H_{j-1} = 0 \qquad j = 1, 2, \ldots, N-1 \qquad (6\text{-}104b) \\
&H_0 = 1
\end{aligned}
$$

where the second subscript, 0, for the functions $H_{j,0}$ has been omitted for brevity, and

$$
\begin{aligned}
\cosh \psi_N &= \frac{1}{2}\left[1 - \frac{\omega^2 m_N - i\omega c_N}{k(1 + i\alpha)} \right] \\
\cosh \psi &= \frac{1}{2}\left[2 - \frac{\omega^2 m - i\omega c}{k(1 + i\alpha)} \right]
\end{aligned} \qquad (6\text{-}105)
$$

The solution for $H_j, j = 1, 2, \ldots, N-1$ may be written as

$$
H_j = C_1 \cosh j\psi + C_2 \sinh j\psi \qquad j = 1, 2, \ldots, N-1 \qquad (6\text{-}106)
$$

where the constants C_1 and C_2 are arbitrary. These constants can be determined so that the same expression also applies to the cases $j = 0$ and $j = N$. From the last equation in (6-104b) it is clear that $C_1 = 1$. To evaluate C_2, we proceed as follows. We *formally* extend the second equation in (6-104b) to $j = N$; that is, we write

$$
H_{N+1} - 2H_N \cosh \psi + H_{N-1} = 0 \qquad (6\text{-}107)
$$

‡ If the excitation were taken to be a sinusoidal ground acceleration with a unit amplitude, we should change $G(t)$ to $-\omega^{-2} \exp{(i\omega t)}$. Then the last equation in (6-104) would read $H_{0,0} = -\omega^{-2}$. Of course, the frequency response functions thus obtained would have a different physical meaning from those obtained from the present Eqs. (6-104).

Subtracting the first equation in (6-104b) from Eq. (6-107), we obtain

$$H_{N+1} - 2H_N(\cosh \psi - \cosh \psi_N) = 0 \qquad (6\text{-}108)$$

Equation (6-108) can be used as a condition to determine C_2:

$$C_2 = - \frac{2 \cosh N\psi \cosh \psi_N - \cosh (N - 1)\psi}{2 \sinh N\psi \cosh \psi_N - \sinh (N - 1)\psi} \qquad (6\text{-}109)$$

Therefore,

$$H_j = \cosh j\psi - \frac{2 \cosh N\psi \cosh \psi_N - \cosh (N - 1)\psi}{2 \sinh N\psi \cosh \psi_N - \sinh (N - 1)\psi} \sinh j\psi \qquad (6\text{-}110)$$

This expression for H_j is quite concise in comparison with one obtainable from, say, the transfer matrix method. Of course, the price we pay for a simpler result is the limitation that the interior construction of the structure be divisible into identical units.

The impulse response function $h_j(t)$ may be obtained from the Fourier transformation of Eq. (6-110). This is possible, provided that the zeros of the denominator $2 \sinh N\psi \cosh \psi_N - \sinh (N - 1)\psi$ can be found and the integration performed, say, by use of the method of residues. To show this we consider the special case $m_N = m$ and $c_N = c$. Then $\cosh \psi_N = -\frac{1}{2} + \cosh \psi$, and Eq. (6-110) reduces to

$$H_j(\omega) = \frac{\cosh (N + \frac{1}{2} - j)\psi}{\cosh (N + \frac{1}{2})\psi} \qquad (6\text{-}111)$$

Therefore,

$$h_j(t) = \frac{1}{2\pi} \int_{-\infty}^{\infty} \frac{\cosh (N + \frac{1}{2} - j)\psi}{\cosh (N + \frac{1}{2})\psi} \exp (i\omega t) \, d\omega \qquad (6\text{-}112)$$

The poles of the integrand in Eq. (6-112) are obtained from

$$\cosh (N + \tfrac{1}{2})\psi = 0$$

the solution of which is

$$\psi = i\lambda_n = \frac{i\pi(2n - 1)}{2N + 1} \qquad n = 1, 2, \ldots, N \qquad (6\text{-}113)$$

The poles corresponding to $n > N$ are merely repetitions of those given in (6-113), and they should not be included in the evaluation of Eq. (6-112). It can be seen that in the undamped case each pole would correspond to a natural frequency. Therefore, the contributions to the value of the integral in (6-112) in the lightly damped case should be roughly those of N normal modes. This provides a physical reason for restricting $n \leq N$. Substituting (6-113) into the second of Eqs. (6-105) and changing ω to a complex variable ζ, we find the poles

$$\zeta_n = \pm \xi_n + i\left(\frac{c}{2m} \pm \eta_n\right) \tag{6-114}$$

where

$$\xi_n = \left\{\left[2\frac{k}{m}(1 - s_n) - \frac{c^2}{4m^2}\right]^2 + \left[2\frac{k\alpha}{m}(1 - s_n)\right]^2\right\}^{\frac{1}{4}} \cos\frac{\theta}{2}$$

$$\eta_n = \left\{\left[2\frac{k}{m}(1 - s_n) - \frac{c^2}{4m^2}\right]^2 + 2\left[\frac{k\alpha}{m}(1 - s_n)\right]^2\right\}^{\frac{1}{4}} \sin\frac{\theta}{2}$$

$$\theta = \tan^{-1}\frac{2k\alpha(1 - s_n)}{2k(1 - s_n) - c^2/4m} \tag{6-115}$$

$$s_n = \cos\frac{\pi(2n - 1)}{2N + 1}$$

In the expressions for ξ_n and η_n the quartic root is the one which is real and positive. Assume that $|\eta_n| < c/2m$ for all n. Then all the poles are in the upper ζ plane. Then the method of residues leads to

$$h_j(t) = \frac{2k(\alpha - i)}{2N + 1} \sum_{n=1}^{N} (-1)^{n+1} \frac{\cos\left[(N + \frac{1}{2} - j)\lambda_n\right] \sin\lambda_n}{m(\xi_n + \eta_n)}$$

$$\left(\exp\left\{\left[-\left(\frac{c}{2m} + \eta_n\right) + i\xi_n\right]t\right\} - \exp\left\{\left[-\left(\frac{c}{2m} - \eta_n\right) - i\xi_n\right]t\right\}\right)$$

$$t \geq 0 \tag{6-116}$$

It is understood that only the real part of Eq. (6-116) gives the function $h_j(t)$ and that $h_j(t) = 0$ for $t < 0$. Furthermore, if either $c/2m + \eta_n$ or $c/2m - \eta_n$ is negative for a certain n, then the associated exponential function in Eq. (6-116) should not be included in the summation, since the pole corresponding to this term is in the lower ζ plane.

Once the $h_j(t)$ are determined, the cumulant functions of the responses at various floors can be computed in a straightforward manner from the cumulant functions of the ground excitation. If the second-order property of the ground excitation is specified by its generalized spectral density,‡ then the frequency response functions $H_j(\omega)$ can be conveniently used to obtain the generalized cross spectral densities for the random motions of the various floors.

In the case of wind or blast loading, the inputs are generally fed in at all floors. We shall then require the frequency response functions $H_{jp}(\omega)$ and/or the impulse response functions $h_{jp}(t)$, where both j and p range from 1 to N (assuming that the ground floor is motionless for all time¶). The method of difference equations still applies to this more

---

‡ Presumably, a nonstationary model is more acceptable for the earthquake analysis.
¶ If this is not the case, p ranges from 0 to N; but, of course, $p = 0$ has just been considered.

general case. We shall discuss the determination of the frequency response functions. The impulse response functions follow from integral transformations by use of the method of residues, in a manner similar to that described above.

To determine $H_{jp}(\omega)$, the pth floor is assumed to be excited by a deterministic force exp $(i\omega t)$. The system of difference equations can now be written as follows:

$$-2H_{N,p}\cosh\psi_N + H_{(N-1),p} = 0$$
$$\cdot\;\cdot\;\cdot\;\cdot\;\cdot\;\cdot\;\cdot\;\cdot\;\cdot\;\cdot\;\cdot\;\cdot\;\cdot\;\cdot\;\cdot\;\cdot$$
$$H_{(q+1),p} - 2H_{q,p}\cosh\psi + H_{(q-1),p} = 0$$
$$\cdot\;\cdot\;\cdot\;\cdot\;\cdot\;\cdot\;\cdot\;\cdot\;\cdot\;\cdot\;\cdot\;\cdot\;\cdot\;\cdot\;\cdot\;\cdot\;\cdot\;\cdot$$
$$H_{(p+2),p} - 2H_{(p+1),p}\cosh\psi + H_{p,p} = 0 \qquad\qquad (6\text{-}117)$$
$$H_{(p+1),p} - 2H_{p,p}\cosh\psi + H_{(p-1),p} = -[k(1 + i\alpha)]^{-1}$$
$$H_{p,p} - 2H_{(p-1),p}\cosh\psi + H_{(p-2),p} = 0$$
$$\cdot\;\cdot\;\cdot\;\cdot\;\cdot\;\cdot\;\cdot\;\cdot\;\cdot\;\cdot\;\cdot\;\cdot\;\cdot\;\cdot\;\cdot\;\cdot\;\cdot\;\cdot$$
$$H_{2,p} - 2H_{1,p}\cosh\psi = 0$$

where $\cosh\psi$ and $\cosh\psi_N$ have been given in (6-105). The general solutions to these equations for $p < j < N$ and for $1 \le j < p$ are given by

$$H_{jp} = \begin{cases} A\cosh(j - p)\psi + B\sinh(j - p)\psi & p < j < N \\ C\cosh j\psi + D\sinh j\psi & 1 \le j < p \end{cases} \qquad (6\text{-}118)$$

The arbitrary constants A, B, C, D are determined by satisfying the conditions

$$H_{(N+1),p} - 2H_N(\cosh\psi - \cosh\psi_N) = 0$$
$$H_{(p+1),p} - 2H_{p,p}\cosh\psi + H_{(p-1),p} = -[k(1 + i\alpha)]^{-1} \qquad (6\text{-}119)$$
$$H_{0,p} = 0$$

The first and third conditions are to be satisfied by the first and second expressions in (6-118), respectively; and the second condition is to be satisfied by both expressions in (6-118). Imposition of these conditions yields

$$A = \frac{S_p}{\Delta}\sinh p\psi[k(1 + i\alpha)\sinh\psi]^{-1}$$

$$B = \frac{-C_p}{\Delta}\sinh p\psi[k(1 + i\alpha)\sinh\psi]^{-1}$$

$$C = 0 \qquad\qquad\qquad\qquad\qquad\qquad\qquad\qquad\qquad (6\text{-}120)$$

$$D = \frac{S_p}{\Delta}[k(1 + i\alpha)\sinh\psi]^{-1}$$

where

$$S_p = 2\cosh\psi_N\sinh(N - p)\psi - \sinh(N - p - 1)\psi$$
$$C_p = 2\cosh\psi_N\cosh(N - p)\psi - \cosh(N - p - 1)\psi \qquad (6\text{-}121)$$
$$\Delta = 2\cosh\psi_N\sinh N\psi - \sinh(N - 1)\psi$$

With these values for A, B, C, and D, the validity of the first expression in (6-118) is extended to $j = p$ and $j = N$, and the validity of the second expression in (6-118) is extended to $j = p$ and $j = 1$. It is interesting to note that the common denominator for both expressions, Δ, is the same as that appearing in Eq. (6-110). This is to be expected since the zeros of Δ in the undamped case correspond to the natural frequencies which are characteristics of the system independent of the location of the excitation.

6.6 / THE MARKOV-VECTOR APPROACH

The theory of Markov random vectors can be used to advantage if the excitations to an n-degrees-of-freedom system satisfy

$$E[F_j(t)] = 0$$
$$E[F_j(t_1)F_k(t_2)] = J_{jk}(t_1)\,\delta(t_1 - t_2) \qquad j, k = 1, 2, \ldots, n \qquad (6\text{-}122)$$

If, in addition, the excitations $F_j(t)$ are Gaussian, then it is clear that the responses $X_k(t)$ and their time derivatives $(d/dt)\,X_k(t)$ constitute a Markov vector in a $2n$-dimensional phase space. Without the Gaussian assumption, $X_k(t)$ and $(d/dt)\,X_k(t)$ are components of a wide-sense Markov vector.

A system of excitations having the properties specified in Eqs. (6-122) will be called a *vector* shot noise, which we shall denote by the symbol $\mathbf{S} = \{S_1(t), S_2(t), \ldots, S_n(t)\}$. Under the excitation of a vector shot noise the matrix equation of motion

$$\mathbf{m\ddot{X}} + \mathbf{c\dot{X}} + \mathbf{kX} = \mathbf{S} \qquad (6\text{-}123)$$

can be rewritten in the same form as Eq. (5-79a),

$$\frac{d}{dt}\mathbf{Y} = \mathbf{gY} + \mathbf{F} \qquad (5\text{-}79a)$$

with, say,

$$\begin{aligned} Y_j &= X_j \\ Y_{j+n} &= \frac{d}{dt}Y_j = \dot{X}_j \end{aligned} \qquad (6\text{-}124)$$

It can easily be seen that the $2n \times 2n$ matrix $\mathbf{g}$ is

$$\mathbf{g} = \left[\begin{array}{c|c} \mathbf{0} & \mathbf{I} \\ \hline -\mathbf{m}^{-1}\mathbf{k} & -\mathbf{m}^{-1}\mathbf{c} \end{array} \right] \qquad (6\text{-}125)$$

and that the forcing column $\mathbf{F}$ is

$$\mathbf{F} = \left\{ \begin{array}{c} \mathbf{0} \\ \hline \mathbf{m}^{-1}\mathbf{S} \end{array} \right\} \qquad (6\text{-}126)$$

The expectation and the covariance matrix of $\mathbf{Y}$ under the condition that $\mathbf{Y}(t_0) = \mathbf{y}_0$ are still given by Eqs. (5-109) and (5-113), respectively:

$$E[\mathbf{Y}(t)] = \exp[\mathbf{g}(t - t_0)]\mathbf{y}_0 \tag{5-109}$$

$$\hat{\mathbf{S}} = \int_{t_0}^{t} \exp[\mathbf{g}(t - \tau)]\mathbf{B} \exp[\mathbf{g}'(t - \tau)]\, d\tau \tag{5-113}$$

It is only necessary to use Eq. (6-125) for the matrix $\mathbf{g}$ and to note that $\mathbf{B}$ is now

$$\mathbf{B} = \begin{bmatrix} \mathbf{0} & \mathbf{0} \\ \hline \mathbf{0} & \mathbf{m}^{-1}\mathbf{J}(\tau)\mathbf{m}'^{-1} \end{bmatrix} \tag{6-127}$$

where $\mathbf{J}(\tau)$ is the $n \times n$ matrix of $J_{jk}(\tau)$'s which appear in (6-122). When $\mathbf{J}$ is a constant matrix, that is, when the vector shot noise is a vector white noise, Eqs. (5-109) and (5-113) give the results obtained by Wang and Uhlenbeck.‡

Extension to the case in which the excitation vector is a *filtered* shot-noise vector is immediate. By a filtered shot-noise vector, we mean that the excitation vector $\mathbf{G}(t)$ is obtainable from

$$\mathbf{QG}(t) = \mathbf{S}(t) \tag{6-128}$$

and a set of initial conditions concerning $\mathbf{G}(t)$. Here $\mathbf{Q}$ is an $n \times n$ matrix of differential operators, which can be written specifically as

$$\mathbf{Q} = \sum_{l=0}^{N} \mathbf{L}_l \frac{d^l}{dt^l} \tag{6-129}$$

where the $\mathbf{L}_l$ are constant matrices. The matrix equation of motion is therefore

$$\mathbf{Qm\ddot{X}} + \mathbf{Qc\dot{X}} + \mathbf{QkX} = \mathbf{S} \tag{6-130}$$

Denote

$$Y_j = X_j$$

$$Y_{j+n} = \frac{d}{dt} Y_j = \dot{X}_j$$

$$Y_{j+2n} = \frac{d}{dt} Y_{j+n} = \ddot{X}_j \tag{6-131}$$

$$\cdots \cdots \cdots \cdots \cdots$$

$$Y_{j+(M-1)n} = \frac{d}{dt} Y_{j+(M-2)n} = \frac{d^{M-1}}{dt^{M-1}} X_j$$

$$j = 1, 2, \ldots, n; M = N + 2$$

‡ M. C. Wang and G. E. Uhlenbeck, On the Theory of the Brownian Motion II, *Rev. Mod. Phys.*, **17**(2, 3):323–342 (1945). Collected in N. Wax (ed.), "Selected Papers on Noise and Stochastic Processes," Dover, New York, 1954.

Equation (6-130) can be rearranged to read

$$\mathbf{P}_M \frac{d}{dt} \left\{ \begin{matrix} Y_{1+(M-1)n} \\ Y_{2+(M-1)n} \\ \cdot \\ \cdot \\ \cdot \\ Y_{Mn} \end{matrix} \right\} + \mathbf{P}_{M-1} \left\{ \begin{matrix} Y_{1+(M-1)n} \\ Y_{2+(M-1)n} \\ \cdot \\ \cdot \\ \cdot \\ Y_{Mn} \end{matrix} \right\}$$

$$+ \mathbf{P}_{M-2} \left\{ \begin{matrix} Y_{1+(M-2)n} \\ Y_{2+(M-2)n} \\ \cdot \\ \cdot \\ \cdot \\ Y_{(M-1)n} \end{matrix} \right\} + \cdots + \mathbf{P}_0 \left\{ \begin{matrix} Y_1 \\ Y_2 \\ \cdot \\ \cdot \\ \cdot \\ Y_n \end{matrix} \right\} = \left\{ \begin{matrix} S_1 \\ S_2 \\ \cdot \\ \cdot \\ \cdot \\ S_n \end{matrix} \right\} \qquad (6\text{-}132)$$

Combination of Eqs. (6-131) and (6-132) results again in a form the same as Eq. (5-79a). It suffices to note that in the present case

$$\mathbf{g} = \begin{bmatrix} 0 & I & 0 & \cdots & 0 \\ 0 & 0 & I & \cdots & 0 \\ \cdot & \cdot & \cdot & \cdot & \cdot \\ \cdot & \cdot & \cdot & \cdot & \cdot \\ \cdot & \cdot & \cdot & \cdot & \cdot \\ 0 & 0 & 0 & \cdots & I \\ -\mathbf{P}_M^{-1}\mathbf{P}_0 & -\mathbf{P}_M^{-1}\mathbf{P}_1 & -\mathbf{P}_M^{-1}\mathbf{P}_2 & \cdots & -\mathbf{P}_M^{-1}\mathbf{P}_{M-1} \end{bmatrix} \qquad (6\text{-}133)$$

which is an $(Mn) \times (Mn)$ matrix since the $\mathbf{Y}$ vector is (Mn)-dimensional, and the forcing column $\mathbf{F}$ is

$$\mathbf{F} = \left\{ \begin{matrix} 0 \\ \hline 0 \\ \hline \cdot \\ \cdot \\ \cdot \\ \hline 0 \\ \hline \mathbf{P}_M^{-1}\mathbf{S} \end{matrix} \right\} \qquad (6\text{-}134)$$

We have assumed, of course, that $\mathbf{P}_M^{-1}$ exists. Equations (5-109) and (5-113) remain valid with $\mathbf{g}$ specified in Eq. (6-133) and $\mathbf{B}$ given by

$$
\mathbf{B} = \begin{bmatrix}
0 & 0 & \cdots & 0 \\
0 & 0 & \cdots & 0 \\
\cdot & \cdot & \cdot & \cdot \\
\cdot & \cdot & \cdot & \cdot \\
\cdot & \cdot & \cdot & \cdot \\
\cdot & \cdot & \cdot & \cdot \\
0 & 0 & \cdots & \mathbf{P}_M^{-1}\mathbf{J}(\tau)\mathbf{P}_M'^{-1}
\end{bmatrix}
\qquad (6\text{-}135)
$$

EXERCISES

6-1. Let the heavy block supported by a uniform massless cantilever beam, shown in Fig. 6.1, be excited by a vertical white noise which passes through the centroid of the block. Compute the variance of the stationary state deflection $X_1(t)$ at the end of the cantilever beam. Use the frequency response function extracted from Eq. (6-32).

6-2. For the same structure and the same excitation as described in Exercise 6-1, find the variance of the stationary state rotation $X_2(t)$ at the end of the cantilever beam.

6-3. Determine the frequency response functions for the moment and the shear at the clamped end of the cantilever beam, as shown in Fig. 6.1. The excitation is assumed to be a vertical force passing through the centroid of the heavy block. Use the method of transfer matrices.

6-4. Outline the procedure and give necessary formulas for computing the generalized spectral density and the covariance function of the random fixed end moment in Exercise 6-3. Assume that the excitation is nonstationary with a known generalized spectral density and a known covariance function.

6-5. As shown in Fig. 6.15, N particles with equal masses are supported at equal distances by a massless taut string.

Fig. 6.15.

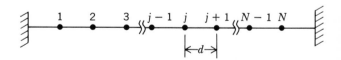

Let m be the mass of each particle, c the damping coefficient, d the distance between particles, and T the tension in the string, which is assumed to be unchanged for small particle deflections. The equations of motion are given by

$$
m\ddot{W}_j + c\dot{W}_j - \frac{T}{d}(W_{j-1} - 2W_j + W_{j+1}) = F_j(t) \qquad j = 1, 2, \ldots, N
$$

$$
W_0 = W_{N+1} = 0
$$

Determine the frequency response functions $H_{jk}(\omega)$ and the impulse response functions $h_{jk}(t)$ by using a finite-difference approach.

6-6. In Exercise 6-5, if the excitations F_j are uncorrelated and if each of the excitations is stationary with a common spectral density function $\Phi_{FF}(\omega)$, find the spectral densities of the responses W_j.

6-7. A two-degrees-of-freedom system is shown in Fig. 6.16. The exciting forces are random Gaussian shot noise, and

$$E[F_j(t)] = 0 \qquad j = 1, 2$$
$$E[F_j(t_1)F_k(t_2)] = J_{jk}(t_1)\,\delta(t_1 - t_2) \qquad j, k = 1, 2$$

Derive the Fokker-Planck equation for the joint transition probability density for the random displacements and velocities $X_1(t)$, $X_2(t)$, $\dot{X}_1(t)$, $\dot{X}_2(t)$ of the two masses.

Fig. 6.16.

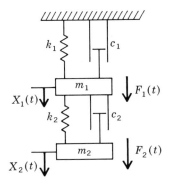

6-8.‡ Let the excitations $F_j(t)$ in Exercise 6-5 be Gaussian shot noise, and
$$E[F_j(t)] = 0$$

$$E[F_j(t_1)F_k(t_2)] = J_{jk}(t_1)\,\delta(t_1 - t_2)$$

Derive the Fokker-Planck equation for the joint transition probability density for the random displacements W_j and the random velocities $\dot{W}_j$.

‡ Compare with M. R. Spiegal, The Random Vibrations of a String, *Quart. Appl. Math.*, **X**(1):25–33 (1952).]

7 | LINEAR CONTINUOUS STRUCTURES

7.1 / A GENERAL ANALYTICAL FRAMEWORK

A linear continuous structure assumed to be a time-invariant deterministic system can be characterized by either the *impulse influence function* $h(\mathbf{r}, \varrho; t)$ or the *frequency influence function* $H(\mathbf{r}, \varrho; \omega)$, where $\mathbf{r}$ and ϱ are position vectors belonging to an uncountable set $\Re$ which is the domain of the structure. These functions are generalizations of the matrix of impulse response functions and the matrix of frequency response functions, respectively which are discussed in Sec. 6.1. Thus the impulse influence function describes the motion at location $\mathbf{r}$ due to a unit impulse applied at location ϱ at time $t = 0$, assuming that the structure is at rest prior to the excitation. The frequency influence function is, again, based on the steady-state response due to a single sinusoidal excitation. Let this excitation be $A \exp(i\omega t)$, which is applied at location ϱ. Then the steady-state response at location $\mathbf{r}$ may be written as

$$A H(\mathbf{r}, \varrho; \omega) \exp(i\omega t)$$

Therefore, the frequency influence function is simply the ratio (generally complex-valued) between such a response and such an excitation. The absolute value of the frequency influence function is the ratio of the amplitudes, and the negative value of the phase angle of this function is the time lag between the excitation and the trailing response, times the frequency ω. Again, we limit our attention to stable structures, that is, those structures whose motions gradually diminish after their excitations have been terminated. That a continuous structure is a system with an uncountably infinite number of degrees of freedom is reflected in the fact that $\Re$ is uncountable. Naturally,

$$h(\mathbf{r}, \varrho; t) = 0 \quad \text{for either } t < 0, \text{ or } \mathbf{r} \notin \Re, \text{ or } \varrho \notin \Re$$
$$H(\mathbf{r}, \varrho; \omega) = 0 \quad \text{for either } \mathbf{r} \notin \Re \text{ or } \varrho \notin \Re \tag{7-1}$$

Analogous to the case of a finite number of degrees of freedom, the impulse influence function and the frequency influence function are related by

$$h(\mathbf{r}, \varrho; t) = \frac{1}{2\pi} \int_{-\infty}^{\infty} H(\mathbf{r}, \varrho; \omega) \exp(i\omega t) \, d\omega$$
$$H(\mathbf{r}, \varrho; \omega) = \int_{-\infty}^{\infty} h(\mathbf{r}, \varrho; t) \exp(-i\omega t) \, dt \tag{7-2}$$

Let the random excitation be $P(\mathbf{r}, t)$ and denote the random response by $W(\mathbf{r}, t)$. If the initial conditions $W(\mathbf{r}, 0)$ and $\dot{W}(\mathbf{r}, 0)$ are known, then by invoking the superposition principle in a linear problem we may consider that the structure is at rest prior to the commencement of the excitation; that is, $W(\mathbf{r}, 0) = \dot{W}(\mathbf{r}, 0) = 0$. Then with the knowledge of the impulse influence function we find that the nth moment function and the nth cumulant function of the response are, respectively,

$$E[W(\mathbf{r}_1, t_1) \cdots W(\mathbf{r}_n, t_n)]$$
$$= \int_0^{t_1} \cdots \int_0^{t_n} \int_{\mathfrak{R}} \cdots \int_{\mathfrak{R}} h(\mathbf{r}_1, \varrho_1; t_1 - \tau_1) \cdots h(\mathbf{r}_n, \varrho_n; t_n - \tau_n)$$
$$E[P(\varrho_1, \tau_1) \cdots P(\varrho_n, \tau_n)] \, d\varrho_1 \cdots d\varrho_n \, d\tau_1 \cdots d\tau_n$$
$$\kappa_n[W(\mathbf{r}_1, t_1) \cdots W(\mathbf{r}_n, t_n)] \qquad\qquad (7\text{-}3)$$
$$= \int_0^{t_1} \cdots \int_0^{t_n} \int_{\mathfrak{R}} \cdots \int_{\mathfrak{R}} h(\mathbf{r}_1, \varrho_1; t_1 - \tau_1) \cdots h(\mathbf{r}_n, \varrho_n; t_n - \tau_n)$$
$$\kappa_n[P(\varrho_1, \tau_1) \cdots P(\varrho_n, \tau_n)] \, d\varrho_1 \cdots d\varrho_n \, d\tau_1 \cdots d\tau_n$$

These functions exist if the respective multifold Riemann integrals on the right-hand sides exist, and each of these functions is equal to zero if any of the $\mathbf{r}_j$ is not in $\mathfrak{R}$ or if any of the t_j is negative, in view of the first restriction specified in (7-1). In particular, the first and second cumulant functions, which are identical to the mean and the covariance function, respectively, are

$$E[W(\mathbf{r}, t)] = \int_0^t \int_{\mathfrak{R}} h(\mathbf{r}, \varrho; t - \tau) E[P(\varrho, \tau)] \, d\varrho \, d\tau$$
$$\kappa_{WW}(\mathbf{r}_1, t_1; \mathbf{r}_2, t_2) = \int_0^{t_1} \int_0^{t_2} \int_{\mathfrak{R}} \int_{\mathfrak{R}} h(\mathbf{r}_1, \varrho_1; t_1 - \tau_1) h(\mathbf{r}_2, \varrho_2; t_2 - \tau_2) \qquad (7\text{-}4)$$
$$\kappa_{PP}(\varrho_1, \tau_1; \varrho_2, \tau_2) \, d\varrho_1 \, d\varrho_2 \, d\tau_1 \, d\tau_2$$

Let us introduce a generalized cross spectral density of the response,

$$\hat{\Phi}_{WW}(\mathbf{r}_1, \omega_1; \mathbf{r}_2, \omega_2) = \frac{1}{(2\pi)^2} \int_{-\infty}^{\infty} \int_{-\infty}^{\infty} \kappa_{WW}(\mathbf{r}_1, t_1; \mathbf{r}_2, t_2)$$
$$\exp\left[-i(\omega_1 t_1 - \omega_2 t_2)\right] dt_1 \, dt_2 \qquad (7\text{-}5)$$

and a similarly defined generalized cross spectral density of the excitation. We obtain, similar to Eq. (6-5), the frequency-domain relation

$$\hat{\Phi}_{WW}(\mathbf{r}_1, \omega_1; \mathbf{r}_2, \omega_2)$$
$$= \int_{\mathfrak{R}} \int_{\mathfrak{R}} \hat{\Phi}_{PP}(\varrho_1, \omega_1; \varrho_2, \omega_2) H(\mathbf{r}_1, \varrho_1; \omega_1) H^*(\mathbf{r}_2, \varrho_2; \omega_2) \, d\rho_1 \, d\rho_2 \qquad (7\text{-}6)$$

The covariance function of the response can be recovered, at least in principle, from an inverse transformation of Eq. (7-6). Equations (7-3), (7-4), and (7-6) are useful for the determination of the transient statistical properties of the response to arbitrary random excitations. The validity of Eq. (7-6) is, of course, subject to the additional requirement that the generalized cross spectral densities involved in this equation exist.

If the excitation is weakly stationary, then

$$\phi_{PP}(\varrho_1, \tau_1; \varrho_2, \tau_2) = R_{PP}(\varrho_1, \varrho_2; \tau_1 - \tau_2)$$
$$\kappa_{PP}(\varrho_1, \tau_1; \varrho_2, \tau_2) = \Gamma_{PP}(\varrho_1, \varrho_2; \tau_1 - \tau_2) \qquad (7\text{-}7)$$

where ϕ_{PP} denotes the correlation function of $P(\varrho, \tau)$. Under the usual restrictions of a Fourier representation, we may write

$$R_{PP}(\varrho_1, \varrho_2; \tau_1 - \tau_2) = \int_{-\infty}^{\infty} \Phi_{PP}(\varrho_1, \varrho_2; \omega) \exp\left[i\omega(\tau_1 - \tau_2)\right] d\omega \qquad (7\text{-}8)$$

where

$$\Phi_{PP}(\varrho_1, \varrho_2; \omega) = \frac{1}{2\pi} \int_{-\infty}^{\infty} R_{PP}(\varrho_1, \varrho_2; u) \exp\left(-i\omega u\right) du \qquad (7\text{-}9)$$

is the cross spectral density of the weakly stationary excitation. If Eq. (7-8) is substituted into the expression for the correlation function of the response, we have

$$\phi_{WW}(\mathbf{r}_1, t_1; \mathbf{r}_2, t_2) = \int_0^{t_1} \int_0^{t_2} \int_{\mathfrak{R}} \int_{\mathfrak{R}} h(\mathbf{r}_1, \varrho_1; t_1 - \tau_1) h(\mathbf{r}_2, \varrho_2; t_2 - \tau_2)$$
$$R_{PP}(\varrho_1, \varrho_2; \tau_1 - \tau_2)\, d\varrho_1\, d\varrho_2\, d\tau_1\, d\tau_2 \qquad (7\text{-}10)$$

Thus we may obtain, analogous to Eq. (6-10),

$$\phi_{WW}(\mathbf{r}_1, t_1; \mathbf{r}_2, t_2)$$
$$= \int_{-\infty}^{\infty} \int_{\mathfrak{R}} \int_{\mathfrak{R}} \Phi_{PP}(\varrho_1, \varrho_2; \omega) \mathfrak{IC}(\mathbf{r}_1, \varrho_1; \omega, t_1) \mathfrak{IC}^*(\mathbf{r}_2, \varrho_2; \omega, t_2)$$
$$\exp\left[i\omega(t_1 - t_2)\right] d\varrho_1\, d\varrho_2\, d\omega \qquad (7\text{-}11)$$

where

$$\mathfrak{IC}(\mathbf{r}, \varrho; \omega, t) = \int_0^t h(\mathbf{r}, \varrho; u) \exp\left(-i\omega u\right) du$$
$$= \int_{-\infty}^{t} h(\mathbf{r}, \varrho; u) \exp\left(-i\omega u\right) du \qquad (7\text{-}12)$$

and $\mathfrak{IC}(\mathbf{r}, \varrho; \omega, \infty) = H(\mathbf{r}, \varrho; \omega)$. Equation (7-11) is useful for computing the transient nonstationary response under weakly stationary excitations. As t_1 and t_2 approach infinity, but the difference $t_1 - t_2$ is kept finite, Eq. (7-11) yields the correlation function of the weakly stationary response,

$$R_{WW}(\mathbf{r}_1, \mathbf{r}_2; t_1 - t_2)$$
$$= \int_{-\infty}^{\infty} \int_{\mathfrak{R}} \int_{\mathfrak{R}} \Phi_{PP}(\varrho_1, \varrho_2; \omega) H(\mathbf{r}_1, \varrho_1; \omega)$$
$$H^*(\mathbf{r}_2, \varrho_2; \omega) \exp\left[i\omega(t_1 - t_2)\right] d\varrho_1\, d\varrho_2\, d\omega \qquad (7\text{-}13)$$

If we introduce the cross spectral density of the weakly stationary response, defined in the same way as in Eq. (7-9), we see that

$$\Phi_{WW}(\mathbf{r}_1, \mathbf{r}_2; \omega)$$
$$= \int_{\mathfrak{R}} \int_{\mathfrak{R}} \Phi_{PP}(\varrho_1, \varrho_2; \omega) H(\mathbf{r}_1, \varrho_1; \omega) H^*(\mathbf{r}_2, \varrho_2; \omega)\, d\varrho_1\, d\varrho_2 \qquad (7\text{-}14)$$

Equations (7-13) and (7-14) are applicable after the weakly stationary excitation has operated for a sufficiently long time that the transient portion of the response is adequately damped out.

In certain engineering applications, the forcing field can be assumed to be weakly homogeneous in space. Then the correlation function $\phi_{PP}(\varrho_1, \tau_1; \varrho_2, \tau_2)$ of the excitation is a function of the difference vector $\varrho_1 - \varrho_2$. The same statement can also be made for the generalized cross spectral density or the cross spectral density, as the case may be. Consider, first, an excitation which is weakly stationary in time and weakly homogeneous in space. Denote

$$\Phi_{PP}(\varrho_1, \varrho_2; \omega) = \Theta_{PP}(\varrho_1 - \varrho_2; \omega) \qquad (7\text{-}15)$$

Then, again, under the usual restrictions of a Fourier representation we may write

$$\Theta_{PP}(\varrho_1 - \varrho_2; \omega) = \int \Psi_{PP}(\mathbf{k}; \omega) \exp\left[i\mathbf{k} \cdot (\varrho_1 - \varrho_2)\right] d\mathbf{k} \qquad (7\text{-}16)$$

where $\mathbf{k} \cdot (\varrho_1 - \varrho_2)$ denotes the dot product of the two vectors, and the integration is over the entire range of $\mathbf{k}$. The vector $\mathbf{k}$ is known as a *wave-number vector*. The inversion of Eq. (7-16) is

$$\Psi_{PP}(\mathbf{k}; \omega) = \frac{1}{(2\pi)^\alpha} \int \Theta_{PP}(\mathbf{u}; \omega) \exp\left(-i\mathbf{k} \cdot \mathbf{u}\right) d\mathbf{u} \qquad (7\text{-}17)$$

where $\mathbf{u} = \varrho_1 - \varrho_2$, α is the number of dimensions in $\mathbf{k}$ (or in $\mathbf{u}$), and the integral covers the range of $\mathbf{u}$.

Recall that the spectral density of a time-parametered weakly stationary random process describes the energy distribution over the frequency domain ω. It is clear that $\Psi_{PP}(\mathbf{k}; \omega)$ gives the energy distribution of a time-and-space-parametered weakly stationary and weakly homogeneous random process in the product domain of $\mathbf{k}$ and ω. While the frequency ω is one-dimensional, $\mathbf{k}$ is generally three-dimensional. A given $\mathbf{k}$ value corresponds to a spatial sinusoidal variation in the direction of $\mathbf{k}$ and with a wavelength $2\pi/|k|$, hence the name wave number. It is clear that the function $\Psi_{PP}(\mathbf{k}; \omega)$ is real and nonnegative, and it is an even function of ω and of any component of $\mathbf{k}$. If the cross spectral density of the excitation in Eq. (7-14) is replaced by its alternative form of Eq. (7-16), the integrations on ϱ_1 and ϱ_2 yield

$$\Phi_{WW}(\mathbf{r}_1, \mathbf{r}_2; \omega) = \int \Psi_{PP}(\mathbf{k}; \omega) G(\mathbf{r}_1, \mathbf{k}, \omega) G^*(\mathbf{r}_2, \mathbf{k}, \omega) \, d\mathbf{k} \qquad (7\text{-}18)$$

where

$$\begin{aligned}
G(\mathbf{r}, \mathbf{k}, \omega) &= \int_{\mathcal{R}} H(\mathbf{r}, \varrho; \omega) \exp\left(i\mathbf{k} \cdot \varrho\right) d\varrho \\
&= \int_{-\infty}^{\infty} \int_{\mathcal{R}} h(\mathbf{r}, \varrho; u) \exp\left[-i(\omega u - \mathbf{k} \cdot \varrho)\right] du \, d\varrho \qquad (7\text{-}19)
\end{aligned}$$

The function $G(\mathbf{r}, \mathbf{k}, \omega)$ is merely a characteristic of a structure; and, for each structure, it can be evaluated once and for all. This function will be called the *sensitivity function* since it represents the sensitivity of a structure, as manifested at point $\mathbf{r}$, to a harmonic excitation having a frequency ω and a sinusoidal spacewise variation specified by a wave-number vector $\mathbf{k}$.

In the case of a time nonstationary and spatially nonhomogeneous excitation, it is sometimes useful to employ the relations

$$\hat{\Phi}_{PP}(\varrho_1, \omega_1; \varrho_2, \omega_2)$$
$$= \iint \hat{\Psi}_{PP}(\mathbf{k}_1, \omega_1; \mathbf{k}_2, \omega_2) \exp\left[i(\mathbf{k}_1 \cdot \varrho_1 - \mathbf{k}_2 \cdot \varrho_2)\right] d\mathbf{k}_1 \, d\mathbf{k}_2 \quad (7\text{-}20)$$

and

$$\hat{\Psi}_{PP}(\mathbf{k}_1, \omega_1; \mathbf{k}_2, \omega_2)$$
$$= \frac{1}{(2\pi)^{2\alpha}} \int_{\mathfrak{R}} \int_{\mathfrak{R}} \hat{\Phi}_{PP}(\varrho_1, \omega_1; \varrho_2, \omega_2) \exp\left[-i(\mathbf{k}_1 \cdot \varrho_1 - \mathbf{k}_2 \cdot \varrho_2)\right] d\varrho_1 \, d\varrho_2$$
$$= \frac{1}{(2\pi)^{2\alpha+2}} \int_{-\infty}^{\infty} \int_{-\infty}^{\infty} \int_{\mathfrak{R}} \int_{\mathfrak{R}} \kappa_{PP}(\varrho_1, \tau_1; \varrho_2, \tau_2)$$
$$\exp\left[-i(\omega_1\tau_1 - \omega_2\tau_2 + \mathbf{k}_1 \cdot \varrho_1 - \mathbf{k}_2 \cdot \varrho_2)\right] d\varrho_1 \, d\varrho_2 \, d\tau_1 \, d\tau_2 \quad (7\text{-}21)$$

provided that the transformations in (7-20) and (7-21) are legitimate. Then Eq. (7-6) becomes

$$\hat{\Phi}_{WW}(\mathbf{r}_1, \omega_1; \mathbf{r}_2, \omega_2)$$
$$= \iint \hat{\Psi}_{PP}(\mathbf{k}_1, \omega_1; \mathbf{k}_2, \omega_2) G(\mathbf{r}_1, \mathbf{k}_1, \omega_1) G^*(\mathbf{r}_2, \mathbf{k}_2, \omega_2) \, d\mathbf{k}_1 \, d\mathbf{k}_2 \quad (7\text{-}22)$$

Developments for the case of a time stationary but spatially nonhomogeneous excitation and for the case of a time nonstationary but spatially homogeneous excitation are similar.

7.2 / THE NORMAL-MODE APPROACH

If the required statistical properties of the excitation are known, then to compute the response statistical properties by use of the above analytical framework we must first determine the impulse influence function $h(\mathbf{r}, \varrho; t)$ or the frequency influence function $H(\mathbf{r}, \varrho; \omega)$. This task may or may not be simple, depending largely on the type of structure in question. As is true in the case of a linear structure with finitely many degrees of freedom (Chap. 6), the existence of normal modes is not always guaranteed for a linear continuous structure if damping is present. This will be demonstrated below. We anticipate that if the normal modes do indeed exist, the determination of the impulse influence function and the frequency influence function of the structure will be simple. In the present section we shall confine ourselves to this class of structure.

Let the equation of motion be

$$m\ddot{W} + c\dot{W} + \mathfrak{L}(W) = P \quad (7\text{-}23)$$

where m and c in general are functions of the spatial coordinates, and $\mathfrak{L}$ is a linear differential operator in the spatial variables. For example,

$$
\mathcal{L} = \begin{cases} -T\left(\dfrac{\partial^2}{\partial x^2}\right) & \text{for a taut string} \\[2ex] D\left(\dfrac{\partial^4}{\partial x^4} + 2\dfrac{\partial^4}{\partial x^2\,\partial y^2} + \dfrac{\partial^4}{\partial y^4}\right) & \text{for a uniform flat plate} \end{cases} \tag{7-24}
$$

In the first of (7-24), T is the tensile force in the string; and in the second of (7-24), D is the bending rigidity of the plate. The impulse influence function $h(\mathbf{r}, \varrho; t)$ satisfies the equation

$$
m\ddot{h} + c\dot{h} + \mathcal{L}(h) = \delta(\mathbf{r} - \varrho)\,\delta(t) \tag{7-25}
$$

and the restriction that it vanish for either $t < 0$, or $\mathbf{r} \notin \Re$, or $\varrho \notin \Re$, as stated in the first of (7-1). The right-hand side of Eq. (7-25) indicates that a unit impulse is applied to the structure at the location $\mathbf{r} = \varrho$ and at time $t = 0$. Try a solution to Eq. (7-25) in the form of

$$
h(\mathbf{r}, \varrho; t) = \sum_{j=1}^{\infty} a_j(\varrho; t) f_j(\mathbf{r}) \tag{7-26}
$$

Substituting Eq. (7-26) into Eq. (7-25), we have

$$
m\sum_{j=1}^{\infty} \ddot{a}_j f_j + c\sum_{j=1}^{\infty} \dot{a}_j f_j + \sum_{j=1}^{\infty} a_j \mathcal{L}(f_j) = \delta(\mathbf{r} - \varrho)\,\delta(t) \tag{7-25a}
$$

If the $f_j(\mathbf{r})$ are the normal modes corresponding to the undamped free vibrations of the structure, then they satisfy the equation

$$
m\ddot{b}_j f_j + b_j \mathcal{L}(f_j) = 0 \tag{7-27}
$$

Since the undamped free motion in each normal mode is simple harmonic,

$$
\ddot{b}_j = -\omega_j^2 b_j \tag{7-28}
$$

The combination of Eqs. (7-27) and (7-28) yields

$$
m\omega_j^2 f_j = \mathcal{L}(f_j) \tag{7-29}
$$

Equation (7-29) states an important property of the normal modes, i.e., when a normal mode is operated upon by the linear differential operator in the spatial variables, $\mathcal{L}$, the result is the same normal mode multiplied by the mass density m and the squared value of the corresponding natural frequency. If this property is used in Eq. (7-25a), we obtain

$$
m\sum_{j=1}^{\infty} \ddot{a}_j f_j + c\sum_{j=1}^{\infty} \dot{a}_j f_j + m\sum_{j=1}^{\infty} a_j \omega_j^2 f_j = \delta(\mathbf{r} - \varrho)\,\delta(t) \tag{7-25b}
$$

Another important property of the normal modes is the orthogonality relation

$$\int_{\Re} m f_j(\mathbf{r}) f_l(\mathbf{r})\, d\mathbf{r} = \begin{cases} m_j & \text{if } j = l \\ 0 & \text{if } j \neq l \end{cases} \tag{7-30}$$

This relation is true if the governing differential equation (7-29) and the required boundary conditions constitute a *self-adjoint* eigenvalue problem,‡ which we shall assume to be the case here. The constant m_j is called the generalized mass in the jth mode. The orthogonality property Eq. (7-30) can be used to separate different modes in Eq. (7-25b), if and only if the following is also true:

$$\int_{\Re} c f_j(\mathbf{r}) f_l(\mathbf{r})\, d\mathbf{r} = \begin{cases} c_j & \text{if } j = l \\ 0 & \text{if } j \neq l \end{cases} \tag{7-31}$$

where c_j is called the generalized damping in the jth mode. The condition that the integral is zero for different normal modes is analogous to the condition of being able to simultaneously diagonalize the matrices $\mathbf{m}^{-1}\mathbf{k}$ and $\mathbf{m}^{-1}\mathbf{c}$ in a system with a finite number of degrees of freedom. This condition is satisfied, for example, when c is proportional to m. In practical applications, the normal-mode approach is widely used provided that the structure is lightly damped, in which case we simply disregard the coupled damping in different modes; i.e., for $j \neq l$, we substitute zero for the integral even when it is not zero.

If Eqs. (7-30) and (7-31) are both valid, Eq. (7-25b) then reduces to a system of uncoupled equations

$$m_j \ddot{a}_j + c_j \dot{a}_j + m_j \omega_j^2 a_j = f_j(\varrho)\, \delta(t) \tag{7-32}$$

The solution to Eq. (7-32), which satisfies the restrictions $a_j = 0$ for $t < 0$ or $\varrho \notin \Re$, is known to be¶

$$a_j = \begin{cases} \dfrac{f_j(\varrho)}{m_j \omega_{jd}} \exp\left(-\zeta_j \omega_j t\right) \sin \omega_{jd} t & \varrho \in \Re \text{ and } t \geq 0 \\ 0 & \varrho \notin \Re \text{ or } t < 0 \end{cases} \tag{7-33}$$

where $\zeta_j = c_j / (2 m_j \omega_j)$ is the ratio of the damping to the critical damping in the jth mode, and $\omega_{jd} = (1 - \zeta_j^2)^{\frac{1}{2}} \omega_j$ is the damped natural frequency in the jth mode. More simply,

$$a_j = \begin{cases} f_j(\varrho) h_j(t) & \varrho \in \Re \\ 0 & \varrho \notin \Re \end{cases} \tag{7-33a}$$

where $h_j(t)$ may be called the impulse response function in the jth mode.

‡ See, for example, R. L. Bisplinghoff and H. Ashley, "Principles of Aeroelasticity," p. 50, Wiley, New York, 1962.

¶ Compare with Eq. (5-10a).

Substituting (7-33a) into Eq. (7-26), we find that the impulse influence function of the entire structure is

$$h(\mathbf{r}, \boldsymbol{\varrho}; t) = \begin{cases} \sum_{j=1}^{\infty} f_j(\mathbf{r}) f_j(\boldsymbol{\varrho}) h_j(t) & \mathbf{r} \text{ and } \boldsymbol{\varrho} \in \mathfrak{R} \\ 0 & \mathbf{r} \text{ or } \boldsymbol{\varrho} \notin \mathfrak{R} \end{cases} \qquad (7\text{-}34)$$

The frequency influence function is obtained from the transformation

$$H(\mathbf{r}, \boldsymbol{\varrho}; \omega) = \int_{-\infty}^{\infty} h(\mathbf{r}, \boldsymbol{\varrho}; t) \exp(-i\omega t)\, dt$$

$$= \begin{cases} \sum_{j=1}^{\infty} f_j(\mathbf{r}) f_j(\rho) H_j(\omega) & \mathbf{r} \text{ and } \boldsymbol{\varrho} \in \mathfrak{R} \\ 0 & \mathbf{r} \text{ or } \boldsymbol{\varrho} \notin \mathfrak{R} \end{cases} \qquad (7\text{-}35)$$

where $H_j(\omega) = m_j^{-1}(\omega_j{}^2 - \omega^2 + 2i\zeta_j\omega\omega_j)^{-1}$ may be called the frequency response function in the jth mode. When the transient response of a structure due to a weakly stationary excitation is of interest, the function $\mathfrak{K}(\mathbf{r}, \boldsymbol{\varrho}; \omega, t)$ as defined in Eq. (7-12) is required. The indicated integration yields

$$\mathfrak{K}(\mathbf{r}, \boldsymbol{\varrho}; \omega, t) = \begin{cases} \sum_{j=1}^{\infty} f_j(\mathbf{r}) f_j(\boldsymbol{\varrho}) H_j(\omega) \left[1 - \exp(-\zeta_j\omega_j t - i\omega t) \right. \\ \qquad \left. \left(\cos \omega_{jd} t + \frac{\zeta_j\omega_j + i\omega}{\omega_{jd}} \sin \omega_{jd} t \right) \right] & \mathbf{r} \text{ and } \boldsymbol{\varrho} \in \mathfrak{R} \\ 0 & \mathbf{r} \text{ or } \boldsymbol{\varrho} \notin \mathfrak{R} \end{cases}$$
$$(7\text{-}36)$$

As expected, $\mathfrak{K}(\mathbf{r}, \boldsymbol{\varrho}; \omega, t)$ approaches to $H(\mathbf{r}, \boldsymbol{\varrho}; \omega)$ as t increases.

The sensitivity function obtained from an integral transformation of Eq. (7-35) is simply

$$G(\mathbf{r}, \mathbf{k}, \omega) = \begin{cases} \sum_{j=1}^{\infty} f_j(\mathbf{r}) S_j(\mathbf{k}) H_j(\omega) & \mathbf{r} \in \mathfrak{R}. \\ 0 & \mathbf{r} \notin \mathfrak{R} \end{cases} \qquad (7\text{-}37)$$

where

$$S_j(\mathbf{k}) = \int_{\mathfrak{R}} f_j(\boldsymbol{\varrho}) \exp(i\mathbf{k} \cdot \boldsymbol{\varrho})\, d\boldsymbol{\varrho} \qquad (7\text{-}38)$$

The normal-mode approach in the study of the response of continuous structures under random loading dates back to the work by Van Lear and Uhlenbeck[‡] in 1931. Recent authors using this approach include Lyon, Eringen, Thomson and Barton, Powell, Samuels, Dyer, Bogdanoff

‡ G. A. Van Lear, Jr., and G. E. Uhlenbeck, The Brownian Motion of Strings and Elastic Rods, *Phys. Rev.*, **38**:1583–1598 (1931).

and Goldberg, and Lin, to name only a few.‡ Each of these authors placed emphasis on different aspects of the general problem. The work by Powell was aimed at the evaluation of the response of aircraft panels to jet-engine noise, and it has attracted the attention of aeronautical engineers who are charged with the design of airplanes powered by jet engines. In view of its practical interest, we shall deduce Powell's central result from the more general formulation outlined above.

The excitation field considered by Powell is weakly stationary; therefore, Eq. (7-11) applies. Introduce the integral

$$I_{jk}(\omega) = \int_{\Re} \int_{\Re} \Phi_{PP}(\varrho_1, \varrho_2; \omega) f_j(\varrho_1) f_k(\varrho_2) \, d\varrho_1 \, d\varrho_2 \qquad (7\text{-}39)$$

which is the cross spectral density of the generalized forces in the modes j and k. A combination of Eqs. (7-36) and (7-11) then gives

$$\phi_{WW}(\mathbf{r}_1, t_1; \mathbf{r}_2, t_2)$$

$$= \int_{-\infty}^{\infty} \sum_{j,k=1}^{\infty} f_j(\mathbf{r}_1) f_k(\mathbf{r}_2) H_j(\omega) H_k^*(\omega) I_{jk}(\omega)$$

$$\left\{ 1 - \exp\left[-\zeta_j \omega_j t_1 - \zeta_k \omega_k t_2 - i\omega(t_1 - t_2) \right] \left(\cos \omega_{jd} t_1 \right.\right.$$

$$\left. + \frac{\zeta_j \omega_j + i\omega}{\omega_{jd}} \sin \omega_{jd} t_1 \right) \left(\cos \omega_{kd} t_2 + \frac{\zeta_k \omega_k - i\omega}{\omega_{kd}} \sin \omega_{kd} t_2 \right) \right\}$$

$$\exp\left[i\omega(t_1 - t_2) \right] d\omega \qquad (7\text{-}40)$$

This is the crosscorrelation function of the response at locations $\mathbf{r}_1$ and $\mathbf{r}_2$ in the transient nonstationary state. As t_1 and t_2 increase but $t_1 - t_2$ is kept finite, the response tends to be weakly stationary. Then Eq. (7-40) reduces to

$$R_{WW}(\mathbf{r}_1, \mathbf{r}_2; t_1 - t_2) = \int_{-\infty}^{\infty} \sum_{j,k=1}^{\infty} f_j(\mathbf{r}_1) f_k(\mathbf{r}_2) H_j(\omega) H_k^*(\omega) I_{jk}(\omega)$$

$$\exp\left[i\omega(t_1 - t_2) \right] d\omega \qquad (7\text{-}41)$$

‡ R. H. Lyon, Response of Strings to Random Noise Fields, *J. Acoust. Soc. Am.*, **28**:391–398 (1956); A. C. Eringen, Response of Beams and Plates to Random Loads, *J. Appl. Mech.*, **24**:46–52 (1957); W. T. Thomson and M. V. Barton, The Response of Mechanical Systems to Random Excitations, *J. Appl. Mech.*, **24**:248–251 (1957); A. Powell, On the Fatigue Failure of Structures Due to Vibrations Excited by Random Pressure Fields, *J. Acoust. Soc. Am.*, **30**:1130–1135 (1958); J. C. Samuels and A. C. Eringen, Response of a Simply Supported Timoshenko Beam to a Purely Random Gaussian Process, *J. Appl. Mech.*, **25**:496–500 (1958); I. Dyer, Response of Plates to a Decaying and Convecting Random Pressure Field, *J. Acoust. Soc. Am.*, **31**:922–928 (1959); J. L. Bogdanoff and J. E. Goldberg, On the Bernoulli-Euler Beam Theory with Random Excitation, *J. Aerospace Sci.*, **27**:371–376 (1960); Y. K. Lin, Nonstationary Response of Continuous Structures to Random Loading, *J. Acoust. Soc. Am.* **35**:222–227 (1963).

Equivalently, the cross spectral density of the response at r_1 and r_2 is

$$\Phi_{WW}(r_1, r_2; \omega) = \sum_{j,k=1}^{\infty} f_j(r_1) f_k(r_2) H_j(\omega) H_k^*(\omega) I_{jk}(\omega) \qquad (7\text{-}42)$$

It is interesting to note that in the special case $r_1 = r_2 = r$ the double sum in Eq. (7-42) is real. This conclusion is based on the observation that $I_{jk}(\omega)$ is hermitian, i.e.,

$$I_{jk}(\omega) = I_{kj}^*(\omega)$$

Therefore, the imaginary parts cancel in Eq. (7-42) when $r_1 = r_2$.

Equation (7-42) is essentially Powell's central result. In his original version, however, the cross spectral density of the generalized forces, $I_{jk}(\omega)$, is modified and normalized to a nondimensional function, called the *joint acceptance*, which, in the present notation, is defined as

$$J_{jk}^2(\omega) = \Re^{-2}[\Phi_{PO}(\omega)]^{-1} I_{jk}(\omega) \exp(-i\omega\tau_{jk}) \qquad (7\text{-}43)$$

where $\Re$ denotes $\int_{\Re} d\varrho$, $\Phi_{PO}(\omega)$ is the spectral density of the forcing field at a reference point O, and τ_{jk} is the difference in response-time lag between the jth and kth modes, i.e.,

$$\tau_{jk} = \frac{1}{\omega}\left(\tan^{-1}\frac{2\zeta_j\omega_j\omega}{\omega_j^2 - \omega^2} - \tan^{-1}\frac{2\zeta_k\omega_k\omega}{\omega_k^2 - \omega^2}\right) \qquad (7\text{-}44)$$

Equation (7-42) can then be written as

$$\Phi_{WW}(r_1, r_2; \omega) = \sum_{j,k=1}^{\infty} f_j(r_1) f_k(r_2) \Re^2 \Phi_{PO}(\omega) J_{jk}^2(\omega) |H_j(\omega)| \, |H_k(\omega)| \qquad (7\text{-}42a)$$

The function $J_{jj}^2(\omega)$ gives the relative effectiveness of a random forcing field in exciting the jth mode, and the function $J_{jk}^2(\omega)$, $j \neq k$, represents the contribution from the coupling effect between the two different modes. The fact that $J_{jk}^2(\omega)$ is generally not zero indicates that the random responses in two different modes are generally dependent on each other.

To further appreciate the relationship between responses in different modes, we note, by a combination of Eqs. (7-9), (7-39), and (7-43), that

$$J_{jk}^2(\omega)\Re^2\Phi_{PO}(\omega)$$
$$= I_{jk}(\omega)\exp(-i\omega\tau_{jk})$$
$$= \frac{1}{2\pi}\int_{\Re}\int_{\Re}\int_{-\infty}^{\infty} f_j(\varrho_1) f_k(\varrho_2) R_{PP}(\varrho_1, \varrho_2; u)\exp[-i\omega(u + \tau_{jk})]$$
$$du \, d\varrho_1 \, d\varrho_2$$
$$= \frac{1}{2\pi}\int_{\Re}\int_{\Re}\int_{-\infty}^{\infty} f_j(\varrho_1) f_k(\varrho_2) R_{PP}(\varrho_1, \varrho_2; v - \tau_{jk})$$
$$\exp(-i\omega v)\, dv \, d\varrho_1 \, d\varrho_2 \qquad (7\text{-}45)$$

Now the integral

$$\tilde{\Phi}_{PP}(\varrho_1, \varrho_2; \omega, \tau_{jk}) = \frac{1}{2\pi} \int_{-\infty}^{\infty} R_{PP}(\varrho_1, \varrho_2; v - \tau_{jk}) \exp\,(-i\omega v)\,dv \qquad (7\text{-}46)$$

is essentially a cross spectral density computed from a *shifted* crosscorrelation function‡ such as depicted in Fig. 7.1a. This cross spectral density, modified to incorporate a difference in the response-time lag τ_{jk}, is responsible for the correlation between the responses in modes j and k. Equation (7-45) is seen to give the modified cross spectral density for the generalized forces in these two modes.

Return to Eq. (7-39) and consider, for the moment, that the forcing field is weakly stationary in time and weakly homogeneous in space.

‡ Expression (7-46) is generally complex even when $\varrho_1 = \varrho_2$, since a shifted auto-correlation function, as shown in Fig. 7.1b, is generally unsymmetrical.

Fig. 7.1 (a) Shifted crosscorrelation function and (b) shifted autocorrelation function of a forcing field for use in computing joint acceptances.

$$R_{PP}(\varrho_1, \varrho_2; \tau_1 - \tau_2 - \tau_{jk})$$

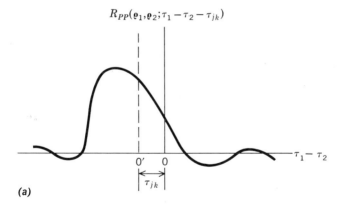

(a)

$$R_{PP}(\varrho, \varrho; \tau_1 - \tau_2 - \tau_{jk})$$

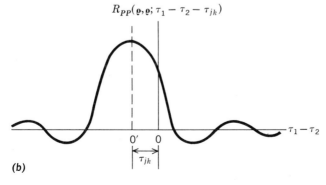

(b)

Then

$$I_{jl}(\omega) = \int_{\mathbf{k}} \Psi_{PP}(\mathbf{k}; \omega) S_j(\mathbf{k}) S_l^*(\mathbf{k}) \, d\mathbf{k} \tag{7-47}$$

where $\Psi_{PP}(\mathbf{k}; \omega)$ and $S_j(\mathbf{k})$ are defined in Eqs. (7-17) and (7-38), respectively, and the integration is over the entire range of $\mathbf{k}$. For $j = l$, we have

$$I_{jj}(\omega) = \int_{\mathbf{k}} \Psi_{PP}(\mathbf{k}; \omega) |S_j(\mathbf{k})|^2 \, d\mathbf{k} \tag{7-48}$$

Recall that the function $\Psi_{PP}(\mathbf{k}; \omega)$ is nonnegative. For a given ω, the integral in (7-48) yields a large value if the major peak of the function $\Psi_{PP}(\mathbf{k}; \omega)$ coincides with the peak of $|S_j(\mathbf{k})|^2$. This means that the jth mode is effectively excited by the forcing field. Similar observations can be made for the integral in Eq. (7-47) for $j \neq l$; but since the integrand is complex, we can only talk about the upper bound of the absolute value of $I_{jl}(\omega)$. It may be noted, however, that in practical computations Eqs. (7-47) and (7-48) may or may not be more convenient to use than the original Eq. (7-39), which is also valid for a forcing field nonhomogeneous in space.

In the application of Eq. (7-42) or (7-42a) to a practical problem, the infinite sum is replaced by a partial sum. This is generally permissible if $|I_{jk}(\omega)|$ is bounded for any pair of j and k. A simple calculation will show that for the usual underdamped case (that is, $\zeta_j < 1$), the absolute value of $H_j(\omega)$ is bounded by $(2m_j \zeta_j \omega_j^2)^{-1} (1 - \zeta_j^2)^{-\frac{1}{2}}$. Since the natural frequency ω_j of the jth mode increases as the mode order j increases, we can always find a sufficiently large number N that Eq. (7-42) can be adequately approximated by

$$\sum_{j,k=1}^{N} f_j(\mathbf{r}_1) f_k(\mathbf{r}_2) H_j(\omega) H_k^*(\omega) I_{jk}(\omega)$$

For lower modes, the terms that contribute more to the double sum are often those for which the maxima of at least two of the three functions $|H_j(\omega)|$, $|H_k(\omega)|$, and $|I_{jk}(\omega)|$ are very close to each other. It is also interesting to note that if the structure is uniform and if the forcing field is spatially uncorrelated and weakly homogeneous, then the coupling terms in Eq. (7-42) or (7-42a) are zero regardless of the magnitude of damping. This statement can be verified by substituting

$$\Phi_{PP}(\varrho_1, \varrho_2; \omega) = A(\omega) \, \delta(\varrho_1 - \varrho_2)$$

and by noting that the orthogonality property for the normal modes of a uniform structure now reads

$$\int_{\mathfrak{R}} f_j(\varrho) f_k(\varrho) \, d\varrho = 0 \qquad j \neq k \tag{7-30a}$$

If the structure is *lightly damped* and if the natural frequencies in the various normal modes are *well separated*, then the cross terms are usually negligible. In such a case the integral over $|H_j(\omega)|^2$ and $|H_k(\omega)|^2$ usually exceeds that over $2|H_j(\omega)|\,|H_k(\omega)|$.

Powell‡ has given a physical interpretation of the cross terms in Eq. (7-42) when the structure is uniform and when $\mathbf{r_1} = \mathbf{r_2}$. In this case the equation becomes

$$\Phi_{WW}(\mathbf{r};\,\omega) = \sum_{j,k=1}^{\infty} f_j(\mathbf{r}) f_k(\mathbf{r}) H_j(\omega) H_k^*(\omega) I_{jk}(\omega) \tag{7-42b}$$

If the response spectral density is averaged over the space domain of the structure, $\mathfrak{R}$, the cross terms contribute nothing to this average because of the orthogonality condition; i.e.,

$$\frac{1}{\mathfrak{R}} \int_{\mathfrak{R}} \Phi_{WW}(\mathbf{r};\,\omega) \, d\mathbf{r} = \sum_{j=1}^{\infty} |H_j(\omega)|^2 I_{jj}(\omega) \frac{1}{\mathfrak{R}} \int_{\mathfrak{R}} f_j^2(\mathbf{r}) \, d\mathbf{r} \tag{7-49}$$

Therefore, the cross terms account for the local variation of the response spectral density from this average. Thus if the excitation is applied to a limited area on a structure and if one pair of the cross terms makes a positive contribution to the response spectral density at a point well within the loaded area, it then must make essentially a negative contribution outside the loaded area, since the average over the structure is zero. Of course, the terms involving each mode, that is, $f_j^2(\mathbf{r})|H_j(\omega)|^2 I_{jj}(\omega)$, must always make a positive contribution to the response spectral density at a point either within or without the loaded area. Since a spectral density is always positive, the sum of the positive contributions cannot be smaller than the sum of the negative contributions.

To illustrate some of the theoretical points discussed in this section, let us consider a uniform beam governed by the equation

$$EI \frac{\partial^4 W}{\partial x^4} + c\dot{W} + m\ddot{W} = P(x,\,t)$$

where EI, c, and m are assumed to be constants. Further assume that both ends of the beam are simply supported. Then, as is well known, the normal modes are described by the functions

$$f_j(x) = \sin\frac{j\pi x}{l}$$

‡ *Loc. cit.*

where l is the span length of the beam and x is the distance from a reference support. It can be shown that the generalized mass, the generalized damping coefficient, and the natural frequency in each mode are, respectively,

$$m_j = \frac{ml}{2}$$

$$c_j = \frac{cl}{2}$$

$$\omega_j = \sqrt{\frac{EI}{m}} \left(\frac{j\pi}{l}\right)^2$$

Write the impulse influence function according to Eq. (7-34); i.e., write

$$h(x, \xi; t) = \begin{cases} \sum_{j=1}^{\infty} \sin\frac{j\pi x}{l} \sin\frac{j\pi \xi}{l} h_j(t) & 0 \leq x, \xi \leq l \\ 0 & \text{otherwise} \end{cases}$$

The impulse response function in the jth mode, $h_j(t)$, is found to be

$$h_j(t) = \begin{cases} \frac{2}{ml} \left[\frac{EI}{m} \left(\frac{j\pi}{l}\right)^4 - \left(\frac{c}{2m}\right)^2\right]^{-\frac{1}{2}} \\ \exp\left(-\frac{c}{2m}t\right) \sin\sqrt{\frac{EI}{m} \left(\frac{j\pi}{l}\right)^4 - \left(\frac{c}{2m}\right)^2}\, t & t \geq 0 \\ 0 & t < 0 \end{cases}$$

On the other hand, if the continuous system is characterized by the frequency influence function expressed as

$$H(x, \xi, \omega) = \begin{cases} \sum_{j=1}^{\infty} \sin\frac{j\pi x}{l} \sin\frac{j\pi \xi}{l} H_j(\omega) & 0 \leq x, \xi \leq l \\ 0 & \text{otherwise} \end{cases}$$

we find that

$$H_j(\omega) = \frac{2}{l} \left[EI \left(\frac{j\pi}{l}\right)^4 - \omega^2 m + ic\omega\right]^{-1}$$

It will be assumed that the random load $P(x, t)$ is weakly stationary and weakly homogeneous and that its correlation function can be idealized as

$$E[P(\xi_1, \tau_1)P(\xi_2, \tau_2)] = R_{PP}(\xi_1 - \xi_2, \tau_1 - \tau_2)$$
$$= \sigma^2 \exp\left(-a|\xi_1 - \xi_2|\right) \delta(\tau_1 - \tau_2) \qquad a > 0$$

What we have assumed is that the random load $P(\xi, \tau)$ is a white noise with respect to the time parameter τ, and it has an exponential-decay type of correlation with respect to the space parameter ξ. Correspondingly, the cross spectral density of the random load is

$$\Phi_{PP}(\xi_1 - \xi_2, \omega) = \frac{\sigma^2}{2\pi} \exp(-a|\xi_1 - \xi_2|)$$

Then the cross spectral density of the generalized forces in the modes j and k can be computed according to Eq. (7-39);‡ i.e.,

$$
\begin{aligned}
I_{jk}(\omega) &= \frac{\sigma^2}{2\pi} \left\{ \int_0^l d\xi_1 \int_0^{\xi_1} \sin\frac{j\pi\xi_1}{l} \sin\frac{k\pi\xi_2}{l} \exp\left[-a(\xi_1 - \xi_2)\right] d\xi_2 \right. \\
&\qquad \left. + \int_0^l d\xi_2 \int_0^{\xi_2} \sin\frac{j\pi\xi_1}{l} \sin\frac{k\pi\xi_2}{l} \exp\left[-a(\xi_2 - \xi_1)\right] d\xi_1 \right\} \\
&= \frac{\sigma^2}{2\pi} \left\{ \frac{al}{2} \left[\frac{1}{a^2 + (j\pi/l)^2} + \frac{1}{a^2 + (k\pi/l)^2} \right] \delta_{jk} \right. \\
&\qquad \left. + \frac{j\pi}{l} \frac{k\pi}{l} \frac{2 + e^{-al}[(-1)^{j+1} + (-1)^{k+1}]}{[a^2 + (j\pi/l)^2][a^2 + (k\pi/l)^2]} \right\}
\end{aligned}
$$

where δ_{jk} is a Kronecker delta; i.e.,

$$
\delta_{jk} = \begin{cases} 1 & j = k \\ 0 & j \ne k \end{cases}
$$

The cross spectral density of the response in the weakly stationary state is obtained by use of Eq. (7-42):

$$
\begin{aligned}
\Phi_{WW}(x_1, x_2; \omega) &= \frac{2\sigma^2}{\pi l^2} \sum_{j,k=1}^{\infty} \sin\frac{j\pi x_1}{l} \sin\frac{k\pi x_2}{l} \left\{ \frac{al}{2} \left[\frac{1}{a^2 + (j\pi/l)^2} \right. \right. \\
&\quad \left. + \frac{1}{a^2 + (k\pi/l)^2} \right] \delta_{jk} + \frac{j\pi}{l} \frac{k\pi}{l} \frac{2 + e^{-al}[(-1)^{j+1} + (-1)^{k+1}]}{[a^2 + (j\pi/l)^2][a^2 + (k\pi/l)^2]} \right\} \\
&\quad \left[EI\left(\frac{j\pi}{l}\right)^4 - \omega^2 m + ic\omega \right]^{-1} \left[EI\left(\frac{k\pi}{l}\right)^4 - \omega^2 m - ic\omega \right]^{-1}
\end{aligned}
$$

If, for the above expression, we let $x_1 = x_2 = x$ and integrate over ω, we obtain the mean-square value of the stationary deflection $W(x, t)$, which is

$$
\begin{aligned}
E[W^2(x, t)] &= \frac{32c\sigma^2}{\pi^4 m^2 EI} \sum_{j,k=1}^{\infty} \sin\frac{j\pi x}{l} \sin\frac{k\pi x}{l} \left\{ \frac{al}{2} \left[\frac{1}{a^2 + (j\pi/l)^2} \right. \right. \\
&\quad \left. + \frac{1}{a^2 + (k\pi/l)^2} \right] \delta_{jk} + \frac{j\pi}{l} \frac{k\pi}{l} \frac{2 + e^{-al}[(-1)^{j+1} + (-1)^{k+1}]}{[a^2 + (j\pi/l)^2][a^2 + (k\pi/l)^2]} \right\} \\
&\quad \left[\frac{EI}{m} \left(\frac{\pi}{l}\right)^4 (j^4 - k^4) + 2\left(\frac{c}{m}\right)^2 (j^4 + k^4) \right]^{-1}
\end{aligned}
$$

‡ In principle Eq. (7-47) can also be used, but the integral is more troublesome.

7.3 / PANEL VIBRATIONS INDUCED
BY BOUNDARY-LAYER TURBULENCE

To further illustrate the use of a normal-mode approach, consider a somewhat more complicated example than the one just discussed, namely, the vibration of a rectangular flat panel induced by exposure to boundary-layer turbulence. A simplified model of the physical setup is shown in Fig. 7.2. The panel, which forms one side of an enclosed space, is assumed to be simply supported on four edges. The panel may be viewed as an idealization of a fuselage panel of an aircraft or a submarine.

The boundary-layer turbulence results when the vehicle travels at high speeds. The random pressure fluctuation in the turbulent flow excites the panel. The vibrating panel, in turn, radiates noise (random sound pressure) to the surrounding medium. It is conceivable that the panel motion may cause some change in the structure of the boundary layer; however, such a change is negligible for panel deflections much smaller than the boundary-layer thickness. In what follows, we shall assume that the boundary-layer pressure is independent of the panel behavior. On the other hand, the sound radiated by a vibrating panel and the panel vibration itself are closely related, and they must be considered together. Therefore, the analysis for the panel vibration also yields information about, for example, the noise inside the enclosed space. Actually the latter problem, called the *cabin noise problem*, was the

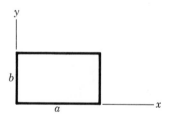

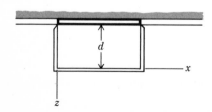

Fig. 7.2

incentive for many pioneering analyses, notably the works by Ribner,[‡] Corcos and Liepmann,[¶] Kraichnan,[§] Dyer,[‡‡] and Lyon.[¶¶]

The statistical properties of boundary-layer pressure fields have been sampled by a number of investigators,[§§] both on actual vehicles and on wind-tunnel models. These measurements showed the following general results:

1. Except near the ends or near the irregularities of a vehicle, a boundary-layer pressure field is nearly weakly stationary in time.
2. The correlation of a boundary-layer pressure field is characterized by a time decay as well as by a convection velocity in the direction of the free stream. The convection speed v is equal to about $0.83u$ for subsonic flow and about $0.72u$ for supersonic flow, where u is the free-stream velocity.
3. The root-mean-square pressure of a boundary-layer pressure field is about $0.006q$ for subsonic flow, and it decreases to about $0.003q$ in the Mach-number range 2 to 5, where q is the dynamic pressure of the free flow (that is, $q = \frac{1}{2}\rho u^2$).

Based on the above evidence, it is plausible to assume a covariance function of the following form[‡‡‡] for the boundary-layer pressure field:

$$\Gamma_{PP}(x_1, y_1; x_2, y_2; t_1 - t_2) = \sigma^2 \exp\left\{-\frac{\pi}{4L^2}[(\xi - v\tau)^2 + \eta^2] - \left(\frac{\tau}{\theta}\right)^2\right\}$$
$$\xi = x_1 - x_2, \ \eta = y_1 - y_2, \ \tau = t_1 - t_2 \quad (7\text{-}50)$$

This covariance function is characterized by the parameters σ^2, L, v, and θ, which are the variance of the pressure field, the scale of turbulence, the convection speed, and the life expectancy of the turbulence eddies, respectively. Although this covariance function is a function of

$$\xi = x_1 - x_2$$

‡ H. S. Ribner, Boundary-layer-induced Noise in the Interior of Aircraft, *Univ. Toronto, UTIA Rept.* 37, April, 1956.

¶ G. M. Corcos and H. W. Liepmann, On the Contribution of Turbulent Boundary Layers to the Noise Inside a Fuselage, *NACA* TM 1420, December, 1956.

§ R. H. Kraichnan, Noise Transmission from Boundary Layer Pressure Fluctuations, *J. Acoust. Soc. Am.*, **29**(1): 1957.

‡‡ *Loc. cit.* ¶¶ *Loc. cit.*

§§ E. J. Richards, M. K. Bull, and J. L. Willis, Boundary Layer Noise Research in the U.S.A. and Canada, Univ. Southampton Rep. 131, 1960.

‡‡‡ This is a variation of the following form suggested by Dyer:

$$\sigma^2 \exp\left[-\kappa \sqrt{(\xi - v\tau)^2 + \eta^2} - \frac{|\tau|}{\theta}\right]$$

The pressure field corresponding to Dyer's covariance function, however, is not mean-square differentiable.

it is not an even function of ξ. Therefore, a boundary-layer pressure field is not weakly homogeneous in the direction of convection. It has been mentioned in Sec. 6.4 that the scale of turbulence, L, is a measure of the average eddy size in the turbulent flow. In the limiting case when the life expectancy of the turbulence eddies is infinitely long, i.e., when $\theta \to \infty$, Eq. (7-50) becomes

$$\lim_{\theta \to \infty} \Gamma_{PP} = \sigma^2 \exp\left\{ -\frac{\pi}{4L^2} [(\xi - v\tau)^2 + \eta^2] \right\} \qquad (7\text{-}51)$$

This limiting case corresponds to a *frozen pattern* of a pressure field which is convected at a velocity v in the x direction. On the other hand, if the eddy sizes are very small in comparison with the length or the width of the panel, we can make the approximation that $L \to 0$ while keeping the product $\sigma^2 L^2 = A^2$ finite. Then by use of the representation‡

$$\lim_{L \to 0} \frac{1}{2L} \exp\left(-\frac{\pi}{4L^2} \zeta^2 \right) = \delta(\zeta) \qquad (7\text{-}52)$$

we have

$$\lim_{L \to 0} \Gamma_{PP} = 4A^2 \, \delta(\xi - v\tau) \, \delta(\eta) \exp\left[-\left(\frac{\tau}{\theta}\right)^2 \right] \qquad (7\text{-}53)$$

The cross spectral density of the weakly stationary panel response is given by Eq. (7-42), which for the present case reads

$$\Phi_{WW}(x_1, y_1; x_2, y_2; \omega)$$

$$= \sum_{j=1}^{\infty} \sum_{l=1}^{\infty} \sum_{r=1}^{\infty} \sum_{s=1}^{\infty} f_{jl}(x_1, y_1) f_{rs}(x_2, y_2) H_{jl}(\omega) H_{rs}^*(\omega) \, I_{(jl)(rs)}(\omega) \qquad (7\text{-}42c)$$

Here, we use double indices to represent each normal mode, since for a panel with uniform thickness and simply supported on four edges

$$f_{jl}(x, y) = \sin\frac{j\pi x}{a} \sin\frac{l\pi y}{b} \qquad (7\text{-}54)$$

The function $I_{(jl)(rs)}(\omega)$ appearing in Eq. (7-42c) is the cross spectral density of the generalized forces in modes (jl) and (rs). From Eq. (7-39)

$$I_{(jl)(rs)}(\omega) = \int_0^a dx_1 \int_0^a dx_2 \int_0^b dy_1 \int_0^b dy_2$$
$$\Phi_{PP}(x_1, y_1; x_2, y_2; \omega) f_{jl}(x_1, y_1) f_{rs}(x_2, y_2) \qquad (7\text{-}55)$$

We shall be concerned only with the portion of the pressure fluctuating from the mean pressure. Then $E[P(x, y, t)] = 0$, and the covariance function Γ_{PP} is the same as the correlation function R_{PP}. For simplicity,

‡ Compared with Eq. (V-5), Appendix V.

consider a correlation function having the limiting form given by Eq. (7-53). The cross spectral density of the pressure field can be readily computed; it is

$$
\Phi_{PP}(x_1, y_1; x_2, y_2; \omega)
$$
$$
= \frac{2A^2}{\pi} \int_{-\infty}^{\infty} \delta(\xi - v\tau)\, \delta(\eta)\, \exp\left[-\left(\frac{\tau}{\theta}\right)^2 - i\omega\tau \right] d\tau
$$
$$
= \frac{2A^2}{\pi v} \delta(\eta)\, \exp\left[-\frac{1}{\theta^2}\left(\frac{\xi}{v}\right)^2 - i\omega\left(\frac{\xi}{v}\right) \right] \qquad \xi = x_1 - x_2,\ \eta = y_1 - y_2
$$
$$
(7\text{-}56)
$$

Substituting Eq. (7-56) into Eq. (7-55) and integrating on y_1 and y_2, we obtain

$$
I_{(jl)(rs)} = \frac{A^2 b}{\pi v}\, \delta_{l,s} \int_0^a \int_0^a \exp\left[-\frac{1}{\theta^2}\left(\frac{\xi}{v}\right)^2 - i\omega\left(\frac{\xi}{v}\right) \right]
$$
$$
\sin\frac{j\pi x_1}{a} \sin\frac{r\pi x_2}{a}\, dx_1\, dx_2 \qquad (7\text{-}57)
$$

where $\delta_{l,s}$ is a Kronecker delta.

The integrations on x_1 and x_2 are straightforward but somewhat tedious. It can be shown‡ that

$$
I_{(jl)(rs)} = \frac{2A^2 ab}{\pi^2 v(r^2 - j^2)}\, \delta_{l,s} \int_0^a \cos\frac{\omega\xi}{v}\left(r\sin\frac{j\pi\xi}{a} - j\sin\frac{r\pi\xi}{a} \right)
$$
$$
\exp\left[-\frac{1}{\theta^2}\left(\frac{\xi}{v}\right)^2 \right] d\xi \qquad r \neq j,\ r - j = \text{even} \quad (7\text{-}58a)
$$

$$
I_{(jl)(rs)} = \frac{2iA^2 ab}{\pi^2 v(r^2 - j^2)}\, \delta_{l,s} \int_0^a \sin\frac{\omega\xi}{v}\left(r\sin\frac{j\pi\xi}{a} + j\sin\frac{r\pi\xi}{a} \right)
$$
$$
\exp\left[-\frac{1}{\theta^2}\left(\frac{\xi}{v}\right)^2 \right] d\xi \qquad r - j = \text{odd} \quad (7\text{-}58b)
$$

$$
I_{(jl)(rs)} = \frac{A^2 b}{\pi v}\, \delta_{l,s} \int_0^a \cos\frac{\omega\xi}{v}\left(-\xi + \frac{a}{j\pi}\sin\frac{j\pi\xi}{a} \right)
$$
$$
\exp\left[-\frac{1}{\theta^2}\left(\frac{\xi}{v}\right)^2 \right] d\xi \qquad r = j \quad (7\text{-}58c)
$$

The integrals in (7-58a) to (7-58c) may be conveniently expressed in terms of the error functions of a complex argument by use of the formulas¶

‡ A procedure similar to the one for the integration of Eq. (3-78) may be used.

¶ W. Grobner and N. Hofreiter, "Integraltafel, Erster Teil, Unbestimmte Integrale," p. 109, Springer, Wien und Innsbruck, 1957. The error functions with complex arguments are tabulated in M. Abramowitz and I. A. Stegun (eds.), "Handbook of Mathematical Functions," National Bureau of Standards, Applied Mathematics, Series 55, Washington, D.C., June, 1964.

$$\int e^{-x^2} \cos \alpha x \, dx$$

$$= \frac{\sqrt{\pi}}{4} \exp\left(-\frac{\alpha^2}{4}\right)\left[\operatorname{erf}\left(x - \frac{i\alpha}{2}\right) + \operatorname{erf}\left(x + \frac{i\alpha}{2}\right)\right] + C$$

$$\int e^{-x^2} \sin \alpha x \, dx \tag{7-59}$$

$$= -\frac{i\sqrt{\pi}}{4} \exp\left(-\frac{\alpha^2}{4}\right)\left[\operatorname{erf}\left(x - \frac{i\alpha}{2}\right) - \operatorname{erf}\left(x + \frac{i\alpha}{2}\right)\right] + C$$

where the error function is defined as

$$\operatorname{erf} x = \frac{2}{\sqrt{\pi}} \int_0^x e^{-t^2} \, dt$$

$$= \frac{2}{\sqrt{\pi}}\left(x - \frac{x^3}{3} + \frac{1}{2!}\frac{x^5}{5} - \frac{1}{3!}\frac{x^7}{7} + \cdots\right) \tag{7-60}$$

Thus

$$I_{(jl)(rs)} = \frac{-iA^2\theta ab}{4\pi^{\frac{3}{2}}(r^2 - j^2)}\delta_{l,s}\left\{r\exp\left(-\beta_{j+}{}^2\right)\left[\operatorname{erf}\left(\frac{a}{\theta v} - i\beta_{j+}\right)\right.\right.$$

$$\left. - \operatorname{erf}\left(\frac{a}{\theta v} + i\beta_{j+}\right) - \operatorname{erf}\left(-i\beta_{j+}\right) + \operatorname{erf}\left(i\beta_{j+}\right)\right] + r\exp\left(-\beta_{j-}{}^2\right)$$

$$\left[\operatorname{erf}\left(\frac{a}{\theta v} - i\beta_{j-}\right) - \operatorname{erf}\left(\frac{a}{\theta v} + i\beta_{j-}\right) - \operatorname{erf}\left(-i\beta_{j-}\right) + \operatorname{erf}\left(i\beta_{j-}\right)\right]$$

$$- j\exp\left(-\beta_{r+}{}^2\right)\left[\operatorname{erf}\left(\frac{a}{\theta v} - i\beta_{r+}\right) - \operatorname{erf}\left(\frac{a}{\theta v} + i\beta_{r+}\right)\right.$$

$$\left. - \operatorname{erf}\left(-i\beta_{r+}\right) + \operatorname{erf}\left(i\beta_{r+}\right)\right] - j\operatorname{erf}\left(-\beta_{r-}{}^2\right)\left[\operatorname{erf}\left(\frac{a}{\theta v} - i\beta_{r-}\right)\right.$$

$$\left.\left. - \operatorname{erf}\left(\frac{a}{\theta v} + i\beta_{r+}\right) - \operatorname{erf}\left(-i\beta_{r-}\right) + \operatorname{erf}\left(i\beta_{r-}\right)\right]\right\}$$

$$r \neq j, \ r - j = \text{even} \tag{7-61a}$$

$$I_{(jl)(rs)} = \frac{iA^2\theta ab}{4\pi^{\frac{3}{2}}(r^2 - j^2)}\delta_{l,s}\left\{r\exp\left(-\beta_{j-}{}^2\right)\left[\operatorname{erf}\left(\frac{a}{\theta v} - i\beta_{j-}\right)\right.\right.$$

$$\left. + \operatorname{erf}\left(\frac{a}{\theta v} + i\beta_{j-}\right) - \operatorname{erf}\left(-i\beta_{j-}\right) - \operatorname{erf}\left(i\beta_{j-}\right)\right] - r\exp\left(-\beta_{j+}{}^2\right)$$

$$\left[\operatorname{erf}\left(\frac{a}{\theta v} - i\beta_{j+}\right) + \operatorname{erf}\left(\frac{a}{\theta v} + i\beta_{j+}\right) - \operatorname{erf}\left(-\beta_{j+}\right) - \operatorname{erf}\left(i\beta_{j+}\right)\right]$$

$$+ j\exp\left(-\beta_{r-}{}^2\right)\left[\operatorname{erf}\left(\frac{a}{\theta v} - i\beta_{r-}\right) + \operatorname{erf}\left(\frac{a}{\theta v} + i\beta_{r-}\right)\right.$$

$$\left. - \operatorname{erf}\left(-i\beta_{r-}\right) - \operatorname{erf}\left(i\beta_{r-}\right)\right] - j\exp\left(-\beta_{r+}{}^2\right)\left[\operatorname{erf}\left(\frac{a}{\theta v} - i\beta_{r+}\right)\right.$$

$$\left.\left. + \operatorname{erf}\left(\frac{a}{\theta v} + i\beta_{r+}\right) - \operatorname{erf}\left(-i\beta_{r+}\right) - \operatorname{erf}\left(i\beta_{r+}\right)\right]\right\}$$

$$r - j = \text{odd} \tag{7-61b}$$

$$I_{(jl)(jl)} = \frac{A^2\theta^2 vb}{2\pi} \left\{ \cos\frac{\omega a}{v} \exp\left(-\frac{a^2}{\theta^2 v^2}\right) - 1 - \frac{i\sqrt{\pi}\,\theta^2 v\omega}{4} \right.$$

$$\exp\left(-\frac{\theta^2\omega^2}{4}\right)\left[\operatorname{erf}\left(\frac{a}{\theta v} - \frac{i\omega\theta}{2}\right) - \operatorname{erf}\left(\frac{a}{\theta v} + \frac{i\omega\theta}{2}\right)\right.$$

$$\left.- \operatorname{erf}\left(-\frac{i\omega\theta}{2}\right) + \operatorname{erf}\left(\frac{i\omega\theta}{2}\right)\right]\right\} - \frac{iA^2\theta ab}{8\pi^3 j}\left\{\exp\left(-\beta_{j+}{}^2\right)\right.$$

$$\left[\operatorname{erf}\left(\frac{a}{\theta v} - i\beta_{j+}\right) - \operatorname{erf}\left(\frac{a}{\theta v} + i\beta_{j+}\right) - \operatorname{erf}\left(-i\beta_{j+}\right) + \operatorname{erf}\left(i\beta_{j+}\right)\right]$$

$$+ \exp\left(-\beta_{j-}{}^2\right)\left[\operatorname{erf}\left(\frac{a}{\theta v} - i\beta_{j-}\right) - \operatorname{erf}\left(\frac{a}{\theta v} - i\beta_{j-}\right)\right.$$

$$\left.\left.- \operatorname{erf}\left(-i\beta_{j-}\right) + \operatorname{erf}\left(i\beta_{j-}\right)\right]\right\} \qquad r = j \quad (7\text{-}61c)$$

where

$$\beta_{j+} = \frac{\theta v}{2}\left(\frac{j\pi}{a} + \frac{\omega}{v}\right)$$

$$\beta_{j-} = \frac{\theta v}{2}\left(\frac{j\pi}{a} - \frac{\omega}{v}\right)$$

$$\beta_{r+} = \frac{\theta v}{2}\left(\frac{r\pi}{a} + \frac{\omega}{v}\right) \qquad\qquad (7\text{-}62)$$

$$\beta_{r-} = \frac{\theta v}{2}\left(\frac{r\pi}{a} - \frac{\omega}{v}\right)$$

Equation (7-61c) gives the spectral density of the generalized force in each mode. It can be seen that the spectral densities and the cross spectral densities, as given in Eqs. (7-61a) to (7-61c), are sensitive to the values $\beta_{j\pm}$ and $\beta_{r\pm}$, which, besides appearing in the error functions, enter into these equations in the form of $\exp\left(-\beta^2\right)$. We anticipate, therefore, that a spectral density or the absolute value of a cross spectral density is large when one of the β's vanishes; for example, when $\beta_{j-} = j\pi/a - \omega/v = 0$. This occurs when the convection frequency of the pressure field, $j\pi v/a$, is equal to the frequency of the panel vibration, ω. If ω is also very near to the natural frequency of the panel corresponding to the same mode, then a large response will result in this mode. The phenomenon is known as the *coincidence effect*.

Equations (7-61a) to (7-61c) have been obtained for the special case where the eddy sizes of the turbulence field are much smaller than either the length or the width of the panel. In the more general case, the covariance function Eq. (7-50) should be used. Then the computation of the cross spectral density of the generalized forces would be more tedious, although it is clear that similar steps can be followed to obtain the required results.

We turn now to the determination of the frequency response function of mode (jl) for use in Eq. (7-42c). This function can be obtained by considering the steady-state motion of the system under a *suitable* deterministic simple harmonic excitation, for which we choose the following plane sound pressure wave traveling in a direction normal to, and toward, the panel from the free-space side of the panel,

$$p_1 = A_1 \exp\left[i\left(\omega t - \frac{\omega}{c_0} z\right)\right] \qquad (7\text{-}63)$$

where c_0 is the speed of sound in the fluid. It is seen from this expression that the attenuation of sound when propagating through a fluid medium is neglected. Figure 7.3 shows this incident sound wave, the scattered wave p_2 from the panel, and the transmitted wave p_3 into the enclosed space. For the present analysis the interior surfaces of the enclosed space, with the exception of the panel, are assumed to be pressure-release surfaces.

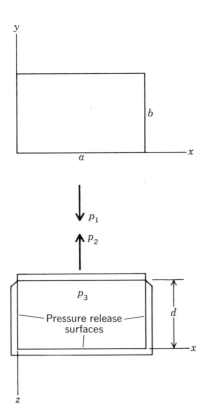

Fig. 7.3.

The transmitted pressure field p_3 will be determined first. In the absence of sources the wave equation reads

$$\frac{\partial^2 p_3}{\partial t^2} - c_i^2 \nabla^2 p_3 = 0 \tag{7-64}$$

where $\nabla^2 = \dfrac{\partial^2}{\partial x^2} + \dfrac{\partial^2}{\partial y^2} + \dfrac{\partial^2}{\partial z^2}$ is the Laplacian operator and c_i is the speed of sound in the enclosure. Equation (7-64) is to be solved with the boundary conditions

$$p_3 = 0 \quad \begin{cases} x = 0, a \\ y = 0, b \\ z = 0 \end{cases}$$

$$\left(\frac{\partial}{\partial z} p_3\right)_{z=-d} = -\frac{\partial}{\partial t}(\rho_i \dot{w}) \tag{7-65}$$

where ρ_i is the mass density of the enclosed fluid. The last condition in (7-65) is merely a statement of Newton's second law of motion. In a linear theory of sound propagation, the variation of ρ_i is neglected. Thus

$$\frac{\partial}{\partial t}(\rho_i \dot{w}) = \rho_i \ddot{w}$$

Furthermore, for the purpose of determining the modal frequency response function $H_{jl}(\omega)$, only the panel motion in the (jl) mode and with a frequency ω is considered. Thus

$$w = q_{jl} \sin\frac{j\pi x}{a} \sin\frac{l\pi y}{b} \exp(i\omega t) \tag{7-66}$$

The last equation in (7-65) then becomes

$$\left(\frac{\partial}{\partial z} p_3\right)_{z=-d} = \rho_i \omega^2 q_{jl} \sin\frac{j\pi x}{a} \sin\frac{l\pi y}{b} \exp(i\omega t) \tag{7-67}$$

The solution to Eq. (7-64) which corresponds to a single frequency ω and which satisfies all the boundary conditions is found to be

$$p_3 = \frac{\rho_i \omega^2 q_{jl}}{k_{jl,i} \cos k_{jl,i} d} \sin\frac{j\pi x}{a} \sin\frac{l\pi y}{b} (\sin k_{jl,i} z) \exp(i\omega t) \tag{7-68}$$

where

$$k_{jl,i}^2 = \left(\frac{\omega}{c_i}\right)^2 - \left(\frac{j\pi}{a}\right)^2 - \left(\frac{l\pi}{b}\right)^2 \tag{7-69}$$

The determination of the scattered pressure field p_2 is more involved. It is intuitively clear that the propagation of the scattered field must be three-dimensional. However, since we are interested only in the behavior of p_2 in the proximity of the panel, a one-dimensional analysis will yield a useful approximation. In this neighborhood we shall assume that p_2 can be approximated in the form

$$p_2 = A_2 \sin \frac{j\pi x}{a} \sin \frac{l\pi y}{b} \exp [i(\omega t + k_{jl,0}z)] \qquad (7\text{-}70)$$

where

$$k_{jl,0}^2 = \left(\frac{\omega}{c_0}\right)^2 - \left(\frac{j\pi}{a}\right)^2 - \left(\frac{l\pi}{b}\right)^2 \qquad (7\text{-}71)$$

The constant A_2 will be determined from the boundary condition at the panel, i.e.,

$$\left[\frac{\partial}{\partial z}(p_1 + p_2)\right]_{z=-d} = -\rho_0 \ddot{w} \qquad (7\text{-}72)$$

where ρ_0 is the mass density of the fluid in the free space. Substitution of Eqs. (7-63), (7-66), and (7-70) into Eq. (7-72) gives

$$A_2 = \left\{\frac{A_1(\omega/c_0) \exp [i(\omega/c_0)d]}{\sin (j\pi x/a) \sin (l\pi y/b)} - i\rho_0\omega^2 q_{jl}\right\} \frac{\exp (ik_{jl,0}d)}{k_{jl,0}} \qquad (7\text{-}73)$$

Therefore,

$$p_2 = \left[A_1 \left(\frac{\omega}{c_0}\right) \exp \left(i\frac{\omega d}{c_0}\right) - i\rho_0\omega^2 q_{jl} \sin \frac{j\pi x}{a} \sin \frac{l\pi y}{b}\right]$$
$$\frac{\exp \{i[\omega t + k_{jl,0}(d + z)]\}}{k_{jl,0}} \qquad (7\text{-}74)$$

Now the equation of motion for the panel may be written as follows:

$$D\left(\frac{\partial^4}{\partial x^4} + 2\frac{\partial^4}{\partial x^2 \partial y^2} + \frac{\partial^4}{\partial y^4}\right) w = -m\ddot{w} + (p_1 + p_2 - p_3)_{z=-d} \qquad (7\text{-}75)$$

where D is the bending rigidity‡ and m the mass per unit area of the panel. Substituting Eqs. (7-63), (7-66), (7-68), and (7-74) into Eq. (7-75), we obtain

$$q_{jl}\left\{D\left[\left(\frac{j\pi}{a}\right)^2 + \left(\frac{l\pi}{b}\right)^2\right]^2 - m\omega^2 + \frac{i\rho_0\omega^2}{k_{jl,0}} - \frac{\rho_i\omega^2}{k_{jl,i}}\tan k_{jl,i}d\right\} \sin \frac{j\pi x}{a} \sin \frac{l\pi y}{b}$$
$$= A_1\left(1 + \frac{\omega}{k_{jl,0}c_0}\right)\exp\left(i\frac{\omega d}{c_0}\right) \qquad (7\text{-}76)$$

The frequency response function $H_{jl}(\omega)$ is the ratio of $q_{jl} \exp (i\omega t)$ to the generalized force

$$\int_0^a \int_0^b (p_1)_{z=-d} \sin \frac{j\pi x}{a} \sin \frac{l\pi y}{b} \, dx \, dy$$

‡ The structural damping may be accounted for by use of a complex D.

Therefore,

$$
H_{jl}(\omega) = \frac{4}{ab}\left(1 + \frac{\omega}{k_{jl,0}c_0}\right)\left\{D\left[\left(\frac{j\pi}{a}\right)^2 + \left(\frac{l\pi}{b}\right)^2\right]^2 - m\omega^2 \right.
$$
$$
\left. + \frac{i\rho_0\omega^2}{k_{jl,0}} - \frac{\rho_i\omega^2}{k_{jl,i}}\tan k_{jl,i}d\right\}^{-1} \quad (7\text{-}77)
$$

Some comments about the result obtained in Eq. (7-77) are in order. We note that if the excitation frequency ω is sufficiently high that

$$
\left(\frac{\omega}{c_0}\right)^2 > \left(\frac{j\pi}{a}\right)^2 + \left(\frac{l\pi}{b}\right)^2
$$

then $k_{jl,0}$ is real. The term $i\rho_0\omega^2/k_{jl,0}$ plays the role of a damping term for the panel motion; that is, the panel radiates energy to the free space. This type of damping is called *acoustic damping*. At low frequencies

$$
\left(\frac{\omega}{c_0}\right)^2 < \left(\frac{j\pi}{a}\right)^2 + \left(\frac{l\pi}{b}\right)^2
$$

$k_{jl,0}$ is imaginary. Then the impedance provided by the fluid in the free-space is represented by an *apparent mass* equal to $\rho_0/|k_{jl,0}|$ per unit area of the panel. Therefore at low frequencies the scatter wave does not carry energy away from the panel. The boundary frequency computed from

$$
\omega_c = c_0\left[\left(\frac{j\pi}{a}\right)^2 + \left(\frac{l\pi}{b}\right)\right]^{\frac{1}{2}} \quad (7\text{-}78)
$$

is called the *cutoff* frequency of the panel. On the other hand, the effect of the fluid in the enclosure is always represented by an *apparent mass* regardless of the value of the excitation frequency. This apparent mass is

$$
\frac{\rho_i}{k_{jl,i}}\tan k_{jl,i}d \qquad \text{for real } k_{jl,i}
$$

and is

$$
\frac{\rho_i}{|k_{jl,i}|}\tan h|k_{jl,i}d| \qquad \text{for imaginary } k_{jl,i}
$$

It was pointed out previously that the analysis for panel vibration also results in information about the noise (i.e., the random pressure fluctuation) transmitted into the enclosed space. The link is provided in Eq. (7-68). Let the noise pressure be denoted by $N(x, y, z, t)$. Then the cross spectral density of the noise pressure may be computed from

$$
\Phi_{NN}(x_1, y_1, z_1; x_2, y_2, z_2; \omega)
$$
$$
= \sum_{j=1}^{\infty}\sum_{l=1}^{\infty}\sum_{r=1}^{\infty}\sum_{s=1}^{\infty}\rho_i{}^2\omega^4[k_{jl,i}k_{rs,i}^* \cos(k_{jl,i}d)\cos(k_{rs,i}^*d)]^{-1}f_{jl}(x_1, y_1)
$$
$$
f_{rs}(x_2, y_2)\sin(k_{jl,i}z_1)\sin(k_{rs,i}^*z_2)H_{jl}(\omega)H_{rs}^*(\omega)I_{(jl)(rs)}(\omega) \quad (7\text{-}79)
$$

This cross spectral density can be used to compute the pressure correlation, etc. In particular, the mean-square pressure is obtained by equating $x_1 = x_2$, $y_1 = y_2$, $z_1 = z_2$ in Eq. (7-79) and integrating on ω. The mean-square noise pressure is a useful measure, for example, in determining whether or not an aircraft cabin is too noisy to be tolerable to passengers. For such purposes, the mean-square noise pressure is often expressed in terms of a logarithmic scale called the *decibel* (db) scale, which is defined as

$$\text{db} = 10 \log_{10} \frac{E[N^2]}{p_0{}^2}$$

where the reference pressure p_0 is 1 microbar (that is, 1 dyne/cm^2). Correspondingly, the spectral density of the noise pressure is expressed in decibels per octave.

7.4 / METHOD OF TRANSFER MATRICES

It has been pointed out in Sec. 7.3 that if damping is present in a linear structure it is not always possible to find suitable normal coordinates such that the equations of motion written in these coordinates are strictly uncoupled. However, when the damping is light, it is generally permissible to compute the normal modes on the basis of an undamped system and to neglect the coupling in damping, if there is any, between such normal coordinates when computing the response. Since we do not wish to rule out the possibility of using *moderately* damped structures, it is desirable to devise other methods in dealing with the cases for which a normal-mode approach is clearly unjustified or, at least, questionable. Unfortunately, such other methods are not available for arbitrary structures. For beams and beamlike structures, however, the method of transfer matrices can be used. This method was introduced in Chap. 6, in which were treated structures with concentrated inertia forces. It now will be extended to the case of a distributed mass.

Consider the equation of motion of a nonuniform beam

$$\frac{\partial^2}{\partial x^2} \left(EI \frac{\partial^2 W}{\partial x^2} \right) + c\dot{W} + m\ddot{W} = P(x, t) \tag{7-80}$$

where EI, c, and m are generally functions of x. Assume that it is permissible to take the Fourier transforms of both sides of Eq. (7-80). Then the Fourier transform of W, that is,

$$\bar{W} = \frac{1}{2\pi} \int_{-\infty}^{\infty} W \exp\left(-i\omega t\right) dt$$

satisfies the equation

$$\frac{d^2}{dx^2} \left(EI \frac{d^2 \bar{W}}{dx^2} \right) + (i\omega c - \omega^2 m)\bar{W} = \bar{P} \tag{7-80a}$$

where $\bar{P}$ is the Fourier transform of P. It is convenient to replace Eq. (7-80a) by the following first-order matrix equation for the vector $\bar{Z} = \{\bar{W}, \bar{W}', EI\bar{W}'', (EI\bar{W}'')'\} = \{\bar{W}, \bar{\theta}, \bar{M}, \bar{V}\}$, where a prime denotes one differentiation with respect to x:

$$\frac{d}{dx}\bar{Z} = A\bar{Z} + \bar{B} \tag{7-81}$$

with

$$A = \begin{bmatrix} 0 & 1 & 0 & 0 \\ 0 & 0 & \dfrac{1}{EI} & 0 \\ 0 & 0 & 0 & 1 \\ \omega^2 m - i\omega c & 0 & 0 & 0 \end{bmatrix} \tag{7-82}$$

$$\bar{B}(x) = \begin{Bmatrix} 0 \\ 0 \\ 0 \\ \bar{P}(x, \omega) \end{Bmatrix}$$

Suppose that the complementary solution for Eq. (7-81) has the form $T(x, 0)C$, where T is a square matrix and C is a column of arbitrary constants. Then the complete solution for Eq. (7-81) may be written as follows:

$$\bar{Z}(x) = T(x, 0)\bar{Z}(0) + \int_0^x T(x, s)\bar{B}(s)\,ds \tag{7-83}$$

It is clear that the matrix $T(x, 0)$ is a transfer matrix which relates the state vectors at $x = 0$ and at an arbitrary x when the beam is unloaded. Similarly, the matrix $T(x, s)$ in the integrand in Eq. (7-83) transfers a jump in the value of the state vector equal to $\bar{B}(s)\,ds$ from s to x. Thus a solution of Eq. (7-81) for a given problem depends on the possibility of finding the transfer matrix $T(x, s)$.

Let us postpone the determination of the transfer matrix $T(x, s)$ and take up first the question of the boundary conditions. To illustrate, let the beam be simply supported at one end and elastically supported at the other, as shown in Fig. 7.4. The elastic support also allows for structural damping, which may be accounted for by introducing an imaginary part to each of the two spring constants. The boundary conditions require that

$$\bar{Z}(0) = \begin{Bmatrix} 0 \\ \bar{\theta}(0) \\ 0 \\ \bar{V}(0) \end{Bmatrix} \qquad \bar{Z}(l+) = \begin{Bmatrix} \bar{W}(l) \\ \bar{\theta}(l) \\ 0 \\ 0 \end{Bmatrix} \tag{7-84}$$

where $x = l+$ denotes the location at the immediate right of the elastic support.

Let $x = l+$ in Eq. (7-83). We obtain

$$\begin{Bmatrix} \bar{W}(l) \\ \bar{\theta}(l) \\ 0 \\ 0 \end{Bmatrix} = \mathbf{T}(l+, 0) \begin{Bmatrix} 0 \\ \bar{\theta}(0) \\ 0 \\ \bar{V}(0) \end{Bmatrix} + \int_0^l \mathbf{T}(l+, s)\bar{\mathbf{B}}(s) \, ds \qquad (7\text{-}85)$$

Extracting the third and the fourth rows from Eq. (7-85),

$$\begin{Bmatrix} 0 \\ 0 \end{Bmatrix} = {}_{l+}\begin{bmatrix} t_{32} & t_{34} \\ t_{42} & t_{44} \end{bmatrix}_0 \begin{Bmatrix} \bar{\theta}(0) \\ \bar{V}(0) \end{Bmatrix} + \int_0^l {}_{l+}\begin{Bmatrix} t_{34} \\ t_{44} \end{Bmatrix}_s \bar{P}(s, \omega) \, ds \qquad (7\text{-}86)$$

where each t_{jk} is the (j, k) element of a transfer matrix $\mathbf{T}$, the arguments of which are indicated at the corners of the matrix symbol. For example, the matrix

$$_{+l}\begin{bmatrix} t_{32} & t_{34} \\ t_{42} & t_{44} \end{bmatrix}_0$$

is constructed by using the elements t_{32}, t_{34}, t_{42}, and t_{44} of the transfer matrix $\mathbf{T}(l+, 0)$.

For the present boundary conditions at $x = 0$, Eq. (7-83) can also be written as

$$\bar{\mathbf{Z}}(x) = {}_x\begin{bmatrix} t_{12} & t_{14} \\ t_{22} & t_{24} \\ t_{32} & t_{34} \\ t_{42} & t_{44} \end{bmatrix}_0 \begin{Bmatrix} \bar{\theta}(0) \\ \bar{V}(0) \end{Bmatrix} + \int_0^x {}_x\begin{Bmatrix} t_{14} \\ t_{24} \\ t_{34} \\ t_{44} \end{Bmatrix}_s \bar{P}(s, \omega) \, ds \qquad (7\text{-}87)$$

Fig. 7.4

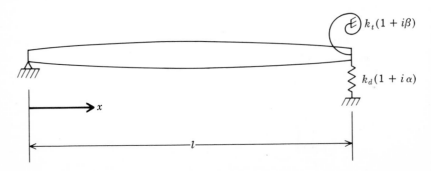

Elimination of the vector $\{\bar{\theta}(0),\ \bar{V}(0)\}$ from Eqs. (7-86) and (7-87) yields

$$\bar{Z}(x) = -\begin{bmatrix} t_{12} & t_{14} \\ t_{22} & t_{24} \\ t_{32} & t_{34} \\ t_{42} & t_{44} \end{bmatrix}_x \left(\begin{bmatrix} t_{32} & t_{34} \\ t_{42} & t_{44} \end{bmatrix}_0\right)^{-1}$$

$$\int_0^l \begin{Bmatrix} t_{34} \\ t_{44} \end{Bmatrix}_s \bar{P}(s,\ \omega)\ ds + \int_0^x \begin{Bmatrix} t_{14} \\ t_{24} \\ t_{34} \\ t_{44} \end{Bmatrix}_s \bar{P}(s,\ \omega)\ ds \qquad (7\text{-}88)$$

Equation (7-88) can be used to compute the generalized cross spectral densities or the cross spectral densities of the responses, as the case may be. For simplicity let $E[P(x,\ t)] = 0$. Then $E[\bar{P}(x,\ \omega)] = 0$ and $E[\bar{Z}(x)] = \mathbf{0}$. It can be seen easily that if the structure is originally at rest the matrix of the generalized cross spectral densities of the response at x_1 and at x_2 is given by

$$\hat{\mathbf{\Phi}}_Z(x_1,\ \omega_1;\ x_2,\ \omega_2) = E[\bar{Z}(x_1,\ \omega_1)\bar{Z}^{*\prime}(x_2,\ \omega_2)] \qquad (7\text{-}89)$$

In the case of a weakly stationary excitation, the matrix of the cross spectral densities of the weakly stationary response may be computed from

$$\mathbf{\Phi}_Z(x_1,\ x_2;\ \omega) = \lim_{L\to\infty} \frac{\pi}{L} E[\bar{Z}_L(x_1,\ \omega)\bar{Z}_L^{*\prime}(x_2,\ \omega)] \qquad (7\text{-}90)$$

where $\bar{Z}_L$ is a truncated Fourier transform of Z, defined as

$$\bar{Z}_L = \frac{1}{2\pi} \int_{-L}^L Z \exp\left(-i\omega t\right) dt \qquad (7\text{-}91)$$

Of course, $\bar{Z}_L$ can also be computed from Eq. (7-88) if $\bar{P}$ is replaced by $\bar{P}_L$, which is a truncated Fourier transform of P defined in the same way as in Eq. (7-91).

It is of interest to note that the frequency influence function $H(x,\ \xi,\ \omega)$ can be obtained by letting the excitation be a *deterministic* concentrated load $P(x,\ t) = 2\pi\ \delta(x - \xi)\ \delta(t)$, for which $\bar{P}(x,\ \omega) = \delta(x - \xi)$. Then the response vector $Z(x,\ t)$ has the components $2\pi\{h,\ h',\ EIh'',\ (EIh'')'\}$, where h is the impulse influence function $h(x,\ \xi,\ t)$. Since $H = 2\pi\bar{h}$, it follows, by substituting $\bar{P}(s,\ \omega) = \delta(s - \xi)$ in Eq. (7-88) and keeping only the first row, that

$$H(x,\ \xi;\omega) = \begin{cases} -\,_x\lfloor t_{12} & t_{14} \rfloor_0 \left(\begin{bmatrix} t_{32} & t_{34} \\ t_{42} & t_{44} \end{bmatrix}_0\right)^{-1} \begin{Bmatrix} t_{34} \\ t_{44} \end{Bmatrix}_\xi & x \leq \xi \\[4mm] -\,_x\lfloor t_{12} & t_{14} \rfloor_0 \left(\begin{bmatrix} t_{32} & t_{34} \\ t_{42} & t_{44} \end{bmatrix}_0\right)^{-1} \begin{Bmatrix} t_{34} \\ t_{44} \end{Bmatrix}_\xi \\[4mm] \qquad\qquad + \,_x\lfloor t_{14} \rfloor_\xi & x > \xi \end{cases} \qquad (7\text{-}92)$$

In principle, the impulse influence function may be obtained by a Fourier transformation of Eq. (7-92), although to actually carry out the transformation is usually quite difficult.

We now turn to the determination of the transfer matrix $\mathbf{T}(x, s)$. We observe that this matrix is the fundamental solution of Eq. (7-81). Unfortunately, such a solution is not available for an arbitrary nonuniform beam. However, a nonuniform beam can always be approximated by one with piecewise uniform sections, as shown in Fig. 7.5. The approximation can be improved to any desired degree of accuracy by increasing the number of uniform sections. The damping coefficient is assumed to be a constant within each uniform section. Referring to Fig. 7.5, we find that the equation governing $\bar{W}$, the Fourier transform of the displacement within a typical uniform section, say section k (between stations $k - 1$ and k), is as follows:

$$(EI)_k \frac{d^4\bar{W}}{dx^4} - (\omega^2 m_k - i\omega c_k)\bar{W} = 0 \qquad (7\text{-}93)$$

Note that, for the purpose of obtaining the fundamental solution, the external load is assumed to be absent from this section. Let

$$\sigma_k{}^4 = \frac{\omega^2 m_k - i\omega c_k}{(EI)_k} \qquad (7\text{-}94)$$

A solution to Eq. (7-93) may be constructed from four independent parts:

$$\cosh \sigma_k x_k \qquad \sinh \sigma_k x_k \qquad \cos \sigma_k x_k \qquad \sin \sigma_k x_k$$

where x_k is a local coordinate, as shown in Fig. 7.5. Note that although there are four quartic roots for the right-hand side of Eq. (7-94), we may

Fig. 7.5 A piecewise uniform beam.

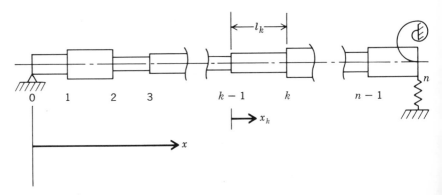

choose any one‡ of these roots for σ_k. Write

$$\bar{W} = \frac{\Lambda_0}{2} \left(\cosh \sigma_k x_k + \cos \sigma_k x_k\right) + \frac{\Lambda_1}{2\sigma_k} \left(\sinh \sigma_k x_k + \sin \sigma_k x_k\right)$$

$$+ \frac{\Lambda_2}{2\sigma_k{}^2} \left(\cosh \sigma_k x_k - \cos \sigma_k x_k\right) + \frac{\Lambda_3}{2\sigma_k{}^3} \left(\sinh \sigma_k x_k - \sin \sigma_k x_k\right) \quad (7\text{-}95)$$

It can easily be shown that the symbols Λ_0, Λ_1, Λ_2, Λ_3 are $\bar{W}$, $\bar{W}'$, $\bar{W}''$, $\bar{W}'''$ evaluated at $x_k = 0$, respectively. Thus

$$\bar{Z}(x_k = 0) = \{\Lambda_0, \Lambda_1, EI\Lambda_2, EI\Lambda_3\}$$

Introduce the following abbreviations:

$$C_0(x_k) = \frac{\cosh \sigma_k x_k + \cos \sigma_k x_k}{2}$$

$$C_2(x_k) = \frac{\cosh \sigma_k x_k - \cos \sigma_k x_k}{2\sigma_k{}^2}$$

$$S_1(x_k) = \frac{\sinh \sigma_k x_k + \sin \sigma_k x_k}{2\sigma_k}$$

$$S_3(x_k) = \frac{\sinh \sigma_k x_k - \sin \sigma_k x_k}{2\sigma_k{}^3}$$

$$(7\text{-}96)$$

Now we are able to write

$$\bar{Z}(x_k) = \mathbf{F}_k(x_k)\bar{Z}(x_k = 0) \quad (7\text{-}97)$$

where

$$\mathbf{F}_k(x_k) = \begin{bmatrix} C_0 & S_1 & \dfrac{C_2}{EI} & \dfrac{S_3}{EI} \\[2mm] \sigma^4 S_3 & C_0 & \dfrac{S_1}{EI} & \dfrac{C_2}{EI} \\[2mm] \sigma^4 EI C_2 & \sigma^4 EI S_3 & C_0 & S_1 \\[2mm] \sigma^4 EI S_1 & \sigma^4 EI C_2 & \sigma^4 S_3 & C_0 \end{bmatrix}_k \quad (7\text{-}98)$$

The subscript k associated with the square matrix on the right-hand side of (7-98) indicates that $\sigma = \sigma_k$, $EI = (EI)_k$, $C_0 = C_0(x_k)$, etc. Equation (7-97) can be verified by performing the matrix multiplication on the right-hand side of this equation and comparing the results with the left-hand side.

The matrix $\mathbf{F}_k(x_k)$ transfers the state vector $\bar{Z}$ from $x_k = 0$ to an arbitrary x_k within a uniform section. It may be noted that $\mathbf{F}_k$ is symmetrical about its cross diagonal. This special form of a transfer matrix within a uniform section can always be obtained by properly arranging

---

‡ Since a complete set of four independent solutions, $\cosh \sigma_k x_k$, $\sinh \sigma_k x_k$, $\cos \sigma_k x_k$, $\sin \sigma_k x_k$, can be constructed from any one of these quartic roots.

the order of the components of the state vector and by suitably assigning a positive direction to each component. This property has been noted in Chap. 6. More generally, if both x_k and s_k are local coordinates within the k section, we have

$$\bar{\mathbf{Z}}(x_k) = \mathbf{F}_k(x_k - s_k)\bar{\mathbf{Z}}(s_k) \tag{7-97a}$$

Since inversion of a transfer matrix implies a transfer of state in the opposite direction, then within a uniform section

$$\mathbf{F}_k^{-1}(x_k - s_k) = \mathbf{F}_k(s_k - x_k) \tag{7-99}$$

Equation (7-99) can be verified by actually carrying out the matrix inversion. As a partial check we see that $\mathbf{F}_k(s_k - x_k)$ reduces to an identity matrix as $x_k = s_k$.

Since the basic transfer matrices $\mathbf{F}_k$ for $k = 1, 2, \ldots, n$ have been determined, the general transfer matrix $\mathbf{T}(x, s)$ for transfer of state from s to x along the beam from the left to the right can be constructed. Let

$$x = x_q + \sum_{j=1}^{q-1} l_j \qquad s = s_p + \sum_{j=1}^{p-1} l_j$$

Then, for x and s in the interval $[0, l)$,

$$\mathbf{T}(x, s) = \begin{cases} \mathbf{F}_q(x_q)\mathbf{F}_{q-1}(l_{q-1})\mathbf{F}_{q-2}(l_{q-2}) \cdots \mathbf{F}_{p+1}(l_{p+1})\mathbf{F}_p(l_p - s_p) \\ \qquad\qquad\qquad\qquad\qquad\qquad\qquad\qquad\qquad q > p \quad (7\text{-}100) \\ \mathbf{F}_q(x_q - s_q) \qquad\qquad\qquad\qquad\qquad\qquad\qquad\qquad q = p \end{cases}$$

The inversion of Eq. (7-100) results in a matrix for transferring the state from x to s,

$$\mathbf{T}(s, x) = \mathbf{T}^{-1}(x, s)$$
$$= \begin{cases} \mathbf{F}_p(s_p - l_p)\mathbf{F}_{p+1}(-l_{p+1}) \cdots \mathbf{F}_{q-1}(-l_{q-1})\mathbf{F}_q(-x_q) & q > p \\ \mathbf{F}_q(s_q - x_q) & q = p \end{cases} \tag{7-101}$$

For $x = l+$, the constraints and the structural damping provided at the elastic support must be taken into consideration. It is convenient to use a point transfer matrix at this support. Thus

$$\mathbf{Z}(l+) = \mathbf{S}\mathbf{Z}(l-) \tag{7-102}$$

where

$$\mathbf{S} = \begin{bmatrix} 1 & 0 & 0 & 0 \\ 0 & 1 & 0 & 0 \\ 0 & k_t(1 + i\beta) & 1 & 0 \\ -k_d(1 + i\alpha) & 0 & 0 & 1 \end{bmatrix} \tag{7-103}$$

Such a point transfer matrix has been disussed in Chap. 6. We then have

$$\mathbf{T}(l+, 0) = \mathbf{S}\mathbf{T}(l-, 0)$$
$$\mathbf{T}(l+, s) = \mathbf{S}\mathbf{T}(l-, s)$$
$$(7\text{-}104)$$

These transfer matrices are needed for the application of Eqs. (7-88) and (7-92).

The foregoing formulation has been based on a particular set of boundary conditions. Other boundary conditions can be treated analogously. Furthermore, if intermediate elastic supports and/or concentrated masses are present along the beam, then additional point transfer matrices must be introduced to account for the discontinuities in transferring the state vector across the stations with such supports and/or concentrated masses. Computational difficulties may arise when the intermediate elastic supports are extremely stiff. Some useful measures devised to circumvent such difficulties may be found in Pestel and Leckie.‡ In this book the case of rigid intermediate supports is also discussed.

It is of interest to compare the results from a normal-mode approach and from a transfer-matrix approach when both methods are applicable. We shall do this for a beam with a uniform cross section and a uniform viscous damping coefficient throughout its length, and simply supported at both ends. For this case

$$T(x, s) = F(x - s) \tag{7-105}$$

and it can be shown that corresponding to the stated boundaries the frequency influence function when $x \leq \xi$ is given by

$$H(x, \xi; \omega) = - \,_x\lfloor t_{12} \quad t_{14} \rfloor_0 \left(\begin{bmatrix} t_{12} & t_{14} \\ t_{32} & t_{34} \end{bmatrix}_0 \right)^{-1} \begin{Bmatrix} t_{14} \\ t_{34} \end{Bmatrix}_\xi \qquad x \leq \xi \tag{7-106}$$

With the help of Eq. (7-98), we find that

$$H(x, \xi; \omega) = (2EI\sigma^3 \sin \sigma l \sin \sigma l)^{-1}[\sinh \sigma l \sin \sigma x \sin \sigma(l - \xi)$$
$$- \sinh \sigma x \sin \sigma l \sin \sigma(l - \xi)] \qquad x \leq \xi \tag{7-106a}$$

To determine the impulse influence function from

$$h(x, \xi; t) = \frac{1}{2\pi} \int_{-\infty}^{\infty} H(x, \xi; \omega) \exp(i\omega t) \, d\omega$$

we shall use the method of residues. By expanding the sine and hyperbolic sine functions in power series it can be seen that the simple poles are located at those values of ω which cause $\sinh \sigma l \sin \sigma l$ to vanish, other

‡ E. C. Pestel and F. A. Leckie, "Matrix Methods in Elastomechanics," p. 192, McGraw-Hill, New York, 1963.

than at $\sigma = 0$, that is, at $\sigma = n\pi/l$, and $\sigma = in\pi/l$, $n = \pm 1, \pm 2, \ldots$. Now σ and ω are related as

$$\sigma^4 = \frac{\omega^2 m - i\omega c}{EI}$$

Therefore the poles are found from the equation

$$\omega_p{}^2 m - i\omega_p c - EI \left(\frac{n\pi}{l}\right)^4 = 0 \tag{7-107}$$

Solving for ω_p,

$$\omega_p = \frac{ic}{2m} \pm \sqrt{\frac{EI}{m}\left(\frac{n\pi}{l}\right)^4 - \frac{c^2}{4m^2}} \tag{7-108}$$

Assume that‡

$$\frac{c}{2m} < \left(\frac{n\pi}{l}\right)^2 \sqrt{\frac{EI}{m}} = \omega_n$$

where ω_n is the undamped natural frequency in the nth mode. Then all the poles are located in the upper complex plane. Note that

$$\frac{c}{2m\omega_n} = \frac{c_n}{2m_n\omega_n} = \zeta_n \tag{7-109}$$

Equation (7-108) may be written more simply as

$$\omega_p = i\zeta_n\omega_n \pm \omega_{nd} \tag{7-108a}$$

It is known that the residue for a function

$$\frac{N(\omega)}{D(\omega)} \exp{(i\omega t)}$$

at a simple pole ω_p is

$$\frac{N(\omega_p)}{D'(\omega_p)} \exp{(i\omega_p t)} \tag{7-110}$$

where $D'(\omega_p)$ is the derivative of $D(\omega)$ evaluated at $\omega = \omega_p$. Let the simple pole $\omega_p = i\zeta_n\omega_n + \omega_{nd}$ be associated with $\sigma = n\pi/l$, and note that

$$\frac{d\sigma}{d\omega} = \frac{2\omega m - ic}{4EI\sigma^3}$$

‡ This assumption implies that the damping is smaller than the critical damping in all the normal modes.

It can be shown by use of (7-110) that the residue at this simple pole is

$$(\text{Res})_{+n} = \frac{-\sin(n\pi x/l)\sin(n\pi\xi/l)}{m\omega_{nd}l} \exp\left[(-\zeta_n\omega_n + i\omega_{nd})t\right] \qquad (7\text{-}111)$$

Similarly, the residue at a simple pole $\omega_p = i\zeta_n\omega_n - \omega_{nd}$ associated with $\sigma = in\pi/l$ is

$$(\text{Res})_{-n} = \frac{\sin(n\pi x/l)\sin(n\pi\xi/l)}{m\omega_{nd}l} \exp\left[(-\zeta_n\omega_n - i\omega_{nd})t\right] \qquad (7\text{-}112)$$

It follows that

$$
\begin{aligned}
h(x,\xi;t) &= i\sum_{n=1}^{\infty}\left[(\text{Res})_{+n} + (\text{Res})_{-n}\right] \\
&= \sum_{n=1}^{\infty}\frac{\sin(n\pi x/l)\sin(n\pi\xi/l)}{m_n\omega_{nd}}\exp\left(-\zeta_n\omega_n t\right)\sin\omega_{nd}t \quad t \ge 0 \quad (7\text{-}113)
\end{aligned}
$$

where all quantities are real, and $m_n = m/2$ is the generalized mass in the nth mode. Although this impulse influence function has been obtained for $x \le \xi$, it can be shown that the same expression is obtained for $x > \xi$. This result agrees with Eq. (7-33) when $f_n(x) = \sin(n\pi x/l)$.

7.5 / MULTISPANNED PANEL SYSTEM

With a small variation, the method of transfer matrices can be used to analyze a rather complicated problem, namely, the random vibration of a multispanned panel system. Figure 7.6 shows a plan view of a row of rectangular panels supported by a number of stringers running parallel to the x axis and by two frames at $x = 0$ and $x = l$. The configuration resembles a typical bay of fuselage panels of a large aircraft. It is known that the fuselage panels located to the rear of jet engines vibrate randomly because of the excitation of engine noise. The vibration is especially intense during takeoffs when the engines are operated at maximum power. In due course, fatigue failures may result in such panels. This phenomenon is called *acoustical fatigue*. To estimate the fatigue life, we need to know the statistical properties of the random vibrations of the panels.

Experience has shown that the acoustical-fatigue failures of a fuselage panel usually occur near the span center of a supporting stringer. This is due to the common practice whereby the stringers are spaced about two to three times closer than the frames. Therefore the stress excursion in a panel is largest near the center of a stringer. If our interest is limited to such critical locations, we can make the analysis more tractable by considering only a row of panels in one bay between two frames, as pictured in Fig. 7.6. Further, we shall assume that the panels are simply supported at the frames. Of course, these simplifications would not be acceptable if the stresses near the frames were of interest. Note that the coupling of motion between two neighboring panels across a common supporting frame is disregarded in this simplified structural model. Although fuselage panels are curved, we shall omit the effects of curvature in the present discussion; i.e., each panel is treated as a thin plate.

Two basic transfer matrices are required in this formulation: the matrix relating two state vectors across an unloaded panel and the matrix relating two state vectors across a stringer. Consider first an unloaded panel with a uniform thickness. The equation of motion is given by

$$\frac{\partial^4 W}{\partial x^4} + 2\,\frac{\partial^4 W}{\partial x^2\,\partial y^2} + \frac{\partial^4 W}{\partial y^4} + c\dot{W} + \frac{m}{D}\,\ddot{W} = 0 \qquad (7\text{-}114)$$

Fig. 7.6 A multispanned panel system.

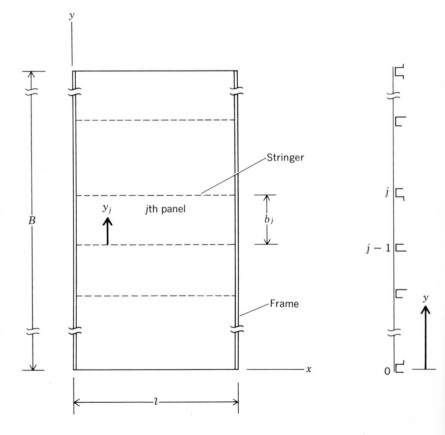

where the mass density per unit panel area, m, may include the *apparent mass*, and the damping coefficient c may include the effect of the acoustic damping.‡ Since the two sides $x = 0$ and $x = l$ of this panel are simply supported, the solution to Eq. (7-114) may be written as

$$W = \sum_{n=1}^{\infty} W_n = \sum_{n=1}^{\infty} Y_n(y, t) \sin \frac{n\pi x}{l} \qquad (7\text{-}115)$$

Substitution of (7-115) into (7-114) and application of the orthogonality condition of the sine functions yield a system of uncoupled equations for the determination of the functions $Y_n(y, t)$ as follows:

$$\frac{\partial^4 Y_n}{\partial y^4} - 2\left(\frac{n\pi}{l}\right)^2 \frac{\partial^2 Y_n}{\partial y^2} + \left(\frac{n\pi}{l}\right)^4 Y_n + c\dot{Y}_n + \frac{m}{D}\ddot{Y}_n = 0 \qquad (7\text{-}116)$$

For the purpose of obtaining the frequency influence functions we seek a solution to the Fourier transform of Eq. (7-116), namely,

$$\bar{Y}_n{}^{(4)} - 2\left(\frac{n\pi}{l}\right)^2 \bar{Y}_n'' + \left[\left(\frac{n\pi}{l}\right)^4 - \frac{m\omega^2}{D} + ic\omega\right]\bar{Y}_n = 0 \qquad (7\text{-}117)$$

where each prime indicates one differentiation with respect to y. It can easily be seen that a solution to Eq. (7-117) can be constructed from a linear combination of four independent components

$$\cosh \sigma_1 y_j \qquad \sinh \sigma_1 y_j \qquad \cos \sigma_2 y_j \qquad \sin \sigma_2 y_j \qquad (7\text{-}118)$$

where

$$\sigma_1 = \left[\left(\frac{m\omega^2}{D} - ic\omega\right)^{\frac{1}{2}} + \left(\frac{n\pi}{l}\right)^2\right]^{\frac{1}{2}}$$

$$\sigma_2 = \left[\left(\frac{m\omega^2}{D} - ic\omega\right)^{\frac{1}{2}} - \left(\frac{n\pi}{l}\right)^2\right]^{\frac{1}{2}} \qquad (7\text{-}119)$$

and y_j is a local coordinate in the y direction (cf. Fig. 7.6). As can be seen from Eqs. (7-119), the evaluation of σ_1 and σ_2 involves taking square roots of complex quantities; therefore the values obtained are not unique. However, it is permissible to use any pair of σ_1 and σ_2 values as long as the four components in (7-118) are independent solutions of Eq. (7-117).

For the present purpose, it is convenient to write

$$\bar{Y}_n(y_j) = \frac{\Lambda_0}{s^2}\left(\sigma_2{}^2 \cosh \sigma_1 y_j + \sigma_1{}^2 \cos \sigma_2 y_j\right) + \frac{\Lambda_1}{s^2}\left(\frac{\sigma_2{}^2}{\sigma_1}\sinh \sigma_1 y_j + \frac{\sigma_1{}^2}{\sigma_2}\sin \sigma_2 y_j\right)$$

$$+ \frac{\Lambda_2}{s^2}\left(\cosh \sigma_1 y_j - \cos \sigma_2 y_j\right) + \frac{\Lambda_3}{s^2}\left(\frac{1}{\sigma_1}\sinh \sigma_1 y_j - \frac{1}{\sigma_2}\sin \sigma_2 y_j\right) \qquad (7\text{-}120)$$

‡ The apparent mass and the acoustic damping can be evaluated approximately by use of a one-dimensional theory of sound propagation; cf. Sec. 7.3.

where

$$s^2 = \sigma_1{}^2 + \sigma_2{}^2 = 2\left(\frac{m\omega^2}{D} - ic\omega\right)^{\frac{1}{2}} \tag{7-121}$$

It can easily be shown that the coefficients Λ_0, Λ_1, Λ_2, Λ_3 are $\bar{Y}_n$, $\bar{Y}_n'$, $\bar{Y}_n''$, $\bar{Y}_n'''$ evaluated at $y_j = 0$, respectively. Then these functions evaluated at y_j are

$$\begin{Bmatrix} \bar{Y}_n \\ \bar{Y}_n' \\ \bar{Y}_n'' \\ \bar{Y}_n''' \end{Bmatrix}_{y_j} = \begin{bmatrix} \mathcal{C}_0 & \mathcal{S}_{-1} & \mathcal{C}_{-2} & \mathcal{S}_{-3} \\ \mathcal{S}_1 & \mathcal{C}_0 & \mathcal{S}_{-1}' & \mathcal{C}_{-2} \\ \mathcal{C}_2 & \mathcal{S}_1 & \mathcal{C}_0' & \mathcal{S}_{-1}' \\ \mathcal{S}_3 & \mathcal{C}_2 & \mathcal{S}_1' & \mathcal{C}_0' \end{bmatrix}_j \begin{Bmatrix} \bar{Y}_n \\ \bar{Y}_n' \\ \bar{Y}_n'' \\ \bar{Y}_n''' \end{Bmatrix}_{y_j=0} \tag{7-122}$$

where we have used the abbreviations

$$\mathcal{C}_{-2} = \frac{1}{s^2}\left(\cosh \sigma_1 y_j - \cos \sigma_2 y_j\right)$$

$$\mathcal{C}_0 = \frac{1}{s^2}\left(\sigma_2{}^2 \cosh \sigma_1 y_j + \sigma_1{}^2 \cos \sigma_2 y_j\right)$$

$$\mathcal{C}_0' = \frac{1}{s^2}\left(\sigma_1{}^2 \cosh \sigma_1 y_j + \sigma_2{}^2 \cos \sigma_2 y_j\right)$$

$$\mathcal{C}_2 = \frac{\sigma_1{}^2\sigma_2{}^2}{s^2}\left(\cosh \sigma_1 y_j - \cos \sigma_2 y_j\right)$$

$$\mathcal{S}_{-3} = \frac{1}{s^2}\left(\frac{1}{\sigma_1}\sinh \sigma_1 y_j - \frac{1}{\sigma_2}\sin \sigma_2 y_j\right)$$

$$\mathcal{S}_{-1} = \frac{1}{s^2}\left(\frac{\sigma_2{}^2}{\sigma_1}\sinh \sigma_1 y_j + \frac{\sigma_1{}^2}{\sigma_2}\sin \sigma_2 y_j\right) \tag{7-123}$$

$$\mathcal{S}_{-1}' = \frac{1}{s^2}\left(\sigma_1 \sinh \sigma_1 y_j + \sigma_2 \sin \sigma_2 y_j\right)$$

$$\mathcal{S}_1 = \frac{\sigma_1\sigma_2}{s^2}\left(\sigma_2 \sinh \sigma_1 y_j - \sigma_1 \sin \sigma_2 y_j\right)$$

$$\mathcal{S}_1' = \frac{1}{s^2}\left(\sigma_1{}^3 \sinh \sigma_1 y_j - \sigma_2{}^3 \sin \sigma_2 y_j\right)$$

$$\mathcal{S}_3 = \frac{\sigma_1{}^2\sigma_2{}^2}{s^2}\left(\sigma_1 \sinh \sigma_1 y_j + \sigma_2 \sin \sigma_2 y_j\right)$$

The subscript j attached to the square matrix in Eq. (7-122) signifies that the physical constants of the jth panel should be used to compute this matrix.

The column $\{\bar{Y}_n,\ \bar{Y}_n',\ \bar{Y}_n'',\ \bar{Y}_n'''\}$ can be converted to the column $\bar{Z}_n = \{\bar{Y}_n,\ \bar{Y}_n',\ \bar{M}_n,\ \bar{V}_n\}$ or vice versa, where $\bar{M}_n$ and $\bar{V}_n$ describe the variations in the y direction of the Fourier transforms of the unit moment and the unit shear, respectively, corresponding to the panel displacement

W_n [cf. Eq. (7-115)]; i.e.,

$$D \left(\frac{\partial^2 \bar{W}_n}{\partial y^2} + \nu \frac{\partial^2 \bar{W}_n}{\partial x^2} \right) = \bar{M}_n \sin \frac{n\pi x}{l}$$

$$D \frac{\partial}{\partial y} \left[\frac{\partial^2 \bar{W}_n}{\partial y^2} + (2 - \nu) \frac{\partial^2 \bar{W}_n}{\partial x^2} \right] = \bar{V}_n \sin \frac{n\pi x}{l} \tag{7-124}$$

A simple calculation shows that

$$\bar{\mathbf{Z}}_n = \begin{bmatrix} 1 & 0 & 0 & 0 \\ 0 & 1 & 0 & 0 \\ -D \left(\dfrac{n\pi}{l} \right)^2 \nu & 0 & D & 0 \\ 0 & -D(2 - \nu) \left(\dfrac{n\pi}{l} \right)^2 & 0 & D \end{bmatrix}_j \begin{Bmatrix} \bar{Y}_n \\ \bar{Y}'_n \\ \bar{Y}''_n \\ \bar{Y}'''_n \end{Bmatrix} \tag{7-125}$$

and

$$\begin{Bmatrix} \bar{Y}_n \\ \bar{Y}'_n \\ \bar{Y}''_n \\ \bar{Y}'''_n \end{Bmatrix} = \begin{bmatrix} 1 & 0 & 0 & 0 \\ 0 & 1 & 0 & 0 \\ \left(\dfrac{n\pi}{l} \right)^2 \nu & 0 & \dfrac{1}{D} & 0 \\ 0 & (2 - \nu) \left(\dfrac{n\pi}{l} \right)^2 & 0 & \dfrac{1}{D} \end{bmatrix}_j \bar{\mathbf{Z}}_n \tag{7-126}$$

Equations (7-122), (7-125), and (7-126) may be combined to give

$$\bar{\mathbf{Z}}_n(y_j) = \mathbf{F}_j(y_j) \bar{\mathbf{Z}}_n(0) \tag{7-127}$$

where

$$\mathbf{F}_j(y_j) = \begin{bmatrix} 1 & 0 & 0 & 0 \\ 0 & 1 & 0 & 0 \\ -D \left(\dfrac{n\pi}{l} \right)^2 \nu & 0 & D & 0 \\ 0 & -D(2 - \nu) \left(\dfrac{n\pi}{l} \right)^2 & 0 & D \end{bmatrix}_j$$

$$\begin{bmatrix} \mathcal{C}_0 & \mathcal{S}_{-1} & \mathcal{C}_{-2} & \mathcal{S}_{-3} \\ \mathcal{S}_1 & \mathcal{C}_0 & \mathcal{S}'_{-1} & \mathcal{C}_{-2} \\ \mathcal{C}_2 & \mathcal{S}_1 & \mathcal{C}_0 & \mathcal{S}'_{-1} \\ \mathcal{S}_3 & \mathcal{C}_2 & \mathcal{S}'_1 & \mathcal{C}'_0 \end{bmatrix}_j \begin{bmatrix} 1 & 0 & 0 & 0 \\ 0 & 1 & 0 & 0 \\ \left(\dfrac{n\pi}{l} \right)^2 \nu & 0 & \dfrac{1}{D} & 0 \\ 0 & (2 - \nu) \left(\dfrac{n\pi}{l} \right)^2 & 0 & \dfrac{1}{D} \end{bmatrix}_j \tag{7-128}$$

The matrix $\mathbf{F}_j(y_j)$ transfers a state vector in the y direction from $y_j = 0$ to an arbitrary y_j, assuming that the value of the state vector varies as sin $(n\pi x/l)$ in the x direction. To account for structural damping in the panel a complex value may be used for the bending rigidity D in Eq. (7-128). It is of interest to note the similarity between Eqs. (7-97) and (7-127).

The transfer of state across a stringer supporting two neighboring panels can be studied by a consideration of the interaction between the panels and the stringer. For the sake of light weight and ease of fabrication and maintenance, the stringers used in aircraft construction are generally thin members with an open-shape cross section. The ⌐ shape and ⌐⌐ shape cross sections are frequent examples. When the panels vibrate, the supporting stringers also vibrate in bending and torsion. Figure 7.7a shows a stringer cross section in both the undisplaced position and a displaced position. The points C and O are the centroid and the shear center of the stringer cross section, respectively. When the stringer is deformed, the elastic forces of the stringer may be summed into resultant vertical and horizontal forces through O and a resultant torque about O. The inertial forces of the stringer, however, are more conveniently summed into similar resultants through and about the centroid C. In addition, there are forces and a moment transmitted from the skin panels to the stringer at the point of attachment S (cf. Fig. 7.7b), assumed to be directly beneath the shear center O. The equations gov-

Fig. 7.7 (a) Stringer cross section showing undisplaced and displaced positions; (b) forces and moment transmitted from skin to stringer.

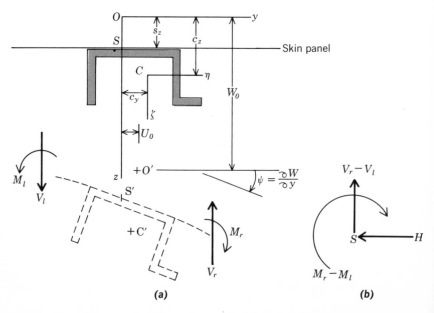

erning the motion of the stringer can then be expressed as follows:

$$EC_w \frac{\partial^4 \psi}{\partial x^4} - GC \frac{\partial^2 \psi}{\partial x^2} = -\rho I_C \ddot{\psi} - \rho A c_y \ddot{W}_C + H s_z + \rho A c_z \ddot{U}_C + M_r - M_l$$

$$EI_\eta \frac{\partial^4}{\partial x^4} W_O + EI_{\eta\zeta} \frac{\partial^4}{\partial x^4} U_O = -\rho A \ddot{W}_C - (V_r - V_l) \qquad (7\text{-}129)$$

$$EI_\zeta \frac{\partial^4}{\partial x^4} U_O + EI_{\eta\zeta} \frac{\partial^4}{\partial x^4} W_O = -\rho A \ddot{U}_C - H$$

where, besides the symbols indicated in Fig. 7.7, we designate the following physical constants of the stringer:

A = cross-sectional area

C = Saint Venant constant of uniform torsion

C_w = warping constant with respect to shear center

E, G = moduli of elasticity

I_C = polar moment of inertia about the centroid

$I_\eta, I_\zeta, I_{\eta\zeta}$ = centroidal moments of inertia and product moment of inertia

ρ = mass density

In Eqs. (7-129) the subscript r (or l) associated with M or V signifies that the moment or shear is transmitted from the skin panel on the right (or left) of the stringer considered. These equations are written essentially for the torsional displacement ψ and the vertical and horizontal displacements W_O and U_O of the shear center. Since the point S is considered as the point of attachment between the stringer and the skin, the motion of point S is the same as the skin motion at S, which has the components W and U. For small displacements, the component $U = 0$ and

$$W_O = W + s_z(1 - \cos \psi) \approx W$$
$$U_O = s_z \psi$$
$$W_C = W + c_y \psi \qquad (7\text{-}130)$$
$$U_C = -(c_z - s_z)\psi$$

Substituting these relations into Eqs. (7-129) and eliminating H,

$$EC_{ws} \frac{\partial^4}{\partial x^4} \psi - GC \frac{\partial^2}{\partial x^2} \psi$$

$$= -\rho I_S \ddot{\psi} - \rho A c_y \ddot{W} - EI_{\eta\zeta} s_z \frac{\partial^4}{\partial x^4} W + (M_r - M_l) \qquad (7\text{-}131)$$

$$EI_\eta \frac{\partial^4}{\partial x^4} W + EI_{\eta\zeta} s_z \frac{\partial^4}{\partial x^4} \psi = -\rho A (\ddot{W} + c_y \ddot{\psi}) - (V_r - V_l)$$

where use has been made of the following relations:

$$C_{ws} = C_w + s_z{}^2 EI_\zeta$$
$$I_S = I_C + A[c_y{}^2 + (c_z - s_z)^2]$$

For the present sign conventions,

$$\psi = \frac{\partial W}{\partial y}$$

$$M = D\left(\frac{\partial^2 W}{\partial y^2} + \nu \frac{\partial^2 W}{\partial x^2}\right)$$

$$V = D\frac{\partial}{\partial y}\left[\frac{\partial^2 W}{\partial y^2} + (2 - \nu)\frac{\partial^2 W}{\partial x^2}\right]$$

Equations (7-131) may be rewritten as

$$EC_{ws}\frac{\partial^5 W}{\partial x^4 \partial y} - GC\frac{\partial^3 W}{\partial x^2 \partial y} + \rho I_s\frac{\partial^3 W}{\partial t^2 \partial y} + \rho A c_y\frac{\partial^2 W}{\partial t^2} + EI_{\eta\zeta}s_z\frac{\partial^4 W}{\partial x^4}$$

$$= \left[D\left(\frac{\partial^2 W}{\partial y^2} + \nu\frac{\partial^2 W}{\partial x^2}\right)\right]_r - \left[D\left(\frac{\partial^2 W}{\partial y^2} + \nu\frac{\partial^2 W}{\partial x^2}\right)\right]_l$$

$$EI_{\eta}\frac{\partial^4 W}{\partial x^4} + EI_{\eta\zeta}s_z\frac{\partial^5 W}{\partial x^4 \partial y} + \rho A\frac{\partial^2}{\partial t^2}\left(W + c_y\frac{\partial W}{\partial y}\right)$$
$$\tag{7-132}$$

$$= -\left\{D\frac{\partial}{\partial y}\left[\frac{\partial^2 W}{\partial y^2} + (2 - \nu)\frac{\partial^2 W}{\partial x^2}\right]\right\}_r + \left\{D\frac{\partial}{\partial y}\left[\frac{\partial^2 W}{\partial y^2} + (2 - \nu)\frac{\partial^2 W}{\partial x^2}\right]\right\}_l$$

Furthermore, the deflection and the slope must remain continuous; that is,

$$W_l = W_r$$
$$\left(\frac{\partial W}{\partial y}\right)_l = \left(\frac{\partial W}{\partial y}\right)_r$$
$$\tag{7-133}$$

Equations (7-132) are the equilibrium conditions and Eqs. (7-133) the continuity conditions which two adjoining panels must satisfy at the common supporting stringers. Upon substitution of the expression for W, Eq. (7-115), into Eqs. (7-132) and (7-133), it is readily seen that these conditions must be met by each $W_n = Y_n \sin(n\pi x/l)$ in the sum. A simple algebraic manipulation will show that the Fourier transforms $\bar{Y}_n$, $\bar{Y}'_n$, $\bar{M}_n$, $\bar{V}_n$ must satisfy

$$(\bar{Y}_n)_r = (\bar{Y}_n)_l = \bar{Y}_n$$
$$(\bar{Y}'_n)_r = (\bar{Y}'_n)_l = \bar{Y}'_n$$
$$(\bar{M}_n)_r = (\bar{M}_n)_l + d\bar{Y}_n + c\bar{Y}'_n$$
$$(\bar{V}_n)_r = (\bar{V}_n)_l - e\bar{Y}_n - d\bar{Y}'_n$$
$$\tag{7-134}$$

where

$$c = EC_{ws}\left(\frac{n\pi}{l}\right)^4 + GC\left(\frac{n\pi}{l}\right)^2 - \rho I_s\omega^2$$

$$d = EI_{\eta\zeta}s_z\left(\frac{n\pi}{l}\right)^4 - Ac_y\omega^2$$
$$\tag{7-135}$$

$$e = EI_{\eta}\left(\frac{n\pi}{l}\right)^4 - \rho A\omega^2$$

which are basically the elastic and inertial properties of the supporting stringer. Write Eqs. (7-134) in the matrix form

$$(\bar{Z}_n)_r = S_j(\bar{Z}_n)_l \tag{7-134a}$$

where the vector $\bar{Z}_n$ is, of course, $\{\bar{Y}_n, \bar{Y}_n', \bar{M}_n, \bar{V}_n\}$ and

$$S_j = \begin{bmatrix} 1 & 0 & 0 & 0 \\ 0 & 1 & 0 & 0 \\ d & c & 1 & 0 \\ -e & -d & 0 & 1 \end{bmatrix}_j \tag{7-136}$$

The subscript j associated with the matrix S signifies that the physical constants of the jth stringer should be used to compute the elements of this matrix. As is represented in Eq. (7-134a), the matrix S_j transfers a state vector from the left side of the jth stringer to the right side of the stringer. To account for the structural damping of the stringer, the elastic moduli of the stringer, E and G, appearing in Eqs. (7-135) may be replaced by $E(1 + i\alpha)$ and $G(1 + i\gamma)$, respectively.

Having determined the basic transfer matrices F_j and S_j for every panel and every stringer, we can now construct the general transfer matrix $T_n(y, s)$ for transfer of state from s to y in the y direction. Let

$$y = y_q + \sum_{j=1}^{q-1} b_j \qquad s = s_p + \sum_{j=1}^{p-1} b_j$$

Then for both y and s corresponding to two locations within the panel row

$$T_n(y, s) = \begin{cases} F_q(y_q)S_{q-1}F_{q-1}(b_{q-1}) \cdots F_{p+1}(b_{p+1})S_pF_p(b_p - s_p) & q > p \\ F_q(y_q - s_q) & q = p \end{cases} \tag{7-137}$$

The inversion of Eq. (7-137) results in a matrix for transferring the state from y to s; that is,

$$T_n(s, y) = T_n^{-1}(y, s) \tag{7-138}$$

When carrying out the inversion it is useful to note that

$$F_j^{-1}(y_j) = F_j(-y_j) \tag{7-139}$$

and that

$$S_j^{-1} = \begin{bmatrix} 1 & 0 & 0 & 0 \\ 0 & 1 & 0 & 0 \\ -d & -c & 1 & 0 \\ e & d & 0 & 1 \end{bmatrix}_j \tag{7-140}$$

The frequency influence function of the panel row, $H(x, y; r, s; \omega)$, can now be obtained from the transfer matrix $T_n(y, s)$. For this purpose, consider the excitation to be a *deterministic* concentrated load

$$P(x, y, t) = 2\pi \, \delta(x - r) \, \delta(y - s) \, \delta(t)$$

then the frequency influence function is the Fourier transform of the response to this excitation. Let an excitation be represented by

$$P(x, y, t) = \int_{-\infty}^{\infty} \sum_{n=1}^{\infty} \bar{P}_n(y, \omega) \sin \frac{n\pi x}{l} \exp (i\omega t) \, d\omega \qquad (7\text{-}141)$$

or, equivalently, let the Fourier transform of P be represented by

$$\bar{P}(x, y, \omega) = \frac{1}{2\pi} \int_{-\infty}^{\infty} P(x, y, t) \exp (-i\omega t) \, dt$$
$$= \sum_{n=1}^{\infty} \bar{P}_n(y, \omega) \sin \frac{n\pi x}{l} \qquad (7\text{-}142)$$

It is readily seen that for the present case,

$$\bar{P}_n(y, \omega) = \frac{2}{l} \sin \frac{n\pi r}{l} \, \delta(y - s) \qquad (7\text{-}143)$$

Thus

$$\bar{P}(x, y, \omega) = \frac{2}{l} \sum_{n=1}^{\infty} \sin \frac{n\pi r}{l} \sin \frac{n\pi x}{l} \, \delta(y - s) \qquad (7\text{-}144)$$

Corresponding to each term of this sum, i.e., for each n, we may write relations for the Fourier transforms of the response state vectors as follows:

$$\bar{Z}_n(y) = \begin{cases} \mathbf{T}_n(y, 0)\bar{Z}_n(0) & y \leq s \\[2mm] \mathbf{T}_n(y, 0)\bar{Z}_n(0) + \mathbf{T}_n(y, s) \begin{Bmatrix} 0 \\ 0 \\ 0 \\ \dfrac{2}{l} \sin \dfrac{n\pi r}{l} \end{Bmatrix} & y > s \end{cases} \qquad (7\text{-}145)$$

and

$$\bar{Z}_n(B) = \mathbf{T}_n(B, 0)\bar{Z}_n(0) + \mathbf{T}_n(B, s) \begin{Bmatrix} 0 \\ 0 \\ 0 \\ \dfrac{2}{l} \sin \dfrac{n\pi r}{l} \end{Bmatrix} \qquad (7\text{-}146)$$

In Eqs. (7-145) and (7-146) the common factor $\sin (n\pi x/l)$ has been dropped for brevity. From these equations an explicit expression for $\bar{Z}_n(y)$ can be derived when the boundary conditions at $y = 0$ and $y = B$ are specified. The procedure is similar to the derivation of Eq. (6-59) for the case of a Myklestad beam. For the purpose of discussion, let both ends of the panel row, i.e., $y = 0$ and $y = B$, be simply supported on rigid supports. Then

$$\bar{Z}_n(0) = \begin{Bmatrix} 0 \\ \bar{Y}'_n(0) \\ 0 \\ \bar{V}_n(0) \end{Bmatrix} \qquad \bar{Z}_n(B) = \begin{Bmatrix} 0 \\ \bar{Y}'_n(B) \\ 0 \\ \bar{V}_n(B) \end{Bmatrix} \qquad (7\text{-}147)$$

Inserting (7-147) into (7-146) and rearranging, we obtain

$$\begin{Bmatrix} \bar{Y}'_n(0) \\ \bar{V}_n(0) \end{Bmatrix} = - \left({}_B\begin{bmatrix} t_{12} & t_{14} \\ t_{32} & t_{34} \end{bmatrix}_0 \right)^{-1} {}_B\begin{Bmatrix} t_{14} \\ t_{34} \end{Bmatrix}_s \frac{2}{l} \sin \frac{n\pi r}{l} \qquad (7\text{-}148)$$

where, as before, each t_{jk} is the (j, k) element of a transfer matrix $\mathbf{T}_n$, the arguments of which are indicated at the corners of the matrix symbol. Using (7-148) in Eq. (7-145) and keeping only the first row, i.e., the expression for $\bar{Y}_n(y)$, we find that

$$\bar{Y}_n(y) = \begin{cases} -{}_y\lfloor\, t_{12} \quad t_{14}\,\rfloor_0 \left({}_B\begin{bmatrix} t_{12} & t_{14} \\ t_{32} & t_{34} \end{bmatrix}_0 \right)^{-1} {}_B\begin{Bmatrix} t_{14} \\ t_{34} \end{Bmatrix}_s \frac{2}{l} \sin \frac{n\pi r}{l} & y \le s \\[2em] -{}_y\lfloor\, t_{12} \quad t_{14}\,\rfloor_0 \left({}_B\begin{bmatrix} t_{12} & t_{14} \\ t_{32} & t_{34} \end{bmatrix}_0 \right)^{-1} {}_B\begin{Bmatrix} t_{14} \\ t_{34} \end{Bmatrix}_s \frac{2}{l} \sin \frac{n\pi r}{l} & (7\text{-}149) \\[2em] \qquad + {}_y\lfloor\, t_{14}\,\rfloor_s \frac{2}{l} \sin \frac{n\pi r}{l} & y > s \end{cases}$$

Thus the required frequency influence function

$$H(x, y; r, s; \omega) = \sum_{n=1}^{\infty} \bar{Y}_n(y) \sin \frac{n\pi x}{l}$$

$$= \begin{cases} -\sum_{n=1}^{\infty} {}_y\lfloor\, t_{12} \quad t_{14}\,\rfloor_0 \left({}_B\begin{bmatrix} t_{12} & t_{14} \\ t_{32} & t_{34} \end{bmatrix}_0 \right)^{-1} {}_B\begin{Bmatrix} t_{14} \\ t_{34} \end{Bmatrix}_s \frac{2}{l} \sin \frac{n\pi r}{l} \sin \frac{n\pi x}{l} & y \le s \\[2em] & (7\text{-}150) \\[1em] -\sum_{n=1}^{\infty} {}_y\lfloor\, t_{12} \quad t_{14}\,\rfloor_0 \left({}_B\begin{bmatrix} t_{12} & t_{14} \\ t_{32} & t_{34} \end{bmatrix}_0 \right)^{-1} {}_B\begin{Bmatrix} t_{14} \\ t_{34} \end{Bmatrix}_s \frac{2}{l} \sin \frac{n\pi r}{l} \sin \frac{n\pi x}{l} \\[2em] \qquad + \sum_{n=1}^{\infty} {}_y\lfloor\, t_{14}\,\rfloor_s \frac{2}{l} \sin \frac{n\pi r}{l} \sin \frac{n\pi x}{l} & y > s \end{cases}$$

Finally, the generalized cross spectral density or the cross spectral density of the response under random excitation follows from an application of Eq. (7-6) or Eq. (7-14).

In the foregoing analysis the thickness of each panel was assumed to be uniform. It is not difficult to modify the formulation for the case of piecewise uniform panel thickness. An alternative scheme‡ is to lump

‡ Y. K. Lin, Response of Multi-spanned Beam and Panel Systems under Noise Excitation, Air Force Systems Command, AFML-TR-64-348, Part I, Wright-Patterson Air Force Base, Ohio, February, 1965.

the distributed mass of each panel as well as the excitations along straight lines parallel to the x axis. Then the resulting expression for the response cross spectral density or generalized cross spectral density is analogous to that obtained in Sec. 6.3 for a beam with similarly lumped masses and excitations.

To take into account the effect of the curvature of the panels requires a basic transfer matrix for curved panels. The technique for obtaining this transfer matrix was discussed by Lin, McDaniel, Donaldson, Vail, and Dwyer.‡

7.6 / THE METHOD OF DIFFERENCE EQUATIONS

In Sec. 6.5, the method of difference equations was used to analyze a one-dimensional structure with finitely many degrees of freedom, the interior of which was composed of identical units. We shall now show that under the same general conditions this type of formulation also applies to continuous structures.

As an example, consider a uniform beam supported on an arbitrary number of uniformly spaced hinges,¶ as shown in Fig. 7.8. The beam is subjected to random moments $M_0(t)$ and $M_N(t)$ at the two exterior ends. Let the equations of motion be

$$EI \frac{\partial^4 W_k}{\partial x_k{}^4} + c\dot{W}_k + m\ddot{W}_k = 0 \qquad k = 1, 2, \ldots, N \qquad (7\text{-}151)$$

where each x_k is a local coordinate, such that

$$x_k = x - (k - 1)l \qquad (k - 1)l \leq x \leq kl$$

‡ Y. K. Lin, T. J. McDaniel, B. K. Donaldson, C. F. Vail, and W. J. Dwyer, Free Vibration of Continuous Skin-stringer Panels with Non-uniform Stringer Spacing and Panel Thickness, Air Force Systems Command, AFML-TR-64-347, Wright-Patterson Air Force Base, Ohio, February, 1965.

¶ The undamped free vibrations of such a beam have been considered by Miles. See J. W. Miles, Vibrations of Beams on Many Supports, *J. Eng. Mech. Div., Am. Soc. Civil Engrs.*, **82**(EM 1):1–9 (1956).

Fig. 7.8 A uniform beam supported by uniformly spaced hinges.

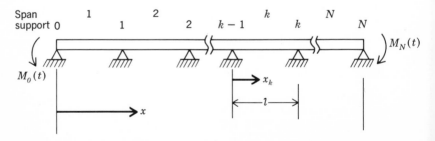

Equation (7-151) is to be solved in conjunction with the conditions

$$W_1''(0, t) = (EI)^{-1}M_0(t)$$
$$W_N''(l, t) = (EI)^{-1}M_N(t)$$
$$(7\text{-}152)$$

For simplicity, assume that the beam is originally at rest and that the exciting moments have zero expectations. Then

$$E[W_k(x_k, t)] = 0 \qquad (7\text{-}153)$$

For the determination of the generalized cross spectral density or the cross spectral density of the response we need to solve the transformed version of Eq. (7-151), that is,

$$EI \frac{d^4\bar{W}_k}{dx_k{}^4} - (m\omega^2 - ic\omega)\bar{W}_k = 0 \qquad k = 1, 2, \ldots, N \qquad (7\text{-}151a)$$

subject to the conditions

$$\bar{W}_1''(0) = (EI)^{-1}\bar{M}_0$$
$$\bar{W}_N''(l) = (EI)^{-1}\bar{M}_N$$
$$(7\text{-}152a)$$

where an upper bar indicates the Fourier transform or the truncated Fourier transform of W_k, as the case may be.

A general solution to Eq. (7-151a) satisfying $\bar{W}_k(0) = \bar{W}_k(l) = 0$, $k = 1, 2, \ldots, N$, as required at the hinged supports, may be written as follows:

$$\bar{W}_k = A_k(\sinh \sigma l \sin \sigma x_k - \sin \sigma l \sinh \sigma x_k)$$
$$+ B_k[\sinh \sigma l \sin \sigma(l - x_k) - \sin \sigma l \sinh \sigma(l - x_k)] \qquad (7\text{-}154)$$

where

$$\sigma^4 = \frac{m\omega^2 - ic\omega}{EI} \qquad (7\text{-}155)$$

As was mentioned in Sec. 7.4, it is permissible to use any of the four quartic roots of the right-hand side of (7-155) for the value of σ in computations. At each of the interior supports the continuity of slope and the equilibrium in moment require that

$$\left.\begin{array}{l}\bar{W}_k'(l) = \bar{W}_{k+1}'(0) \\ \bar{W}_k''(l) = \bar{W}_{k+1}''(0)\end{array}\right\} \qquad k = 1, 2, \ldots, N - 1 \qquad (7\text{-}156)$$

The imposition of the equilibrium condition, i.e., the second equation in (7-156), yields

$$A_k = B_{k+1} \qquad (7\text{-}157)$$

Then from the slope continuity condition, i.e., the first equation in (7-156), we obtain

$$A_{k+1} - 2\cos\theta A_k + A_{k-1} = 0 \qquad (7\text{-}158)$$

where‡

$$\cos \theta = \frac{\sinh \sigma l \cos \sigma l - \sin \sigma l \cosh \sigma l}{\sinh \sigma l - \sin \sigma l} \qquad (7\text{-}159)$$

Equation (7-158) is written in a standard form¶ for symmetrical difference equations. Corresponding to this standard form, the general solution for A_k may be written as

$$A_k = \Lambda_1 \cos k\theta + \Lambda_2 \sin k\theta \qquad (7\text{-}160)$$

This solution satisfies the conditions at the interior supports with arbitrary Λ_1 and Λ_2. In order that the conditions at the exterior supports can be satisfied also, we further impose Eqs. (7-152a), which require

$$\Lambda_1 = -\frac{\bar{M}_0}{2EI\sigma^2 \sinh \sigma l \sin \sigma l}$$

$$\Lambda_2 = \frac{\bar{M}_0 \cos N\theta - \bar{M}_N}{2EI\sigma^2 \sinh \sigma l \sin \sigma l \sin N\theta} \qquad (7\text{-}161)$$

The combination of Eqs. (7-154), (7-157), (7-160), and (7-161) gives

$$\begin{aligned}
\bar{W}_k = (2EI\sigma^2 \sinh \sigma l \sin \sigma l)^{-1} \Big\{ &-\bar{M}_0 \sinh \sigma l [\cos k\theta \sin \sigma x_k \\
&+ \cos (k-1)\theta \sin \sigma (l - x_k)] \\
&+ \bar{M}_0 \sin \sigma l [\cos k\theta \sinh \sigma x_k + \cos (k-1)\theta \sinh \sigma (l - x_k)] \\
&+ \frac{(\bar{M}_0 \cos N\theta - \bar{M}_N) \sinh \sigma l}{\sin N\theta} [\sin k\theta \sin \sigma x_k \\
&+ \sin (k-1)\theta \sin \sigma (l - x_k)] - \frac{(\bar{M}_0 \cos N\theta - \bar{M}_N) \sin \sigma l}{\sin N\theta} \\
&[\sin k\theta \sinh \sigma x_k + \sin (k-1)\theta \sinh \sigma (l - x_k)] \Big\} \qquad (7\text{-}162)
\end{aligned}$$

Of course, Eq. (7-162) reduces to an expression for the frequency response function $H(x, N; \omega)$ or $H(x, 0; \omega)$, where N and 0 indicate, respectively, that the input moment is applied either at station N or at station 0. For example, $H(x, N; \omega)$ is obtained by letting $\bar{M}_0 = 0$ and $\bar{M}_N = 1$. Thus

$$\begin{aligned}
H(x, N; \omega) = (2EI\sigma^2 \sinh \sigma l \sin \sigma l \sin N\theta)^{-1} \{ &\sin \sigma l [\sin k\theta \sinh \sigma x_k \\
&+ \sin (k-1)\theta \sinh \sigma (l - x_k)] - \sinh \sigma l [\sin k\theta \sin \sigma x_k \\
&+ \sin (k-1)\theta \sin \sigma (l - x_k)] \} \qquad (7\text{-}163)
\end{aligned}$$

However, the inversion of Eq. (7-163) to obtain $h(x, N; t)$ for an arbitrary N appears to be rather involved.

The method of difference equations also applies when the intermedi-

---

‡ Since σ and, consequently, θ are complex-valued, the choice of calling this expression $\cos \theta$ or $\cosh \theta$ is entirely arbitrary.

¶ Compare with Eq. (6-104b).

ate hinged rigid supports of the beam are replaced by elastic supports. The governing difference equation in this more general case is one of a fourth order‡ rather than of a second order such as Eq. (7-158). It is also possible to consider an input moment applied at an intermediate support, either rigid or elastic, or an input vertical load at an elastic intermediate support. The general scheme to be used is analogous to the one employed in Sec. 6.5 for the determination of the frequency response functions in the case of a wind loading on a tall building.

EXERCISES

7-1. Let the motion of a simply supported beam with a uniform cross section be governed by the equation

$$EI \frac{\partial^4 W}{\partial x^4} + c\dot{W} + m\ddot{W} = P(x, t)$$

where EI, c, and m are constants, and the excitation $P(x, t)$ is a weakly stationary and weakly homogeneous random process characterized by

$$E[P(x, t)] = 0$$
$$E[P(x_1, t_1)P(x_2, t_2)] = R_{PP}(x_1 - x_2, t_1 - t_2)$$
$$= \sigma^2 \exp\left(-\alpha|t_1 - t_2|\right)\delta(x_1 - x_2)$$

Compute the crosscorrelation function and the cross spectral density of the weakly stationary deflection of the beam, i.e.,

$$E[W(x_1, t_1)W(x_2, t_2)] = R_{WW}(x_1, x_2; t_1 - t_2)$$

and

$$\Phi_{WW}(x_1, x_2; \omega) = \frac{1}{2\pi} \int_{-\infty}^{\infty} R_{WW}(x_1, x_2; \tau) \exp\left(-i\omega\tau\right) d\tau$$

7-2. Under the same general assumptions as those in Exercise 7-1, compute the crosscorrelation function of the deflection of the beam in the transient nonstationary state. The beam is initially at rest.

7-3.¶ As shown in Fig. 7.9, in the analysis of its response to earthquake excitations the tower of a suspension bridge is idealized as a beam column. Denote the random ground motion in the horizontal direction by $Q(t)$ and the horizontal displacement of the beam column by

$$W(x, t) = W_0(x, t) + Q(t)$$

The name *response* will here refer to $W_0(x, t)$, which is directly related to the bending moment of the beam column. Assume that the ground motion can be modeled as

$$Q(t) = \int_0^t (e^{-\alpha\tau} - e^{-\beta\tau})G(\tau) d\tau$$

where $G(\tau)$ is a stationary Gaussian random process with a zero expectation and a

---

‡ For the formulation of such an equation see Y. K. Lin, Free Vibrations of a Continuous Beam on Elastic Supports, *Intern. J. Mech. Sci.*, **4**:409–423 (1962). See also Y. K. Lin, I. D. Brown, and P. C. Deutschle, Free Vibrations of a Finite Row of Continuous Skin-stringer Panels, *J. Sound Vibration*, **1**:14–27 (1964).

¶ See M. Shinozuka and L. Henry, Random Vibration of a Beam Column, *J. Eng. Mech. Div.*, *Am. Soc. Civil Engrs.*, **91**(EM 5):123–143 (1965).

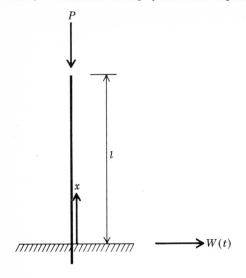

Fig. 7.9

spectral density $\Phi_{GG}(\omega)$, and that the equation of motion of the beam column is given by

$$EI\,\frac{\partial^4 W_0}{\partial x^4} + P\,\frac{\partial^2 W_0}{\partial x^2} + c\dot{W}_0 + m\ddot{W}_0 = F(t)$$

where EI, P, c, m are constants and

$$F(t) = -m\ddot{Q} - c\dot{Q}$$

Find the expression for the crosscorrelation function of the response

$$E[W_0(x_1,\,t_1)W_0(x_2,\,t_1)]$$

by use of a normal-mode approach.

7-4. Determine the frequency influence function of a beam consisting of two uniform sections, as shown in Fig. 7.10. One end of the beam is clamped, and the other is simply supported. The damping coefficient c is assumed to be a constant throughout the entire span length l. Express the spectral density of the random bending moment at the clamped support in terms of the spectral density of the concentrated load $P(t)$.

Fig. 7.10

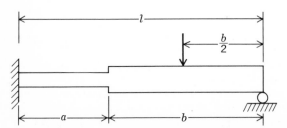

8 | NONLINEAR STRUCTURES

Two types of nonlinear problems are encountered in the study of structural response to random excitations; one is represented by nonlinear differential equations and the other by nonlinear algebraic equations. An example of a problem of the first type is a single-degree-of-freedom system characterized by the following differential equation:

$$\ddot{X} + g(X, \dot{X}) = F(t) \qquad (8\text{-}1)$$

where g is a nonlinear function of the displacement X and the velocity $\dot{X}$. Since the input $F(t)$ at an earlier time will affect the output at a later time, where the output may be viewed as the vector $\{X, \dot{X}\}$ on a phase plane, such a nonlinear system is sometimes said to be one *with memory*. On the other hand, a nonlinear algebraic relationship between input and output such as

$$Y = g(X) \qquad (8\text{-}2)$$

represents a system *without memory*. In this equation the value of the output, $Y(t)$, is determined from the instantaneous value of the input, $X(t)$, and $X(t)$ has no aftereffect on $Y(t)$. Equation (8-2) arises, for example, when the stress at a point on an elastic structure is a nonlinear function of the displacement. We are concerned, of course, with the situation where input and output are random. Then for a system without memory, the transformation between the random processes $X(t)$ and $Y(t)$ is the same as the transformation between random variables. The required technique for such a transformation has been discussed in Chap. 3. We shall elaborate somewhat upon the problem of nonlinear stress in Sec. 8.6.

The relatively general nonlinear systems with memory represented by Eq. (8-1) may be further specialized. The case of nonlinear stiffness is one in which g is nonlinear only with respect to X, that is,

$$g(X, \dot{X}) = \beta \dot{X} + f_1(X) \qquad (8\text{-}3)$$

Analogously, the case of nonlinear damping is the one where

$$g(X, \dot{X}) = f_2(\dot{X}) + kX \qquad (8\text{-}4)$$

In Eqs. (8-3) and (8-4), f represents a nonlinear function.

To show how the problem of nonlinear stiffness may arise and be dealt with, consider a rectangular plate supported by immovable hinges along its four edges. In a linear theory, it is assumed that the deflections are small in comparison with the thickness of the plate. This assumption ensures the negligibility of the membrane forces which are developed in the plate when it is deformed. If the deflections of the plate are of the same order of magnitude as the plate thickness, the omission of membrane forces is no longer justifiable. In fact, the corresponding membrane strains are of such a magnitude that they contribute considerable resistance to the deformation, thus causing a nonlinear load-deflection relationship. The nonlinearity as described is completely attributable to large deflections. However, in this problem we shall assume that the stresses in the plate are moderate so that the stress-strain relation remains linear.

The governing equations of motion for a nonlinear plate can best be derived from energy considerations. Referring to the coordinate system shown in Fig. 8.1, we have, for the tensile and shearing strains in the midsurface of the plate‡ (synonymously called the membrane strains),

$$\epsilon_x = u_{,x} + \tfrac{1}{2}w_{,x}^2$$
$$\epsilon_y = v_{,y} + \tfrac{1}{2}w_{,y}^2 \qquad\qquad (8\text{-}5)$$
$$\gamma_{xy} = u_{,y} + v_{,x} + w_{,x}w_{,y}$$

‡ See, for example, S. Timoshenko, "Theory of Plates and Shells," p. 342, McGraw-Hill, New York, 1940.

Fig. 8.1 (*a*) Coordinates; (*b*) displacements.

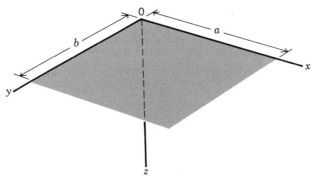

(a)

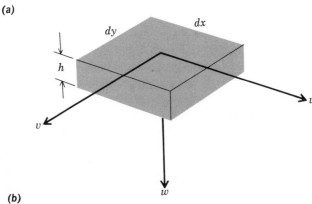

(b)

where u, v, w are the displacements of a plate element in the x, y, z directions, respectively, and a comma preceding a subscript indicates partial differentiation with respect to that subscript. Expressions (8-5) are written with the assumption that the vertical deflection of the plate (i.e., the displacement w) is of the same order of magnitude as that of the plate thickness but of a smaller order of magnitude than that of the plate length or width. This assumption also justifies the usual approximation for the curvatures of the deformed plate, namely,

$$\rho_x = w_{,xx}$$
$$\rho_y = w_{,yy} \qquad\qquad (8\text{-}6)$$
$$\rho_{xy} = w_{,xy}$$

The following internal forces acting on a plate element are obtained from the foregoing expressions for strains and curvatures:

N_x = unit membrane tension in x direction

$$= \frac{Eh}{1 - \nu^2}[u_{,x} + \tfrac{1}{2}w_{,x}^2 + \nu(v_{,y} + \tfrac{1}{2}w_{,y}^2)]$$

N_y = unit membrane tension in y direction

$$= \frac{Eh}{1 - \nu^2}[v_{,y} + \tfrac{1}{2}w_{,y}^2 + \nu(u_{,x} + \tfrac{1}{2}w_{,x}^2)]$$

N_{xy} = unit membrane shear in x direction acting on a cross section perpendicular to y axis

= unit membrane shear in y direction acting on a cross section perpendicular to x axis

$$= \frac{Eh}{2(1 + \nu)}(u_{,y} + v_{,x} + w_{,x}w_{,y}) \qquad\qquad (8\text{-}7)$$

M_x = unit bending moment acting about y axis on a cross section perpendicular to x axis

$$= D(w_{,xx} + \nu w_{,yy})$$

M_y = unit bending moment acting about x axis on a cross section perpendicular to y axis

$$= D(w_{,yy} + \nu w_{,xx})$$

M_{xy} = unit twisting moment acting on a cross section perpendicular to x axis

= unit twisting moment acting on a cross section perpendicular to y axis

$$= D(1 - \nu)w_{,xy}$$

where E = modulus of elasticity

ν = Poisson ratio

h = plate thickness

D = plate rigidity = $\dfrac{Eh^3}{12(1 - \nu^2)}$

The strain energy in the deformed plate is given by

$$V = \tfrac{1}{2} \int_0^a \int_0^b [N_x(u_{,x} + \tfrac{1}{2}w_{,x}^2) + N_y(v_{,y} + \tfrac{1}{2}w_{,y}^2)$$
$$+ N_{xy}(u_{,y} + v_{,x} + w_{,x}w_{,y}) + M_x w_{,xx} + M_y w_{,yy} + 2M_{xy}w_{,xy}]\, dx\, dy \qquad (8\text{-}8)$$

which is reducible to the strain energy expression in the linear theory if the membrane forces N_x, N_y, N_{xy} are set to zero. To calculate the kinetic energy of the vibrating plate, we shall neglect the rotary inertia terms, which is a permissible step for plate deflections of the order of the plate thickness. Thus,

$$T = \frac{h\rho}{2} \int_0^a \int_0^b (\dot{u}^2 + \dot{v}^2 + \dot{w}^2)\, dx\, dy \qquad (8\text{-}9)$$

where ρ is the mass density of the plate material. The equations of motion may be derived from Hamilton's principle,

$$\delta \int_{t_1}^{t_2} (T - V)\, dt = 0 \qquad (8\text{-}10)$$

where the integrand $T - V$ is known as the Lagrangian function and δ represents the *first* variation of the integral. If the expressions (8-8) and (8-9) for V and T are substituted into (8-10), the first variation involves a threefold integral with independent variables t, x, y and dependent variables u, v, w. The usual technique of the calculus of variations leads to three Euler-Lagrange equations‡ as follows:

$$u_{,xx} + w_{,x}w_{,xx} + \nu(v_{,xy} + w_{,y}w_{,xy})$$
$$+ \frac{1 - \nu}{2}(u_{,yy} + v_{,xy} + w_{,x}w_{,yy} + w_{,y}w_{,xy}) = \frac{1}{c_p^2}\ddot{u}$$

$$v_{,yy} + w_{,y}w_{,yy} + \nu(u_{,xy} + w_{,x}w_{,xy})$$
$$+ \frac{1 - \nu}{2}(u_{,xy} + v_{,xy} + w_{,x}w_{,xy} + w_{,y}w_{,xx}) = \frac{1}{c_p^2}\ddot{v}$$

$$\frac{h^2}{12}(w_{,xxxx} + 2w_{,xxyy} + w_{,yyyy}) - u_{,x}w_{,xx} - \tfrac{1}{2}(w_{,x})^2 w_{,xx} \qquad (8\text{-}11)$$
$$- \nu[v_{,y}w_{,xx} + \tfrac{1}{2}(w_{,y})^2 w_{,xx}] - v_{,y}w_{,yy} - \tfrac{1}{2}(w_{,y})^2 w_{,yy}$$
$$- \nu[u_{,x}w_{,yy} + \tfrac{1}{2}(w_{,x})^2 w_{,yy}]$$
$$- (1 - \nu)(u_{,y}w_{,xy} + v_{,x}w_{,xy} + w_{,x}w_{,y}w_{,xy})$$
$$= \frac{1}{c_p^2}(w_{,x}\ddot{u} + w_{,y}\ddot{v} - \ddot{w})$$

where $c_p^2 = E/\rho(1 - \nu^2)$. Equations (8-11) govern the undamped free vibrations of a nonlinear plate. These equations were first derived by Chu and Herrmann.¶

‡ See, for example, A. E. H. Love, "Mathematical Theory of Elasticity," 4th ed., p. 166, Dover, New York, 1944.
¶ H. N. Chu and G. Herrmann, Influence of Large Amplitudes on Free Flexural Vibration of Rectangular Elastic Plates, *J. Appl. Mech.* **23**(4):532–540 (1956).

The exact solution to Eqs. (8-11) is unknown. However, for a plate hinged along four immovable edges, a condition corresponding to the boundary conditions

$$u = w = w_{,xx} = 0 \quad \text{at } x = 0, a$$
$$v = w = w_{,yy} = 0 \quad \text{at } y = 0, b \tag{8-12}$$

it is plausible to assume that the dominant mode in the vertical displacement is

$$w = \zeta(t) \sin \frac{\pi x}{a} \sin \frac{\pi y}{b} \tag{8-13a}$$

Then under the assumption that w is of the order of the plate thickness h and that u and v are of the order of h^2, Chu and Herrmann‡ have shown that

$$u = \frac{\pi \zeta^2(t)}{16a} \left(\cos \frac{2\pi y}{b} - 1 + \nu r^2 \right) \sin \frac{2\pi x}{a} \tag{8-13b}$$

$$v = \frac{\pi \zeta^2(t)}{16b} \left(r \cos \frac{2\pi x}{a} - r + \frac{\nu}{r} \right) \sin \frac{2\pi y}{b} \tag{8-13c}$$

where $r = a/b$. Expressions (8-13a) to (8-13c) satisfy Eqs. (8-11) approximately to an order of h^2. It should be noted that although the coupling effect in the displacements u, v, w is taken into account, the approximate solution admits only *one* degree of freedom, the degree of freedom corresponding to the generalized coordinate ζ. Of course, one must be careful about treating a continuous structure as a single-degree-of-freedom system. Experimental evidence is often required to substantiate a severe assumption such as this when applied to a practical problem.

The equation for the forced motion will now be derived from a Lagrangian formulation within the framework of a single-degree-of-freedom representation. Since we shall be interested only in lightly damped systems, the usual assumption is made that the forced motion is of the same mode as that of the free motion. Substituting (8-13a) through (8-13c) into the expressions for the strain and kinetic energies, we have

$$V = \frac{Eh\zeta^4\pi}{128(1 - \nu^2)} \left[\frac{1}{ra^2} \left(\frac{3}{2} + \frac{\nu^2}{2} r^4 \right) + \frac{2\nu r}{a^2} \left(1 - \frac{\nu}{2r^2} - \frac{\nu}{2} r^2 \right) \right.$$
$$\left. + \frac{r^3}{a^2} \left(\frac{3}{2} + \frac{\nu^2}{2r^4} \right) \right] + \frac{Eh^3}{96(1 - \nu^2)} \frac{\zeta^2\pi^4}{ra} (1 + r^2)^2 \tag{8-14}$$

$$T = \frac{\rho}{2} \left(\frac{\zeta\dot{\zeta}}{8} \right)^2 \left[\frac{h}{r} \left(\frac{3}{4} + \nu^2 r^4 - 2\nu r^2 \right) + hr \left(\frac{3}{4} + \frac{\nu^2}{r^4} - \frac{2\nu}{r^2} \right) \right]$$
$$+ \rho \frac{(\dot{\zeta})^2}{8} \frac{a^2}{r} h \tag{8-15}$$

‡ *Ibid.*

The Lagrange equation of motion is

$$\frac{d}{dt}\frac{\partial L}{\partial \dot{\zeta}} - \frac{\partial L}{\partial \zeta} = Q(t) \tag{8-16}$$

where $L = T - V$ is the Lagrangian function and Q is the generalized force computed from

$$Q(t) = \lim_{\Delta \zeta \to 0} \frac{\Delta W}{\Delta \zeta} \tag{8-17}$$

In this definition, ΔW includes the virtual work done by all the external forces (including damping forces) as a result of the virtual displacement $\Delta \zeta$. Substitution of (8-14) and (8-15) into (8-16) gives

$$\ddot{\zeta} + \omega_0^2(\zeta + \alpha \zeta^3) = \psi(t) \tag{8-18}$$

where

$$\omega_0^2 = \frac{D\pi^4}{\rho h a^4}(1 + r^2)^2$$

$$\alpha = \frac{3}{2}\left(\frac{1}{1+r^2}\right)^2 \frac{1}{h^2}\left[\left(\frac{3}{2} - \frac{\nu^2}{2}\right)(1 + r^4) + 2\nu r^2\right] \tag{8-19}$$

$$\psi(t) = \frac{4r}{\rho a^2 h} Q(t)$$

In Eq. (8-18), the nonlinearity is evident in that the elastic force is represented by the sum of a linear term and a cubic term. The nonlinear equation of this particular form is called the *Duffing equation*. It usually occurs in a structure treated as a single-degree-of-freedom system when the nonlinearity is solely due to large deflections. If more than one degree of freedom needs to be considered, it is generally not possible to represent the behavior of the structure by a Duffing equation. However, under certain conditions, the normal modes of vibration can be "uncoupled," and each uncoupled equation also takes the form of (8-18). The "uncoupling" of normal modes as referred to here is to be broadly interpreted. It implies the possibility of obtaining one equation for each mode which is solvable, although the coefficients of the equation may involve all the other modes [see Eq. (8-49)].

The characteristics of a nonlinear structure if representable by a Duffing equation are determined by the parameters ω_0^2 and α. These parameters may be computed from the dimensions and material properties of the structure, and in the case of a nonlinear plate the relations are given explicitly in (8-19). It must be remembered that the expressions in (8-19) were derived for a simply supported plate. Other boundary conditions can be treated similarly if appropriate mode shapes, such as those given in (8-13a) to (8-13c), can be intelligently assumed. However, the problem of assuming a mode shape for a nonlinear structure is not as simple as it appears to be. For example, consider a beam which is clamped at both ends. When the amplitude of vibration is of a smaller order of magnitude than the beam depth, the normal modes for vertical deflections w are the well-known linear bending modes and are given in almost any standard textbook on vibrations. On the other hand, if the amplitude of vibration is much greater than the beam depth, then the membrane tension in the beam prevails and the structure behaves more like a string than a beam; thus the normal modes for w must be closer to those of a string. For a case in between the two extremes, the w modes must lie between those of linear bending and those of pure membrane tension. From this example, it is obvious that the nonlinear modes of a beam change with the amplitude unless, of course, the bending modes are identical with the membrane tension modes. The latter is exactly true if a beam is hinged on both ends. The same argument applies to hinge-supported plates such as the one just discussed. Since the assumption of hinge supports is not always justifiable for many practical structures, it may be desirable to develop techniques for arbitrarily supported beams or plates by which the variation of normal modes with the deflection amplitude can be assessed. It has been found‡ that the computed parameters ω_0^2 and α can be quite different for different assumed mode shapes.

The stiffness nonlinearity discussed in the above example of a thin plate is due solely to large deflections with the stress-strain relationship assumed to be linear. Of course, a nonlinear equation, similar to Eq. (8-18) but not necessarily of the Duffing type, will result if the stress-strain law is nonlinear, whether or not this is accompanied by large deflections. However, if the stiffness characteristics are the same for either a positive or a negative generalized displacement $\zeta(t)$, then a more general version of Eq. (8-18) is

$$\ddot{\zeta} + f_1(\zeta) = \psi(t) \qquad (8\text{-}20)$$

where $f_1(\zeta)$ is an odd function. Klein¶ has presented an analysis based on

$$f_1(\zeta) = K \tan \frac{\pi \zeta}{2d} \qquad -d < \zeta < d \qquad (8\text{-}21)$$

a mathematical model for nonlinear stiffness attributed to Mindlin.§

‡ P. N. Smith, Jr., C. I. Malme, and C. M. Gogos, Nonlinear Response of a Simple Clamped Panel, *J. Acoust. Soc. Am.*, **33**:1476–1486 (1962).

¶ G. H. Klein, Random Excitation of a Nonlinear System with Tangent Elasticity Characteristics, *J. Acoust. Soc. Am.*, **36**(11):2095–2105 (1964).

§ R. D. Mindlin, Dynamics of Package Cushioning, *Bell System Tech. J.*, **24**:353–461 (1945).

It is interesting to note that in Mindlin's model the generalized displacement is restricted to $(-d, d)$, whereas it is allowed to vary over $(-\infty, \infty)$ in the Duffing model. For small ζ/d, however, Mindlin's model departs from Duffing's model only in the order of $(\zeta/d)^5$, as can be seen from the power-series representation of a tangent function.

The problem of nonlinear damping is not so clear-cut. There are usually three sources of damping which affect an actual structure: the surrounding fluid, the internal friction of the structural material, and the relative slippage of different parts of the structure which are fastened together by rivets and bolts. We shall call the damping due to the first source *ambient damping*, that due to the second source *material damping*, and that due to the third source *interface damping*. Material and interface damping are often referred to collectively as structural damping. One type of ambient damping, namely, acoustic damping, has been studied under certain idealized conditions in Sec. 7.3. From the result‡ obtained there, we expect that for a thin plate vibrating simply harmonically in a fluid, the induced acoustic damping is approximately linear, provided that the amplitude of the plate motion is sufficiently small to justify the assumption of a constant speed of sound in the fluid. An analysis similar to the one leading to Eq. (7-77) will show that this is also true if the structure is a thin cylindrical or spherical shell. On the other hand, when the amplitude of the structural motion is not sufficiently small and/or when the shape of the structure is different from those mentioned above, the ambient damping is generally nonlinear. Since analytical studies of the laws of ambient damping for such cases are as a rule difficult, empirical relations are usually the only relief.

The actual characteristics of structural damping are also complicated, and the bulk of information about these characteristics has been obtained from experimental studies. Usually a cyclic loading is applied to a specimen for the purpose of measuring the energy loss per cycle. For material damping, Lazan and Goodman¶ have suggested the empirical formula

$$D = \left(\frac{s}{s_e}\right)^{2.3} + 6 \left(\frac{s}{s_e}\right)^8 \tag{8-22}$$

where D (called the specific damping) is the energy loss per unit volume of the material per cycle, s is the stress amplitude for the cycle, and s_e is

‡ Refer to Eq. (7-77). Note, in particular, the term $i\rho_0\omega^2/k_{jl,0}$.

¶ B. J. Lazan and L. E. Goodman, Material and Interface Damping, in C. M. Harris and C. E. Crede (eds.), "Shock and Vibration Handbook," vol. II, Chap. 36, p. 36-34, McGraw-Hill, New York, 1961.

the fatigue strength at 2×10^7 cycles for the material. This equation follows closely the geometric mean of a band within which are located most of the test-data points of a large variety of structural materials. If the material damping were truly linear, the specific damping would be proportional to $(s/s_e)^2$. Equation (8-22) shows that the material damping is not far from linear at low stress amplitudes when the first term in Eq. (8-22) predominates. It becomes highly nonlinear at stress amplitudes near or over s_e. Crandall, Khabbaz, and Manning‡ have shown that an alternative empirical formula

$$D = 0.7 \left[\left(\frac{s}{s_e}\right)^2 + 6 \left(\frac{s}{s_e}\right)^8 \right]$$ (8-22a)

also closely resembles the geometric mean of the test data for a number of materials.

The interface damping depends heavily on the existing pressure at the interface. Theoretically, energy dissipation due to this type of damping is zero for either zero or a large interface pressure; it attains a maximum value when the pressure is somewhere in between. When slippage does occur, it is usually limited to only a portion of the interface. Analyses based on the assumption of partial slippage show that the energy dissipation is essentially proportional to the third power of the applied force amplitude.¶ Therefore, the interface damping is basically nonlinear.

For most structural problems, slippage at the joints does not occur at low stresses. Then in a low-stress range, the material damping accounts entirely for the structural damping present, and a linear damping assumption for analyses is, perhaps, acceptable for most purposes. When the stress level is high, not only does the material damping become essentially nonlinear, but interface damping contributes to the dissipation of energy. Depending on the configuration of a structure and the fabrication process used in its construction, it is possible that as the intensity of an excitation increases, the structural damping will depart appreciably from linearity far before the stiffness nonlinearity is initiated. The reasons for the inadequate discussion of damping nonlinearity in the literature are the lack of sufficient detailed knowledge of damping mechanisms and the greater difficulty in analyzing such problems.

‡ S. H. Crandall, G. R. Khabbaz, and J. E. Manning, Random Vibration of an Oscillator with Nonlinear Damping, *J. Acoust. Soc. Am.*, **36**(7):1330–1334 (1964).

¶ L. E. Goodman, A Review of Progress in Analysis of Interfacial Slip Damping, in "Structural Damping," American Society of Mechanical Engineers, New York, December, 1959. See also T. H. H. Pian and F. C. Hallowell, Jr., Structural Damping in a Simple Built-up Beam, *Proc. First Natl. Congr. Appl. Mech.*, June, 1951.

8.2 / THE MARKOV–VECTOR APPROACH‡
SINGLE DEGREE OF FREEDOM

If the excitation $F(t)$ in Eq. (8-1) is a sequence of independent and independently arriving impulses (one type of shot noise), then the random displacement $X(t)$ and the random velocity $\dot{X}(t)$ are components of a Markov vector. This conclusion is based on the fact that the cause for the change in the vector $\{X, \dot{X}\}$, the excitation, has independent values at any two different times; therefore, the vector is one of independent increments. We have made the same observation previously in regard to a linear system (Sec. 5.6).

Let $X = Y_1$ and $\dot{X} = Y_2$, and denote $\mathbf{Y} = \{Y_1, Y_2\}$. Equation (8-1) is equivalent to two first-order equations

$$\dot{Y}_1 = Y_2$$
$$\dot{Y}_2 = -g(Y_1, Y_2) + S(t) \qquad (8\text{-}23)$$

where the shot noise $S(t)$ has replaced $F(t)$. It can easily be shown that if $S(t)$ is also Gaussian, then the Fokker-Planck equation governing the transition probability density $q_{\{Y\}}(\mathbf{y}, t|\mathbf{y}_0, t_0)$ is

$$\frac{\partial q}{\partial t} + y_2 \frac{\partial q}{\partial y_1} - \frac{\partial}{\partial y_2}[qg(y_1, y_2)] - \frac{I(t)}{2}\frac{\partial^2 q}{\partial y_2{}^2} = 0 \qquad (8\text{-}24)$$

where $I(t)$ is the intensity function of the shot noise, i.e.,

$$E[S(t)S(t + \tau)] = I(t)\,\delta(\tau)$$

Unfortunately, no solution has been found for Eq. (8-24), not even when the excitation has been limited to a Gaussian white noise [i.e., when $I(t) = $ const] and the nonlinear g function has been specialized.

The possibility of solving Eq. (8-24) is greatly increased if $I(t)$ is a constant and if the first term in this equation, $\partial q/\partial t$, can be set to zero. The physical implication of dropping this term is that the transition time $t - t_0$ is sufficiently long that the Markov vector $\mathbf{Y}$ has reached a stationary state. In this state, the probability structure is necessarily independent of the pretransition state $\mathbf{y}_0$ at time t_0. Equation (8-24) then reduces to one to be solved for the first-order probability density $p_{\{Y\}}(\mathbf{y})$ of a stationary Markov vector, i.e.,

$$y_2 \frac{\partial p}{\partial y_1} - \frac{\partial}{\partial y_2}[pg(y_1, y_2)] - \pi K \frac{\partial^2 p}{\partial y_2{}^2} = 0 \qquad (8\text{-}25)$$

---

‡ The Markov-vector approach was first applied to the case of nonlinear systems by A. Andronov, L. Pontryagin, and A. Witt in their paper, On the Statistical Investigation of Dynamical Systems, (in Russian), *Zh. Eksperim. i. Teor.*, **3**:165–180 (1933). See also A. Andronov, "Selected Works," pp. 142–160, Academy of Sciences, USSR, 1956.

where K is the constant spectral density of the Gaussian white noise. Although it is regrettable that it is necessary to consider the reduced case, Eq. (8-25), the first-order probability density p, if obtained, is still very useful. This probability density governs the joint behavior of the stationary random displacement and velocity at the same time t.

Let us consider first the case of a nonlinear stiffness, i.e., the case where the g function is given by Eq. (8-3). If

$$g(y_1, y_2) = \beta y_2 + f_1(y_1)$$

is substituted into Eq. (8-25), we obtain‡

$$y_2 \frac{\partial p}{\partial y_1} - [\beta y_2 + f_1(y_1)] \frac{\partial p}{\partial y_2} - \beta p - \pi K \frac{\partial^2 p}{\partial y_2{}^2} = 0 \qquad (8\text{-}26)$$

It is known that in a stationary state, $Y_1(t)$ and $Y_2(t)$ are orthogonal, i.e.,

$$E[Y_1(t)Y_2(t)] = 0 \qquad (8\text{-}27)$$

Furthermore, since the expectation of the excitation, the white noise, is zero, in the stationary state

$$E[Y_1(t)] = E[Y_2(t)] = 0 \qquad (8\text{-}28)$$

Equation (8-27) implies that $Y_1(t)$ and $Y_2(t)$ are uncorrelated. Although two uncorrelated random processes may or may not be independent, we shall try a solution to Eq. (8-26) in the form of

$$p_{\{Y\}}(y_1, y_2) = p_1(y_1)p_2(y_2) \qquad (8\text{-}29)$$

If such a solution is admissible, then we shall have verified indirectly that $Y_1(t)$ and $Y_2(t)$ are truly independent. Substituting (8-29) into Eq. (8-26) and dividing the resulting equation by $p_1(y_1)p_2(y_2)$, we obtain

$$y_2 \frac{p_1'}{p_1} - [\beta y_2 + f_1(y_1)] \frac{p_2'}{p_2} - \beta - \pi K \frac{p_2''}{p_2} = 0 \qquad (8\text{-}30)$$

where a prime indicates one differentiation with respect to the argument. In order for the separation of the variables to be possible, it is necessary that

$$y_2 \frac{p_1'}{p_1} = f_1(y_1) \frac{p_2'}{p_2} \qquad (8\text{-}31)$$

or

$$\frac{1}{f_1(y_1)} \frac{p_1'}{p_1} = \frac{1}{y_2} \frac{p_2'}{p_2} = -A \text{ (a constant)} \qquad (8\text{-}31a)$$

‡ This equation is sometimes referred to as the stationary form of the Kramers equation. See his pioneering work: H. A. Kramers, Brownian Motion in a Field of Force and the Diffusion Model of Chemical Reactions, *Physica*, **7**:284–304 (1940).

Integration of (8-31a) gives

$$p_1(y_1) = C_1 \exp \left[-A \int_0^{y_1} f_1(u) \, du \right]$$

$$p_2(y_2) = C_2 \exp \left(\frac{-A y_2{}^2}{2} \right) \tag{8-32}$$

The value for the constant A can be obtained by substituting (8-32) into Eq. (8-30). The substitution yields

$$\beta A y_2{}^2 - \beta + \pi K (A - A^2 y_2{}^2) = 0 \tag{8-33}$$

This is a quadratic equation for A. One of the two roots of Eq. (8-33) is truly a constant, viz.,

$$A = \frac{\beta}{\pi K} \tag{8-34}$$

The nonconstant root should be discarded since it contradicts Eq. (8-31a). It is to be noted that if both the roots for A were nonconstant, it would imply that a solution to the Fokker-Planck equation could not be written in a product form such as that in Eq. (8-29). The above analysis thus establishes that for a single-degree-of-freedom system with nonlinear stiffness and linear damping which is exposed to Gaussian-white-noise excitations, the stationary displacement and velocity are truly independent and that their joint probability density is given by

$$p = C \exp \left\{ -\frac{\beta}{\pi K} \left[\frac{y_2{}^2}{2} + \int_0^{y_1} f_1(u) \, du \right] \right\} \tag{8-35}$$

This probability density has been obtained independently by several authors.‡ The constant C in Eq. (8-35) is determined from the normalization condition

$$\int_{-\infty}^{\infty} \int_{-\infty}^{\infty} p \, dy_1 \, dy_2 = 1$$

Some comments about this simple result, Eq. (8-35), are in order. Besides the already-mentioned independence between the stationary displacement and velocity we note that the velocity process $Y_2(t)$ at an arbitrary t is a Gaussian random *variable*, whereas the displacement process $Y_1(t)$ is not. However, $Y_2(t)$ cannot be a Gaussian random *process* because its mean-square integral $Y_1(t)$ is not. In particular, $Y_2(t_1)$ and $Y_2(t_2)$ are not jointly distributed Gaussian random variables. Secondly, the two terms $y_2{}^2/2$ and $\int_0^{y_1} f_1(u) \, du$ are essentially the kinetic energy and the

‡ See, for example, T. K. Caughey, Derivation and Application of the Fokker-Planck Equation to Discrete Nonlinear Dynamic Systems Subjected to White Random Excitation, *J. Acoust. Soc. Am.*, **35**:1683–1692 (1963).

strain energy of the system. If we write

$$\mathcal{E} = \frac{y_2{}^2}{2} + \int_0^{y_1} f_1(u) \, du \tag{8-36}$$

and Eq. (8-35) as

$$p = C \exp{(-A\mathcal{E})} \tag{8-35a}$$

we see that in the stationary state the energy level as a random process is exponentially distributed. This probability distribution, having a density function (8-35a), is known in the kinetic theory of gases as the *Maxwell-Boltzmann distribution*, and it describes the kinetic energy of the molecules of a gas. Thirdly, since energies are nonnegative, the integral representing the strain energy in Eq. (8-36) is nonnegative for either positive or negative y_1. Of particular interest is the case where the integrand, i.e., the spring force f_1, is an odd function; then the strain energy is an even function of y_1. Finally, since the Fokker-Planck equation (8-26) is linear and is associated with inaccessible natural boundary conditions, the solution (8-35) is unique.

It is interesting to investigate what types of second-order dynamic systems, when responding to a Gaussian white-noise excitation, have closed-form stationary solutions to their associated Fokker-Planck equations. This is an inverse problem, and it amounts to finding the class of g functions from Eq. (8-25) that allows such solutions subject to the general condition that p is a probability density of jointly stationary random processes Y_1 and Y_2. A straightforward integration of Eq. (8-25) yields

$$\int y_2 \frac{\partial p}{\partial y_1} \, dy_2 - pg(y_1, y_2) - \pi K \frac{\partial p}{\partial y_2} + M(y_1) = 0 \tag{8-37}$$

or

$$g(y_1, y_2) = \frac{1}{p} \left[\int y_2 \frac{\partial p}{\partial y_1} \, dy_2 - \pi K \frac{\partial p}{\partial y_2} + M(y_1) \right] \tag{8-37a}$$

where $M(y_1)$ is an arbitrary function of y_1. In the case $M(y_1) = 0$, it can be seen by direct substitution that if the displacement and velocity are independent, i.e., if their joint probability density is of the form of Eq. (8-29), then the separation

$$g(y_1, y_2) = f_1(y_1) + f_2(y_2) \tag{8-38}$$

must be accompanied by

$$p_2(y_2) = C_2 \exp{(-ky_2{}^2)}$$

From this velocity distribution it immediately follows that the damping must be linear. Conversely, if the damping is nonlinear, we expect that either the simultaneous stationary displacement and stationary velocity are dependent, or the spring and damping forces cannot be separated in the manner of Eq. (8-38), or both. For example, for the hypothetical probability density

$$p = C \exp \left\{ - \frac{\beta}{\pi K} \left[|y_2| + k \frac{\beta}{\pi K} \int_0^{y_1} f_1(u) \, du \right] \right\} \tag{8-39}$$

a possible expression for the damping and spring forces is

$$g(y_1, y_2) = \beta(\text{sgn } y_2) + k \left(\frac{\beta}{\pi K} |y_2| + 1 \right) f_1(y_1) \tag{8-40}$$

Equation (8-40) is obtained by substituting (8-39) into (8-37a) and letting $M(y_1) = 0$. The first term on the right-hand side of (8-40) indicates Coulomb damping, and the second term shows that the spring force is dependent upon the ratio of the absolute magnitude of the instantaneous velocity and the excitation spectral density, $|y_2|/K$. As another example, we mention Caughey's solution,[‡] which includes Eq. (8-35a) as a special case. If a probability density may be written as

$$p = C \exp \left[- \frac{\beta}{\pi K} \int_0^\varepsilon h(\zeta) \, d\zeta \right] \tag{8-41}$$

where ε is the sum of the kinetic and strain energies as given in Eq. (8-36) and h is a positive monotonically increasing function, then we find from Eq. (8-37a) that

$$g(y_1, y_2) = \beta y_2 h(\varepsilon) + f_1(y_1) \tag{8-42}$$

We remark that the joint probability density p of the displacement $Y_1(t)$ and the velocity $Y_2(t)$ is required to compute the expected number of times per unit time that $Y_1(t)$ crosses an arbitrary threshold level (see Sec. 9.2), which in turn is a useful item of information for the estimation of the fatigue damage to a structure (see Sec. 9.6). However, since this probability density describes the random nature of $Y_1(t)$ and $Y_2(t)$ at just one arbitrary time, it can be used to compute only the one-time statistical properties such as $E[Y_1(t)]$, $E[Y_1^2(t)]$, and $E[Y_1(t)Y_2(t)]$. The two-time statistical properties such as $E[Y_1^m(t)Y_1^n(t_0)]$ must be obtained by other means, one of which we shall now explore.¶ With a Markov

‡ T. K. Caughey, On the Response of a Class of Nonlinear Oscillators to Stochastic Excitation, *Proc. Colloq. Intern. du Centre National de la Recherche Scientifique*, No. 148, pp. 393–402, Marseille, September, 1964.

¶ See L. E. Wolaver, Second Order Properties of Nonlinear Systems Driven by Random Noise, *USAF Aerospace Res. Lab.* ARL-65-61, Wright-Patterson Air Force Base, Ohio, April, 1965.

model, we can again make use of the Fokker-Planck equation. To show this, recall that

$$E[Y_1^m(t)Y_1^n(t_0)] = \int_{-\infty}^{\infty} \int_{-\infty}^{\infty} y_1^m \eta_1^n p_{\{Y_1\}}(y_1, t; \eta_1, t_0) \, dy_1 \, d\eta_1 \qquad (8\text{-}43)$$

Now if $\mathbf{Y} = \{Y_1, Y_2\}$ is a Markov vector, we have

$$p_{\{Y_1\}}(y_1, t; \eta_1, t_0) = \int_{-\infty}^{\infty} \int_{-\infty}^{\infty} q_{\{Y\}}(y_1, y_2, t|\eta_1, \eta_2, t_0) p_{\{Y\}}(\eta_1, \eta_2, t_0) \, dy_2 \, d\eta_2$$

$$(8\text{-}44)$$

Substituting Eq. (8-44) into Eq. (8-43) and letting

$$v(y_1, y_2, t, t_0) = \int_{-\infty}^{\infty} \int_{-\infty}^{\infty} \eta_1^n q_{\{Y\}}(y_1, y_2, t|\eta_1, \eta_2, t_0) p_{\{Y\}}(\eta_1, \eta_2, t_0) \, d\eta_1 \, d\eta_2$$

$$(8\text{-}45)$$

we have

$$E[Y_1^m(t)Y_1^n(t_0)] = \int_{-\infty}^{\infty} \int_{-\infty}^{\infty} y_1^m v(y_1, y_2, t, t_0) \, dy_1 \, dy_2 \qquad (8\text{-}46)$$

It is important to note that the function $v(y_1, y_2, t, t_0)$ and the transition probability density $q_{\{Y\}}(y_1, y_2, t|\eta_1, \eta_2, t_0)$ both satisfy the same equation, namely, the Fokker-Planck equation (8-24). This can be seen from the defining expression (8-45), since the right-hand side of this expression simply consists of an operation on the transition probability density, but this operation does not involve the independent variables y_1, y_2, and t of the Fokker-Planck equation. Now the initial condition for q is

$$q_{\{Y\}}(y_1, y_2, t_0|\eta_1, \eta_2, t_0) = \delta(y_1 - \eta_1)\,\delta(y_2 - \eta_2) \qquad (8\text{-}47)$$

However, the initial condition to be satisfied by the function v is

$$v(y_1, y_2, t_0, t_0) = y_1^n p_{\{Y\}}(y_1, y_2, t_0) \qquad (8\text{-}48)$$

which is obtained by using Eq. (8-47) in Eq. (8-45). We recall that a similar situation was encountered when we discussed the Kolmogorov backward equation (4-128). For the two different conditions at $t = t_0$ cited there, the Kolmogorov backward equation yields either the transition probability density function or the transition probability distribution function. Analogously, if a solution for v can be obtained subject to the initial condition Eq. (8-48), then the moment function $E[Y_1^m(t)Y_1^n(t_0)]$ can be computed by the indicated integration in Eq. (8-46).

There is a certain advantage to having a well-behaved function such as expression (8-48) as an initial condition. This is so because it is then possible to devise a numerical solution to the differential equation, a very desirable feature in the age of electronic computers.

8.3 / THE MARKOV–VECTOR APPROACH
MULTIPLE DEGREES OF FREEDOM

The results obtained in Sec. 8.2 can be extended to multiple-degrees-of-freedom nonlinear systems under certain restrictions. We shall discuss first the extension of Eq. (8-35) since it, again, has an interesting analogy in the kinetic theory of gases. We consider, therefore, the case of nonlinear stiffness and linear damping, and impose the additional restrictions that there exist suitable generalized coordinates such that (1) the generalized excitations are uncorrelated white Gaussian processes, (2) neither the generalized damping forces nor the generalized inertia forces are coupled, and (3) the ratio of the spectral density of every generalized excitation to the corresponding generalized damping coefficient is the same constant. Under restriction (2), the equations of motion for the generalized displacements X_j may be written as follows:

$$m_j \ddot{X}_j + m_j \beta_j \dot{X}_j + \frac{\partial U}{\partial X_j} = W_j(t) \qquad j = 1, 2, \ldots, n \qquad (8\text{-}49)$$

where the m_j are generalized mass terms, the $m_j \beta_j$ are generalized damping terms, and U is the potential energy of the structure. Under restriction (1), the excitations $W_j(t)$ satisfy

$$
\begin{aligned}
E[W_j(t)] &= 0 \\
E[W_j(t + \tau)W_j(t)] &= 2\pi K_{jj}\, \delta(\tau) \\
E[W_j(t + \tau)W_k(t)] &= 0 \qquad j \neq k
\end{aligned}
\qquad (8\text{-}50)
$$

Equations (8-49) may be replaced by $2n$ first-order equations

$$
\left.
\begin{aligned}
\dot{Y}_j &= Y_{j+n} \\
\dot{Y}_{j+n} &= -\beta_j Y_{j+n} - \frac{1}{m_j}\frac{\partial U}{\partial Y_j} + \frac{1}{m_j} W_j(t)
\end{aligned}
\right\}
\qquad j = 1, 2, \ldots, n \qquad (8\text{-}51)
$$

From a physical basis, we conclude as before that the vector

$$\mathbf{Y} = \{Y_1, Y_2, \ldots, Y_n, Y_{n+1}, \ldots, Y_{2n}\}$$

is a Markov vector. For a *stable* system, $\mathbf{Y}$ approaches stationarity when the duration of the white-noise excitations is long. To construct the Fokker-Planck equation associated with this system we require the derivate moments A_j and B_{jk}, which can be obtained by use of Eqs. (8-51):

$$
\begin{aligned}
A_j &= y_{j+n} \\
A_{j+n} &= -\beta_j y_{j+n} - \frac{1}{m_j}\frac{\partial U(y_1, y_2, \ldots, y_n)}{\partial y_j} \\
B_{jk} &= 0 \qquad j \neq k \\
B_{jj} &= 0 \qquad j \leq n \\
B_{j+n,\, j+n} &= \frac{2\pi}{m_j{}^2} K_{jj}
\end{aligned}
\qquad (8\text{-}52)
$$

where K_{jj} is the value of the constant spectral density of the generalized excitation, the white noise $W_j(t)$. Thus the Fokker-Planck equation for the stationary case is given by

$$\sum_{j=1}^{n} \frac{\partial}{\partial y_j} (y_{j+n} p) - \sum_{j=1}^{n} \frac{\partial}{\partial y_{j+n}} \left\{ \left[\beta_j y_{j+n} + \frac{1}{m_j} \frac{\partial U(y_1, \ldots, y_n)}{\partial y_j} \right] p \right\}$$

$$- \sum_{j=1}^{n} \frac{\pi K_{jj}}{m_j^2} \frac{\partial^2 p}{\partial y_{j+n}^2} = 0 \quad (8\text{-}53)$$

where p is the abbreviation for the probability density of the stationary Markov vector $p_{\{Y\}}(\mathbf{y})$. Recall restriction (3) in the statement of the problem. We have

$$\frac{m_j \beta_j}{K_{jj}} = \gamma \quad \text{for every } j$$

Then the solution to Eq. (8-53) may be written as follows:

$$p = C \exp \left\{ - \frac{\gamma}{\pi} \left[\tfrac{1}{2} \sum_{j=1}^{n} m_j y_{j+n}^2 + U(y_1, \ldots, y_n) \right] \right\} \quad (8\text{-}54)$$

as can be verified by substituting it into Eq. (8-53). Equation (8-54) reduces to Eq. (8-35) in the case of a single degree of freedom.

Note from Eq. (8-54) that the kinetic energy in each generalized coordinate is identically distributed. In particular, the expected value of the kinetic energy in each coordinate is the same, namely, π/γ. This result is analogous to the principle of equipartitioned energy[‡] in the kinetic theory of gases. Note also that Eq. (8-54) has the same form as Eq. (8-35a). The total energy in the system is now

$$\mathcal{E} = \tfrac{1}{2} \sum_{j=1}^{n} m_j y_{j+n}^2 + U(y_1, \ldots, y_n) \quad (8\text{-}55)$$

The probability density (8-54) was obtained by Ariaratnam[¶] for a two-degrees-of-freedom system, and it was extended to the present general form by Caughey.[§]

The restrictions imposed for obtaining Eq. (8-54) are fulfilled, for example, by a viscously damped uniform beam pinned at both ends and subjected to a Gaussian-white-noise excitation which is spatially homo-

[‡] See, for example, C. Kittel, "Elementary Statistical Physics," p. 59, Wiley, New York, 1958.

[¶] S. T. Ariaratnam, Random Vibration of Nonlinear Suspensions, *J. Mech. Eng. Sci.*, **2**(3):195–201 (1960).

[§] Caughey, Derivation and Application of the Fokker-Planck Equation to Discrete Nonlinear Dynamic Systems Subjected to White Random Excitation.

geneous and uncorrelated. This problem was considered by Herbert.‡ Let this excitation process be denoted by $P(x, t)$. Then

$$E[P(x, t)] = 0$$
$$E[P(x_1, t_1)P(x_2, t_2)] = 2\pi B \, \delta(x_1 - x_2) \, \delta(t_1 - t_2) \tag{8-56}$$

We shall choose the generalized displacements $X_j(t)$ such that the transverse deflection of the beam may be written as

$$W(x, t) = \sum_{j=1}^{\infty} X_j(t) \sin \frac{j\pi x}{l} \tag{8-57}$$

where l is the span length of the beam. The generalized mass and the generalized damping in each mode are computed from

$$m_j = \int_0^l \rho A \sin^2 \frac{j\pi x}{l} \, dx = \frac{\rho A l}{2}$$
$$m_j \beta_j = \int_0^l c \sin^2 \frac{j\pi x}{l} \, dx = \frac{cl}{2} \tag{8-58}$$

where ρ is the mass density of the beam material, A the beam cross section, and c the damping coefficient. Both the generalized mass and the generalized damping terms are uncoupled in different modes. The cross spectral density of the generalized forces is obtained from

$$\Phi_{jk}(\omega) = \frac{1}{2\pi} \int_{-\infty}^{\infty} \int_0^l \int_0^l 2\pi B \, \delta(x_1 - x_2) \, \delta(\tau)$$
$$\sin \frac{j\pi x_1}{l} \sin \frac{k\pi x_2}{l} \exp(-i\omega\tau) \, dx_1 \, dx_2 \, d\tau$$
$$= \frac{l}{2} B \delta_{jk} \tag{8-59}$$

The cross spectral density for any two different generalized forces is seen to be zero. The individual spectral densities are

$$K_{jj} = \frac{l}{2} B$$

Therefore the conditions (1) through (3) listed in the beginning of this section are satisfied; thus the joint probability density for the stationary generalized displacements and the stationary generalized velocities must have the same form as Eq. (8-54). It is necessary only to note that, in the present example,

$$\frac{m_j \beta_j}{K_{jj}} = \gamma = \frac{c}{B} \tag{8-60}$$

---

‡ R. E. Herbert, Random Vibrations of a Nonlinear Elastic Beam, *J. Acoust. Soc. Am.*, **36**(11):2090–2094 (1964).

and the kinetic and potential energies of the system are, respectively,

$$T = \frac{\rho A}{2} \int_0^l \left(\sum_{j=1}^{\infty} z_j \sin \frac{j\pi x}{l} \right)^2 dx = \frac{\rho A l}{4} \sum_{j=1}^{\infty} z_j^2 \qquad (8\text{-}61)$$

$$U = \frac{EI}{2} \int_0^l \left(\frac{d^2}{dx^2} \sum_{j=1}^{\infty} y_j \sin \frac{j\pi x}{l} \right)^2 dx + \frac{AE}{2l} \left[\frac{1}{2} \int_0^l \left(\frac{d}{dx} \sum_{j=1}^{\infty} y_j \sin \frac{j\pi x}{l} \right)^2 dx \right]^2$$

$$= \frac{\pi^4 EI}{4l^3} \sum_{j=1}^{\infty} j^4 y_j^2 + \frac{\pi^4 AE}{32l^3} \left(\sum_{j=1}^{\infty} j^2 y_j^2 \right)^2 \qquad (8\text{-}62)$$

where y_j denotes the state variable for $X_j(t)$, and z_j denotes the state variable for $\dot{X}_j(t)$. Then

$$p = C \exp \left\{ -\frac{c}{\pi B} \left[\frac{1}{2} \frac{\rho A l}{2} \sum_{j=1}^{\infty} z_j^2 \right] \right.$$

$$\left. + \frac{\pi^4 EI}{4l^3} \left[\sum_{j=1}^{\infty} j^4 y_j^2 + \frac{1}{8r^2} \sum_{j=1}^{\infty} \sum_{k=1}^{\infty} j^2 k^2 y_j^2 y_k^2 \right] \right\} \qquad (8\text{-}63)$$

where $r = (I/A)^{\frac{1}{2}}$ is the radius of gyration of the beam cross section.

As can be seen from Eq. (8-54) for the special class of problems discussed above, the velocity processes are mutually independent and independent of the displacement processes. This is generally not true if the damping in the system is nonlinear. Caughey‡ has shown that if the equations of motion can be expressed as

$$m_j \ddot{X}_j + m_j \beta_j h(\mathcal{E}) \dot{X}_j + \frac{\partial U}{\partial X_j} = W_j(t) \qquad j = 1, 2, \ldots, n \qquad (8\text{-}64)$$

where the excitations $W_j(t)$ are uncorrelated with one another, where each $W_j(t)$ is a Gaussian white noise with spectral density K_{jj}, where $h(\mathcal{E})$ is a positive monotonically increasing function of $\mathcal{E}$ which is defined in Eq. (8-55), and where the constants $m_j \beta_j$ satisfy the condition

$$\frac{m_j \beta_j}{K_{jj}} = \gamma \qquad \text{for every } j$$

then a solution for the joint probability density of the stationary displacements and velocities can be obtained. Note that Eqs. (8-64) describe a system which satisfies the restrictions (1) through (3) stated on page 268 except for the matter of damping. Here the damping is nonlinear, and when it is expressed in each generalized coordinate it has

‡ Caughey, *On the Response of a Class of Nonlinear Oscillators to Stochastic Excitation.*

the special form $m_j \beta_j h(\mathcal{E}) \dot{X}_j$. Again, by denoting X_j by Y_j and $\dot{X}_j$ by Y_{j+n}, the Fokker-Planck equation for the joint probability density of the stationary displacements and velocities may be shown to be

$$\sum_{j=1}^{n} \frac{\partial}{\partial y_j} (y_{j+n} p) - \sum_{j=1}^{n} \frac{\partial}{\partial y_{j+n}} \left\{ \left[\beta_j h(\mathcal{E}) y_j + \frac{1}{m_j} \frac{\partial U}{\partial y_j} \right] p \right\}$$

$$- \sum_{j=1}^{n} \frac{\pi K_{jj}}{m_j^2} \frac{\partial^2 p}{\partial y_{j+n}^2} = 0 \quad (8\text{-}65)$$

The solution to Eq. (8-65) is

$$p = C \exp \left[- \frac{\gamma}{\pi} \int_0^{\mathcal{E}} h(\zeta) \, d\zeta \right] \quad (8\text{-}66)$$

Equation (8-66) is a generalization of Eq. (8-41) in the sense that the total energy level $\mathcal{E}$ in Eq. (8-66) is given by expression (8-55) whereas in Eq. (8-41) it is given by expression (8-36).

8.4 / THE PERTURBATION METHOD‡

The perturbation method is suitable for treating those cases in which the nonlinear terms in the governing equations are small. Consider the following equation for a single-degree-of-freedom system

$$\ddot{X} + 2\zeta \omega_0 \dot{X} + \omega_0^2 X + \epsilon \eta(X, \dot{X}) - F(t) = 0 \quad (8\text{-}67)$$

where η is a nonlinear function and ϵ is a parameter which is sufficiently small that the perturbation scheme is applicable. Assume that a solution to Eq. (8-67) may be expressed as a power series in ϵ; that is,

$$X(t) = X_0(t) + \epsilon X_1(t) + \epsilon^2 X_2(t) + \cdots \quad (8\text{-}68)$$

Substituting (8-68) into (8-67) and grouping terms having the same power of ϵ leads to a set of linear equations for $X_0, X_1, X_2, \ldots$:

$$\ddot{X}_0 + 2\zeta \omega_0 \dot{X}_0 + \omega_0^2 X_0 - F(t) = 0$$
$$\ddot{X}_1 + 2\zeta \omega_0 \dot{X}_1 + \omega_0^2 X_1 + \eta(X_0, \dot{X}_0) = 0 \quad (8\text{-}69)$$
$$\cdots \cdots \cdots \cdots \cdots \cdots \cdots \cdots$$

If we assume that the excitation process $F(t)$ is weakly stationary and that after the excitation has operated for a sufficiently long time there exists a weakly stationary solution to Eq. (8-67), then this solution can

‡ The development in this section follows closely a paper by S. H. Crandall, "The Spectrum of Random Vibration of a Nonlinear Oscillator," presented at the Eleventh International Congress of Applied Mechanics, Munich, August 30–September 5, 1964.

be constructed from the weakly stationary solutions to Eqs. (8-69), i.e.,

$$X_0(t) = \int_{-\infty}^{\infty} F(t - \tau)h(\tau)\, d\tau$$

$$X_1(t) = -\int_{-\infty}^{\infty} \eta_0(t - \tau)h(\tau)\, d\tau \qquad\qquad (8\text{-}70)$$

. . . .

where we have used the abbreviation $\eta_0(\tau)$ for $\eta[X_0(\tau), \dot{X}_0(\tau)]$, and h is the impulse response function corresponding to $\epsilon = 0$. Equations (8-70) can be used to compute various statistical properties of the response $X(t)$, for example, the mean function and the correlation function. The expectation of $X(t)$ is simply

$$E[X(t)] = E[X_0(t)] + \epsilon E[X_1(t)] + \epsilon^2 E[X_2(t)] + \cdots \qquad (8\text{-}71)$$

Substitution of (8-70) into (8-71) yields

$$E[X(t)] = \int_{-\infty}^{\infty} E[F(t - \tau)]h(\tau)\, d\tau - \epsilon \int_{-\infty}^{\infty} E[\eta_0(t - \tau)]h(\tau)\, d\tau + \cdots$$
$$(8\text{-}72)$$

Usually, results from a perturbation method are obtained only to the first order of the perturbation parameter ϵ, in which case only the first two terms on the right-hand side of Eq. (8-72) are retained. The auto-correlation of the response, computed to the first order of ϵ, is

$$E[X(t + \tau)X(t)] = E[X_0(t + \tau)X_0(t)] + \epsilon E[X_0(t + \tau)X_1(t)]$$
$$+ \epsilon E[X_0(t)X_1(t + \tau)] \quad (8\text{-}73)$$

or

$$R_{XX}(\tau) = R_{X_0 X_0}(\tau) + \epsilon[R_{X_0 X_1}(\tau) + R_{X_1 X_0}(\tau)] \qquad (8\text{-}73a)$$

It follows from Eqs. (8-70) that

$$R_{X_0 X_0}(\tau) = \int_{-\infty}^{\infty}\int_{-\infty}^{\infty} E[F(t + \tau - \theta_1)F(t - \theta_2)]h(\theta_1)h(\theta_2)\, d\theta_1\, d\theta_2$$

$$R_{X_0 X_1}(\tau) = -\int_{-\infty}^{\infty}\int_{-\infty}^{\infty} E[F(t + \tau - \theta_1)\eta_0$$
$$(t - \theta_2)]h(\theta_1)h(\theta_2)\, d\theta_1\, d\theta_2 \quad (8\text{-}74)$$

$$R_{X_1 X_0}(\tau) = -\int_{-\infty}^{\infty}\int_{-\infty}^{\infty} E[F(t - \theta_1)\eta_0(t + \tau - \theta_2)]h(\theta_1)h(\theta_2)\, d\theta_1\, d\theta_2$$

It is simpler, however, to compute either $R_{X_0 X_1}(\tau)$ or $R_{X_1 X_0}(\tau)$ and then use the symmetry relationship

$$R_{X_1 X_0}(\tau) = R_{X_0 X_1}(-\tau)$$

The spectral density of the response is obtained by taking the Fourier transform of Eq. (8-73a), i.e.,

$$\Phi_{XX}(\omega) = \Phi_{X_0 X_0}(\omega) + 2\epsilon \operatorname{Re} \left[\Phi_{X_0 X_1}(\omega) \right] \tag{8-75}$$

where use has been made of the fact that the cross spectral density of two jointly weakly stationary random processes is hermitian.

As an example, consider the equation of motion

$$\ddot{X} + 2\zeta \omega_0 \dot{X} + \omega_0{}^2 (X + \epsilon X^n) = F(t) \tag{8-76}$$

where n is an odd integer and $F(t)$ is a stationary Gaussian random process. This equation represents a system with a small stiffness non-linearity. To begin, let us compute $R_{X_0 X_0}(\tau)$; its computation is the same as that for a linear system, as discussed in Sec. 5.3. To proceed, let the spectral density of the excitation be $\Phi_{FF}(\omega)$. By substituting

$$E[F(t + \tau - \theta_1) F(t - \theta_2)] = R_{FF}(\tau - \theta_1 + \theta_2)$$
$$= \int_{-\infty}^{\infty} \Phi_{FF}(\omega) \exp \left[i\omega(\tau - \theta_1 + \theta_2) \right] d\omega$$

into the first equation in (8-74) we obtain

$$R_{X_0 X_0}(\tau) = \int_{-\infty}^{\infty} \Phi_{FF}(\omega) |H(\omega)|^2 \exp (i\omega\tau) \, d\omega \tag{8-77}$$

where $H(\omega)$ is the frequency response function corresponding to $\epsilon = 0$ and we have used the relation

$$H(\omega) = \int_{-\infty}^{\infty} h(\theta) \exp (-i\omega\theta) \, d\theta$$

To evaluate $R_{X_0 X_1}(\tau)$, we note that, for the present example,

$$E[F(t + \tau - \theta_1)\eta_0(t - \theta_2)] = \omega_0{}^2 E[F(t + \tau - \theta_1) X_0{}^n(t - \theta_2)] \tag{8-78}$$

Since $F(t)$ and $X_0(t)$ are jointly Gaussian, the expectation on the right-hand side of Eq. (8-78) can be evaluated by use of the Gaussian property Eq. (4-49). For simplicity, let $E[F(t)] = 0$, so that $E[X_0(t)] = 0$. Therefore

$$E[F(t + \tau - \theta_1)\eta_0(t - \theta_2)]$$
$$= m\omega_0{}^2 E[F(t + \tau - \theta_1) X_0(t - \theta_2)] E[X_0{}^{n-1}(t - \theta_2)] \tag{8-79}$$

The factor m on the right-hand side of (8-79) is the number of ways by which we can pick an $X_0(t - \theta_2)$ from the product $X_0{}^n(t - \theta_2)$; that is, $m = n$ here. Since $X_0(t)$ is weakly stationary and since $E[X_0(t)] = 0$,

$$E[X_0{}^{n-1}(t)] = \sigma_{X_0}{}^{n-1}(n - 2)(n - 4) \cdots 5 \cdot 3 \cdot 1 \tag{8-80}$$

We recall that n is an odd integer here. More concisely,

$$E[X_0{}^{n-1}(t)] = \frac{(\sqrt{2}\,\sigma_{X_0})^{n-1}}{\sqrt{\pi}}\,\Gamma\left(\frac{n}{2}\right) \qquad (8\text{-}80a)$$

where use has been made of the recurrence relation

$$\Gamma(\nu) = (\nu - 1)\Gamma(\nu - 1)$$

and $\Gamma(\tfrac{1}{2}) = \sqrt{\pi}$. Furthermore,

$$E[F(t + \tau - \theta_1)X_0(t - \theta_2)]$$
$$= \int_{-\infty}^{\infty} E[F(t + \tau - \theta_1)F(t - \theta_2 - \theta_3)]h(\theta_3)\,d\theta_3$$
$$= \int_{-\infty}^{\infty} R_{FF}(\tau - \theta_1 + \theta_2 + \theta_3)h(\theta_3)\,d\theta_3 \qquad (8\text{-}81)$$

Therefore,

$$E[F(t + \tau - \theta_1)\eta_0(t - \theta_2)] = \omega_0{}^2 \left(\frac{2^{n+1}}{\pi}\right)^{\frac{1}{2}} \sigma_{X_0}{}^{n-1}\Gamma\left(\frac{n+2}{2}\right)$$
$$\int_{-\infty}^{\infty} R_{FF}(\tau - \theta_1 + \theta_2 + \theta_2)h(\theta_3)\,d\theta_3 \qquad (8\text{-}82)$$

Substituting (8-82) into the second equation in (8-74) and letting

$$R_{FF}(\tau - \theta_1 + \theta_2 + \theta_3) = \int_{-\infty}^{\infty} \Phi_{FF}(\omega) \exp\left[i\omega(\tau - \theta_1 + \theta_2 + \theta_3)\right]d\omega$$

we obtain, after interchanging the order of integration,

$$R_{X_0 X_1}(\tau) = -\omega_0{}^2 \left(\frac{2^{n+1}}{\pi}\right)^{\frac{1}{2}} \sigma_{X_0}{}^{n-1}\Gamma\left(\frac{n+2}{2}\right)$$
$$\int_{-\infty}^{\infty} \Phi_{FF}(\omega)|H(\omega)|^2 H^*(\omega) \exp\,(i\omega\tau)\,d\omega \qquad (8\text{-}83)$$

The crosscorrelation function $R_{X_1 X_0}(\tau)$ is obtained by replacing τ by $-\tau$ in Eq. (8-83). Finally, the autocorrelation function of the nonlinear response $X(t)$, computed to the first order of ϵ, is

$$R_{XX}(\tau) = \int_{-\infty}^{\infty} \Phi_{FF}(\omega)|H(\omega)|^2 \left[\exp\,(i\omega\tau) - 2\epsilon\omega_0{}^2 \left(\frac{2^{n+1}}{\pi}\right)^{\frac{1}{2}}\right.$$
$$\left. \sigma_{X_0}{}^{n-1}\Gamma\left(\frac{n+2}{2}\right) H^*(\omega)\cos\omega\tau\right]d\omega \qquad (8\text{-}84)$$

The spectral density of the response is simply

$$\Phi_{XX}(\omega) = \Phi_{FF}(\omega)|H(\omega)|^2 \left\{1 - 2\epsilon\omega_0{}^2 \left(\frac{2^{n+1}}{\pi}\right)^{\frac{1}{2}} \sigma_{X_0}{}^{n-1}\Gamma\left(\frac{n+2}{2}\right) \mathrm{Re}\,[H(\omega)]\right\}$$
$$(8\text{-}85)$$

These results, Eqs. (8-84) and (8-85), for the system represented by Eq. (8-67) can be somewhat generalized. If the dynamic system is governed by the more general equation

$$\ddot{X} + 2\zeta\omega_0\dot{X} + \omega_0^2 \left(X + \epsilon \sum_{n=3,5,\ldots} g_n X^n \right) = F(t) \qquad (8\text{-}86)$$

then the autocorrelation function and the spectral density of the response to the first order in ϵ are

$$R_{XX}(\tau) = \int_{-\infty}^{\infty} \Phi_{FF}(\omega)|H(\omega)|^2[\exp\,(i\omega\tau) - 2\epsilon\omega_0^2 M H^*(\omega)\,\cos\,\omega\tau]\,d\omega \qquad (8\text{-}87)$$

$$\Phi_{XX}(\omega) = \Phi_{FF}(\omega)|H(\omega)|^2\{1 - 2\epsilon\omega_0^2 M\,\mathrm{Re}\,[H(\omega)]\} \qquad (8\text{-}88)$$

where

$$M = \sum_{n=3,5,\ldots} g_n \left(\frac{2^{n+1}}{\pi}\right)^{\frac{1}{2}} \sigma_{X_0}^{n-1} \Gamma\left(\frac{n+2}{2}\right) \qquad (8\text{-}89)$$

In the case of a white-noise excitation, Eqs. (8-87) and (8-88) become, respectively,

$$R_{XX}(\tau) = \sigma_{X_0}^2 \exp\,(-\zeta\omega_0\tau) \left\{ \left(\cos\,\omega_d\tau + \frac{\zeta}{\sqrt{1-\zeta^2}}\,\sin\,\omega_d\tau \right)(1 - \epsilon M) \right.$$
$$\left. - \epsilon\frac{M}{2}(1-\zeta^2)^{-1}\left[\left(\omega_d\tau + \frac{\zeta}{\sqrt{1-\zeta^2}} \right)\sin\,\omega_d\tau - \zeta\omega_0\tau\,\cos\,\omega_d\tau \right] \right\} \qquad (8\text{-}90)$$

$$\Phi_{XX}(\omega) = \frac{K}{(\omega_0^2 - \omega^2)^2 + (2\zeta\omega\omega_0)^2}\left[1 - 2\epsilon\omega_0^2 M\,\frac{\omega_0^2 - \omega^2}{(\omega_0^2 - \omega^2)^2 + (2\zeta\omega\omega_0)^2} \right]$$
$$(8\text{-}91)$$

where the spectral density K of the exciting white noise is related to the variance (same as the mean-square value in this case) of the linear response $\sigma_{X_0}^2$ as follows:

$$\sigma_{X_0}^2 = \frac{\pi K}{2\zeta\omega_0^3}$$

Equations (8-90) and (8-91) were first obtained by Crandall.‡

It is interesting to remark that if the nonlinear stiffness term in Eq. (8-86) is replaced by a nonlinear damping term which is a power series in terms of the velocity, then the resulting autocorrelation function and spectral density of the response are similar in form to Eqs. (8-87) and (8-88). Specifically, if the dynamic system is represented by

$$\ddot{X} + 2\zeta_0\omega_0 \left(\dot{X} + \epsilon \sum_{n=3,5,\ldots} k_n \dot{X}^n \right) + \omega_0^2 X = F(t) \qquad (8\text{-}92)$$

‡ Crandall, The Spectrum of Random Vibration of a Nonlinear Oscillator.

a procedure analogous to that used in dealing with the nonlinear stiffness case yields

$$R_{XX}(\tau) = \int_{-\infty}^{\infty} \Phi_{FF}(\omega)|H(\omega)|^2[\exp(i\omega\tau) + 4\epsilon N\zeta_0\omega_0(i\omega)H^*(\omega)\cos\omega\tau]\,d\omega \tag{8-93}$$

and

$$\Phi_{XX}(\omega) = \Phi_{FF}(\omega)|H(\omega)|^2\{1 + 4\epsilon N\zeta_0\omega_0 \operatorname{Re}[i\omega H^*(\omega)]\} \tag{8-94}$$

where

$$N = \sum_{n=3,5,\ldots} k_n\left(\frac{2^{n+1}}{\pi}\right)^{\frac{1}{2}} \sigma_{\dot X_0}{}^{n-1}\Gamma\left(\frac{n+2}{2}\right)$$

$$\sigma_{\dot X_0} = \left[\int_{-\infty}^{\infty} \omega^2\Phi_{FF}(\omega)|H(\omega)|^2\,d\omega\right]^{\frac{1}{2}} \tag{8-95}$$

There is certain practical interest in a nonlinearly damped dynamic system represented by Eq. (8-92). Crandall, Khabbaz, and Manning,‡ have shown that if the damping force is assumed to be

$$F_d(t) = c\dot s(1 + \epsilon|\dot s|^m) \tag{8-96}$$

then the energy loss per cycle in a cyclic motion has the same general form as Eq. (8-22a). Equation (8-96) agrees with Eq. (8-92) when the stress is proportional to the displacement and when the sum $\Sigma k_n\dot X^n$ is reduced to a single term $k_{m+1}\dot X^{m+1}$.

In principle, the perturbation method can be applied to any non-linear problem in which the nonlinear terms are small and for which the corresponding linear problem (i.e., when the nonlinear terms are dropped) is solvable. For example, let the potential energy U of the structure in Eqs. (8-49) be separable as

$$U = U_0 + \epsilon U_1$$

where U_0 is quadratic in the generalized displacements. Then in the expression

$$\frac{\partial U}{\partial X_j} = \frac{\partial U_0}{\partial X_j} + \epsilon\frac{\partial U_1}{\partial X_j}$$

the first and the second terms represent, respectively, the linear and non-linear spring forces. Assuming the existence of the power series

$$X_j = X_{j0} + \epsilon X_{j1} + \epsilon^2 X_{j2} + \cdots \qquad j = 1, 2, \ldots, n \tag{8-97}$$

‡ S. H. Crandall, G. R. Kabbaz, and J. E. Manning, Random Vibration of an Oscillator with Nonlinear Damping, *J. Acoust. Soc. Am.*, **36**(7):1330–1334 (1964).

we obtain from Eq. (8-49)

$$m_j \ddot{X}_{j0} + m_j \beta_j \dot{X}_{j0} + \left(\frac{\partial U_0}{\partial X_j}\right)_0 = F_j(t)$$

$$m_j \ddot{X}_{j1} + m_j \beta_j \dot{X}_{j1} + \left(\frac{\partial U_0}{\partial X_j}\right)_1 = - \left(\frac{\partial U_1}{\partial X_j}\right)_0 \qquad j = 1, 2, \ldots, n$$

$$(8\text{-}98)$$

for use in the first-order perturbation solutions in ϵ, where $(\partial U_r/\partial X_j)_s$, r, $s = 0$, 1, denotes the derivative $\partial U_r/\partial X_j$ evaluated at $X_1 = X_{1s}$, $X_2 = X_{2s}$, $\ldots$, $X_n = X_{ns}$, and the $F_j(t)$ are the excitations which need not be restricted to white noise. The statistical properties of the X_j can be computed easily if the excitations are stationary and Gaussian.

In Eqs. (8-98), the inertia forces and the damping forces are both uncoupled in the generalized coordinates, but the perturbation scheme is useful even when coupling in inertia or in damping is present. It can be applied either to a finite-degrees-of-freedom system or to a continuum, although in a complicated case the algebraic operations may become so unwieldy that the method is no longer practical. An example of a continuous system treated by use of a perturbation procedure may be found in a paper by Lyon.‡ At this point, as an example, we shall present in some detail a two-degrees-of-freedom case which is a simplified analysis of the response of an airplane when taxied on a rough runway.¶

Let the airplane be moving at a constant horizontal speed along a runway whose profile is assumed to be a homogeneous random process. We idealize the airplane as a two-degrees-of-freedom system, as shown in Fig. 8.2. The mass of the wheels is represented by m_2; and the lumped mass of the airplane, cargo, passengers, etc., is represented by m_1. The tire spring force and the damping force in the landing-gear system are assumed to be linear; but the spring force in the landing-gear system is considered to have a Duffing-type nonlinearity. As the airplane moves, the system senses an excitation which is a stationary random motion of its support. From this model we write the equations of motion as follows:

$$m_1 \ddot{Z}_1 + c(\dot{Z}_1 - \dot{Z}_2) + k_1[(Z_1 - Z_2) + \epsilon(Z_1 - Z_2)^3] = 0$$
$$m_2 \ddot{Z}_2 - c(\dot{Z}_1 - \dot{Z}_2) - k_1[(Z_1 - Z_2) + \epsilon(Z_1 - Z_2)^3]$$
$$+ k_2 Z_2 = k_2 \Delta(vt)$$

$$(8\text{-}99)$$

where ϵ is a sufficiently small perturbation parameter. To the first order

‡ R. H. Lyon, Response of a Nonlinear String to Random Excitation, *J. Acoust. Soc. Am.*, **32**(8):953–960 (1960).

¶ This problem was considered by C. C. Tung, J. Penzien, and R. Horonjeff. See their paper, The Effect of Runway Unevenness on the Dynamic Response of Supersonic Transports, *NASA* CR-119, University of California, Berkeley, 1964.

of the perturbation parameter, we can write

$$Z_1 = Z_{10} + \epsilon Z_{11}$$
$$Z_2 = Z_{20} + \epsilon Z_{21} \tag{8-100}$$

and we find the matrix equations for Z_{10}, Z_{11}, Z_{20}, and Z_{21} are

$$[m] \begin{Bmatrix} \ddot{Z}_{10} \\ \ddot{Z}_{20} \end{Bmatrix} + [c] \begin{Bmatrix} \dot{Z}_{10} \\ \dot{Z}_{20} \end{Bmatrix} + [k] \begin{Bmatrix} Z_{10} \\ Z_{20} \end{Bmatrix} = \begin{Bmatrix} 0 \\ k_2 \Delta \end{Bmatrix}$$

$$[m] \begin{Bmatrix} \ddot{Z}_{11} \\ \ddot{Z}_{21} \end{Bmatrix} + [c] \begin{Bmatrix} \dot{Z}_{11} \\ \dot{Z}_{21} \end{Bmatrix} + [k] \begin{Bmatrix} Z_{11} \\ Z_{21} \end{Bmatrix} = \begin{Bmatrix} -k_1(Z_{10} - Z_{20})^3 \\ k_1(Z_{10} - Z_{20})^3 \end{Bmatrix} \tag{8-101}$$

where

$$[m] = \begin{bmatrix} m_1 & 0 \\ 0 & m_2 \end{bmatrix} \qquad [c] = \begin{bmatrix} c & -c \\ -c & c \end{bmatrix} \qquad [k] = \begin{bmatrix} k_1 & -k_1 \\ -k_1 & k_1 + k_2 \end{bmatrix}$$

A solution to Eqs. (8-101) may be expressed in terms of the matrix of the impulse response functions. It can be shown that these equations cannot be uncoupled by linear transformations; therefore the matrix of the impulse response functions must be computed by use of Eq. (6-22) or Eq. (6-26). Let us choose Eq. (6-22), i.e.,

$$\mathbf{h}(t) = \begin{cases} [\mathbf{0} \mathbin{\vdots} \mathbf{I}] \exp{(-\mathbf{g}t)} \begin{bmatrix} \mathbf{m}^{-1} \\ \hdashline \mathbf{0} \end{bmatrix} & t \geq 0 \\ \mathbf{0} & t < 0 \end{cases} \tag{6-22}$$

To evaluate $\exp{(-\mathbf{g}t)}$ we require the eigenvalues and the eigenvectors

Fig. 8.2 Simplified model for airplane taxiing analysis.

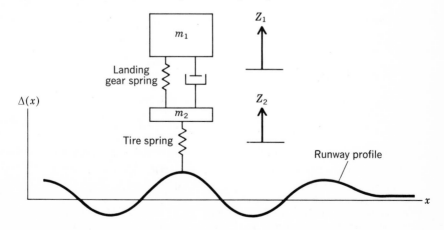

(modal columns) of $\mathbf{g}$, which, for the present example, is given by

$$\mathbf{g} = \begin{bmatrix} \dfrac{c}{m_1} & -\dfrac{c}{m_1} & \dfrac{k_1}{m_1} & -\dfrac{k_1}{m_1} \\[2mm] -\dfrac{c}{m_2} & \dfrac{c}{m_2} & -\dfrac{k_1}{m_2} & \dfrac{k_1}{m_2}+\dfrac{k_2}{m_2} \\[2mm] -1 & 0 & 0 & 0 \\[2mm] 0 & -1 & 0 & 0 \end{bmatrix} \qquad (8\text{-}102)$$

The eigenvalues λ of this matrix can be computed from its characteristic equation

$$\lambda^4 - \lambda^3\left(\frac{c}{m_1}+\frac{c}{m_2}\right) + \lambda^2\left(\frac{2k_1}{m_1}+\frac{k_2}{m_2}\right) - \lambda\,\frac{c}{m_1}\frac{k_2}{m_2} + \frac{k_1}{m_1}\frac{k_2}{m_2} = 0 \qquad (8\text{-}103)$$

We remark that the real parts of the four roots of Eq. (8-103) are positive if the damping coefficient c is positive, as can be detected easily by an application of the well-known Routh-Hurwitz criterion.‡ This implies that the structure is a stable system. As a practical matter, however, the actual solution of Eq. (8-103) can be carried out only when the numerical values for c, m_1, m_2, k_1, and k_2 are given. For every root $\lambda = \lambda_n$, it can be shown easily that the associated modal column is

$$\left\{ \begin{array}{c} -(k_1 - c\lambda_n)\dfrac{\lambda_n}{m_1} \\[3mm] -\lambda_n{}^2 - (k_1 - c)\dfrac{\lambda_n}{m_1} \\[3mm] \dfrac{k_1 - c\lambda_n}{m_1} \\[3mm] \lambda_n + \dfrac{k_1 - c}{m_1} \end{array} \right\}$$

Thus, we have all the necessary ingredients to construct the matrix of the impulse response functions $\mathbf{h}(t)$ according to Eq. (6-22). In this case this matrix is 2×2. Then we may write for the stationary solutions

$$Z_{10} = \int_{-\infty}^{\infty} h_{12}(t - \tau)k_2\,\Delta(v\tau)\,d\tau$$

$$Z_{20} = \int_{-\infty}^{\infty} h_{22}(t - \tau)k_2\,\Delta(v\tau)\,d\tau$$

$$Z_{11} = \int_{-\infty}^{\infty} k_1[h_{12}(t - \tau) - h_{11}(t - \tau)][Z_{10}(\tau) - Z_{20}(\tau)]^3\,d\tau \qquad (8\text{-}104)$$

$$Z_{21} = \int_{-\infty}^{\infty} k_1[h_{22}(t - \tau) - h_{21}(t - \tau)][Z_{10}(\tau) - Z_{20}(\tau)]^3\,d\tau$$

where h_{ij} is the (i, j) element of the matrix $\mathbf{h}$. Equations (8-104) can be used to compute the statistical properties for $Z_1(t)$ and $Z_2(t)$ in a way similar to that in which Eqs. (8-70) were used in Eqs. (8-73), (8-74), etc.

‡ See, for example, G. A. Korn and T. M. Korn, "Mathematical Handbook for Scientists and Engineers," p. 17, McGraw-Hill, New York, 1961.

For example, the mean-square values of $Z_1(t)$ and $Z_2(t)$ computed to the first order in ϵ are given by

$$E[Z_1{}^2(t)] = E[Z_{10}{}^2(t)] + 2\epsilon E[Z_{10}(t)Z_{11}(t)]$$
$$E[Z_2{}^2(t)] = E[Z_{20}{}^2(t)] + 2\epsilon E[Z_{20}(t)Z_{21}(t)]$$

$$(8\text{-}105)$$

To proceed further, let us assume that the stationary excitation $\Delta(vt)$ is Gaussian and has a zero mean. Substituting Eqs. (8-104) into Eqs. (8-105) and using the Gaussian property

$$E\{\Delta(v\tau_1)[Z_{10}(\tau_2) - Z_{20}(\tau_2)]^3\}$$
$$= 3E\{[Z_{10}(\tau_2) - Z_{20}(\tau_2)]^2\}E\{\Delta(v\tau_1)[Z_{10}(\tau_2) - Z_{20}(\tau_2)]\}$$

we obtain

$$E[Z_1{}^2(t)]$$
$$= \int_{-\infty}^{\infty} d\tau_1 \int_{-\infty}^{\infty} d\tau_2\, k_2{}^2 h_{12}(t - \tau_1)h_{12}(t - \tau_2)E[\Delta(v\tau_1)\,\Delta(v\tau_2)]$$
$$+ 6\epsilon k_1 k_2{}^4 \int_{-\infty}^{\infty} d\tau_1 \int_{-\infty}^{\infty} d\tau_2 \int_{-\infty}^{\infty} du_1 \int_{-\infty}^{\infty} du_2 \int_{-\infty}^{\infty} du_3$$
$$h_{12}(t - \tau_1)[h_{12}(t - \tau_2) - h_{11}(t - \tau_2)][h_{12}(\tau_2 - u_1)$$
$$- h_{22}(\tau_2 - u_1)][h_{12}(\tau_2 - u_2) - h_{22}(\tau_2 - u_2)][h_{12}(\tau_2 - u_3)$$
$$- h_{22}(\tau_2 - u_3)]E[\Delta(vu_1)\,\Delta(vu_2)]E[\Delta(v\tau_1)\,\Delta(vu_3)]$$

$$E[Z_2{}^2(t)]$$

$$(8\text{-}106)$$

$$= k_2{}^2 \int_{-\infty}^{\infty} d\tau_1 \int_{-\infty}^{\infty} d\tau_2\, h_{22}(t - \tau_1)h_{22}(t - \tau_2)E[\Delta(v\tau_1)\,\Delta(v\tau_2)]$$
$$+ 6\epsilon k_1 k_2{}^4 \int_{-\infty}^{\infty} d\tau_1 \int_{-\infty}^{\infty} d\tau_2 \int_{-\infty}^{\infty} du_1 \int_{-\infty}^{\infty} du_2 \int_{-\infty}^{\infty} du_3$$
$$h_{22}(t - \tau_1)[h_{22}(t - \tau_2) - h_{21}(t - \tau_2)][h_{12}(\tau_2 - u_1)$$
$$- h_{22}(\tau_2 - u_1)][h_{12}(\tau_2 - u_2) - h_{22}(\tau_2 - u_2)][h_{12}(\tau_2 - u_3)$$
$$- h_{22}(\tau_2 - u_3)]E[\Delta(vu_1)\,\Delta(vu_2)]E[\Delta(v\tau_1)\,\Delta(vu_3)]$$

Tung‡ has computed these mean-square values by assuming the correlation function of the runway profile to be

$$E[\Delta(vu_1)\,\Delta(vu_2)] = R_{\Delta\Delta}(u_1 - u_2)$$
$$= R_{\Delta\Delta}(0) \exp\left(-\eta v|u_1 - u_2|\right)$$

Using the following preliminary data for a large jet transport and an average international airport,

$$m_1 = 955 \text{ lb-sec}^2/\text{in.}$$
$$m_2 = 12 \text{ lb-sec}^2/\text{in.}$$
$$c = 1{,}500 \text{ lb-sec/in.}$$
$$k_1 = 187{,}500 \text{ lb/in.}$$
$$k_2 = 96{,}000 \text{ lb/in.}$$
$$\epsilon = 0.15$$
$$v = 1{,}200 \text{ in./sec}$$
$$\eta = 0.00179 \text{ in.}^{-1}$$
$$R_{\Delta\Delta}(0) = 0.475 \text{ in.}^2$$

‡ *Op. cit.*

he found that $E[Z_1^2(t)] = 7.34$ in.^{2} and $E[Z_2^2(t)] = 3.60$ in.^{2} for the stationary response.

These statistical properties of the random displacements $Z_1(t)$ and $Z_2(t)$, although computed from a simplified model, are useful in preliminary design to predict whether or not an airplane will fulfill certain of its intended functions. For example, if the airplane under study were being considered as a commercial transport, then a large mean-square value for $Z_1(t)$ would indicate that such an airplane would most likely be too bumpy for the passengers' comfort. A more accurate prediction for this design criterion can be made from the information provided by the spectral density of $Z_1(t)$, since it is known that human sensitivity to an up-and-down motion differs for different frequency components. In addition to the above, we mention the statistical properties of the relative displacement $Z_1(t) - Z_2(t)$, which are more important to the designer of the landing-gear system than those of $Z_1(t)$ and $Z_2(t)$ separately since it is this difference which gives rise to the stresses in the landing-gear system.

In spite of the versatility enjoyed by the perturbation method, certain subtle questions about this method remain unanswered. The power-series expansion for the nonlinear response, Eq. (8-68), is valid if the response is analytic in ϵ and the series converges in mean square, or in probability, or with probability 1, or in distribution. Obviously, the criteria for convergence in any of the above senses must include the magnitude of the perturbation parameter ϵ. No such criteria have been established. At the present time confidence in the perturbation method can be gained only by comparing the results with those from another method whose applicability does not depend on the smallness of the nonlinear terms, such as the method of Fokker-Planck. We shall show that the comparison is indeed satisfactory in the case of a nonlinear stiffness system subjected to a Gaussian-white-noise excitation.

As the basis for discussion we choose as the equation of motion Eq. (8-86) with the excitation $F(t)$ specialized to a white noise $W(t)$. The mean-square response (same as the variance of the response in this case) may be computed by letting $\tau = 0$ in Eq. (8-90):

$$\sigma_X^2 = \sigma_{X_0}^2 \left[1 - \sum_{n=3,5,\ldots} g_n \left(\frac{2^{n+1}}{\pi} \right)^{\frac{1}{2}} \sigma_{X_0}^{n-1} \Gamma \left(\frac{n+2}{2} \right) \right] \tag{8-107}$$

From a Fokker-Planck approach, the probability density of the stationary response is found to be [refer to Eqs. (8-32)]

$$p_{\{X\}}(x) = C \exp\left[-\frac{1}{\sigma_{X_0}^2} \int_0^x \left(u + \epsilon \sum_{n=3,5,\ldots} g_n u^n \right) du \right]$$

$$= C \exp\left[-\frac{1}{\sigma_{X_0}^2} \left(\frac{x^2}{2} + \epsilon \sum_{n=3,5,\ldots} \frac{g_n x^{n+1}}{n+1} \right) \right] \tag{8-108}$$

To the first order in ϵ, this probability density is approximated as

$$p_{\{X\}}(x) \approx C \left(1 - \frac{\epsilon}{\sigma_{X_0}^2} \sum_{n=3,5,\ldots} \frac{g_n}{n+1} x^{n+1} \right) \exp \left(- \frac{x^2}{2\sigma_{X_0}^2} \right) \qquad (8\text{-}108a)$$

The normalization factor C satisfying

$$\int_{-\infty}^{\infty} p_{\{X\}}(x) \, dx = 1$$

can be readily evaluated:

$$C \approx \left[\sqrt{2\pi} \, \sigma_{X_0} - \epsilon \sum_{n=3,5,\ldots} \frac{g_n}{n+1} (\sqrt{2})^{n+2} \sigma_{X_0}^n \Gamma \left(\frac{n+2}{2} \right) \right]^{-1} \qquad (8\text{-}109)$$

Finally, the mean-square response is obtained from

$$\sigma_X^2 = \int_{-\infty}^{\infty} x^2 p_{\{X\}}(x) \, dx$$

$$\approx C \left[\sqrt{2\pi} \, \sigma_{X_0}^3 - \epsilon \sum_{n=3,5,\ldots} \frac{g_n}{n+1} (2^{(n+4)/2}) \sigma_X^{n+2} \Gamma \left(\frac{n+4}{2} \right) \right]$$

$$\approx \sigma_{X_0}^2 \left[1 - \epsilon \sum_{n=3,5,\ldots} g_n \left(\frac{2^{n+1}}{\pi} \right)^{\frac{1}{2}} \sigma_{X_0}^{n-1} \Gamma \left(\frac{n+2}{2} \right) \right] \qquad (8\text{-}110)$$

which agrees with Eq. (8-107).

8.5 / METHOD OF EQUIVALENT LINEARIZATION

The method of equivalent linearization was originated by Krylov and Bogoliubov‡ for the treatment of nonlinear systems under deterministic excitations. It was first applied to the problems of random oscillations by Booton¶ and Caughey§ and later was used on several occasions by Crandall‡‡ and many others. To show how this method is adapted to a single-degree-of-freedom system such as the one represented by Eq. (8-1), we assume that an approximate solution to Eq. (8-1) can be obtained from the linearized equation

$$\ddot{X} + \beta_e \dot{X} + k_e X = F(t) \qquad (8\text{-}111)$$

‡ N. Krylov and N. Bogoliubov, Introduction à la mécanique nonlineaire: les méthodes approachées et asymptotiques, *Ukr. akad. nauk Inst. de la mécanique, Chaire de phys. math. Ann.*, t. 1-2, 1937; translated by S. Lefshetz in Annals of Mathematical Studies No. 11," Princeton, Princeton, N.J., 1947.

¶ R. C. Booton, Jr., Nonlinear Control Systems with Random Inputs, *IRE Trans. Circuit Theory*, **CT-1**:9–18 (1954).

§ For a review of his work see T. K. Caughey, Equivalent Linearization Techniques, *J. Acoust. Soc. Am.*, **35**(11):1706–1711 (1963).

‡‡ See, for example, S. H. Crandall, Random Vibration of Systems with Nonlinear Restoring Forces, *Proc. Intern. Symp. Nonlinear Vibrations, Kiev, September, 1961*, **1**:306–314 (1963).

The error of linearization, a random process, is

$$\mathcal{E} = g(X, \dot{X}) - \beta_e \dot{X} - k_e X \qquad (8\text{-}112)$$

which is the difference between Eqs. (8-1) and (8-111). The method of attack is to minimize this error in a suitable way, for example, to make $E[\mathcal{E}^2]$ or $E[|\mathcal{E}|]$ as small as possible. The usual choice is to minimize the mean-square error, which can be accomplished by requiring that

$$\frac{\partial}{\partial \beta_e} E[\mathcal{E}^2] = 0$$

$$\frac{\partial}{\partial k_e} E[\mathcal{E}^2] = 0 \qquad (8\text{-}113)$$

Substituting Eq. (8-112) into Eqs. (8-113) and interchanging the order of differentiation and expectation, we obtain

$$E[\dot{X}g(X, \dot{X})] - \beta_e E[\dot{X}^2] - k_e E[X\dot{X}] = 0$$
$$E[Xg(X, \dot{X})] - \beta_e E[X\dot{X}] - k_e E[X^2] = 0 \qquad (8\text{-}114)$$

Solving for the equivalent damping and stiffness constants β_e and k_e, we find

$$\beta_e = \frac{E[X^2]E[\dot{X}g(X, \dot{X})] - E[X\dot{X}]E[Xg(X, \dot{X})]}{E[X^2]E[\dot{X}^2] - (E[X\dot{X}])^2}$$

$$k_e = \frac{E[\dot{X}^2]E[Xg(X, \dot{X})] - E[X\dot{X}]E[\dot{X}g(X, \dot{X})]}{E[X^2]E[\dot{X}^2] - (E[X\dot{X}])^2} \qquad (8\text{-}115)$$

Note that Eqs. (8-115) are not explicit expressions for β_e and k_e, since the expectations appearing on the right-hand sides depend on β_e and k_e. It is possible to see, however, that the conditions (8-113) truly lead to the minimization of the mean-square error, since‡

$$\frac{\partial^2}{\partial \beta_e^2} E[\mathcal{E}^2] = 2E[\dot{X}^2]$$

$$\frac{\partial^2}{\partial k_e^2} E[\mathcal{E}^2] = 2E[X^2]$$

$$\frac{\partial^2}{\partial \beta_e \, \partial k_e} E[\mathcal{E}^2] = 2E[X\dot{X}]$$

and that the quadratic form

$$\frac{1}{2}\left\{ (\Delta\beta_e)^2 \frac{\partial^2}{\partial \beta_e^2} E[\mathcal{E}^2](\Delta\beta_e)^2 + \frac{\partial^2}{\partial k_e^2} E[\mathcal{E}^2](\Delta k_e)^2 \right.$$
$$\left. + 2 \frac{\partial^2}{\partial \beta_e \, \partial k_e} E[\mathcal{E}^2] \right\} = E[(X \, \Delta k_e + \dot{X} \, \Delta\beta_e)^2]$$

is nonnegative.

‡ See, for example, Korn and Korn, *op. cit.*, p. 318.

In order for the following discussion to be reasonably brief but still retain the essence of the equivalent-linearization method, we shall assume that the excitation $F(t)$ is stationary, is Gaussian, and has a zero expectation. Then the approximate displacement and velocity, X and $\dot{X}$, computed from the linearized equation (8-111), are also Gaussian, and they approach stationarity if the dynamical system is stable. For the remainder of this section, we shall be concerned only with the stationary response.

Therefore when we take X and $\dot{X}$ to be jointly stationary, we have $E[X\dot{X}] = 0$. Equations (8-115) then reduce to

$$\beta_e = \frac{E[\dot{X}g(X, \dot{X})]}{E[\dot{X}^2]}$$

$$k_e = \frac{E[Xg(X, \dot{X})]}{E[X^2]} \tag{8-115a}$$

Let us further restrict ourselves to the case where the nonlinearities in stiffness and in damping are separable; i.e., let

$$g(X, \dot{X}) = f_1(X) + f_2(X)$$

Since for Gaussian processes being uncorrelated implies being independent, Eqs. (8-115a) become

$$\beta_e = \frac{E[\dot{X}f_2(\dot{X})]}{E[\dot{X}^2]}$$

$$k_e = \frac{E[Xf_1(X)]}{E[X^2]} \tag{8-115b}$$

Furthermore, if the system nonlinearity is confined to the stiffness characteristics of the system, i.e., if $f_2(\dot{X}) = \beta\dot{X}$, then $\beta_e = \beta$. Similarly, if the system nonlinearity is present only in the damping term, i.e., if $f_1(X) = kX$, then $k_e = k$. Therefore, for either of these special cases, only one of the two conditions in (8-113) needs to be used.

As an example, consider a nonlinearly damped system governed by the equation

$$\ddot{X} + \beta_0(\dot{X} + \epsilon \sum_{n=3,5,\ldots} k_n\dot{X}^n) + \omega_0^2 X = F(t) \tag{8-92a}$$

This equation has been treated previously by use of a perturbation method. We shall show that the equivalent-linearization method leads to a result which is in agreement with that from the perturbation method to the first order in ϵ. Since the nonlinear term in Eq. (8-92a) involves only damping, we need consider only the first equation in (8-115b), i.e.,

$$\beta_e = \frac{E[\dot{X}f_2(\dot{X})]}{E[\dot{X}^2]}$$

$$= \beta_0 \left\{ 1 + \epsilon \sum_{n=3,5,\ldots} k_n \frac{E[\dot{X}^{n+1}]}{E[\dot{X}^2]} \right\} \tag{8-116}$$

The approximate velocity process $\dot{X}(t)$ computed from a linearized equation is Gaussian; therefore,

$$\frac{E[\dot{X}^{n+1}]}{E[\dot{X}^2]} = \sigma_{\dot{X}}^{n-1} n(n-2)(n-4) \cdots 5 \cdot 3 \cdot 1$$

$$= \sqrt{\frac{2^{n+1}}{\pi}} \sigma_{\dot{X}}^{n-1} \Gamma\left(\frac{n+2}{2}\right) \qquad n = 3, 5, \ldots$$

Here, we have used again the special Gaussian property (4-49) and the fact that $E[\dot{X}] = 0$. The equivalent damping constant is then

$$\beta_e = \beta_0(1 + \epsilon \bar{N}) \tag{8-117}$$

where

$$\bar{N} = \sum_{n=3,5,\ldots} k_n \sqrt{\frac{2^{n+1}}{\pi}} \sigma_{\dot{X}}^{n-1} \Gamma\left(\frac{n+2}{2}\right) \tag{8-118}$$

In terms of this equivalent damping constant the spectral density of the displacement $X(t)$ is given by

$$\Phi_{XX}(\omega) = \Phi_{FF}|H_e(\omega)|^2 \tag{8-119}$$

where

$$|H_e(\omega)|^2 = [(\omega_0^2 - \omega^2)^2 + (\beta_e \omega)^2]^{-1} \tag{8-120}$$

To the first order of ϵ,

$$|H_e(\omega)|^2 = |H(\omega)|^2 + \epsilon \bar{N}\beta_0 \frac{\partial}{\partial \beta_0}|H(\omega)|^2 \tag{8-121}$$

which is obtained by considering $|H_e(\omega)|^2$ to be a function of β_e, expanding it into a Taylor series about β_0 (note $\beta_e - \beta_0 = \epsilon \bar{N}\beta_0$), and keeping only the first two terms. It is easy to show that

$$\frac{\partial}{\partial \beta_0}|H(\omega)|^2 = -2\omega^2 \beta_0 |H(\omega)|^4$$

$$= 2|H(\omega)|^2 \operatorname{Re}[i\omega H^*(\omega)] \tag{8-122}$$

Therefore,

$$\Phi_{XX}(\omega) = \Phi_{FF}(\omega)|H(\omega)|^2\{1 + 2\epsilon\bar{N}\beta_0 \operatorname{Re}[i\omega H^*(\omega)]\} \tag{8-123}$$

This result will agree with (8-94), the result obtained from the perturbation method, if

$$\bar{N} = N + 0(\epsilon) \qquad (8\text{-}124)$$

or, equivalently,

$$\sigma_{\dot{X}}{}^{n-1} = \sigma_{\dot{X}_0}{}^{n-1} + 0(\epsilon) \qquad (8\text{-}124a)$$

where $0(\epsilon)$ denotes a remainder which is of order ϵ. That Eq. (8-124a) is true can be seen readily, since

$$\sigma_{\dot{X}}{}^{n-1} = \left[\int_{-\infty}^{\infty} \omega^2 \Phi_{FF}(\omega) |H_e(\omega)|^2 \, d\omega \right]^{(n-1)/2}$$

$$= \left\{ \int_{-\infty}^{\infty} \omega^2 \Phi_{FF}(\omega) [|H(\omega)|^2 + 0(\epsilon)] \, d\omega \right\}^{(n-1)/2} \qquad (8\text{-}125)$$

In the case of a nonlinear stiffness governed by the equation

$$\ddot{X} + \beta_0 \dot{X} + \omega_0{}^2 \left(X + \epsilon \sum_{n=3,5,\ldots} g_n X^n \right) = F(t) \qquad (8\text{-}86a)$$

where $F(t)$ is stationary, is Gaussian, and has a zero expectation, the spectral density of $X(t)$ obtained from the equivalent-linearization method is

$$\Phi_{XX}(\omega) = \Phi_{FF}(\omega) |H(\omega)|^2 \{1 - 2\epsilon\omega_0{}^2 \bar{M} \, \text{Re} \, [H(\omega)]\} \qquad (8\text{-}126)$$

where

$$\bar{M} = \sum_{n=3,5,\ldots} g_n \left(\frac{2^{n+1}}{\pi} \right)^{\frac{1}{2}} \sigma_X{}^{n-1} \Gamma \left(\frac{n+2}{2} \right) \qquad (8\text{-}127)$$

It is also a simple matter to show that

$$\bar{M} = M + 0(\epsilon) \qquad (8\text{-}128)$$

Therefore Eq. (8-126) agrees with Eq. (8-88) to the first order in ϵ. Thus the results from the equivalent-linearization method and those from the perturbation method agree in the case of small nonlinearities.

It should be pointed out that the smallness of the nonlinear term in the original equation was not a presupposition in the development of the equivalent-linearization method. Wolaver[‡] has shown that in the case of a system where only the stiffness law is nonlinear and where the excitation is a Gaussian white noise, the equivalent-linearization method leads to the exact mean-square value for the stationary displacement regardless of the magnitude of the nonlinear term. He also has proved that in this

‡ L. E. Wolaver, Second Order Properties of Nonlinear Systems Driven by Random Noise, *USAF Aerospace Res. Lab.* ARL-65-61, Wright-Patterson Air Force Base, Ohio, April, 1965.

case the MacLaurin series expansion of the approximate autocorrelation function $R_{XX}(\tau)$ of the stationary displacement obtained from equivalent linearization agrees with that of the exact autocorrelation function up to the τ^3 term. These observations give additional confidence in the equivalent-linearization method. However, when the nonlinear term is not small, the equivalent-linearization method is often an iterative procedure. For example, for the application of Eq. (8-126) we must know σ_X, which appears in Eq. (8-127). But σ_X is related to $\Phi_{XX}(\omega)$ by

$$\sigma_X{}^2 = \int_{-\infty}^{\infty} \Phi_{XX}(\omega) \, d\omega$$

We may begin the iteration by substituting M for $\bar{M}$ in Eq. (8-126), which is then integrated to obtain the first approximation for $\sigma_X{}^2$. This approximate result may be used in Eq. (8-127) to find a more accurate $\bar{M}$, thereby completing the first iterative cycle. In certain simple cases, it is possible to obtain an explicit expression for $\sigma_X{}^2$. One such case is a Duffing system under the excitation of a Gaussian white noise. It was shown that a thin plate hinged along immovable edges can be represented as a Duffing system if the motion is essentially that of a single mode. Let us take a closer look at the behavior of such a system. The equation of motion is

$$\ddot{X} + \beta_0 \dot{X} + \omega_0{}^2(X + \alpha X^3) = W(t) \tag{8-129}$$

corresponding to $g_n = 0$ for $n \neq 3$ and $\epsilon g_3 = \alpha$. Then from Eq. (8-127), $\bar{M} = 3\epsilon^{-1}\alpha\sigma_X{}^2$. The spectral density of the response computed from the equivalent-linearization method is

$$\Phi_{XX}(\omega) = K|H(\omega)|^2\{1 - 6\alpha\omega_0{}^2\sigma_X{}^2 \, \text{Re}\,[H(\omega)]\} \tag{8-130}$$

where K is the constant spectral density of the white noise $W(t)$. Equation (8-130) can be rewritten as follows:

$$\Phi_{XX}(\omega) = K\left[|H(\omega)|^2 + \tfrac{3}{2}\alpha\sigma_X{}^2\omega_0 \frac{\partial}{\partial\omega_0} |H(\omega)|^2\right] \tag{8-130a}$$

Integrating Eq. (8-130a) on ω and noting that

$$\sigma_{X_0}{}^2 = K \int_{-\infty}^{\infty} |H(\omega)|^2 \, d\omega = \frac{\pi K}{\beta_0\omega_0{}^2}$$

we obtain

$$\sigma_X{}^2 = \sigma_{X_0}{}^2 - 3\alpha\sigma_X{}^2\sigma_{X_0}{}^2 \tag{8-131}$$

or

$$\sigma_X{}^2 = \sigma_{X_0}{}^2(1 + 3\alpha\sigma_{X_0}{}^2)^{-1} \tag{8-131a}$$

Although Eq. (8-131a) has been obtained for a Gaussian-white-noise excitation, it can be expected to yield a reasonable approximate solution when the spectral density of the excitation is slowly varying in the neighborhood of ω_0 and when the damping in the system is light.

Under certain conditions, the equivalent-linearization method can be applied to a system obeying a hereditary stiffness or damping law or to a system with multiple degrees of freedom. Both extended applications have been considered by Caughey.‡

8.6 / NONLINEAR STRESSES

Sections 8.2 through 8.5 were concerned with the determination of either the probability law or the statistical properties of the nonlinear displacement. However, from a structural-design standpoint, often it is the stresses which are of interest. If a stress $Y(t)$ is related to a displacement $X(t)$ by an algebraic equation such as (8-2), then the transformation is one without memory. To illustrate the nature of such a transformation, let us consider again the example of a thin plate hinged along immovable edges. Within the framework of a single-degree-of-freedom representation we have shown that the displacements of a point on the midsurface in the horizontal directions u and v are proportional to the square of the displacement in the vertical direction w. [Refer to Eqs. (8-13a) to (8-13c).] Choose a generalized displacement $X(t)$, and write

$$
\begin{aligned}
w &= f_1(x, y)X(t) \\
u &= f_2(x, y)X^2(t) \\
v &= f_3(x, y)X^2(t)
\end{aligned}
\tag{8-132}
$$

Then the tensile strains in the plate in the x and y directions are given, respectively, by

$$
\begin{aligned}
\epsilon_x &= \left(u_{,x} + \frac{1}{2}w_{,x}^2\right) - \left(\frac{z}{2}w_{,xx}\right) \\
\epsilon_y &= \left(v_{,y} + \frac{1}{2}w_{,y}^2\right) - \left(\frac{z}{2}w_{,yy}\right)
\end{aligned}
\tag{8-133}
$$

where z denotes the distance from the midsurface, having the same positive direction as w. The stresses in the x and y directions are

$$
\begin{aligned}
Y_x &= \frac{E}{1 - \nu^2}(\epsilon_x + \nu\epsilon_y) \\
Y_y &= \frac{E}{1 - \nu^2}(\epsilon_y + \nu\epsilon_x)
\end{aligned}
\tag{8-134}
$$

We assume that the stresses are such that the linear relations (8-134) are justified. Combining (8-132) to (8-134), we obtain a general expression

‡ Equivalent Linearization Techniques.

for the stress at any point in the plate,

$$Y = D_1 X + D_2 X^2 \qquad (8\text{-}135)$$

where D_1 and D_2 are functions of x, y, and z. This general form is also valid for strains. We shall, however, conduct our discussion in terms of stresses. It can be shown that this general form (8-135) is valid for both normal and shear stresses, and for stresses in any direction. Depending on the type of stress considered, the values for D_1 and D_2 can be determined from the material properties and dimensions of the plate, and the location at which and direction in which the stress is to be measured. For tensile stresses, D_2 must be positive, whereas D_1 may be taken as positive without loss of generality by choosing an appropriate positive direction for the generalized displacement $X(t)$.

In the case of a Gaussian-white-noise excitation the probability density of the stationary generalized displacement has been found to be

$$p_{\{X\}} = C \exp\left[-A \int_0^x f_1(\xi)\,d\xi \right] \qquad (8\text{-}136)$$

where

$$C = \left\{ \int_{-\infty}^{\infty} \exp\left[-A \int_0^x f_1(\xi)\,d\xi \right] dx \right\}^{-1} \qquad (8\text{-}137)$$

It can easily be seen that the distribution function of the stress Y is

$$F_{\{Y\}}(y) = \int_{\alpha_1}^{\alpha_2} p_{\{X\}}(x)\,dx \qquad (8\text{-}138)$$

where

$$\alpha_{1,2} = -\frac{D_1}{2D_2} \mp \left(\frac{D_1^2}{4D_2^2} + \frac{y}{D_2} \right)^{\frac{1}{2}} \qquad \frac{D_1^2}{4D_2} \le y < \infty \qquad (8\text{-}139)$$

A straightforward differentiation of Eq. (8-138) yields

$$p_{\{Y\}}(y) = C(D_1^2 + 4D_2 y)^{-\frac{1}{2}} \left\{ \exp\left[-A \int_0^{\alpha_2} f_1(\xi)\,d\xi \right] \right.$$
$$\left. + \exp\left[-A \int_0^{\alpha_1} f_1(\xi)\,d\xi \right] \right\} \qquad (8\text{-}140)$$

If we are not blessed with a Gaussian-white-noise excitation, we are generally unable to compute the probability density of the generalized displacement; hence, we are unable to compute the probability density of the stress. However, if we can obtain the statistical properties of the generalized displacement, then the statistical properties of the stress may be calculated by use of the relation (8-135). For example, the autocorrelation function of the stationary stress is given by

$$R_{YY}(\tau) = D_1^2 E[X(t+\tau)X(t)] + D_2^2 E[X^2(t+\tau)X^2(t)]$$
$$+ D_1 D_2 \{ E[X(t+\tau)X^2(t)] + E[X^2(t+\tau)X(t)] \} \qquad (8\text{-}141)$$

If $X(t)$ is computed from the equivalent-linearization method, then under a Gaussian excitation the approximate $X(t)$ is Gaussian. The right-hand side of Eq. (8-141) can then be evaluated to give

$$R_{YY}(\tau) = D_1^2 R_{XX}(\tau) + D_2^2[\sigma_X^4 + 2R_{XX}^2(\tau)] \tag{8-142}$$

where we have assumed $E[X(t)] = 0$ for simplicity.

In the above discussion we have assumed that the transformation from displacement to stress is one without memory, as represented by the algebraic equation (8-135) or, more generally, Eq. (8-2). It is conceivable that the displacement-stress transformation can be one with memory as, for example, in the case of a viscoelastic material. The analysis of the latter case is more complicated but appears to be manageable if the material behavior can be represented by a simple linear viscoelastic law.

EXERCISES

8-1. Referring to Fig. 8.1, let the dimensions of the simply supported plate be $a = 10$ in., $b = 20$ in., $h = 0.04$ in.; and let the elastic properties of the material be characterized by $E = 10^7$ psi and $\nu = 0.3$. Assuming that the random excitation on the plate is $P(x, y, t)$ and that viscous damping is present and is proportional to the transverse velocity $\dot{w}$, derive the equation of motion by use of the dominant mode of Chu and Herrmann.‡ Both the random excitation and the damping force are perpendicular to the plate.

8-2.¶ Consider the motion of a single-degree-of-freedom system which is governed by

$$\ddot{X} + 2\zeta\omega_0\dot{X} + \omega_0^2(X + \epsilon \operatorname{sgn} X) = W(t)$$

where $W(t)$ is a Gaussian white noise. Assume that the excitation level is sufficiently high that it is permissible to take $\mathcal{P}\{X = 0\} = 0$. Show that the joint probability density of the random displacement $X(t)$ and the random velocity $\dot{X}(t)$ in the stationary state and at the same time t is given by

$$p_{\{X\}\{\dot{X}\}}(x, \dot{x}) = \left(2\pi\omega_0\sigma_0^2 \exp\frac{\epsilon^2}{2\sigma_0^2} \operatorname{erfc}\frac{\epsilon}{\sqrt{2}\,\sigma_0}\right)^{-1} \exp\left(-\frac{\dot{x}^2}{2\sigma_0^2\omega_0^2} - \frac{x^2}{2\sigma_0^2} - \frac{\epsilon x \operatorname{sgn} x}{\sigma_0^2}\right)$$

$$-\infty < x, \dot{x} < \infty$$

and that the separate probability densities of the stationary deflection and the stationary velocity are given by

$$p_{\{X\}}(x) = \left(\sqrt{2\pi}\,\sigma_0 \exp\frac{\epsilon^2}{2\sigma_0^2} \operatorname{erfc}\frac{\epsilon}{\sqrt{2}\,\sigma_0}\right)^{-1} \exp\left(-\frac{x^2}{2\sigma_0^2} - \frac{\epsilon x \operatorname{sgn} x}{\sigma_0^2}\right)$$

$$-\infty < x < \infty$$

$$p_{\{\dot{X}\}}(\dot{x}) = (\sqrt{2\pi}\,\omega_0\sigma_0)^{-1} \exp\left(-\frac{\dot{x}^2}{2\omega_0^2\sigma_0^2}\right) \qquad -\infty < \dot{x} < \infty$$

where σ_0^2 is the linear mean-square displacement (corresponding to $\epsilon = 0$).

‡ Equations (8-13).

¶ See S. H. Crandall, Random Vibration of a Nonlinear System with a Set-up Spring, *J. Appl. Mech.*, **29**:477–482 (1962).

8-3. Compute the spectral density of the nonlinear system in Exercise 8-2 by use of (1) the perturbation method and (2) the equivalent-linerarization method.

8-4.‡ The equation of motion of a nonlinear system is given by

$$\ddot{X} + 2\zeta\omega_0\dot{X} + \omega_0^2 \left(\frac{2d}{\pi}\right) \tan \frac{\pi X}{2d} = W(t)$$

where $W(t)$ is a Gaussian white noise. Show that the joint probability density of $X(t)$ and $\dot{X}(t)$ in the stationary state and at the same time t is

$$p_{\{X\}\{\dot{X}\}}(x, \dot{x}) = (2\sqrt{2}\, d\sigma_0\omega_0)^{-1} \exp\left(-\frac{\dot{x}^2}{2\sigma_0^2\omega_0^2}\right) \frac{\Gamma(\alpha/2 + 1)}{\Gamma[(\alpha + 1)/2]} \left(\cos \frac{\pi x}{2d}\right)^\alpha$$

$$-d < x < d, \ -\infty < \dot{x} < \infty$$

where $\alpha = \dfrac{4d^2}{\pi^2\sigma_0^2}$

$\sigma_0^2 = \dfrac{\pi K}{2\zeta\omega_0^3}$

‡ See G. H. Klein, Random Excitation of a Nonlinear System with Tangent Elasticity Characteristics, *J. Acoust. Soc. Am.*, **36**(11):2095–2105 (1964).

9 | STRUCTURAL FAILURES RESULTING FROM DYNAMIC RESPONSE AND RELATED TOPICS

9.1 / TYPES OF STRUCTURAL FAILURE

The ultimate purpose in using stochastic-process theory in a structural-response analysis is to be able to judge the reliability of a structure which has been designed to withstand random excitations. Here, reliability means the probability of success (one minus the probability of failure). We shall be concerned only with failures which are the result of the dynamic response of a stable structure; i.e., we shall exclude from present consideration failures under static loads (even when they are random), failures attributable to static or dynamic instability, failures due to corrosion, abrasion, etc.

Let $X(t)$ be the dynamic response (either a deflection, a strain, or a stress) at a critical point in a given structure. We postulate that the structure will fail upon the occurrence of one or the other of the following two events:

1. $X(t)$ reaches, for the first time, either an upper bound level U or a lower bound level $-L$, where U and L are large positive numbers.
2. Damage to the structure accumulated as $X(t)$ fluctuates at small or moderate excursions which are not large enough to cause a failure of the first type, and failure occurs when the accumulated damage reaches a fixed total.

We call the failures due to the first reason *first-excursion failures*, and those due to the second reason *fatigue failures*. It will be shown that for the study of both types of failure it is useful to obtain the probabilistic characteristics of the following two items: (1) within a given time interval the number of times that the random process $X(t)$ crosses a certain threshold; and (2) within a given time interval the number of peaks (or troughs) in $X(t)$ which are above (or below) a certain level. The studies of items (1) and (2) are known as the *threshold-crossing* and the *peak-distribution* problems, respectively. Therefore, as a preliminary to a discussion of structural failures, we shall first consider these problems in some detail.

9.2 / THRESHOLD CROSSINGS

Let $X(t)$ be a continuously valued random process which is also continuous with respect to its parameter t. We shall investigate the statistical properties of an associated counting process $\mathfrak{N}(\xi, t_1, t_2)$ which counts the random number of times that $X(t)$ crosses a threshold ξ from either above or below within a time interval $(t_1, t_2]$. Figure 9.1a shows a sample function of this random process and a given threshold ξ. The study of the counting process $\mathfrak{N}(\xi, t_1, t_2)$ can be facilitated by constructing a three-valued random process

$$Y(t) = \mathbb{1}[X(t) - \xi] \qquad (9\text{-}1)$$

where $\mathbb{1}[\ \ ]$ is Heaviside's step function; that is,

$$Y(t) = \begin{cases} 1 & X(t) > \xi \\ \frac{1}{2} & X(t) = \xi \\ 0 & X(t) < \xi \end{cases} \qquad (9\text{-}1a)$$

Formally differentiate $Y(t)$ with respect to t:

$$\dot{Y}(t) = \dot{X}(t)\, \delta[X(t) - \xi] \qquad (9\text{-}2)$$

where $\delta[\ \ ]$ is Dirac's delta function. This derivative has a formal meaning only in that Eq. (9-1) can be recovered by integrating Eq. (9-2) on t. However, we do require that $\dot{X}(t)$ exist in a suitable sense. We shall

Fig. 9.1

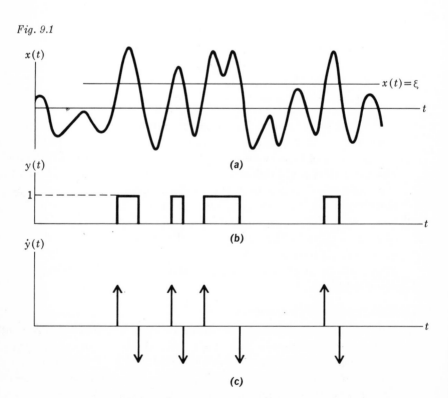

disregard the trivial case‡ $\dot{X}(t) \equiv 0$. In Fig. 9.1, associated typical sample functions of $X(t)$, $Y(t)$, and $\dot{Y}(t)$ are illustrated. We see that the impulses in Fig. 9.1c are unit impulses with alternative signs each of which is located under a threshold crossing in Fig. 9.1a. The counting process $\mathfrak{N}(\xi, t_1, t_2)$ gives the number of such impulses in the time interval $(t_1, t_2]$ without regard to the direction of the impulses. Therefore, this counting process can be expressed as

$$\mathfrak{N}(\xi, t_1, t_2) = \int_{t_1+}^{t_2+} |\dot{X}(t)| \, \delta[X(t) - \xi] \, dt \qquad (9\text{-}3)$$

Equation (9-3) can be used to obtain the statistical properties of $\mathfrak{N}$. For example, the expectation of $\mathfrak{N}$ is given by

$$
\begin{aligned}
E[\mathfrak{N}(\xi, t_1, t_2)] &= \int_{t_1}^{t_2} E\{|\dot{X}(t)| \, \delta[X(t) - \xi]\} \, dt \\
&= \int_{t_1}^{t_2} \int_{-\infty}^{\infty} \int_{-\infty}^{\infty} |\dot{x}| \, \delta(x - \xi) p_{\{X\}\{\dot{X}\}}(x, \dot{x}, t) \, dx \, d\dot{x} \, dt \\
&= \int_{t_1}^{t_2} \int_{-\infty}^{\infty} |\dot{x}| p_{\{X\}\{\dot{X}\}}(\xi, \dot{x}, t) \, d\dot{x} \, dt \qquad (9\text{-}4)
\end{aligned}
$$

We have assumed that $E\{|\dot{X}(t)| \, \delta[X(t) - \xi]\}$ is bounded; therefore, no distinction is made between t_1 and t_1+ and between t_2 and t_2+.

It is often convenient to deal with the rate of threshold crossings per unit time. Write

$$\mathfrak{N}(\xi, t_1, t_2) = \int_{t_1+}^{t_2+} N(\xi, t) \, dt \qquad (9\text{-}5)$$

so that

$$N(\xi, t) = |\dot{X}(t)| \, \delta[X(t) - \xi] \qquad (9\text{-}6)$$

The expectation of $N(\xi, t)$, if it exists, is

$$E[N(\xi, t)] = \int_{-\infty}^{\infty} |\dot{x}| p_{\{X\}\{\dot{X}\}}(\xi, \dot{x}, t) \, d\dot{x} \qquad (9\text{-}7)$$

and the expectation of $\mathfrak{N}(\xi, t_1, t_2)$ is

$$E[\mathfrak{N}(\xi, t_1, t_2)] = \int_{t_1}^{t_2} E[N(\xi, t)] \, dt \qquad (9\text{-}4a)$$

If $X(t)$ is weakly stationary, then the joint probability density of $X(t)$ and $\dot{X}(t)$ is independent of t, and the expected rate of crossings of a given

---

‡ For this trivial case $X(t)$ is equal to the same random variable for all t; that is, the sample functions of $X(t)$ are parallel to the t axis. Since $X(t)$ is continuously valued, the probability of the event $X(t) = \xi$ is generally zero.

threshold is a constant. Equation (9-7) was first obtained by Rice.‡ The above derivation of this equation followed a procedure due to Middleton.¶ Similarly, the correlation function of $N(\xi, t)$ can be computed from

$$\phi_{NN}(\xi, t_1, t_2) = E[N(\xi, t_1)N(\xi, t_2)]$$
$$= \int_{-\infty}^{\infty} \int_{-\infty}^{\infty} |\dot{x}_1| |\dot{x}_2| p_{\{X\}\{\dot{X}\}}(\xi, \dot{x}_1, t_1; \xi, \dot{x}_2, t_2) \, dx_1 \, dx_2 \qquad (9\text{-}8)$$

The required joint probability density of $X(t)$ and $\dot{X}(t)$ here is $p_{\{X\}\{\dot{X}\}}(x_1, \dot{x}_1, t_1; x_2, \dot{x}_2, t_2)$, which involves two different times, t_1 and t_2. When used in Eq. (9-8), both x_1 and x_2 in this joint probability density are replaced by the given threshold value ξ. In principle the mth-order moment function $E[N(\xi, t_1) \cdots N(\xi, t_m)]$ can be expressed as a multifold integral having a joint probability density of $X(t)$ and $\dot{X}(t)$ involving m different times in the integrand; but actually carrying out the integration becomes increasingly more cumbersome as m increases. It can easily be seen that if $X(t)$ is strongly stationary, then so is $N(\xi, t)$; and if $X(t)$ is weakly stationary, then so is $N(\xi, t)$.

In certain applications we only require information about threshold crossings from *below*. Since at such crossings the slopes must be positive, the expected rate of threshold crossings from below is

$$E[N_+(\xi, t)] = \int_0^{\infty} \dot{x} p_{\{X\}\{\dot{X}\}}(\xi, \dot{x}, t) \, d\dot{x} \qquad (9\text{-}9)$$

The correlation of such a crossing rate is

$$\phi_{N_+N_+}(\xi, t_1, t_2) = \int_0^{\infty} \int_0^{\infty} \dot{x}_1 \dot{x}_2 p_{\{X\}\{\dot{X}\}}(\xi, \dot{x}_1, t_1; \xi, \dot{x}_2, t_2) \, d\dot{x}_1 \, d\dot{x}_2 \qquad (9\text{-}10)$$

Equations (9-9) and (9-10) are essentially the same as Eqs. (9-7) and (9-8) except that the average is now taken only over the positive sample space of the derivative process $\dot{X}(t)$. For weakly stationary random processes a positive-slope crossing must be accompanied by a negative-slope crossing at another time. This physical argument enables us to write, for weakly stationary cases,

$$E[N_+(\xi)] = \tfrac{1}{2}E[N(\xi)]$$
$$R_{N_+N_+}(\xi, t_1 - t_2) = \tfrac{1}{4}R_{NN}(\xi, t_1 - t_2) \qquad (9\text{-}11)$$

Therefore, if $X(t)$ is weakly stationary the joint probability density for $X(t)$ and $\dot{X}(t)$ appearing in Eq. (9-9) must be an even function of the

‡ S. O. Rice, Mathematical Analysis of Random Noise, *Bell System Tech. J.*, **23**:282–332 (1944); **24**:46–156 (1945). Reprinted in N. Wax (ed.), "Selected Papers on Noise and Stochastic Processes," Dover, New York, 1954.

¶ D. Middleton, "An Introduction to Statistical Communication Theory," p. 426, McGraw-Hill, New York, 1960.

state variable $\dot{x}$, and the joint probability density appearing in Eq. (9-10) must be an even function for both $\dot{x}_1$ and $\dot{x}_2$.

As an example, let $X(t)$ be stationary and Gaussian and have a zero mean. Then $X(t)$ and $\dot{X}(t)$ are independent, and their joint probability density is

$$p_{\{X\}\{\dot{X}\}}(x, \dot{x}) = \frac{1}{2\pi\sigma_X\sigma_{\dot{X}}} \exp\left(-\frac{x^2}{2\sigma_X{}^2} - \frac{\dot{x}^2}{2\sigma_{\dot{X}}{}^2}\right) \qquad (9\text{-}12)$$

Substitution of Eq. (9-12) into Eq. (9-9) yields

$$E[N_+(\xi)] = \frac{1}{2\pi}\frac{\sigma_{\dot{X}}}{\sigma_X} \exp\left(-\frac{\xi^2}{2\sigma_X{}^2}\right) \qquad (9\text{-}13)$$

To compute the correlation function of N_+, we require the two-time joint probability density of $X(t)$ and $\dot{X}(t)$. For convenience, denote $X(t) = Z_1$, $\dot{X}(t) = Z_2$, $X(t + \tau) = Z_3$, and $\dot{X}(t + \tau) = Z_4$. The matrix of covariances for the Z's is given by

$$\mathbf{S}(\tau) = \begin{bmatrix} \Gamma(0) & 0 & \Gamma(\tau) & \Gamma'(\tau) \\ 0 & -\Gamma''(0) & -\Gamma'(\tau) & -\Gamma''(\tau) \\ \Gamma(\tau) & -\Gamma'(\tau) & \Gamma(0) & 0 \\ \Gamma'(\tau) & -\Gamma''(\tau) & 0 & -\Gamma''(0) \end{bmatrix}$$

where $\Gamma(\tau)$ is the abbreviation for the covariance function of $X(t)$, $\Gamma_{XX}(\tau)$, and each prime indicates one differentiation with respect to the argument. The required probability density can be written in accordance with the standard multidimensional Gaussian form, Eq. (4-28a), viz.,

$$p_Z(\mathbf{z}) = \frac{1}{(2\pi)^2|S|^{\frac{1}{2}}} \exp\left(-\tfrac{1}{2}\mathbf{z}'\mathbf{S}^{-1}\mathbf{z}\right) \qquad (9\text{-}14)$$

Using (9-14) in (9-10) and with x_1 and x_2 replacing z_1 and z_3, $\dot{x}_1$ and $\dot{x}_2$ replacing z_2 and z_4, the integration is seen to be possible but very tedious. We shall not try to produce the result here except to say that it can be expressed in terms of $\Gamma(\tau)$, $\Gamma'(\tau)$, and $\Gamma''(\tau)$.

When the threshold ξ is zero, the problem is known as the zero-crossing problem. In particular, for a stationary Gaussian process with a zero mean, the expected rate of zero crossings from below is

$$E[N_+(0)] = \frac{1}{2\pi}\frac{\sigma_{\dot{X}}}{\sigma_X} \qquad (9\text{-}15)$$

as obtained from Eq. (9-13) by letting $\xi = 0$. Equation (9-15) may be written alternatively as

$$E[N_+(0)] = \frac{1}{2\pi}\left[\frac{\displaystyle\int_{-\infty}^{\infty} \omega^2\Phi_{XX}(\omega)\,d\omega}{\displaystyle\int_{-\infty}^{\infty} \Phi_{XX}(\omega)\,d\omega}\right]^{\frac{1}{2}} \qquad (9\text{-}15a)$$

Now suppose that $X(t)$ is also a narrow-band random process such as the stationary response of a lightly damped single-degree-of-freedom linear system to a broadband excitation. Then a typical sample function of $X(t)$, as depicted in Fig. 9.2, has the general appearance of a sinusoid but has slowly varying amplitude and phase. We may envisage that, between two consecutive zero crossings with positive slope, this sample function varies over an "equivalent" cycle. Therefore, for a narrow-band random process, the expected rate of zero crossings with positive slope is equal to the number of expected equivalent cycles per unit time, say $\dot{f_e}$. Let $f_e = \omega_e/(2\pi)$, where ω_e may be called the *expected equivalent frequency*. When a narrow-band random process is also Gaussian, we have, from Eq. (9-15),

$$\omega_e = \left[\frac{\displaystyle\int_{-\infty}^{\infty} \omega^2 \Phi_{XX}(\omega)\, d\omega}{\displaystyle\int_{-\infty}^{\infty} \Phi_{XX}(\omega)\, d\omega}\right]^{\frac{1}{2}} \tag{9-16}$$

As another example, let $X(t)$ be the stationary response of a linearly damped Duffing system subjected to a Gaussian-white-noise excitation. The joint probability density of $X(t)$ and $\dot{X}(t)$ is given by‡

$$p_{\{X\}\{\dot{X}\}}(x, \dot{x}) = C \exp\left\{-\frac{\beta}{\pi K}\left[\frac{\dot{x}^2}{2} + \omega_0{}^2\left(\frac{x^2}{2} + \epsilon\frac{x^4}{4}\right)\right]\right\} \tag{9-17}$$

where ϵ is assumed to be a positive number; that is, the system exhibits a *hardening-spring* type of nonlinearity. Here $X(t)$ is not Gaussian. However, if the system is lightly damped and if the nonlinearity is small (that is, $\epsilon \ll 1$), then $X(t)$ is still expected to be a narrow-band random

‡ See Eq. (8-35).

Fig. 9.2 Typical sample function of narrow-band random processes.

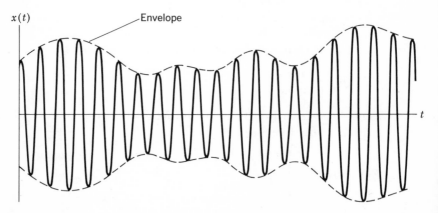

process. Substituting (9-17) into (9-9), we find that

$$E[N_+(\xi)] = C \frac{\pi K}{\beta} \exp\left[- \frac{\beta \omega_0^2}{\pi K} \left(\frac{\xi^2}{2} + \epsilon \frac{\xi^4}{4} \right) \right] \qquad (9\text{-}18)$$

The expected equivalent frequency is

$$\omega_e = 2\pi E[N_+(0)] = \frac{2\pi^2 K}{\beta} C \qquad (9\text{-}19)$$

In order to compare this result with that in a linear case (i.e., when $\epsilon = 0$), we need to know the normalization constant C. Unfortunately, the exact value for C cannot be computed; but for small ϵ, we may approximate Eq. (9-17) by

$$p_{\{X\}\{\dot{X}\}}(x, \dot{x}) = C \left(1 - \epsilon \frac{\beta \omega_0^2}{4\pi K} x^4 + \cdots \right) \exp\left[- \frac{\beta}{2\pi K} (\dot{x}^2 + \omega_0^2 x^2) \right] \qquad (9\text{-}20)$$

Then, to the first order in ϵ,

$$C^{-1} \approx \frac{2\pi^2 K}{\beta \omega_0} \left(1 - \epsilon \frac{3}{4} \frac{\pi K}{\beta \omega_0^2} \right) \qquad (9\text{-}21)$$

Using (9-21) in (9-19), we have

$$\omega_e = \omega_0 \left(1 - \epsilon \frac{3}{4} \frac{\pi K}{\beta \omega_0^2} \right)^{-1} \qquad (9\text{-}22)$$

It is seen that in the linear case where $\epsilon = 0$ the expected equivalent frequency coincides with the undamped natural frequency, and that the nonlinearity considered in the above example has the effect of increasing the expected equivalent frequency. It is not difficult to show that this is true for a system having more general hardening-spring characteristics.‡ Although the above conclusion is based on the case of a white noise, we expect it to be valid for a broadband excitation provided that the excitation spectral density is slowly varying in the neighborhood of ω_0.

9.3 / PEAK DISTRIBUTION

A peak (or a maximum) in a sample function $x(t)$ of a continuously valued random process $X(t)$ which is also continuous with respect to its parameter t occurs when $\dot{x}(t)$ is zero and $\ddot{x}(t)$ is negative. This suggests that information about the peak distribution of $X(t)$ can be obtained from the joint distribution of $X(t)$, $\dot{X}(t)$, and $\ddot{X}(t)$. We shall, therefore, assume that $X(t)$ is at least twice differentiable in the following discussion. It is not difficult to combine a study of both peaks and troughs (the

‡ For example, a system governed by Eq. (8-86), assuming that the g_n are all positive.

extrema) since the extrema in $X(t)$ are the zero crossings of the first derivative $\dot{X}(t)$. Following Middleton,‡ the number of extrema in $X(t)$ above a specified level ξ within the time interval (t_1, t_2) is

$$\mathcal{E}(\xi, t_1, t_2) = \int_{t_1+}^{t_2+} |\ddot{X}(t)| \, \delta[\dot{X}(t)] \mathbb{1}[X(t) - \xi] \, dt \qquad (9\text{-}23)$$

A comparison between this equation and Eq. (9-3) reveals that this equation gives the random number of counts of the zero crossings of $\dot{X}(t)$ when¶ $X(t) > \xi$. [Analogous to the treatment of the threshold-crossing problem, we disregard the trivial case $\ddot{X}(t) \equiv 0$ which is generally associated with probability zero. Then the number of zero crossings of $\dot{X}(t)$ is the number of extrema in $X(t)$.]

Equation (9-23) may be used to compute the statistical properties of the extrema or of the peaks and troughs separately. From here onward, however, we shall be concerned only with the peaks. For convenience, the random number of peaks will be denoted by $\mathfrak{M}$, and the random number of peaks per unit time by M. The expected number of peaks in $X(t)$ above ξ within the time interval (t_1, t_2) is given by

$$E[\mathfrak{M}(\xi, t_1, t_2)] = \int_{t_1}^{t_2} E[M(\xi, t)] \, dt \qquad (9\text{-}24)$$

We assume that $E[M(\xi, t)]$ is bounded; therefore, no distinction is made between t_1 and t_{1+} and between t_2 and t_{2+}. When $E[M(\xi, t)]$ exists, it is given by

$$
\begin{aligned}
E[M(\xi, t)] \\
= &- \int_{-\infty}^{\infty} dx \int_{-\infty}^{\infty} d\dot{x} \int_{-\infty}^{0} p_{\{X\}\{\dot{X}\}\{\ddot{X}\}}(x, \dot{x}, \ddot{x}, t)\ddot{x}\, \delta(\dot{x}) \mathbb{1}(x - \xi) \, d\ddot{x} \\
= &- \int_{\xi}^{\infty} dx \int_{-\infty}^{0} \ddot{x} p_{\{X\}\{\dot{X}\}\{\ddot{X}\}}(x, 0, \ddot{x}, t) \, d\ddot{x}
\end{aligned}
\qquad (9\text{-}25)
$$

Equation (9-25) was first obtained by Rice.§ The expected total number of peaks per unit time, *regardless of their magnitudes*, is obtained from Eq. (9-25) by letting $\xi \to -\infty$; that is,

$$E[M_T(t)] = - \int_{-\infty}^{\infty} dx \int_{-\infty}^{0} \ddot{x} p_{\{X\}\{\dot{X}\}\{\ddot{X}\}}(x, 0, \ddot{x}, t) \, d\ddot{x} \qquad (9\text{-}26)$$

Now $\{E[M_T(t)] - E[M(\xi, t)]\}/E[M_T(t)]$ is the ratio of the expected number of peaks per unit time whose magnitudes are smaller than or equal to ξ to the expected total number of peaks per unit time. A heuristic approach, which is believed to have been used first by Huston

‡ *Op. cit.*

¶ Since $X(t)$ is continuously valued, this condition may be changed to $X(t) \geq \xi$ if the probability for $X(t) = \xi$ is zero.

§ *Loc. cit.*

and Skopinski‡ in the case of Gaussian random processes, is to *assume* that this ratio is equal to the distribution function of the peaks at time t. Let us envisage a sample space, each point of which corresponds to a peak in $X(t)$. Then we can define a probability measure for the peaks at time t which are smaller than or equal to a prescribed level ξ. Strictly speaking, the probability distribution function of the peaks at time t is

$$F_\Xi(\xi, t) = \mathcal{P}[\Xi(t) \leq \xi]$$
$$= 1 - E\left[\frac{M(\xi, t)}{M_T(t)}\right] \tag{9-27}$$

The heuristic assumption states that

$$F_\Xi(\xi, t) = 1 - \frac{E[M(\xi, t)]}{E[M_T(t)]} \tag{9-27a}$$

Thus it implies that

$$E\left[\frac{M(\xi, t)}{M_T(t)}\right] = \frac{E[M(\xi, t)]}{E[M_T(t)]}$$

This assumption has been used by a number of authors, but its implication is seldom noted. The probability density of the peaks, based on the same heuristic assumption, is obtained by differentiating Eq. (9-27a):

$$p_\Xi(\xi, t) = -\frac{1}{E[M_T(t)]} \frac{\partial}{\partial \xi} E[M(\xi, t)]$$
$$= \frac{-1}{E[M_T(t)]} \int_{-\infty}^{0} \ddot{x} p_{\{X\}\{\dot{X}\}\{\ddot{X}\}}(\xi, 0, \ddot{x}, t)\, d\ddot{x} \tag{9-28}$$

As an example, let $X(t)$ be stationary and Gaussian and have a zero expectation. Then the joint probability density of $X(t)$, $\dot{X}(t)$, $\ddot{X}(t)$ may be written in the standard Gaussian form, Eq. (4-28). Note that the matrix of covariances of $X(t)$, $\dot{X}(t)$, and $\ddot{X}(t)$ is given by

$$\mathbf{S} = \begin{bmatrix} \sigma_1^2 & 0 & -\sigma_2^2 \\ 0 & \sigma_2^2 & 0 \\ -\sigma_2^2 & 0 & \sigma_3^2 \end{bmatrix} \tag{9-29}$$

where the variances σ_1^2, σ_2^2, and σ_3^2 can be computed from the spectral density function $\Phi_{XX}(\omega)$ of $X(t)$,

$$\sigma_1^2 = \int_{-\infty}^{\infty} \Phi_{XX}(\omega)\, d\omega$$
$$\sigma_2^2 = \int_{-\infty}^{\infty} \omega^2 \Phi_{XX}(\omega)\, d\omega \tag{9-30}$$
$$\sigma_3^2 = \int_{-\infty}^{\infty} \omega^4 \Phi_{XX}(\omega)\, d\omega$$

‡ W. B. Huston and T. H. Skopinski, Probability and Frequency Characteristics of Some Flight Buffet Loads, *NACA* TN 3733, August, 1956.

It can easily be shown that

$$p_{\{X\}\{\dot{X}\}\{\ddot{X}\}}(x, 0, \ddot{x})$$
$$= \frac{1}{(2\pi)^{\frac{3}{2}}|S|^{\frac{1}{2}}} \exp\left[- \frac{1}{2|S|} (\sigma_2{}^2\sigma_3{}^2x^2 + 2\sigma_2{}^4x\ddot{x} + \sigma_1{}^2\sigma_2{}^2\ddot{x}^2) \right] \quad (9\text{-}31)$$

Note that, except for the trivial case $\Phi_{XX}(\omega) = 0$, the determinant of the matrix of covariances, $|S|$, is positive since

$$|S| = \sigma_1{}^2\sigma_2{}^2\sigma_3{}^2 - \sigma_2{}^6 = \sigma_2{}^2(\sigma_1{}^2\sigma_3{}^2 - \sigma_2{}^4) \quad (9\text{-}32)$$

and

$$\sigma_1{}^2\sigma_3{}^2 - \sigma_2{}^4 = \int_{-\infty}^{\infty} \Phi_{XX}(\omega)\, d\omega \int_{-\infty}^{\infty} \omega^4\Phi_{XX}(\omega)\, d\omega$$
$$- \left[\int_{-\infty}^{\infty} \omega^2\Phi_{XX}(\omega)\, d\omega \right]^2 > 0 \quad (9\text{-}33)$$

The second part of (9-33) stems from the Schwarz inequality. This conclusion, however, is to be expected, since otherwise the joint probability density (9-31) would be meaningless.

The expected total number of peaks per unit time is obtained by substituting (9-31) into (9-26). For the present case, it is simpler to integrate first on x and then on $\ddot{x}$. The result is

$$E[M_T] = \frac{1}{2\pi}\frac{\sigma_3}{\sigma_2} = \frac{1}{2\pi}\left[\frac{\int_{-\infty}^{\infty} \omega^4\Phi_{XX}(\omega)\, d\omega}{\int_{-\infty}^{\infty} \omega^2\Phi_{XX}(\omega)\, d\omega} \right]^{\frac{1}{2}} \quad (9\text{-}34)$$

It is also not difficult to compute the probability density of the peaks according to Eq. (9-28). We evaluate first the integral

$$-\int_{-\infty}^{0} \ddot{x}p_{\{X\}\{\dot{X}\}\{\ddot{X}\}}(\xi, 0, \ddot{x})\, d\ddot{x} = (2\pi)^{-\frac{3}{2}}(\sigma_1\sigma_2)^{-2}\left[|S|^{\frac{1}{2}} \exp\left(\frac{-\sigma_2{}^2\sigma_3{}^2\xi^2}{2|S|} \right) \right.$$
$$\left. + \sigma_2{}^4\xi\left(\frac{\pi}{2\sigma_1{}^2\sigma_2{}^2} \right)^{\frac{1}{2}}\left(1 + \operatorname{erf}\frac{\sigma_2{}^3\xi}{\sqrt{2}\,|S|^{\frac{1}{2}}\sigma_1} \right)\exp\left(-\frac{\xi^2}{2\sigma_1{}^2} \right) \right] \quad (9\text{-}35)$$

Substitution of (9-34) and (9-35) into Eq. (9-28) yields

$$p_{\Xi}(\xi) = (2\pi)^{-\frac{1}{2}}(\sigma_1{}^2\sigma_2\sigma_3)^{-1}\left[|S|^{\frac{1}{2}} \exp\frac{-\sigma_2{}^2\sigma_3{}^2\xi^2}{2|S|} \right.$$
$$\left. + \sigma_2{}^4\xi\left(\frac{\pi}{2\sigma_1{}^2\sigma_2{}^2} \right)^{\frac{1}{2}}\left(1 + \operatorname{erf}\frac{\sigma_2{}^3\xi}{\sqrt{2}\,|S|^{\frac{1}{2}}\sigma_1} \right)\exp\left(-\frac{\xi^2}{2\sigma_1{}^2} \right) \right] \quad (9\text{-}36)$$

An alternative and physically more meaningful expression for $p_{\Xi}(\xi)$ can be obtained by noting that the ratio of the expected number of zero crossings at positive slopes to the expected total number of peaks is

$$\alpha = \frac{E[N_+(0)]}{E[M_T]} = \frac{\sigma_2{}^2}{\sigma_1\sigma_3} \quad (9\text{-}37)$$

Therefore

$$p_\Xi(\xi) = (2\pi)^{-\frac{1}{2}}\sigma_1^{-1}(1 - \alpha^2)^{\frac{1}{2}} \exp\left\{ -\xi^2[2\sigma_1^2(1 - \alpha^2)]^{-1} \right\}$$
$$+ (2\sigma_1^2)^{-1}\alpha\xi \left\{ 1 + \mathrm{erf}\left[\frac{\xi}{\sigma_1} (2\alpha^{-2} - 2)^{-\frac{1}{2}} \right] \right\} \exp \frac{-\xi^2}{2\sigma_1^2} \quad (9\text{-}36a)$$

This alternative form is due to Huston and Skopinski.‡ It can be seen from (9-33) that the ratio α lies between zero and one. The upper limit $\alpha = 1$ corresponds to a narrow-band random process, a typical sample function of which has been pictured in Fig. 9.2. For this special case the number of peaks is equal to the number of zero crossings at positive (or negative) slopes, and the probability density for the peak magnitude reduces to

$$p_\Xi(\xi) = \frac{\xi}{\sigma_1^2} \exp\left(-\frac{\xi^2}{2\sigma_1^2} \right) \qquad 0 \le \xi < \infty \qquad (9\text{-}38)$$

The random variable Ξ is said to have a *Rayleigh distribution*. This distribution is of special practical interest, since the stationary response of a lightly damped single-degree-of-freedom linear system to a stationary Gaussian excitation is often a narrow-band Gaussian process.

On the other hand, when α is very small, corresponding to a situation where the expected number of peaks is much larger than the expected number of zero crossings, Eq. (9-36a) may be approximated by a Gaussian probability density

$$p_\Xi(\xi) \approx \frac{1}{\sqrt{2\pi}\,\sigma_1} \exp\left(-\frac{\xi^2}{2\sigma_1^2} \right) \qquad -\infty < \xi < \infty \qquad (9\text{-}39)$$

Except in these extreme cases the peak distribution of a stationary Gaussian random process is neither Rayleigh nor Gaussian.

Finally, we note from Eqs. (9-25) and (9-35) that the expected number of peaks per unit time above a level ξ for the present example is

$$E[M(\xi)] = (2\pi)^{-\frac{3}{2}}(\sigma_1\sigma_2)^{-2} \int_\xi^\infty \left[|S|^{\frac{1}{2}} \exp \frac{-\sigma_2^2\sigma_3^2 x^2}{2|S|} \right.$$
$$\left. + \sigma_2^4 x \left(\frac{\pi}{2\sigma_1^2\sigma_2^2} \right)^{\frac{1}{2}} \left(1 + \mathrm{erf}\, \frac{\sigma_2^3 x}{2^{\frac{1}{2}}|S|^{\frac{1}{2}}\sigma_1} \right) \exp\left(-\frac{x^2}{2\sigma_1^2} \right) \right] dx \quad (9\text{-}40)$$

The integration of this equation appears to be complicated.

The state of knowledge of the statistical properties and distribution of the peaks in the response of a nonlinear system to random excitations is less complete. As was pointed out before, under a Gaussian excitation neither the displacement response nor the stress response is Gaussian. Although it was possible to obtain the joint probability density for the stationary response $X(t)$ and its derivative $\dot{X}(t)$ when the excitation was

‡ *Ibid.*

a Gaussian white noise, the second derivative $\ddot{X}(t)$ in this case does not exist; therefore, Eqs. (9-25), (9-26), and (9-28) cannot be used. For other types of excitation, we can say even less about the nonlinear response. However, the response of a lightly damped system should be a narrow-band random process, and for this most important case approximate expressions can be obtained for the statistical properties and the distribution of the peaks in the nonlinear response. The approximate method neglects the probability of the occurrence of troughs on positive levels (or peaks on negative levels) in a narrow-band random process. Then the number of crossings over a threshold level at positive (or negative) slopes is nearly the same as the number of peaks above this level; i.e.,

$$M(\xi, t) \approx N_+(\xi, t) \tag{9-41}$$

The expected number of peaks above ξ per unit time is,‡ from Eq. (9-9),

$$E[M(\xi)] \approx \int_0^\infty \dot{x} p_{\{X\}\{\dot{X}\}}(\xi, \dot{x}) \, d\dot{x} \tag{9-42}$$

where only the joint probability density of $X(t)$ and $\dot{X}(t)$ is required in the computation. The expected total number of peaks per unit time regardless of the peak magnitudes is obtained by letting $\xi = 0$ in Eq. (9-42):

$$E[M_T] \approx \int_0^\infty \dot{x} p_{\{X\}\{\dot{X}\}}(0, \dot{x}) \, d\dot{x} \tag{9-43}$$

The probability density for the peak magnitude is

$$p_{\bar{z}}(\xi) \approx - \frac{1}{E[M_T]} \frac{d}{d\xi} \int_0^\infty \dot{x} p_{\{X\}\{\dot{X}\}}(\xi, \dot{x}) \, d\dot{x} \tag{9-44}$$

Powell¶ is generally credited for having suggested the use of Eq. (9-44) for computing the distribution of the higher-level peaks in the structural response, even when the response process is *not* of a narrow band. Such higher peaks are the ones that cause the most damage to a structure. His argument is that there should be few troughs above a sufficiently high threshold; therefore, they can be ignored. Note that following Powell's suggestion is conservative in the assessment of structural damage since, in general, $E[M_T] > E[N_+(0)]$ and the probability of the occurrence of higher peaks is overestimated by use of Eq. (9-44).

The approximate equations (9-42) to (9-44) will now be applied to

‡ Although the following derivation applies to both stationary and nonstationary random processes, we shall use the stationary forms for the probability densities since the nonstationary probability density for the nonlinear response $X(t)$ and its derivative $\dot{X}(t)$ has yet to be found.

¶ A. Powell, On the Fatigue Failure of Structures Due to Vibrations Excited by Random Pressure Fields, *J. Acoust. Soc. Am.*, **30**:1130 (1958).

the stationary displacement response of a system governed by

$$\ddot{X} + 2\zeta\omega_0\dot{X} + \omega_0^2[X + \epsilon g(X)] = W(t) \tag{9-45}$$

where $W(t)$ is a Gaussian white noise. We assume that both ζ and ϵ are sufficiently small that $X(t)$ in its stationary state is a narrow-band random process. The joint probability density of $X(t)$ and $\dot{X}(t)$ was previously determined by a Markov-vector approach and is given in Eq. (8-35). In the present notation,

$$p_{\{X\}\{\dot{X}\}}(x, \dot{x}) = C \exp\left\{-\frac{2\zeta\omega_0}{\pi K}\left[\frac{\omega_0^2 x^2}{2} + \epsilon\omega_0^2 G(x) + \frac{\dot{x}^2}{2}\right]\right\} \tag{9-46}$$

where

$$G(x) = \int_0^x g(u)\, du \tag{9-47}$$

It is a simple matter to show that the expected total number of peaks per unit time computed from the approximate formula (9-43) is

$$E[M_T] \approx C\,\frac{\pi K}{2\zeta\omega_0} \tag{9-48}$$

The expected number of peaks above the level ξ is merely

$$E[M(\xi)] \approx C\,\frac{\pi K}{2\zeta\omega_0} \exp\left\{-\frac{2\zeta\omega_0^3}{\pi K}\left[\frac{\xi^2}{2} + \epsilon G(\xi)\right]\right\} \tag{9-49}$$

This result may be compared with Eq. (9-18), which is the expected number of threshold crossings for the response of a Duffing system under a Gaussian-white-noise excitation. Finally, if the Huston-Skopinski approach‡ is used to find the probability density of the peak magnitude, we obtain

$$p_\Xi(\xi) = -\frac{1}{E[M_T(t)]}\frac{\partial}{\partial\xi}E[M(\xi)]$$
$$= \frac{2\zeta\omega_0^3}{\pi K}[\xi + \epsilon g(\xi)]\exp\left\{-\frac{2\zeta\omega_0^3}{\pi K}\left[\frac{\xi^2}{2} + \epsilon G(\xi)\right]\right\} \tag{9-50}$$

Note that $p_\Xi(\xi)$ reduces to a Rayleigh probability density if $\epsilon = 0$.

From the standpoint of the strength of a nonlinear structure it is perhaps more interesting to study the peak statistics and the distribution of the stress response.¶ Let the transformation from a nonlinear displacement to a nonlinear stress be represented by

$$Y = D_1 X + D_2 X^2 \tag{9-51}$$

---

‡ *op. cit.* The reader is to be reminded of the implication of this approach.

¶ D. A. Smith, T. I. Smits, and R. F. Lambert, Statistical Response of a Bar in Tension, *Wright-Patterson Air Force Base Aeron. Systems Div.* TDR-62-379, April, 1962; Y. K. Lin, Probability Distributions of Stress Peaks in Linear and Nonlinear Structures, *AIAA J.*, **1**(5):1133–1138 (1963).

This is the same as Eq. (8-135). We recall that without loss of generality both D_1 and D_2 in this expression may be taken to be positive constants. It follows from a differentiation of this expression that

$$\dot{Y} = \dot{X}(D_1 + 2D_2X) \tag{9-52}$$

Equations (9-51) and (9-52) can now be used to find the joint probability density of the stress and the stress rate $p_{\{Y\}\{\dot{Y}\}}(y, \dot{y})$ from the joint probability density of the displacement and velocity $p_{\{X\}\{\dot{X}\}}(x, \dot{x})$.

Since Eqs. (9-51) and (9-52) do not specify a one-to-one correspondence in the mapping of the sample spaces for $\{X(t), \dot{X}(t)\}$ and $\{Y(t), \dot{Y}(t)\}$, we begin by finding the distribution function of $Y(t)$ and $\dot{Y}(t)$,

$$F_{\{Y\}\{\dot{Y}\}}(y, \dot{y}) = \mathcal{P}[\{Y(t) \leq y\} \cap \{\dot{Y}(t) \leq \dot{y}\}]$$

It is simple to show that

$$F_{\{Y\}\{\dot{Y}\}}(y, \dot{y}) = \int_{\alpha_1}^{\alpha_2} dx \int_{-\infty}^{\beta} p_{\{X\}\{\dot{X}\}}(x, \dot{x}) \, d\dot{x} \tag{9-53}$$

where

$$\alpha_{1,2} = -\frac{D_1}{2D_2} \mp \left(\frac{D_1{}^2}{4D_2{}^2} + \frac{y}{D_2}\right)^{\frac{1}{2}} \qquad -\frac{D_1{}^2}{4D_2} \leq y < \infty$$
$$\beta = \dot{y}|D_1 + 2D_2x|^{-1} \qquad -\infty < \dot{y} < \infty \tag{9-54}$$

The joint probability density of $Y(t)$ and $\dot{Y}(t)$ is obtained by differentiating Eq. (9-53) with respect to y and $\dot{y}$:

$$p_{\{Y\}\{\dot{Y}\}}(y, \dot{y}) = (D_1{}^2 + 4D_2y)^{-1} \left[p_{\{X\}\{\dot{X}\}}\left(\alpha_2, \frac{\dot{y}}{D_1 + 2D_2\alpha_2}\right) \right.$$
$$\left. + p_{\{X\}\{\dot{X}\}}\left(\alpha_1, \frac{\dot{y}}{D_1 + 2D_2\alpha_1}\right) \right]$$
$$-\frac{D_1{}^2}{4D_2} \leq y < \infty, \, -\infty < \dot{y} < \infty \tag{9-55}$$

We shall again base our discussion on Eq. (9-45), where we assume that the excitation is a Gaussian white noise and that the *response* process is of a narrow band. Then by substituting Eq. (9-46) into Eq. (9-55), we find that

$$p_{\{Y\}\{\dot{Y}\}}(y, \dot{y}) = C(D_1{}^2 + 4D_2y)^{-1} \exp\left[-\frac{\dot{y}^2}{2(D_1{}^2 + 4D_2y)}\right]$$
$$\left\{\exp\left[-\frac{\zeta\omega_0{}^3}{\pi K}\alpha_2{}^2 - \frac{2\epsilon\zeta\omega_0{}^3}{\pi K}G(\alpha_2)\right] + \exp\left[-\frac{\zeta\omega_0{}^3}{\pi K}\alpha_1{}^2 - \frac{2\epsilon\zeta\omega_0{}^3}{\pi K}G(\alpha_1)\right]\right\}$$
$$-\frac{D_1{}^2}{4D_2} \leq y < \infty, \, -\infty < \dot{y} < \infty \tag{9-56}$$

It is interesting to note that although the displacement and the velocity processes $X(t)$ and $\dot{X}(t)$ are independent, the stress and the stress-rate processes $Y(t)$ and $\dot{Y}(t)$ are not. Furthermore, as can be seen from the displacement-stress relationship, Eq. (9-51), a positive peak in $X(t)$ produces a positive peak in $Y(t)$, but a negative trough in $X(t)$ need not result in a negative trough in $Y(t)$. In fact, a trough in $X(t)$ between $-D_1/(2D_2)$ and $-D_1/D_2$ gives rise to a negative peak in $Y(t)$. This situation is illustrated in Fig. 9.3 by the corresponding sample functions $x(t)$ and $y(t)$ of the displacement and the stress processes. Since $X(t)$ is assumed to be of a narrow band, almost all peaks are positive and almost all troughs are negative. On the other hand, we can only assert that

Fig. 9.3 Formation of negative stress peaks in the case of a nonlinear structure.

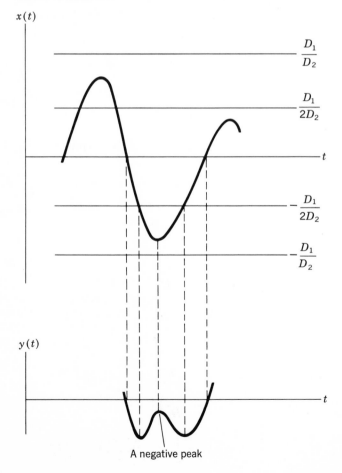

there are almost no positive troughs in $Y(t)$. Therefore, the determination of $E[{}^{s}M_{+}(\eta)]$, the expected number of stress peaks per unit time above a *positive* level η, can be effected by use of Eq. (9-42); i.e.,

$$E[{}^{s}M_{+}(\eta)] \approx \int_{0}^{\infty} \dot{y}p_{\{Y\}\{\dot{Y}\}}(\eta, \dot{y}) \, d\dot{y} \approx C \left\{ \exp\left[-\frac{\zeta\omega_0{}^3}{\pi K}\alpha_2{}^2 - \frac{2\epsilon\zeta\omega_0{}^3}{\pi K}G(\alpha_2) \right] \right.$$

$$\left. + \exp\left[-\frac{\zeta\omega_0{}^3}{\pi K}\alpha_1{}^2 - \frac{2\epsilon\zeta\omega_0{}^3}{\pi K}G(\alpha_1) \right] \right\}$$

$$\eta \geq 0, \; \alpha_{1.2} = -\frac{D_1}{2D_2} \mp \left(\frac{D_1{}^2}{4D_2{}^2} + \frac{\eta}{D_2} \right)^{\frac{1}{2}} \quad (9\text{-}57)$$

where the superscript s and the subscript $+$ associated with the number M signify that the number refers to the *stress* peaks which are above a *positive* level.

We now turn our attention to the negative peaks of $Y(t)$. We observe that the number of negative peaks of $Y(t)$ above a level $\eta < 0$ is equal to the number of troughs in $X(t)$ between $-D_1/D_2$ and

$$\alpha_1 = \frac{-D_1}{2D_2} - \left(\frac{D_1{}^2}{4D_2{}^2} + \frac{\eta}{D_2} \right)^{\frac{1}{2}}$$

If we further impose the assumption that the function $G(x)$ in Eq. (9-46) is an *even* function, then the positive $X(t)$ and the negative $X(t)$ are distributed identically. Thus, the expected number of negative peaks in $Y(t)$ above $\eta < 0$ per unit time is

$$E[{}^{s}M_{-}(\eta)] = \text{expected number of troughs in } X(t) \text{ in the interval} \left(\frac{-D_1}{D_2}, \alpha_1 \right)$$

$$= \text{expected number of peaks in } X(t) \text{ in the interval} \left(-\alpha_1, \frac{D_1}{D_2} \right)$$

$$= \int_{0}^{\infty} \dot{x}p_{\{X\}\{\dot{X}\}}(-\alpha_1, \dot{x}) \, d\dot{x} - \int_{0}^{\infty} \dot{x}p_{\{X\}\{\dot{X}\}} \left(\frac{D_1}{D_2}, \dot{x} \right) d\dot{x} \quad (9\text{-}58)$$

Using (9-46) in (9-58), we obtain

$$E[{}^{s}M_{-}(\eta)] = C \left\{ \exp\left[-\frac{\zeta\omega_0{}^3}{\pi K}\alpha_1{}^2 - \frac{2\epsilon\zeta\omega_0{}^3}{\pi K}G(\alpha_1) \right] \right.$$

$$\left. - \exp\left[-\frac{\zeta\omega_0{}^3}{\pi K}\left(\frac{D_1}{D_2}\right)^2 - \frac{2\epsilon\zeta\omega_0{}^3}{\pi K}G\left(\frac{D_1}{D_2}\right) \right] \right\}$$

$$-\frac{D_1{}^2}{4D_2} \leq \eta \leq 0 \quad (9\text{-}59)$$

The expected total number of stress peaks is computed from

$$E[{}^{s}M_T] = E[{}^{s}M_{+}(0)] + E\left[{}^{s}M_{-}\left(-\frac{D_1{}^2}{4D_2} \right) \right]$$

$$= C \left\{ 1 + \exp\left[-\frac{\zeta\omega_0{}^3}{\pi K}\left(\frac{D_1}{2D_2}\right)^2 - \frac{2\epsilon\zeta\omega_0{}^3}{\pi K}G\left(\frac{D_1}{2D_2}\right) \right] \right\} \quad (9\text{-}60)$$

The probability density of the stress-peak magnituce obtained from the Huston-Skopinski approach is also given by expressions valid either for $\eta \geq 0$ or for $\eta < 0$. They are, respectively,

$$
{}^s p_{\bar{z}}(\eta) = -\frac{1}{E[{}^s M_T]} \frac{d}{d\eta} E[{}^s M_+(\eta)] = \left\{ 1 + \exp\left[-\frac{\zeta\omega_0{}^3}{\pi K} \left(\frac{D_1}{2D_2}\right)^2 \right.\right.
$$
$$
\left.\left. -\frac{2\epsilon\zeta\omega_0{}^3}{\pi K} G\left(\frac{D_1}{2D_2}\right)\right] \right\}^{-1} (D_1{}^2 + 4D_2\eta)^{-\frac{1}{2}} \left\{ \left[\frac{2\zeta\omega_0{}^3\alpha_2}{\pi K} + \frac{2\epsilon\zeta\omega_0{}^3}{\pi K} g(\alpha_2)\right] \right.
$$
$$
\exp\left[-\frac{\zeta\omega_0{}^3}{\pi K}\alpha_2{}^2 - \frac{2\epsilon\zeta\omega_0{}^3}{\pi K} G(\alpha_2)\right] - \left[\frac{2\zeta\omega_0{}^3\alpha_1}{\pi K} + \frac{2\epsilon\zeta\omega_0{}^3}{\pi K} g(\alpha_1)\right]
$$
$$
\left. \exp\left[-\frac{\zeta\omega_0{}^3}{\pi K}\alpha_1{}^2 - \frac{2\epsilon\zeta\omega_0{}^3}{\pi K} G(\alpha_1)\right]\right\} \qquad \eta \geq 0 \quad (9\text{-}61)
$$

$$
{}^s p_{\bar{z}}(\eta) = -\frac{1}{E[{}^s M_T]} \frac{\partial}{\partial\eta} E[{}^s M_-(\eta)] = -\left\{ 1 + \exp\left[-\frac{\zeta\omega_0{}^3}{\pi K} \left(\frac{D_1}{2D_2}\right)^2 \right.\right.
$$
$$
\left.\left. -\frac{2\epsilon\zeta\omega_0{}^3}{\pi K} G\left(\frac{D_1}{2D_2}\right)\right] \right\}^{-1} (D_1{}^2 + 4D_2\eta)^{-\frac{1}{2}} \left[\frac{2\zeta\omega_0{}^3\alpha_1}{\pi K} + \frac{2\epsilon\zeta\omega_0{}^3}{\pi K} g(\alpha_1)\right]
$$
$$
\exp\left[-\frac{\zeta\omega_0{}^3}{\pi K}\alpha_1{}^2 - \frac{2\epsilon\zeta\omega_0{}^3}{\pi K} G(\alpha_1)\right] \qquad \eta < 0 \quad (9\text{-}62)
$$

It is interesting to note that ${}^s p_{\bar{z}}(\eta)$ as given in Eqs. (9-61) and (9-62) is continuous at $\eta = 0$; however, the slope of ${}^s p_{\bar{z}}(\eta)$ is discontinuous at this point. This probability density is plotted in Fig. 9.4 for Duffing's system with the following combinations of the parametric values: (1) $D_1/(D_2\sigma_0) = 2$ and $\epsilon\sigma_0{}^2 = 1$; and (2) $D_1/(D_2\sigma_0) = 2$ and $\epsilon\sigma_0{}^2 = 1.5$, where $\sigma_0 = [\pi K/(2\zeta\omega_0{}^3)]^{\frac{1}{2}}$ is the standard deviation of the linear displacement (i.e., the displacement if $\epsilon = 0$). The first combination corresponds to the stress on the surface and at the center of a nearly square flat plate hinged at its four edges with a deflection of the same order of magnitude as the plate thickness. The second combination represents the same conditions as combination (1), except that the length-to-width ratio of the plate is about 2. The probability density of the linear stress peaks, a Rayleigh probability density, is also included for comparison. Note the difference between the linear and nonlinear stress-peak distributions, especially in the regions of negative peaks and positive peaks smaller than about $2\sigma_0$.

9.4 / ENVELOPE DISTRIBUTION

In Fig. 9.2, which shows a sample function of a narrow-band random process, we have also sketched the envelope of that sample function. An envelope is often conceived to be a curved tangent, but for mathematical analyses a more precise definition is required. Of course, the envelope of a random process is a random process if it can be well defined. A widely accepted definition for the envelope of a *narrow-band* random process is due to Rice.‡ Assume that such a random process can be represented by

$$X(t) = A(t) \cos [\omega_m t + \Theta(t)] \qquad (9\text{-}63)$$

where ω_m is a representative midband frequency of the narrow band, and $A(t)$ and $\Theta(t)$ are random processes which vary much more slowly than $X(t)$ with respect to t. The random process $A(t)$ is the envelope process of $X(t)$ according to Rice's definition. Without loss of generality, we further assume that $A(t)$ is nonnegative. In passing, we note that proper choice of the midband frequency ω_m can be extremely crucial in certain cases. However, if the spectral density of $X(t)$ in the positive (or negative) frequency domain is symmetrical about a frequency ω_s (or $-\omega_s$), then it is clear that $\omega_m = \omega_s$. The critical nature in the choice of ω_m for a nonsymmetrical spectral density will be further noted. ¶

‡ *Loc. cit.*
¶ See the discussion following Eq. (9-97).

Fig. 9.4 Probability densities of stress peaks in linear and nonlinear structures: (1) nonlinear stress peaks, $D_1/(D_2\sigma_0) = 2$, $\epsilon\sigma_0^2 = 1$; (2) nonlinear stress peaks, $D_1/(D_2\sigma_0) = 2$, $\epsilon\sigma_0^2 = 1.5$; (3) linear stress peaks (Rayleigh distribution).

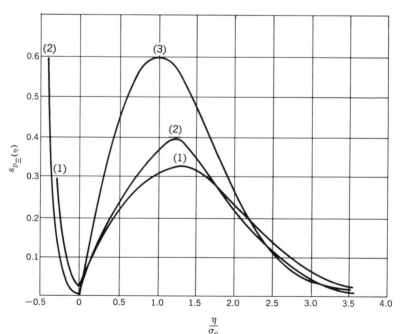

Equation (9-63) may be written alternatively as follows:

$$X(t) = I_c(t) \cos \omega_m t - I_s(t) \sin \omega_m(t) \tag{9-64}$$

where

$$\begin{aligned} I_c(t) &= A(t) \cos [\Theta(t)] \\ I_s(t) &= A(t) \sin [\Theta(t)] \end{aligned} \tag{9-65}$$

Therefore,

$$A(t) = [I_c{}^2(t) + I_s{}^2(t)]^{\frac{1}{2}} \tag{9-66}$$

Equation (9-66) shows that the probability distribution of $A(t)$ can, in principle, be obtained from the joint probability distribution of $I_c(t)$ and $I_s(t)$. It is simpler, however, to use Eqs. (9-65), noting that these equations specify a one-to-one correspondence‡ between the two-dimensional vector processes $\{I_c(t), I_s(t)\}$ and $\{A(t), \Theta(t)\}$. Consequently, the usual technique of transformation of random variables discussed in Sec. 2.9 can be applied here. In particular, the joint probability density of $A(t)$ and $\Theta(t)$ at the same time t is given by

$$p_{\{A\}\{\Theta\}}(a, \theta, t) = |J| p_{\{I_c\}\{I_s\}}(a \cos \theta, a \sin \theta, t) \tag{9-67}$$

where it can be shown that in the present case the Jacobian of the transformation, J, equals a. The first-order probability density of $A(t)$ follows from an integration of (9-67) over the θ domain; i.e.,

$$p_{\{A\}}(a, t) = \int_0^{2\pi} a p_{\{I_c\}\{I_s\}}(a \cos \theta, a \sin \theta, t) \, d\theta \tag{9-68}$$

The above derivation is valid whether or not $X(t)$ is stationary. It is required, however, that the sample functions of $X(t)$ have the general appearance of the one shown in Fig. 9.2; otherwise, the $A(t)$ process would not be a proper definition for the envelope.

As an example, let $I_c(t)$ and $I_s(t)$ be independent and identically distributed stationary Gaussian processes with zero expectation. Then the joint probability density of $I_c(t)$ and $I_s(t)$ may be written as

$$p_{\{I_c\}\{I_s\}}(c, s) = \frac{1}{2\pi\sigma^2} \exp\left(-\frac{c^2 + s^2}{2\sigma^2}\right) \tag{9-69}$$

where σ^2 is the common variance of $I_c(t)$ and $I_s(t)$. In passing we note that it is a simple matter to show that $X(t)$, which is constructed from $I_c(t)$ and $I_s(t)$ in the way specified in Eq. (9-64), has the same first-order

‡ We limit the range for $\Theta(t)$ to, say, $[0, 2\pi)$.

probability density as $I_c(t)$ or $I_s(t)$; that is,

$$p_{\{X\}}(x) = \frac{1}{\sqrt{2\pi}\,\sigma} \exp\left(-\frac{x^2}{2\sigma^2}\right) \tag{9-70}$$

Substitution of Eq. (9-69) into Eq. (9-68) yields

$$p_{\{A\}}(a) = \frac{1}{2\pi\sigma^2} \int_0^{2\pi} a \exp\left(-\frac{a^2}{2\sigma^2}\right) d\theta$$

$$= \frac{a}{\sigma^2} \exp\left(-\frac{a^2}{2\sigma^2}\right) \tag{9-71}$$

This is the Rayleigh probability density which has been shown to be the form of the probability density of the peak magnitude of a narrow band random process obtained from the Huston-Skopinski approach [refer to Eq. (9-38)]. It is plausible that for a stationary narrow-band random process, the probability distributions of the envelope and of the peak magnitude ought to have certain similarities. Thus, the agreement between Eqs. (9-38) and (9-71) shows, in one aspect, the merit of the Huston-Slopinski approach.

The application of Eq. (9-68) to non-Gaussian random processes is not as simple as it might appear. For non-Gaussian cases the first-order distribution of $I_c(t)$ or $I_s(t)$ is generally different from that of $X(t)$. Since $X(t)$ is the given random process in a problem, the first step, a difficult one, would be to find the joint probability density of $I_c(t)$ and $I_s(t)$ which is required in Eq. (9-68). The relation to be used is Eq. (9-64). To avoid taking such a step, Crandall‡ has suggested two alternative definitions for an envelope process. According to his first definition, an envelope is a smooth, gradual curve joining the peaks, and the expected time spent by the envelope between the level a and $a + da$ is just the number of those peaks whose magnitude lies between a and $a + da$ multiplied by the expected period for cycles of amplitude a. According to his second definition, the envelope process $A(t)$ of a random process $X(t)$ is given implicitly by

$$V(A) = \tfrac{1}{2}\dot{X}^2 + V(X) \tag{9-72}$$

The right-hand side of (9-72) is the sum of the kinetic and potential energies per unit mass; therefore, $A(t)$ would be the displacement if the total energy were converted entirely to potential energy. Although both definitions were intended for use in the study of narrow-band random

‡ S. H. Crandall, Zero Crossings, Peaks, and Other Statistical Measures of Random Responses, *J. Acoust. Soc. Am.*, **35**(11):1693–1699 (1963). See also S. H. Crandall, The Envelope of Random Vibration of a Lightly Damped Nonlinear Oscillator, *Zagadnienia drgan nieliniowych* (Nonlinear Vibration Problems), **5**:120–130 (1964).

processes, the second definition, the energy-based definition, does not imply the bandwidth restriction. Crandall has shown that both definitions lead to the same first-order probability density for the envelope of the response of a nonlinear stiffness system to a Gaussian-white-noise excitation. This probability density also reduces to Rice's result when the nonlinear term is set equal to zero. We shall limit our discussion to the energy-based definition. For brevity, we shall consider only stationary random processes.

It can be seen that the first-order distribution function of the envelope process defined in Eq. (9-72) is given by

$$F_{\{A\}}(a) = \mathscr{P}[A(t) \leq a]$$
$$= 4 \int_0^a dx \int_0^{\{2[V(a) - V(x)]\}^{\frac{1}{2}}} p_{\{X\}\{\dot{X}\}}(x, \dot{x}) \, d\dot{x} \tag{9-73}$$

where we have assumed that $p_{\{X\}\{\dot{X}\}}(x, \dot{x})$ is an even function of both x and $\dot{x}$ and that $V(x)$ is an even function of x. The first-order probability density of the envelope follows from a differentiation of Eq. (9-73):

$$p_{\{A\}}(a) = 4V'(a) \int_0^a \{2[V(a) - V(x)]\}^{-\frac{1}{2}} p_{\{X\}\{\dot{X}\}}(x, \{2[V(a) - V(x)]\}^{\frac{1}{2}}) \, dx \tag{9-74}$$

For the case

$$p_{\{X\}\{\dot{X}\}}(x, \dot{x}) = C \exp\left\{-\frac{\beta}{\pi K}\left[\frac{\dot{x}^2}{2} + \int_0^x f_1(u) \, du\right]\right\} \tag{8-35}$$

corresponding to a nonlinear stiffness system excited by a Gaussian white noise, we find‡ that

$$p_{\{A\}}(a) = Cf(a) \left\{4 \int_0^a \left[2 \int_x^a f_1(u) \, du\right]^{-\frac{1}{2}} dx\right\} \exp\left[-\frac{\beta}{\pi K} \int_0^a f_1(u) \, du\right] \tag{9-75}$$

An alternative expression of this equation is

$$p_{\{A\}}(a) = C \left\{4 \int_0^a \left[2 \int_x^a f_1(u) \, du\right]^{-\frac{1}{2}} dx\right\} \left(\frac{\pi K}{\beta}\right) p_{\bar{z}}(a) \tag{9-76}$$

where $p_{\bar{z}}(a)$ is the probability density of the peak magnitude given by

‡ Note that the quantity $4 \int_0^a \left[2 \int_x^a f_1(u) \, du\right]^{-\frac{1}{2}} dx$ is the period corresponding to amplitude a of the undamped free motion, that is, the motion governed by

$$\ddot{x} + f_1(x) = 0$$

See, for example, J. J. Stoker, "Nonlinear Vibration," pp. 20–21, Interscience, New York, 1950.

Eq. (9-50).‡   In particular, for a Duffing system

$$f_1(u) = \omega_0^2(u + \epsilon u^3)$$

The integral in (9-76) can be represented by the elliptic integral of the first kind, which is defined as

$$F(k, \phi) = \int_0^\phi \frac{d\psi}{(1 - k^2 \sin^2 \psi)^{\frac{1}{2}}}$$

where k and ϕ are called the modulus and the amplitude, respectively, of the elliptic integral.   By use of an existing conversion table,¶ it can be shown that for a Duffing system the integral in (9-76) is

$$\int_0^a \frac{dx}{\sqrt{\omega_0^2(a^2 - x^2) + (\epsilon\omega_0^2/2)(a^4 - x^4)}} = \omega_0^{-1}(1 + \epsilon a^2)^{-\frac{1}{2}}F\left(k, \frac{\pi}{2}\right) \quad (9\text{-}77)$$

with a modulus $k = [\epsilon a^2(2 + 2\epsilon a^2)^{-1}]^{\frac{1}{2}}$.   The function $F(k, \pi/2)$ is known as the complete elliptic integral of the first kind.

The constant C in Eq. (9-76) must be determined from the normalization condition of Eq. (8-35).   In the Duffing case

$$C = \left\{2\sqrt{2\pi}\sqrt{\frac{\pi K}{\beta}} \int_0^\infty \exp\left[-\frac{\beta\omega_0^2}{\pi K}\left(\frac{x^2}{2} + \epsilon\frac{x^4}{4}\right)\right] dx\right\}^{-1}$$

Therefore,

$$p_{\{A\}}(a) = \frac{4\sigma_0 F(k, \pi/2)}{2\sqrt{2\pi}\sqrt{1 + \epsilon a^2} \int_0^\infty \exp\left(-\frac{x^2}{2\sigma_0^2} - \epsilon\frac{x^4}{4\sigma_0^2}\right) dx} p_{\mathcal{Z}}(a) \quad (9\text{-}78)$$

where $\sigma_0 = (\pi K/\omega_0^2\beta)^{\frac{1}{2}}$ is the standard deviation of the linear displacement (when $\epsilon = 0$).   It can be shown that only when $\epsilon = 0$ does the factor preceding $p_{\mathcal{Z}}(a)$ on the right-hand side of Eq. (9-78) reduce to unity.

The determination of the second-order probability density of the envelope process is similar in principle, but the actual computation is more complicated.   In the case of a narrow-band random process, if Rice's definition of the envelope of such a process is used, then we may write

$$\begin{aligned} X(t_1) &= I_c(t_1) \cos \omega_m t_1 - I_s(t_1) \sin \omega_m t_1 \\ X(t_2) &= I_c(t_2) \cos \omega_m t_2 - I_s(t_2) \sin \omega_m t_2 \end{aligned} \quad (9\text{-}79)$$

‡ Note that $\beta = 2\zeta\omega_0$ and $\int_0^a f_1(u)\, du = \omega_0^2[a^2/2 + \epsilon G(a)]$ here.

¶ For example, E. Jahnke and F. Emde, "Table of Functions," 4th ed., p. 58, Dover, New York, 1945.

Then, analogous to Eq. (9-68), we have

$$p_{\{A\}}(a_1, t_1; a_2, t_2)$$
$$= \int_0^{2\pi} \int_0^{2\pi} a_1 a_2 p_{\{I_c\}\{I_s\}}(a_1 \cos \theta_1, a_1 \sin \theta_1, t_1;$$
$$a_2 \cos \theta_2, a_2 \sin \theta_2, t_2) \, d\theta_1 \, d\theta_2 \quad (9\text{-}80)$$

When $X(t)$ is stationary and Gaussian and has a zero mean, Rice$\ddagger$ has found that

$$p_{\{A\}}(a_1, t; a_2, t + \tau)$$
$$= \frac{a_1 a_2}{B} I_0 \left[\frac{a_1 a_2}{B} (\mu_{13}{}^2 + \mu_{14}{}^2)^{\frac{1}{2}} \right] \exp \left[-\frac{\sigma^2}{2B} (a_1{}^2 + a_2{}^2) \right] \quad (9\text{-}81)$$

where $I_0[\ \ ]$ is the Bessel function of the first kind with imaginary arguments, and

$$\sigma^2 = E[I_c{}^2(t)] = E[I_s{}^2(t)] = E[X^2(t)]$$
$$= \int_{-\infty}^{\infty} \Phi_{XX}(\omega) \, d\omega$$
$$\mu_{13} = E[I_c(t)I_c(t + \tau)] = E[I_s(t)I_s(t + \tau)]$$
$$= 2 \int_0^{\infty} \Phi_{XX}(\omega) \cos (\omega - \omega_m)\tau \, d\omega \quad (9\text{-}82)$$
$$\mu_{14} = E[I_c(t)I_s(t + \tau)] = -E[I_c(t + \tau)I_s(t)]$$
$$= 2 \int_0^{\infty} \Phi_{XX}(\omega) \sin (\omega - \omega_m)\tau \, d\omega$$
$$B = \sigma^4 - \mu_{13}{}^2 - \mu_{14}{}^2$$

If Crandall's energy-based definition for envelopes is used, the second-order probability distribution function of the envelope of a random process $X(t)$ can be determined if the joint probability density of $X(t)$ and $\dot{X}(t)$ involving two different times is known.

$$F_{\{A\}}(a_1, t_1; a_2, t_2) = \mathcal{P}[A(t_1) \le a_1 \text{ and } A(t_2) \le a_2]$$
$$= \int_{-a_1}^{a_1} dx_1 \int_{-\{2[V(a_1) - V(x_1)]\}^{\frac{1}{2}}}^{\{2[V(a_1) - V(x_1)]\}^{\frac{1}{2}}} d\dot{x}_1 \int_{-a_2}^{a_2} dx_2$$
$$\int_{-\{2[V(a_2) - V(x_2)]\}^{\frac{1}{2}}}^{\{2[V(a_2) - V(x_2)]\}^{\frac{1}{2}}} p_{\{X\}\{\dot{X}\}}(x_1, \dot{x}_1, t_1; x_2, \dot{x}_2, t_2) \, d\dot{x}_2 \quad (9\text{-}83)$$

The second-order probability density of the envelope is obtained as the mixed derivative of $F_{\{A\}}(a_1, t_1; a_2, t_2)$ with respect to a_1 and a_2. The application of Eq. (9-83) when $X(t)$ is non-Gaussian appears to be complicated. In the case of a narrow-band stationary Gaussian process Crandall¶ has shown that the second-order probability density of the energy-based envelope agreed with Rice's result only in the limit as the bandwidth of $X(t)$ was reduced to zero.

$\ddagger$ *Loc. cit.*
¶ *Loc. cit.*

One statistical quantity of some practical interest is the expected number of threshold crossings from below (i.e., at positive slopes) of an envelope process. This problem has been studied by Lyon‡ in the case of a stationary Gaussian random process using Rice's definition of an envelope. As was discussed in Sec. 9.2, the prerequisite to this information is the joint probability density of the envelope $A(t)$ and its derivative $\dot{A}(t)$. If Eqs. (9-65) are differentiated with respect to t, we obtain

$$
\begin{aligned}
\dot{I}_c(t) &= \dot{A}(t) \cos [\Theta(t)] - A(t)\dot{\Theta}(t) \sin [\Theta(t)] \\
\dot{I}_s(t) &= \dot{A}(t) \sin [\Theta(t)] + A(t)\dot{\Theta}(t) \cos [\Theta(t)]
\end{aligned}
\tag{9-84}
$$

Relations (9-65) and (9-84) can now be used to determine the transformation

$$
p_{\{A\}\{\dot{A}\}\{\Theta\}\{\dot{\Theta}\}}(a, \dot{a}, \theta, \dot{\theta}) = p_{\{I_c\}\{I_s\}\{\dot{I}_c\}\{\dot{I}_s\}}(c, s, \dot{c}, \dot{s})|J|
\tag{9-85}
$$

It can readily be shown that the Jacobian of the transformation is $J = a^2$. If $I_c(t)$, $I_s(t)$, $\dot{I}_c(t)$, and $\dot{I}_s(t)$ are independent stationary Gaussian random processes each of which has a zero mean, and if $I_c(t)$ and $I_s(t)$ have a common variance σ^2 and $\dot{I}_c(t)$ and $\dot{I}_s(t)$ have a common variance $\sigma_1{}^2$, then

$$
p_{\{A\}\{\dot{A}\}\{\Theta\}\{\dot{\Theta}\}}(a, \dot{a}, \theta, \dot{\theta}) = \frac{a^2}{(2\pi)^2\sigma^2\sigma_1{}^2} \exp \left(-\frac{a^2}{2\sigma^2} - \frac{\dot{a}^2 + a^2\dot{\theta}^2}{2\sigma_1{}^2} \right)
\tag{9-86}
$$

The required joint probability density of $A(t)$ and $\dot{A}(t)$ is obtained by integrating Eq. (9-86) on θ from 0 to 2π and on $\dot{\theta}$ from $-\infty$ to ∞. The result is

$$
p_{\{A\}\{\dot{A}\}}(a, \dot{a}) = \frac{a}{(2\pi)^{\frac{1}{2}}\sigma^2\sigma_1} \exp \left(-\frac{a^2}{2\sigma^2} - \frac{\dot{a}^2}{2\sigma_1{}^2} \right)
\tag{9-87}
$$

By use of Eq. (9-9), we find the expected number of crossings per unit time over a threshold ξ at positive slopes of the envelope process $A(t)$ to be

$$
E[{}^A N_+(\xi)] = \frac{\xi\sigma_1}{(2\pi)^{\frac{1}{2}}\sigma^2} \exp \left(-\frac{\xi^2}{2\sigma^2} \right)
\tag{9-88}
$$

It has been pointed out that

$$
\sigma^2 = \sigma_X{}^2 = \int_{-\infty}^{\infty} \Phi_{XX}(\omega) \, d\omega
\tag{9-89}
$$

Now since

$$
\dot{X}(t) = \dot{I}_c(t) \cos \omega_m t - \omega_m I_c(t) \sin \omega_m t \\
- \dot{I}_s(t) \sin \omega_m t - \omega_m I_s(t) \cos \omega_m t
\tag{9-90}
$$

‡ R. H. Lyon, On the Vibration Statistics of a Randomly Excited Hard-spring Oscillator. II, *J. Acoust. Soc. Am.*, **33**(10):1395–1403 (1961).

as can be obtained by differentiating Eq. (9-64), and since I_c, I_s, $\dot{I}_c$, and $\dot{I}_s$ are independent, we also have

$$\sigma_{\dot{X}}^2 = E[\dot{X}^2(t)] = \sigma_1^2 + \omega_m^2\sigma^2 \tag{9-91}$$

Thus

$$\begin{aligned}\sigma_1^2 &= \sigma_{\dot{X}}^2 - \omega_m^2\sigma^2 \\ &= \int_{-\infty}^{\infty} (\omega^2 - \omega_m^2)\Phi_{XX}(\omega)\, d\omega\end{aligned} \tag{9-92}$$

Equations (9-89) and (9-92) can be used to compute σ and σ_1 from the spectral density of a given random process, $\Phi_{XX}(\omega)$, for use in Eq. (9-88). It is of interest to note that $\dot{X}(t)$ need not be a narrow-band random process, although Eq. (9-90) has the general form of Eq. (9-64), since $\dot{I}_c$ and $\dot{I}_s$ may be fast-varying with respect to t. Note also that $E[\dot{X}(t)X(t)]$ computed from the left-hand sides of Eqs. (9-64) and (9-90) is equal to zero, as was to be expected.

Once a sample function of a narrow-band random process crosses a given level ξ, it tends to cross again over this level for several excursions. Therefore, for every threshold crossing of an envelope $A(t)$, there are, corresponding to it, several threshold crossings of the narrow-band process $X(t)$ enclosed by the envelope. That is, the threshold crossings of $X(t)$ occur in "clumps." Since every threshold crossing at a positive slope of such a random process almost always results in a peak above this threshold, we may say equivalently that the peaks in $X(t)$ above a given level occur in clumps. Lyon has coined the name *average clump size* for the average number of peaks in a group. From a heuristic argument he suggested that for a narrow-band random process the average clump size could be computed from

$$\langle cs \rangle = \frac{E[N_+(\xi)]}{E[^A N_+(\xi)]} \tag{9-93}$$

By use of Eqs. (9-13), (9-88), we have

$$\langle cs \rangle = \frac{1}{\sqrt{2\pi}\,\xi} \frac{\sigma_{\dot{X}}\sigma_X}{\sigma_1} \tag{9-93a}$$

We shall illustrate the above results by two simple examples. For the first example, assume that

$$\Phi_{XX}(\omega) = \begin{cases} K & 0 \leq \omega_a < |\omega| < \omega_b \\ 0 & \text{otherwise} \end{cases} \tag{9-94}$$

In this case it is clear that $\omega_m = \frac{1}{2}(\omega_a + \omega_b)$. Then

$$\sigma_X{}^2 = 2K(\omega_b - \omega_a)$$

$$\sigma_{\dot{X}}{}^2 = \frac{2}{3}K(\omega_b{}^3 - \omega_a{}^3) \tag{9-95}$$

$$\sigma_1{}^2 = \frac{K}{6}(\omega_b - \omega_a)^3$$

For this case the average clump size for the peaks above ξ is

$$\langle cs \rangle = \frac{2}{\xi(\omega_b - \omega_a)} \left[\frac{K}{\pi}(\omega_b{}^3 - \omega_a{}^3) \right]^{\frac{1}{2}} \tag{9-96}$$

For the second example, assume that

$$\Phi_{XX}(\omega) = K[(\omega_0{}^2 - \omega^2)^2 + (2\zeta\omega_0\omega)^2]^{-1} \tag{9-97}$$

This spectral density corresponds to the displacement response of a single-degree-of-freedom linear oscillator under a white-noise excitation. In this example the spectral density in the positive (or negative) frequency domain is not symmetrical; therefore, the location of the representative midband frequency ω_m is not as clear-cut as in the previous example. It is not accurate enough to use the approximation $\omega_m \approx \omega_0$ for the present purposes, since it would lead to $\sigma_1 = 0$ from Eq. (9-92). In order to circumvent this difficulty, we replace the original spectral density by two rectangles centered respectively at $\pm\omega_0$, as shown in Fig. 9.5. We proportion the rectangles so that they have the same height as that of the peaks of the original spectral density and so that the area of the rectangles is the same as the area under the original spectral density curve ($\sigma_X{}^2$). Having made this change, we can now use

Fig. 9.5 A replacement spectral density for computing $\sigma_1{}^2$.

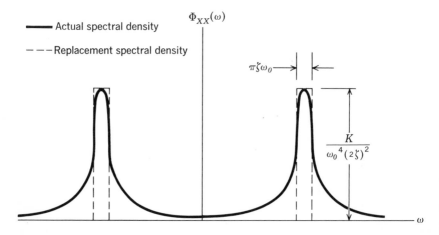

$\omega_m = \omega_0$. Corresponding to the replacement spectral density, we have

$$\sigma_X{}^2 = \frac{\pi K}{2\zeta\omega_0{}^3}$$
$$\sigma_{\dot{X}}{}^2 = \frac{\pi K}{2\zeta\omega_0}\left[1 + \frac{(\pi\zeta)^2}{12}\right] \tag{9-98}$$
$$\sigma_1{}^2 = \frac{\pi^3 K\zeta}{24\omega_0}$$

Note that the new spectral density gives the same mean-square displacement response and nearly the same mean-square velocity response as the original spectral density. The average clump size for the peaks above ξ is obtained by substituting Eqs. (9-98) into Eq. (9-93a),

$$\langle cs\rangle = \frac{1}{\xi}\left(\frac{3K}{\pi^2\zeta^3\omega_0{}^3}\right)^{\frac{1}{2}}\left[1 + \frac{(\pi\zeta)^2}{12}\right]^{\frac{1}{2}} \tag{9-99}$$

or, approximately,

$$\langle cs\rangle \approx \frac{1}{\xi}\left(\frac{3K}{\pi^2\zeta^3\omega_0{}^3}\right)^{\frac{1}{2}} \tag{9-99a}$$

This result agrees with the intuitive notion that the average clump size should be larger for a lower level ξ, or a higher excitation power K, or a smaller damping coefficient ζ.

9.5 / FIRST-EXCURSION FAILURES

We have termed a first-excursion failure to be the event that a random process $X(t)$ passes, for the first time, an upper bound U or a lower bound $-L$. Ideally, we wish to know the probabilistic structure of the random time T when such a failure occurs under suitable initial conditions concerning $X(t)$ and, perhaps, its derivatives. This difficult problem is known as the *first-passage* problem. When $X(t)$ is the response of a damped dynamic system to random excitations, the exact solution to the first-passage problem remains to be found. Therefore, the objective of the present section will be limited to obtaining approximate solutions.

For simplicity we consider first the case where $X(t)$ is stationary and symmetrically distributed in the positive and negative ranges, and where the upper and lower bounds are also symmetrical, that is, $U = L$. Then the probability of failure at time t is

$$\mathcal{P}[\{X(t) \geq U\} \cup \{X(t) \leq -U\}] = \mathcal{P}[\{|X(t)| \geq U\}] = 2\mathcal{P}[X(t) \geq U] \tag{9-100}$$

Although a first-excursion failure of a structure is often destructive, we shall consider an artificial case where the structure can recover immediately after suffering a failure. Then within a time interval, the number of failures is just two times the number of U threshold crossings at positive slopes in the same interval. Further, we shall make another *arbitrary* assumption that such failures arrive independently. Denote by $Q(t)$ the number of failures within the time interval $(0, t]$. Clearly, $Q(t)$ is a Poisson process. When $X(t)$ is stationary, $Q(t)$ is a Poisson process with stationary increments. Referring to Eq. (4-62), we see that the probability function of $Q(t)$ is

$$P_{\{Q\}}(n, t) = \exp(-\lambda t) \frac{(\lambda t)^n}{n!} \qquad (9\text{-}101)$$

The probability of no failure in the time interval $(0, t]$ follows by letting $n = 0$ in Eq. (9-101):

$$P_{\{Q\}}(0, t) = \exp(-\lambda t) \qquad (9\text{-}102)$$

This equation with the failure rate

$$\lambda = 2E[N_+(U)] = E[N(U)] \qquad (9\text{-}103)$$

was first suggested by Coleman‡ as the reliability of a structure against first-excursion failures. Here $E[N_+(U)]$ and $E[N(U)]$ are the expected rates of U threshold crossings at positive slopes and at both positive and negative slopes, respectively. The probability of failure in the time interval $(0, t]$ is simply

$$1 - P_{\{Q\}}(0, t) = 1 - \exp(-\lambda t) \qquad (9\text{-}104)$$

Equation (9-104), however, can be interpreted as the probability that the first passage time is equal to or smaller than t, which is the distribution function¶ of T; that is,

$$F_T(t) = 1 - \exp(-\lambda t) \qquad (9\text{-}105)$$

The probability density of T follows from a differentiation of Eq. (9-105),

$$p_T(t) = \lambda \exp(-\lambda t) \qquad (9\text{-}106)$$

Equation (9-106) can be used to compute the statistical properties of the first-passage time T. In particular, the expectation and the variance of the first-passage time are readily obtained to be

$$E[T] = \int_0^\infty t p_T(t)\, dt = \lambda^{-1}$$
$$\sigma_T{}^2 = \int_0^\infty (t - \lambda^{-1})^2 p_T(t)\, dt = \lambda^{-2} \qquad (9\text{-}107)$$

‡ J. J. Coleman, Reliability of Aircraft Structures in Resisting Chance Failure, *Operations Res.*, **7**(5):639–645 (1959).

¶ This is true provided that the probability of the first-excursion failure in the time interval $(0, t]$ approaches to 1 as t approaches infinity. This condition, however, is not satisfied in certain cases, one of which will be considered later as an example.

The most questionable aspect of the above analysis is the arbitrary assumption that the arrivals of the failures (here the same as the threshold crossings) are independent events.‡ This assumption is especially unacceptable for narrow-band random processes such as the response of lightly damped dynamic systems. We have noted in Sec. 9.4 that threshold crossings for a narrow-band random process occur in clumps. Once there is a crossing over a threshold the probability is high that the following excursion will produce another crossing. However, the crossing of the same threshold by the envelope must precede the first crossing in each clump. When there are many excursions in each clump, the time of a threshold crossing by the envelope is nearly the same as the time of the first crossing in each clump. Since it is more acceptable to treat the threshold crossings of an envelope of a narrow-band random process as independent events, we can improve the above analysis by use of the expected rate of the threshold crossings of the envelope process for λ in Eqs. (9-106) and (9-107). Then

$$p_T(t) = 2E[^4N_+(U)] \exp \{-2tE[^4N_+(U)]\} \qquad (9\text{-}106a)$$
$$E[T] = \{2E[^4N_+(U)]\}^{-1} \qquad (9\text{-}107a)$$
$$\sigma_T{}^2 = \{2E[^4N_+(U)]\}^{-2}$$

Clearly, this improved analysis is somewhat conservative. In the case of a Gaussian random process the expression for $E[^4N_+(U)]$ has been given in Eq. (9-88). Recall, however, that this equation involves the quantity σ_1, which can be precisely computed only when the shape of the spectral density is symmetrical on the positive (or negative) frequency domain. Since the spectral density of a typical stationary response of a structure to random excitations is unsymmetrical, a replacement spectral density of the same general concept as that of Fig. 9.5 is required.

The importance of taking the clustering phenomenon of threshold crossings into consideration is measured by the average clump size

$$\langle cs \rangle = \frac{E[N_+(U)]}{E[^4N_+(U)]} \qquad (9\text{-}93)$$

Let $E_1[T]$ and $E_2[T]$ be the expectations of the first-passage time which are computed by accounting for and ignoring the clustering effect, respectively. Then

$$\frac{E_1[T]}{E_2[T]} = \langle cs \rangle$$

This ratio has been determined, for example, in Eq. (9-99) for the stationary response of a lightly damped single-degree-of-freedom linear

‡ See J. L. Bogdanoff and F. Kozin, Comment on Reliability of Aircraft Structures in Resisting Chance Failure, *Operations Res.*, **9**(1):123–126 (1961).

system due to the excitation of a Gaussian white noise; i.e., under these circumstances

$$\frac{E_1[T]}{E_2[T]} = \frac{1}{U} \left(\frac{3K}{\pi^2 \zeta^3 \omega_0{}^3}\right)^{\frac{1}{2}} \left[1 + \frac{(\pi\zeta)^2}{12}\right]^{\frac{1}{2}} \qquad (9\text{-}108)$$

Let the failure levels $\pm U$ be $\pm n\sigma_X$, where σ_X is the standard deviation of the above response. Recall that

$$\sigma_X{}^2 = \frac{\pi K}{2\zeta\omega_0{}^3}$$

Equation (9-108) may be rewritten as follows:

$$\frac{E_1[T]}{E_2[T]} = \frac{1}{n\zeta} \left\{\frac{6}{\pi^3}\left[1 + \frac{(\pi\zeta)^2}{12}\right]\right\}^{\frac{1}{2}}$$

$$\approx \frac{1}{n\zeta} \sqrt{\frac{6}{\pi^3}} \qquad (9\text{-}108a)$$

For a structure with a typical damping ratio of $\zeta = 0.02$ and designed for an ultimate strength of $U = 5\sigma_X$, Eq. (9-108a) gives

$$\frac{E_1[T]}{E_2[T]} = 4.4$$

Further assume that the undamped natural frequency of the structure is $\omega_0 = 2$ rad/sec. It can be shown that

$$E_1[T] = \sqrt{\frac{6}{\pi}}\frac{1}{n\zeta\omega_0} \exp\left(\frac{n^2}{2}\right) = 1{,}850{,}000 \text{ sec} \approx 21.5 \text{ days}$$

The conservative analysis would lead to

$$E_2[T] \approx 4.9 \text{ days}$$

Without the assumption of independent threshold crossings, either of the response or of the response envelope, it is generally not possible to compute the probability distribution function or the probability density function of the first-passage time. Shinozuka‡ has published a method to determine upper and lower bounds for the probability of the first-excursion failure within an arbitrary semiclosed time interval $(0, t]$. This method is especially suited to treat the case where the excitation is relatively intense only within a short duration. It has been noted before¶ that the probability of the first-excursion failure in $(0, t]$ is the same as the probability distribution function of the first-passage time

‡ M. Shinozuka, Probability of Structural Failure under Random Loading, *J. Eng. Mech. Div., Am. Soc. Civil Engrs.*, **90** (EM 5):147–170 (1964).

¶ See footnote on page 320.

$F_T(t)$, provided that this probability approaches 1 as t approaches infinity. When the computed upper and lower bounds are sufficiently close to each other, they are just as valuable as the mathematically exact value of the probability as a basis for making engineering decisions. Therefore, Shinozuka's analysis will be discussed briefly below.

Let the structural response in question be $X(t)$ with $E[X(t)] = 0$. We define a first-excursion failure as being either the event $\{X(t) \geq U\}$ or the event $\{X(t) \leq -L\}$, where U and L are positive constants. Then the probability of a first-excursion failure is

$$P(t, -L, U) = \mathcal{P}[\{ \inf_{0<\tau\leq t} X(\tau) \leq -L\} \cup \{ \sup_{0<\tau\leq t} X(\tau) \geq U\}] \qquad (9\text{-}109)$$

where inf (abbreviation for *infimum*) and sup (abbreviation for *supremum*) denote a greatest lower bound and a least upper bound within the indicated time interval $(0, t]$, respectively. It is easy to see that

$$\{ \inf_{0<\tau\leq t} X(\tau) \leq -L\} \supset \{X(\tau) \leq -L\} \qquad (9\text{-}110)$$

since every element of the set on the right-hand side belongs to the set on the left-hand side, but the reverse is not always true. Similarly,

$$\{ \sup_{0<\tau\leq t} X(\tau) \geq U\} \supset \{X(\tau) \geq U\} \qquad (9\text{-}111)$$

By use of relations (9-110) and (9-111) we obtain a lower bound for $P(t, -L, U)$ as follows:

$$\begin{aligned}
P(t, -L, U) &\geq \mathcal{P}[\{X(\tau_1) \leq -L\} \cup \{X(\tau_2) \geq U\}] \\
&= \mathcal{P}[\{X(\tau_1) \leq -L\}] + \mathcal{P}[\{X(\tau_2) \geq U\}] \\
&\quad - \mathcal{P}[\{X(\tau_1) \leq -L\} \cap \{X(\tau_2) \geq U\}] \\
&= \int_{-\infty}^{-L} p_{\{X\}}(x, \tau_1)\, dx + \int_{U}^{\infty} p_{\{X\}}(x, \tau_2)\, dx \\
&\quad - \int_{-\infty}^{-L} dx_1 \int_{U}^{\infty} p_{\{X\}}(x_1, \tau_1; x_2, \tau_2)\, dx_2 \quad (9\text{-}112)
\end{aligned}$$

The best lower bound estimate is obtained by a proper choice of the pair τ_1 and τ_2 such that the far right-hand side in relation (9-112) yields its largest value. In the special case where $L = U$ and the probability density of $X(t)$ is symmetrical about $x = 0$, the best lower bound estimate is computed at $\tau^* = \tau_1 = \tau_2$ so that the integrals

$$\int_{-\infty}^{-L} p_{\{X\}}(x, \tau^*)\, dx \qquad \text{and} \qquad \int_{U}^{\infty} p_{\{X\}}(x, \tau^*)\, dx$$

which are now equal, attain their largest value. This conclusion is reached by noting that, at $\tau_1 = \tau_2$,

$$\mathcal{P}[\{X(\tau_1) \leq -L\} \cap \{X(\tau_2) \geq U\}] = 0 \qquad (9\text{-}113)$$

since this probability is one of disjoint events. When $L \neq U$ and/or $X(t)$ is not symmetrically distributed, it is generally necessary to choose two different times $\tau_1 = \tau_1^*$ and $\tau_2 = \tau_2^*$ in order to render $\mathcal{O}[\{X(\tau_1) \leq -L\}]$ and $\mathcal{O}[\{X(\tau_2) \geq U\}]$, that is, the first and second integrals on the far right-hand side of relation (9-112), equal to their respective largest values. Shinozuka has found that although Eq. (9-113) is not strictly valid when $\tau_1^* \neq \tau_2^*$, the value of the left-hand side of this equation is often so small that it is negligible in comparison with $\mathcal{O}[\{x(\tau_1^*) \leq -L\}]$ or $\mathcal{O}[\{X(\tau_2^*) \geq U\}]$. Therefore, as a practical matter, the best lower bound estimate for $P(t, -L, U)$ can often be computed by selecting $\tau_1 = \tau_1^*$ and $\tau_2 = \tau_2^*$ in order to maximize the probabilities $\mathcal{O}[\{X(\tau_1) \leq -L\}]$ and $\mathcal{O}[\{X(\tau_2) \geq U\}]$.

To find an upper bound for $P(t, -L, U)$, we rewrite Eq. (9-109) as follows:

$$P(t, -L, U) = \mathcal{O}[\{ \inf_{0<\tau\leq t} X(\tau) \leq -L\}] + \mathcal{O}[\{ \sup_{0<\tau\leq t} X(\tau) \geq U\}]$$
$$- \mathcal{O}[\{ \inf_{0<\tau\leq t} X(\tau) \leq -L\} \cap \{ \sup_{0<\tau\leq t} X(\tau) \geq U\}] \quad (9\text{-}114)$$

By use of relations (9-110) and (9-111) we obtain the inequality

$$P(t, -L, U) \leq \mathcal{O}[\{ \inf_{0<\tau\leq t} X(\tau) \leq -L\}] + \mathcal{O}[\{ \sup_{0<\tau\leq t} X(\tau) \geq U\}]$$
$$- \mathcal{O}[\{X(\tau_1) \leq -L\} \cap \{X(\tau_2) \geq U\}] \quad 0 < \tau_1, \tau_2 \leq t \quad (9\text{-}115)$$

To proceed further, let us examine first the probability $\mathcal{O}[\{ \sup_{0<\tau\leq t} X(\tau) \geq U\}]$. Clearly, this probability is a function of t; therefore, it is proper to write

$$P(t) = \mathcal{O}[\{ \sup_{0<\tau\leq t} X(\tau) \geq U\}] \quad (9\text{-}116)$$

As t increases to $t + \Delta t$, the value of this probability increases by an increment which is the probability of the joint event

$$\mathcal{E}_1 = \{ \sup_{0<\tau\leq t} X(\tau) < U\} \cap \{ \sup_{t<t'\leq t+\Delta t} X(t') \geq U\} \quad (9\text{-}117)$$

However, this joint event is included in the joint event

$$\mathcal{E}_2 = \{X(t) < U\} \cap \{ \sup_{t<t'\leq t+\Delta t} X(t') \geq U\} \quad (9\text{-}118)$$

since

$$\{X(t) < U\} \supset \{ \sup_{0<\tau\leq t} X(\tau) < U\} \quad (9\text{-}119)$$

Therefore,

$$\mathcal{O}[\mathcal{E}_2] \geq \mathcal{O}[\mathcal{E}_1]$$

We then have

$$P(t + \Delta t) = P(t) + \mathcal{P}[\mathcal{E}_1] \leq P(t) + \mathcal{P}[\mathcal{E}_2] \qquad (9\text{-}120)$$

It will be assumed that when the time increment Δt is sufficiently small the probability for $X(t')$ to cross a given threshold more than once within the time interval $(t, t + \Delta t]$ is negligible compared with the probability for $X(t')$ to cross this threshold only once. Then for such a small Δt, $\mathcal{E}_2$ is the same event as that where $X(t')$ crosses the threshold U from below within the time interval $(t, t + \Delta t]$. This observation enables us to use a known result of the threshold-crossing problem to evaluate $\mathcal{P}[\mathcal{E}_2]$. Specifically, under the above assumption

$$\mathcal{P}[\mathcal{E}_2] \approx \Delta t \, E[N_+(U, t)] \qquad (9\text{-}121)$$

where $E[N_+(U, t)]$ is the expected rate at time t at which $X(t)$ crosses the threshold U from below. This expected rate can be computed from Eq. (9-9). Substituting Eq. (9-121) into inequality (9-120) and transposing, we obtain, as Δt approaches zero,

$$\frac{dP}{dt} \leq E[N_+(U, t)] \qquad (9\text{-}122)$$

Integrating,

$$P(t) \leq \int_{0+}^{t} E[N_+(U, \tau)] \, d\tau + P(0+) \qquad (9\text{-}123)$$

Recall the definition of $P(t)$, Eq. (9-116). Equation (9-123) means that

$$\mathcal{P}[\{ \sup_{0 < \tau \leq t} X(\tau) \geq U \}] \leq \int_{0+}^{t} E[N_+(U, \tau)] \, d\tau$$
$$+ \mathcal{P}[\{ X(0+) \geq U \}] \qquad (9\text{-}123a)$$

In inequalities (9-123) and (9-123a) we used $t = 0+$ as the initial time since we are concerned with the first-excursion failure in the semiclosed time interval $(0, t]$. By use of a procedure similar to the one leading to (9-123a) we can show that

$$\mathcal{P}[\{ \inf_{0 < \tau \leq t} X(\tau) \leq -L \}] \leq \int_{0+}^{t} E[N_-(-L, \tau)] \, d\tau$$
$$+ \mathcal{P}[X(0+) \leq -L] \qquad (9\text{-}124)$$

where $E[N_-(-L, \tau)]$ is the expected rate at time τ at which $X(\tau)$ crosses the threshold $-L$ from above. Similar to Eq. (9-9),

$$E[N_-(-L, \tau)] = \int_{-\infty}^{0} \dot{x} p_{\{X\}\{\dot{X}\}}(-L, \dot{x}, \tau) \, d\dot{x} \qquad (9\text{-}9a)$$

Substituting (9-123a) and (9-124) into (9-115), we obtain an upper-bound expression for the probability of the first-excursion failure in $(0, t]$,

$$P(t, -L, U) \leq \int_{0+}^{t} E[N_+(U, \tau)] \, d\tau + \int_{0+}^{t} E[N_-(-L, \tau)] \, d\tau$$
$$+ \mathcal{P}[\{X(0+) \geq U\}] + \mathcal{P}[\{X(0+) \leq -L\}]$$
$$- \mathcal{P}[\{X(\tau_1) \leq -L\} \cap \{X(\tau_2) \geq U\}] \qquad 0 < \tau_1, \tau_2 \leq t \qquad (9\text{-}125)$$

Note that the sum $\mathcal{P}[\{X(0+) \geq U\}] + \mathcal{P}[\{X(0+) \leq -L\}]$ is the probability of an initial failure. This probability is, of course, zero or 1 if the initial value of $X(t)$ is precisely known. On the other hand, if $X(0+)$ is random, such as the case where $X(t)$ is stationary, then the probability of initial failure is between zero and 1. The best upper bound estimate of $P(t, -L, U)$ is obtained by a choice of $\tau_1 = \tau_1^\dagger$ and $\tau_2 = \tau_2^\dagger$ in the inequality (9-125) such that the probability

$$\mathcal{P}[\{X(\tau_1^\dagger) \leq -L\} \cap \{X(\tau_2^\dagger) \geq U\}]$$

attains its largest value. Of course, an upper-bound value computed from (9-125) is without practical significance if it is greater than 1.

In the special case where $U = L$ and where $X(t)$ and $\dot{X}(t)$ are symmetrically distributed in their respective positive and negative ranges, inequality (9-125) reduces to

$$P(t, -U, U) \leq \int_{0+}^{t} E[N(U, \tau)] \, d\tau + 2\mathcal{P}[\{X(0+) \geq U\}]$$
$$- \mathcal{P}[\{X(\tau_1) \leq -U\} \cap \{X(\tau_2) \geq U\}] \qquad 0 < \tau_1, \tau_2 \leq t \qquad (9\text{-}126)$$

It is interesting to note that to find upper and lower bounds for $P(t, -L, U)$ by use of the above approach we require the joint probability densities for $X(t)$ and $\dot{X}(t)$ and for $X(t_1)$ and $X(t_2)$. The generalization of inequalities (9-112), (9-125), and (9-126) for the case of varying failure boundaries, that is, U and L varying with time, has been achieved by Shinozuka and Yao.‡

To illustrate the usefulness of the above approach Shinozuka¶ chose the example of a single-degree-of-freedom linear system excited by the nonstationary random process

$$F(t) = G(t) \exp(-\alpha\omega_0 t) \mathbf{1}(t) \qquad (9\text{-}127)$$

Of the three factors on the right-hand side of Eq. (9-127) composing the mathematical model of a random excitation, the first is random and the latter two are deterministic. The random factor $G(t)$ is assumed to be stationary and Gaussian and to have a zero mean and a spectral density

‡ M. Shinozuka and J. T. P. Yao, On the Two-sided Time-dependent Barrier Problem, *Columbia Univ. Inst. Study of Fatigue and Reliability*, Tech. Rept. 21, June, 1965.
¶ Probability of Structural Failure under Random Loading.

$\Phi_{GG}(\omega)$. Then $F(t)$ is also Gaussian and has a zero mean. The linear system is characterized by the impulse response function

$$h(t) = \begin{cases} \omega_d^{-1} \exp\left(-\zeta\omega_0 t\right) \sin \omega_d t & t \geq 0 \\ 0 & t < 0 \end{cases}$$

where $\omega_d = \omega_0 \sqrt{1 - \zeta^2}$. Under the condition that the system is at rest at $t = 0$, the response

$$X(t) = \int_0^t h(t - \tau)F(\tau)\, d\tau = \int_0^t h(t - \tau)G(\tau) \exp\left(-\alpha\omega_0\tau\right)\, d\tau$$

is also Gaussian and has a zero expectation; and it is completely characterized by its auto-covariance function

$$\kappa_{XX}(t_1, t_2) = \int_0^{t_1} d\tau_1 \int_0^{t_2} h(t_1 - \tau_1)h(t_2 - \tau_2)E[F(\tau_1)F(\tau_2)]\, d\tau_2$$

$$= \int_0^{t_1} d\tau_1 \int_0^{t_2} d\tau_2 \int_{-\infty}^{\infty} \Phi_{GG}(\omega) \exp\left[(i\omega - \alpha\omega_0)\tau_1 \right.$$
$$\left. - (i\omega + \alpha\omega_0)\tau_2\right]h(t_1 - \tau_1)h(t_2 - \tau_2)\, d\omega \quad (9\text{-}128)$$

The integrations on τ_1 and τ_2 in this equation can be carried out readily by noting the similarity between Eqs. (9-128) and (5-28). Thus

$$\kappa_{XX}(t_1, t_2) = \int_{-\infty}^{\infty} \Phi_{GG}(\omega)\mathfrak{IC}(\omega + i\alpha\omega_0, t_1)\mathfrak{IC}^*(\omega + i\alpha\omega_0, t_2)$$
$$\exp\left[i(\omega + i\alpha\omega_0)(t_1 - t_2)\right] d\omega \quad (9\text{-}128a)$$

where the function $\mathfrak{IC}$ is given by Eq. (5-31). Note that the argument ω in Eq. (5-31) is replaced by $\omega + i\alpha\omega_0$ for use in Eq. (9-128a); i.e.,

$$\mathfrak{IC}(\omega + i\alpha\omega_0, t) = H(\omega + i\alpha\omega_0) \left\{ 1 - \left(\cos \omega_d t \right. \right.$$
$$\left. \left. + \frac{(\zeta - \alpha)\omega_0 + i\omega}{\omega_d} \sin \omega_d t \right) \exp\left[-(\zeta - \alpha)\omega_0 t - i\omega t\right] \right\} \quad (9\text{-}129)$$

and

$$H(\omega + i\alpha\omega_0) = [\omega_0^2 - (\omega + i\alpha\omega_0)^2 + 2i\zeta\omega_0(\omega + i\alpha\omega_0)]^{-1}$$
$$= [\omega_0^2(\zeta - \alpha)^2 + \omega_d^2 - \omega^2 + 2i(\zeta - \alpha)\omega_0\omega]^{-1} \quad (9\text{-}130)$$

The velocity process $\dot{X}(t) = d/dt\, X(t)$ is also Gaussian and has a zero mean. Therefore, it is only necessary to determine the auto-covariance function $\kappa_{\dot{X}\dot{X}}(t_1, t_2)$ and the cross-covariance function $\kappa_{X\dot{X}}(t_1, t_2)$, which can be obtained by differentiating Eq. (9-128a):

$$\kappa_{X\dot{X}}(t_1, t_2) = \frac{\partial}{\partial t_2} \kappa_{XX}(t_1, t_2) \quad (9\text{-}131)$$

and

$$\kappa_{\dot{X}\dot{X}}(t_1, t_2) = \frac{\partial^2}{\partial t_1\, \partial t_2} \kappa_{XX}(t_1, t_2) \quad (9\text{-}132)$$

In the special case where $G(t)$ is a Gaussian white noise, Eqs. (9-128a), (9-131), and (9-132) can be evaluated by the method of residues. The results from the idealized-white-noise analysis are also approximately valid if $\Phi_{GG}(\omega)$ is a smooth function of ω and if the difference between the values of ζ and α is much smaller than 1. This can be understood from the expression for $H(\omega + ia\omega_0)$, Eq. (9-130). If $|\zeta - \alpha| \ll 1$, the function $|H(\omega + ia\omega_0)|^2$ is sharply peaked at $\omega \approx \omega_d$. Then a smooth function $\Phi_{GG}(\omega)$ may be replaced by its value at $\omega = \omega_d$ when evaluating Eqs. (9-128a), (9-131), and (9-132).

If $\kappa_{XX}(t_1, t_2)$, $\kappa_{X\dot{X}}(t_1, t_2)$, and $\kappa_{\dot{X}\dot{X}}(t_1, t_2)$ are known, the probability densities required for the application of inequalities (9-112) and (9-125) may be written in standard Gaussian forms.‡ For the present application it suffices to note that

$$\mu_X = \mu_{\dot{X}} = 0$$
$$\sigma_X{}^2(t) = \kappa_{XX}(t, t)$$
$$\sigma_{\dot{X}}{}^2(t) = \kappa_{\dot{X}\dot{X}}(t, t)$$
$$\rho_{XX}(t_1, t_2) = [\sigma_X(t_1)\sigma_X(t_2)]^{-1}\kappa_{XX}(t_1, t_2)$$
$$\rho_{X\dot{X}}(t, t) = [\sigma_X(t)\sigma_{\dot{X}}(t)]^{-1}\kappa_{X\dot{X}}(t, t)$$

Shinozuka has programmed, on an electronic computer, the computation of the upper and lower bounds subject to the further restrictions that the failure boundaries are symmetrical, that is, $L = U$, and that $G(t)$ is a white noise. Since the excitation tends to diminish exponentially, as is implied in Eq. (9-127), the probability of a first-excursion failure $P(t, -U, U)$ need not approach to 1 as t approaches infinity.¶ This is shown in Fig. 9.6, where the computed upper and lower bounds of the limiting probability $P(\infty, -U, U)$ are plotted versus the ratio k_0 of the ultimate strength U to the greatest root-mean-square response σ_X^*. In the present example, σ_X^* has been found to occur at $\omega_0 t = 1.85$. Note that, in the computation of the best lower bound estimate, we are required to maximize the integral

$$\int_U^\infty \frac{1}{\sqrt{2\pi}\,\sigma_X} \exp\left(-\frac{x^2}{2\sigma_X{}^2}\right) dx = \int_{U/\sigma_X}^\infty \frac{1}{\sqrt{2\pi}} \exp\left(-\frac{u^2}{2}\right) du$$

It is easily seen that this is achieved by letting $U/\sigma_X = U/\sigma_X^* = k_0$. When computing the upper bound, Shinozuka neglected the last member in inequality (9-126). Therefore, the upper bound shown in Fig. 9.6 is not quite the best upper bound which could be obtained from the present approach.

‡ See Eqs. (4-1) and (4-26).
¶ See footnote on page 320.

In the above analyses of the first-excursion time and the probability of a first-excursion failure we have assumed a knowledge of the probability distribution of the structural response $X(t)$ and its derivative $\dot{X}(t)$. When such information is not available but the mean-square values of $X(t)$ and $\dot{X}(t)$ can be computed, an upper bound for the probability of a first-excursion failure $P(t, -U, U)$ can be obtained by use of the generalized Chebyshev inequality (3-13). For simplicity, let $E[X(t)] = 0$. We then have

$$P(t, -U, U) \le \frac{1}{2U^2} [\sigma_X{}^2(0) + \sigma_X{}^2(t)] + \frac{1}{U^2} \int_0^t \sigma_X(t)\sigma_{\dot{x}}(t) \, dt \qquad (9\text{-}133)$$

Since an application of this inequality does not require a knowledge of the detailed probability distribution of $X(t)$ and $\dot{X}(t)$, the computed upper bound will be less accurate than Shinozuka's upper bound, as is illustrated in Fig. 9.6.

As another example, consider the case where $X(t)$ is the weakly stationary response of a lightly damped single-degree-of-freedom linear system under white-noise excitation. For an ultimate strength $U = n\sigma_X$,

Fig. 9.6 Upper and lower bounds of probability of first-excursion-type failure (nonstationary response and infinite time interval).

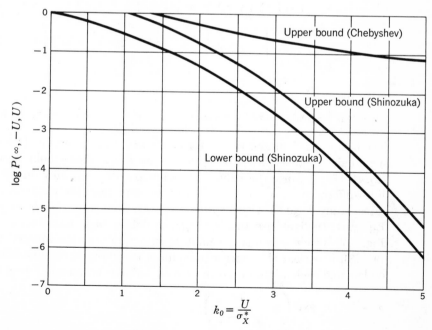

the generalized Chebyshev inequality guarantees that

$$P(t, -n\sigma_X, n\sigma_X) \leq \frac{1}{n^2} (1 + \omega_0 t) \qquad (9\text{-}134)$$

where ω_0 is the undamped natural frequency of the system. If we make an additional assumption for the probability distribution of $X(t)$ and $\dot{X}(t)$, then Shinozuka's method becomes applicable. For what follows we shall again assume that $X(t)$ and $\dot{X}(t)$ are jointly Gaussian. It is simple to see that the best lower bound estimate computed from inequality (9-112) is

$$P(t, -n\sigma_X, n\sigma_X) \geq 2 \int_{n\sigma_X}^{\infty} \frac{1}{\sqrt{2\pi} \, \sigma_X} \exp\left(-\frac{x^2}{2\sigma_X^2}\right) dx = \text{erfc} \, \frac{n}{\sqrt{2}} \qquad (9\text{-}135)$$

which is independent of time. To compute an upper bound by use of inequality (9-126), we note that

$$E[N(n\sigma_X, \tau)] = \frac{1}{\pi} \frac{\sigma_{\dot{X}}}{\sigma_X} \exp\left(-\frac{n^2}{2}\right)$$

$$= \frac{\omega_0}{\pi} \exp\left(-\frac{n^2}{2}\right) \qquad (9\text{-}136)$$

$$2\mathcal{O}[\{X(0+) \geq n\sigma_X\}] = \text{erfc} \, \frac{n}{\sqrt{2}} \qquad (9\text{-}137)$$

and

$$\mathcal{O}[\{X(\tau_1) \leq -n\sigma_X\} \cap \{X(\tau_2) \geq n\sigma_X\}] = \int_{-\infty}^{-n\sigma_X} dx_1 \int_{n\sigma_X}^{\infty} \frac{1}{2\pi\sigma_X^2 \sqrt{1 - \rho^2}}$$

$$\exp\left[-\frac{1}{2\sigma_X^2(1 - \rho^2)} (x_1^2 - 2\rho x_1 x_2 + x_2^2)\right] dx_2 \qquad (9\text{-}138)$$

where

$$\rho = \rho(\tau_1 - \tau_2)$$
$$= \exp(-\zeta\omega_0|\tau_1 - \tau_2|) \left[\cos \omega_d(\tau_1 - \tau_2) + \frac{\zeta\omega_0}{\omega_d} \sin \omega_d|\tau_1 - \tau_2|\right] \qquad (9\text{-}139)$$

The best upper bound estimate for $P(t, -n\sigma_X, n\sigma_X)$ is obtained by selecting a pair of values for τ_1 and τ_2 so as to maximize the twofold integral in Eq. (9-138). Since the value of this integral depends only on the absolute difference $|\tau| = |\tau_1 - \tau_2|$, it can be seen that the extrema of this integral are located where $d\rho/d\tau = 0$. An application of $d\rho/d\tau = 0$ to Eq. (9-139) gives rise to $\tau = \pm m\pi/\omega_d$, where m is an integer. From Fig. 9.7, which shows the domain of integration of the integral in Eq. (9-138), it is clear that each maximum of this integral corresponds to an odd m, and each minimum to an even m. This is because at $\tau = \pm m\pi/\omega_d$

$$\rho = (-1)^m \exp\left(-\frac{m\pi\zeta}{\sqrt{1 - \zeta^2}}\right)$$

and for a negative ρ the probability mass is essentially distributed within the second and the fourth quadrants. However, since both τ_1 and τ_2 lie in the interval $(0, t]$, the difference $\tau = \tau_1 - \tau_2$ must be zero at $t = 0$. Therefore, as t increases from 0 to π/ω_d the value for $|\tau|$ also varies from 0 to π/ω_d; and, in turn, the value for ρ decreases from 1 to $-\exp(-\pi\zeta/\sqrt{1 - \zeta^2})$. By use of a representation of the Dirac delta function, Eq. (V-5) of Appendix V, we can show that the value of the twofold integral in Eq. (9-138) increases from 0, corresponding to $\rho = 1$, to its largest value, corresponding to $\rho = -\exp(-\pi\zeta/\sqrt{1 - \zeta^2})$. For a lightly damped system ($\zeta \ll 1$), the largest value of the integral is approximately $\frac{1}{2}$ erfc $(n/\sqrt{2})$. Substituting Eqs. (9-136) to (9-138) into inequality (9-126), we find that

$$P(t, -U, U) \le \text{erfc}\, \frac{n}{\sqrt{2}} \qquad t = 0+$$

$$P(t, -U, U) \le \frac{1}{2}\, \text{erfc}\left(\frac{n}{\sqrt{2}}\right) + \frac{\omega_0 t}{\pi} \exp\left(-\frac{n^2}{2}\right)$$

$$\left[1 - \frac{1}{2}\, \text{erfc}\, \frac{n}{\sqrt{2}}\right] \frac{\pi}{\omega_0} \exp \frac{n^2}{2} \ge t \ge \frac{\pi}{\omega_d} \qquad \zeta \ll 1$$

$$(9\text{-}140)$$

For $0 < t < \pi/\omega_d$, the best upper bound for $P(t, -U, U)$ must be computed by a numerical procedure. For t greater than $[1 - \frac{1}{2}\, \text{erfc}\, (n/\sqrt{2})](\pi/\omega_0) \exp(n^2/2)$, we take probability 1 as the upper bound.

The results obtained by use of the generalized Chebyshev inequality and of the Shinozuka method are illustrated in Fig. 9.8 for the case $n = 2\sqrt{2}$ and $\omega_0 = 2$ rad/sec. Also shown in this figure is the probability of failure computed from Coleman's formula (9-104). Recall that this equation implies that the crossings of a given threshold are mutually

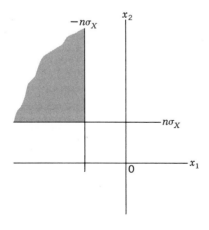

Fig. 9.7

independent, an assumption which is unrealistic, especially for a narrow-band random process. Therefore in using Eq. (9-104) we redefine a failure to be the event that the envelope process crosses either $n\sigma_X$ or $-n\sigma_X$; that is, we use as the failure rate‡

$$\lambda = \frac{1}{E_1[T]} = \sqrt{\frac{\pi}{6}}\, n\zeta\omega_0 \exp\left(-\frac{n^2}{2}\right)$$
$$= 0.0015 \text{ sec}^{-1}$$

corresponding to $n = 2\sqrt{2}$, $\omega_0 = 2$ rad/sec, and a damping ratio $\zeta = 0.02$. Note that the failure rate here is proportional to the damping ratio ζ; therefore, the result obtained from Coleman's method, modified by using an *envelope-based* failure criterion, is highly dependent on the proper choice of the ζ value.

In view of the relatively primitive state of the art of the first-excursion failure analyses, it is desirable that the results from several approaches be compared before reaching an engineering decision.

9.6 / FATIGUE FAILURES

A fatigue failure has been described as the result of cumulative damage that arises when the response of a structure to external excitations fluctuates at small or moderate excursions. The exact nature of fatigue failures

‡ See the expression for $E_1[T]$, page 332.

Fig. 9.8 Probability of first-excursion failure (stationary response and finite time interval).

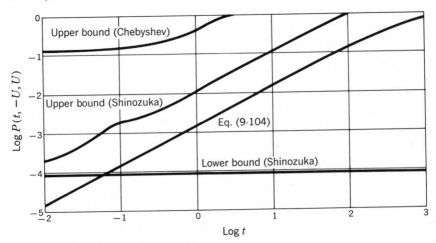

has not been fully understood. To a large extent our sources of information must be experimental data obtained from deterministic loading conditions. For the purposes of the present discussion, however, we shall assume that if the response is deterministic and cyclic, then there is a well-defined relationship between the amplitude of the response and the number of cycles to fatigue failure. Specifically, we shall use the widely adopted formula

$$NS^b = c \qquad\qquad (9\text{-}141)$$

where S is the stress amplitude, N is the number of cycles to fatigue failure, and b and c are positive constants which are material properties. (The constant c must be positive since N and S are positive quantities; b must also be positive since a larger stress amplitude must accompany a smaller number of cycles to fatigue failure.) Represented graphically, relation (9-141) is known as an S-N curve. One such curve is shown in Fig. 9.9. In the discussion to follow, we shall again overlook the fact that the material properties may be random.‡

When the amplitude of the stress is not a constant, Eq. (9-141) cannot be used without additional assumptions. There have been many hypotheses proposed as means of assessing the fatigue damage due to different levels of stress amplitude; however, it has not been established that any of these hypotheses apply to all types of amplitude variations. The simplest theory, proposed independently by Palmgren¶ and Miner,§ has the advantage that it can easily be adapted to the case of random stresses. We shall use this simple theory in the following discussion.

‡ A more general viewpoint would be to regard b and c as random variables, or N as a random process with parameter S. Indeed, wide scatterings of experimental results are usually found in fatigue tests.

¶ A. Palmgren, Die Lebensdauer von Kugellagern, *Ver. deut. Ingr.*, **68**: 339–341 (1924).

§ M. A. Miner, Cumulative Damage in Fatigue, *J. Appl. Mech.*, **12**:A159–A164 (1945).

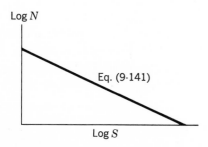

Log N

Eq. (9-141)

Log S

Fig. 9.9 An idealized S-N curve.

The Palmgren-Miner theory postulates that the accumulation of fatigue damage is linear. Thus, the damage due to the application of n_ξ cycles at a stress amplitude ξ is

$$\Delta_\xi = \frac{n_\xi}{N_\xi} \qquad n_\xi \leq N_\xi \tag{9-142}$$

where N_ξ is the number of cycles to fatigue failure at the stress amplitude ξ. Under variable stress amplitudes the total damage is

$$\Delta = \sum \Delta_\xi = \sum \frac{n_\xi}{N_\xi} \tag{9-143}$$

Fatigue failure occurs when Δ reaches unity. Using Eq. (9-141) in Eq. (9-143), we have

$$\Delta = c^{-1} \Sigma n_\xi \xi^b \tag{9-144}$$

Note that the Palmgren-Miner theory implies that the order of application of the different stress levels has no effect on the resulting total damage accumulated, a very desirable property when the theory is used in the case of stationary random stresses.

Since cycles in a random process are generally not recognizable, the interpretation of the Palmgren-Miner theory must be broadened in order for it to apply to the case of random stresses. A logical extended interpretation is obtained by letting the symbol n_ξ in Eqs. (9-142) through (9-144) stand for the number of peaks at the level ξ. The number of peaks is, of course, the same as the number of cycles when the stress is cyclic. It coincides with the number of zero crossings when the stress is a narrow-band random process. For the present time, however, we do not make any restrictions concerning the bandwidth.

‖ Let $D(t)$ denote the random accumulated damage per unit time due to a random stress $X(t)$. Conforming to the pattern of Eq. (9-144), we obtain an expression for the expectation of $D(t)$,

$$E[D(t)] = c^{-1} \int_{-\infty}^{\infty} \xi^b \, d\xi \int_0^{\infty} m p_\Xi(\xi, t|m) p_{M_T}(m, t) \, dm \tag{9-145}$$

where $p_\Xi(\xi, t|m)$ is the probability density of the peak magnitude of the random process $X(t)$ on the condition that the total number of peaks per unit time is m, and $p_{M_T}(m, t)$ is the probability density for the total number of peaks per unit time. Unfortunately, this equation cannot be applied for lack of the knowledge of $p_\Xi(\xi, t|m)$ and $p_{M_T}(m, t)$. However, in the same spirit as the heuristic approach leading to Eqs. (9-27a) and (9-28), we assume that the following relation holds (perhaps only approximately):

$$\int_0^{\infty} m p_\Xi(\xi, t|m) p_{M_T}(m, t) \, dm = E[M_T(t)] p_\Xi(\xi, t) \tag{9-146}$$

Then

$$E[D(t)] = c^{-1}E[M_T(t)] \int_{-\infty}^{\infty} \xi^b p_{\Xi}(\xi, t) \, d\xi \qquad (9\text{-}147)$$

The expected total damage accumulated from $t = 0$ to $t = T$ is

$$E[\mathfrak{D}(t)] = E\left[\int_0^T D(t) \, dt\right] = \int_0^T E[D(t)] \, dt \qquad (9\text{-}148)$$

If the random stress $X(t)$ is stationary, $E[D(t)]$ reduces to a constant. Therefore, for stationary stresses,

$$E[\mathfrak{D}(T)] = TE[D] = TE[M_T]c^{-1} \int_{-\infty}^{\infty} \xi^b p_{\Xi}(\xi) \, d\xi \qquad (9\text{-}149)$$

As an example, let the random stress $X(t)$ be a narrow-band Gaussian stationary random process with a zero mean. Then the peak magnitude of $X(t)$ is Rayleigh distributed and is given in Eq. (9-38):

$$p_{\Xi}(\xi) = \frac{\xi}{\sigma_X{}^2} \exp\left(-\frac{\xi^2}{2\sigma_X{}^2}\right) \qquad 0 \leq \xi < \infty \qquad (9\text{-}38)$$

Substituting Eq. (9-38) into Eq. (9-147) and recalling that b is a positive constant,

$$\begin{aligned} E[D] &= c^{-1}\sigma_X{}^{-2}E[M_T] \int_0^{\infty} \xi^{b+1} \exp\left(-\frac{\xi^2}{2\sigma_X{}^2}\right) d\xi \\ &= c^{-1}E[M_T](\sqrt{2}\,\sigma_X)^b \Gamma\left(\frac{b+2}{2}\right) \end{aligned} \qquad (9\text{-}150)$$

where we have used the formula

$$\Gamma(\nu) = 2 \int_0^{\infty} y^{2\nu-1} \exp(-y^2) \, dy \qquad \nu > 0$$

Since for a narrow-band random process the total number of peaks is almost the same as the number of zero crossings at positive slopes, Eq. (9-150) can also be written as

$$E[D] = c^{-1}E[N_+(0)](\sqrt{2}\,\sigma_X)^b \Gamma\left(\frac{b+2}{2}\right) \qquad (9\text{-}150a)$$

Equation (9-150a) was first derived by Miles.‡

It has been noted before that an approximate probability density of the peak magnitude for a narrow-band random process could be computed from Eq. (9-44), which was derived on the assumption that

‡ J. W. Miles, On Structural Fatigue under Random Loading, *J. Aeron. Sci.*, **21**:753–762 (1954).

every threshold crossing gives rise to a peak above this threshold. Powell suggested that Eq. (9-44) could also be used in Eqs. (9-147) and (9-148) even when the stress process was not of a narrow band. This is a conservative practice since the probability of the occurrence of higher peaks is overestimated[‡] when the random process is not of a narrow band.

Additional information about the random damage $\mathfrak{D}(T)$ can be had by a study of the variance of $\mathfrak{D}(T)$,

$$\sigma_{\mathfrak{D}}{}^2(T) = E[\mathfrak{D}^2(T)] - E^2[\mathfrak{D}(T)]$$
$$= \int_0^T \int_0^T \phi_{DD}(t_1, t_2)\, dt_1\, dt_2 - \left\{ \int_0^T E[D(t)]\, dt \right\}^2 \qquad (9\text{-}151)$$

or

$$\sigma_{\mathfrak{D}}{}^2(T) = \int_0^T \int_0^T \kappa_{DD}(t_1, t_2)\, dt_1\, dt_2 \qquad (9\text{-}151a)$$

We see that the computation of the variance of damage requires either the correlation function or the covariance function of the damage rate, $\phi_{DD}(t_1, t_2)$ or $\kappa_{DD}(t_1, t_2)$. Using a heuristic argument similar to that implied in Eq. (9-147), we may write

$$\phi_{DD}(t_1, t_2) = c^{-2}E^2[M_T(t)] \int_{-\infty}^{\infty} \int_{-\infty}^{\infty} \xi_1{}^b \xi_2{}^b p_{\Xi}(\xi_1, t_1; \xi_2, t_2)\, d\xi_1\, d\xi_2 \qquad (9\text{-}152)$$

This equation contains the second-order probability density of the peak magnitude, which, unfortunately, remains to be found. In the case of a narrow-band Gaussian stress, it may be permissible to replace this probability density by the second-order probability density for the envelope, Eq. (9-81); but even so, the integration in Eq. (9-152) appears to be difficult. Some approximate results for the variance of damage due to narrow-band stresses have been obtained by Crandall, Mark, and Khabbaz[¶] and by Bendat.[§]

The final concern of a design engineer is not the damage or the damage rate, but the fatigue life of a structure. Unfortunately, the determination of the probability distribution or even just the expectation of the fatigue life remains an unsolved problem. The fatigue life, to be

[‡] A. Powell, On the Fatigue Failure of Structures Due to Vibrations Excited by Random Pressure Fields, *J. Acoust. Soc. Am.*, **30**:1130 (1958). See the discussion following Eq. (9-44).

[¶] S. H. Crandall, W. D. Mark, and G. R. Khabbaz, The Variance in Palmgren-Miner Damage Due to Random Vibration, *Proc. 4th U. S. Natl. Congr. Appl. Mech., Berkeley, June,* 1962, **1**:119–126 (1962).

[§] J. S. Bendat, Probability Functions for Random Responses: Prediction of Peaks, Fatigue Damage, and Catastrophic Failures, *NASA* CR-33, Measurement Analysis Corporation, April, 1964.

denoted by L, is the time duration required for the total damage to reach unity, i.e.,

$$\mathfrak{D}(L) = \int_0^L D(t) \, dt = 1 \tag{9-153}$$

This implicit relation between L and $D(t)$ generally cannot be used to compute the statistical properties of L from those of $D(t)$. However, if the random stress is stationary, the damage rate is also stationary. Thus from Eq. (9-149)

$$E[\mathfrak{D}(t)] = TE[D]$$

We may visualize a time duration T_1 which satisfies $E[\mathfrak{D}(T_1)] = 1$. Then in the stationary case

$$T_1 = \frac{1}{E[D]} \tag{9-154}$$

This time duration is the *would-be* fatigue life if the damage rate *were* a constant equal to $E[D]$. In general, $T_1 \neq E[L]$, although

$$E[\mathfrak{D}(T_1)] = E[\mathfrak{D}(L)] = 1$$

This fine point can be appreciated if we consider a hypothetical case where D is a random variable (i.e., it changes from sample function to sample function, but in each sample function it does not change with time). Then $L = 1/D$. But this relation does not imply that

$$E[L] = 1/E[D]$$

However, Crandall, Mark, and Khabbaz‡ have found that when the random stress is of a narrow band, the variance of the total damage $\sigma_{\mathfrak{D}}^2$ is small near the time of failure. Therefore, it is reasonable to expect that T_1 is close to the expected fatigue life for a narrow-band random stress, and it serves as a useful measure in making design decisions.

EXERCISES

9-1. The joint probability density of a stationary random process $X(t)$ and its derivatives $\dot{X}(t)$ and $\ddot{X}(t)$ at the same time t is given by

$$p_{\{x\}\{\dot{x}\}\{\ddot{x}\}}(x, \dot{x}, \ddot{x}) = \frac{1}{8abc} \qquad -a \leq x \leq a, \; -b \leq \dot{x} \leq b, \; -c \leq \ddot{x} \leq c$$

Compute:
  (a) The expected rate at which $X(t)$ crosses a threshold ξ.
  (b) The expected number of peaks in $X(t)$ per unit time above a level ξ.

‡ *Op. cit.*

(c) The probability density of the peak magnitude for $X(t)$ using the Huston-Skopinski approach.

(d) The probability density of the envelope process for $X(t)$ using Crandall's energy-based definition for an envelope. The potential energy is given by

$$V(X) = \tfrac{1}{2}(kX^2)$$

9-2.‡ A narrow-band stationary random process $X(t)$ is the response of a non-linear system to a white-noise excitation. The joint probability density of $X(t)$ and $\dot{X}(t)$ at the same time t is given in Exercise 8-4. Compute the expected rate at which $X(t)$ crosses a threshold ξ. Show that the approximate probability density for the peak magnitude in $X(t)$ is

$$p_\Xi(\xi) = \frac{\alpha\pi}{2d}\left(\sin\frac{\pi\xi}{2d}\right)\left(\cos\frac{\pi\xi}{2d}\right)^{\alpha-1}$$

9-3. The joint probability density of a narrow-band stress and its derivative at the same time t is given by

$$p_{\{x\}\{\dot{x}\}}(x, \dot{x}) = \frac{1}{4\alpha\beta}\exp\left(-\frac{|x|}{\alpha} - \frac{|\dot{x}|}{\beta}\right) \qquad -\infty < x, \dot{x} < \infty\,;\, \alpha, \beta > 0$$

Show that an approximate probability density for the peak magnitude is

$$p_\Xi(\xi) = \frac{1}{\alpha}\exp\left(-\frac{\xi}{\alpha}\right) \qquad 0 \le \xi < \infty$$

Assuming that the material constants in Eq. (9-141) are $b = 10$ and $c = 1$, compute the expected fatigue damage per unit time.

9-4. The joint probability density of a nonstationary stress and its time derivative is given by

$$p_{\{x\}\{\dot{x}\}}(x, \dot{x}, t) = \frac{1}{4f(t)g(t)} \qquad -f(t) \le x \le f(t),\ -g(t) \le \dot{x} \le g(t)$$

where

$$f(t) = t\exp\left(-\frac{t}{\alpha}\right) \qquad \alpha > 0,\, t > 0$$

$$f(t) \to [2\delta(t)]^{-1} \qquad \text{as } t \to 0$$

$$g(t) = \exp\left(-\frac{t}{\beta}\right) \qquad \beta > 0$$

Let the probability of a first excursion be defined as

$$\mathcal{P}\left[\{\inf_{0<\tau\le t} X(\tau) \le -0.8\alpha\} \cup \{\sup_{0<\tau\le t} X(\tau) \ge 0.8\alpha\}\right]$$

Find the upper and lower bounds of this probability by use of inequalities (9-126) and (9-112). Neglect the last term in (9-126). Also compute an upper bound by use of the generalized Chebyshev inequality.

‡ See G. H. Klein, Random Excitation of a Nonlinear System with Tangent Elasticity Characteristics, *J. Acoust. Soc. Am.*, **36**(11):2095–2105 (1964).

APPENDIX I | SOME WELL-KNOWN PROBABILITY FUNCTIONS FOR DISCRETE RANDOM VARIABLES

Distribution	Probability function	Parameters	Admissible x values
Binomial	$P_X(x) = \binom{n}{x} s^x (1-s)^{n-x}$	n number of trials (positive integer) s probability of success for each trial $(0 \leq s \leq 1)$	$x = 0, 1, 2, \ldots, n$
Geometric	$P_X(x) = s(1-s)^{x-1}$	s probability of success of a single trial $(0 \leq s \leq 1)$	$x = 1, 2, \ldots$
Hypergeometric	$P_X(x) = \dfrac{\binom{a}{x}\binom{N-a}{n-x}}{\binom{N}{n}}$	N total population (positive integer) a number of favorable objects in the population (positive integer) n number of objects drawn (positive integer)	$x = 0, 1, 2, \ldots, \min(n, a)$, where $\min(n, a)$ is the smaller of the two numbers n, a if they are different
Poisson	$P_X(x) = e^{-\mu} \dfrac{\mu^x}{x!}$	μ average number of occurrences or successes $(\mu > 0)$	$x = 0, 1, 2, \ldots$
Pascal	$P_X(x) = \binom{n+x-1}{x} s^n (1-s)^x$	n number of successes (positive integer) s probability of success for each trial $(0 \leq s \leq 1)$	$x = 0, 1, 2, \ldots$

APPENDIX II | SOME WELL-KNOWN PROBABILITY DENSITY FUNCTIONS FOR CONTINUOUS RANDOM VARIABLES

Distribution	Probability density	Parameters	Admissible x values
Rectangular (uniform)	$p_X(x) = (b-a)^{-1}$	$-\infty < a < b < \infty$	$a \le x \le b$
Normal (Gaussian)	$p_X(x) = \dfrac{1}{\sigma\sqrt{2\pi}}\exp\left(-\dfrac{(x-\mu)^2}{2\sigma^2}\right)$	$-\infty < \mu < +\infty$ $\sigma > 0$	$-\infty < x < \infty$
Gamma	$p_X(x) = \dfrac{1}{\delta^{(\alpha+1)}\Gamma(\alpha+1)}\,x^\alpha \exp\left(-\dfrac{x}{\delta}\right)$	$\alpha > -1$ $\delta > 0$	$0 \le x < \infty$
Exponential (reducible from gamma distribution)	$p_X(x) = \dfrac{1}{\delta}\exp\left(-\dfrac{x}{\delta}\right)$	$\delta > 0$	$0 \le x < \infty$
Beta	$p_X(x) = \dfrac{1}{\beta(\alpha+1,\,\lambda+1)}\,x^\alpha(1-x)^\lambda$	$\alpha, \lambda > -1$	$0 \le x \le 1$
Rayleigh	$p_X(x) = \dfrac{x}{\sigma^2}\exp\left(-\dfrac{x^2}{2\sigma^2}\right)$	$\sigma > 0$	$0 \le x < \infty$
Chi-square (with n degrees of freedom)	$p_X(x) = \dfrac{1}{2^{n/2}\Gamma(n/2)}\,x^{(n/2-1)}\exp\left(-\dfrac{x}{2}\right)$	n = positive integer	$0 \le x < \infty$
Cauchy	$p_X(x) = \dfrac{a}{(\pi a)^2 + x^2}$	$a > 0$	$-\infty < x < \infty$
Laplace	$p_X(x) = \dfrac{1}{\sqrt{2}\,\sigma}\exp\left(-\dfrac{\sqrt{2}\,|x-\mu|}{\sigma}\right)$	$-\infty < \mu < \infty$ $\sigma > 0$	$-\infty < x < \infty$
F (with m, n degrees of freedom)	$p_X(x) = \dfrac{\Gamma\left(\dfrac{m+n}{2}\right)}{\Gamma\left(\dfrac{m}{2}\right)\Gamma\left(\dfrac{n}{2}\right)}\left(\dfrac{m}{n}\right)^{m/2}\dfrac{x^{(m/2)-1}}{\left(1+\dfrac{m}{n}x\right)^{(m+n)/2}}$	m, n = positive integers	$0 \le x < \infty$
Weibull	$p_X(x) = \dfrac{k}{v-\epsilon}\left(\dfrac{x-\epsilon}{v-\epsilon}\right)^{k-1}\exp\left[-\left(\dfrac{x-\epsilon}{v-\epsilon}\right)^k\right]$	$k > 1$ $v > \epsilon$	$x \ge \epsilon$

APPENDIX III | CORRESPONDING AUTOCORRELATION FUNCTIONS AND SPECTRAL DENSITIES OF SOME WEAKLY STATIONARY RANDOM PROCESSES

$R_{XX}(\tau)$	$\Phi_{XX}(\omega)$
$2\pi K\,\delta(\tau)\qquad K>0$	K
$\sigma^2\exp(-a\lvert\tau\rvert)\qquad a>0$	$\sigma^2 a[\pi(a^2+\omega^2)]^{-1}$
$b^{-1}\sigma^2(b-\lvert\tau\rvert)\quad \lvert\tau\rvert\le b$ $0\qquad\qquad\qquad \lvert\tau\rvert>b$	$(2\pi)^{-1}(b\sigma^2)\left[\dfrac{\sin(\omega b/2)}{\omega b/2}\right]^2$
$\sigma^2\exp(-a\tau^2)\qquad a>0$	$\dfrac{\sigma^2}{2}\sqrt{\pi a}\,\exp\left(\dfrac{-\omega^2}{2a}\right)$
$\sigma^2\left(1-\dfrac{a}{2}\lvert\tau\rvert\right)\exp(-a\lvert\tau\rvert)\qquad a>0$	$(2\pi)^{-1}\sigma^2\left[1+3\left(\dfrac{\omega}{a}\right)^2\right]\left[1+\left(\dfrac{\omega}{a}\right)^2\right]^{-2}$
$\sigma^2(a\tau)^{-1}\sin a\tau\qquad a>0$	$(2a)^{-1}\sigma^2 \quad \lvert\omega\rvert<a$ $0\qquad\qquad \lvert\omega\rvert>a$
$\sigma^2 J_0(a\tau)\qquad a>0$	$\pi^{-1}(a^2-\omega^2)^{-\frac12}\sigma^2 \quad \lvert\omega\rvert<a$ $0\qquad\qquad\qquad\qquad \lvert\omega\rvert>a$
$\sigma^2\exp(-\zeta\omega_0\lvert\tau\rvert)\left(\cos\omega_d\tau+\dfrac{\zeta\omega_0}{\omega_d}\sin\omega_d\lvert\tau\rvert\right)$ $\zeta>0,\ \omega_0>0,\ \omega_d=\sqrt{1-\zeta^2}\,\omega_0$	$\pi^{-1}(2\zeta\omega_0{}^3\sigma^2)[(\omega_0{}^2-\omega^2)^2+(2\zeta\omega\omega_0)^2]^{-1}$
$\sigma^2(b-a)^{-1}[b\exp(-a\lvert\tau\rvert)-a\exp(-b\lvert\tau\rvert)]\qquad a,b>0$	$\sigma^2 ab(a+b)[\pi(a^2+\omega^2)(b^2+\omega^2)]^{-1}$
$\sigma^2\exp(-a\lvert\tau\rvert)\cos\omega_0\tau\qquad a>0$	$\sigma^2 a(\omega^2+\omega_0{}^2+a^2)\{\pi[(\omega^2-\omega_0{}^2-a^2)^2+4a^2\omega^2]\}^{-1}$
$\sigma^2\exp(-a\lvert\tau\rvert)\left(\cos\omega_0\tau+\dfrac{a}{\omega_0}\sin\omega_0\lvert\tau\rvert\right)\qquad a>0$	$\sigma^2 a(\omega_0{}^2+a^2)\{\pi[(\omega^2-\omega_0{}^2-a^2)^2+4a^2\omega^2]\}^{-1}$
$\sigma^2\exp(-a\lvert\tau\rvert)\left(\cos\omega_0\tau-\dfrac{a}{\omega_0}\sin\omega_0\lvert\tau\rvert\right)\qquad a>0$	$\sigma^2 a\omega^2\{\pi[(\omega^2-\omega_0{}^2-a^2)^2+4a^2\omega^2]\}^{-1}$

APPENDIX IV | BASIC SET OPERATIONS

In mathematics the word *set* means a collection of objects. The objects which compose a set are called the *elements* of this set. The statement "*e* is an element of the set *E*" is written as

$$e \in E \quad \text{or} \quad E \ni e \qquad\qquad (IV\text{-}1)$$

which can also be read as "*e* belongs to *E*" or "*E* contains *e*." To indicate that *e* is not an element of the set *E*, we write $e \notin E$ or $E \not\ni e$. A set is said to be *empty* if it contains no elements. The empty set is denoted by ϕ.

When the number of elements in a set is not many, the usual way to specify such a set is to list all the elements it contains within two braces; e.g.,

$$\begin{aligned} E_1 &= \{H, T\} \\ E_2 &= \{1, 2, 3, 4, 5, 6\} \end{aligned} \qquad\qquad (IV\text{-}2)$$

etc. This method of specification is called the roster method. However, the roster method becomes tedious when the number of elements is large, and it becomes inapplicable when the number of elements is infinite. In such cases we may use the rule method by stating the requirements to be satisfied by the elements. For example, the set of integer numbers may be noted by

$$E = \{n: n = \text{integer}\} \qquad\qquad (IV\text{-}3)$$

where the requirement (or requirements) for each element follows the colon sign. It is also possible that the elements in a set are not countable. Then, again, only the rule method is applicable to describe such sets. For example,

$$E = \{x: 0 \leq x \leq a\} \qquad\qquad (IV\text{-}4)$$

denotes a set which contains all points within the closed interval $[0, a]$.

A set containing a finite number of elements is called a finite set. Those illustrated by Eqs. (IV-2) are finite sets. A set containing an infinite but countable number of elements, such as that illustrated by Eq. (IV-3), is called a countable set. A set containing uncountably many elements, such as that of Eq. (IV-4), is called an uncountable set.

Consider two sets *E* and *F*. If every element of *E* also belongs to *F*, we say that *E* is a *subset* of *F*. This subset relationship is represented by

$$E \subset F \quad \text{or} \quad F \supset E \qquad\qquad (IV\text{-}5)$$

which reads "*E* belongs to *F*" or "*F* contains *E*." When it is true that both $E \subset F$ and $E \supset F$, we may write $E = F$. Thus, the above definition of a subset allows us to treat any set as a subset of itself. It is also customary to consider an empty set to be a subset of any set.

Before we can consider set operations, we must first consider the background upon which these operations are defined. This background is the one within which we wish to restrict our attention for a particular study. We call this background the *universal set*. Thus, for a particular study all sets are subsets of the selected universal set.

One basic set operation is that of *complementation*. The concept of complementation can be illustrated best by the well-known *Venn diagram*. In Fig. IV.1, the interior of the rectangle represents the universal set Ω, and the unshaded circular area a set E. Then the complement of E, denoted by $\bar{E}$, is represented by the shaded area within Ω; that is, if $e \in E$, then $e \notin \bar{E}$. It is clear that $\bar{E}$ is also a subset of Ω and that $\bar{\bar{E}} = E$. The complement of the universal set is obviously the empty set; that is, $\bar{\Omega} = \phi$.

In probability theory, the sample space of a random phenomenon is the universal set, the event represented by the entire sample space is a certain event, and the event corresponding to the empty set is an impossible event.

Another basic set operation is denoted by $E_1 \cup E_2$, which reads "E_1 *union* E_2." The union operation gives rise to a set in Ω containing those elements which belong to either E_1 or E_2. Figure IV.2 illustrates such an operation, where the shaded area represents $E_1 \cup E_2$. An example in probability theory is as follows: If E_1 is the event of obtaining an even number, and E_2 the event of obtaining a number greater than 3

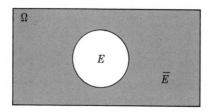

Fig. IV.1   Venn diagram illustrating the complement of E.

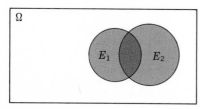

Fig. IV.2   Venn diagram illustrating the union $E_1 \cup E_2$.

in the random experiment of tossing a die, then

$$E_1 \cup E_2 = \{2, 4, 5, 6\}$$

is the event of obtaining either an even number or a number greater than 3.

Although any algebraic manipulation on sets can be carried out by use of the above basic operations, complementation and union, it is convenient to introduce the concepts of two additional operations, namely, those of the *intersection* and *difference*. We denote the intersection of the two sets E_1 and E_2 by $E_1 \cap E_2$, and the result is a set which contains those elements in Ω belonging to both E_1 and E_2. If E_1 and E_2 stand for the previously defined events pertaining to the random experiment of tossing a die, then

$$E_1 \cap E_2 = \{4, 6\}$$

represents the joint event of obtaining an even number greater than 3. A Venn diagram illustrating an intersection operation is shown in Fig. IV.3, where the shaded area corresponds to $E_1 \cap E_2$. It may be seen from this diagram that

$$E_1 \cap E_2 = \overline{\bar{E}_1 \cup \bar{E}_2} \qquad (IV\text{-}6)$$

which shows that an intersection operation can be performed indirectly by use of the operations of complementation and union.

It is interesting to note that the intersection and union operations obey the *commutative*, *associative*, and *distributive* laws. In particular,

$$E_1 \cap E_2 = E_2 \cap E_1 \quad \text{and} \quad E_1 \cup E_2 = E_2 \cup E_1 \qquad (IV\text{-}7)$$
$$E_1 \cap (E_2 \cap E_3) = (E_1 \cap E_2) \cap E_3$$
$$\text{and} \quad E_1 \cup (E_2 \cup E_3) = (E_1 \cup E_2) \cup E_3 \qquad (IV\text{-}8)$$
$$E_1 \cap (E_2 \cup E_3) = (E_1 \cap E_2) \cup (E_1 \cap E_3)$$
$$\text{and} \quad E_1 \cup (E_2 \cap E_3) = (E_1 \cup E_2) \cap (E_1 \cup E_3) \qquad (IV\text{-}9)$$

Since the operations of intersection and union are commutative and associative, it is meaningful to speak of the intersection or the union of

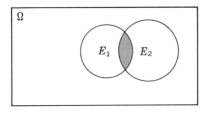

Fig. IV.3 Venn diagram illustrating the intersection $E_1 \cap E_2$.

E_1, E_2, E_3, . . . , E_n. Symbolically, these are written as

$$\bigcap_{j=1}^{n} E_j = E_1 \cap E_2 \cap \cdots \cap E_n \qquad (IV\text{-}10)$$

and

$$\bigcup_{j=1}^{n} E_j = E_1 \cup E_2 \cup \cdots \cup E_n \qquad (IV\text{-}11)$$

The operation (IV-10) results in a set which contains those elements in Ω which are common to E_1, E_2, . . . , E_n. Thus in probability theory (IV-10) denotes the joint event that all the events E_1, E_2, . . . , E_n occur. On the other hand, each element resulting from the union operation of (IV-11) belongs to at least one of the sets E_1, E_2, . . . , E_n. In probability theory (IV-11) represents the *total* event that at least one of the events E_1, E_2, . . . , E_n occurs.

Finally, the difference operation, denoted by $E_1 - E_2$, results in a set which consists of those elements of E_1 which are not in E_2. Figure IV.4 illustrates such an operation, where the shaded area represents $E_1 - E_2$. It can be seen that

$$E_1 - E_2 = \overline{\bar{E}_1 \cup E_2} \qquad (IV\text{-}12)$$

Therefore, a difference operation can be performed indirectly by use of the complementation and union operations.

We also have

$$E_1 - E_2 = E_1 \cap \bar{E}_2$$
$$E_1 \cup E_2 = \overline{\bar{E}_1 \cap \bar{E}_2} \qquad (IV\text{-}13)$$

so that, for example, we could have chosen complementation and intersection as our basic set operations. Equations (IV-6) and the last of (IV-13) are known as De Morgan's laws.

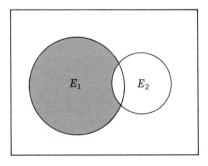

Fig. IV.4 Venn diagram illustrating the difference $E_1 - E_2$.

APPENDIX V | DIRAC DELTA FUNCTION

The Dirac delta function $\delta(x)$ is not an ordinary function in the sense that its values cannot be properly assigned for every x. Therefore, to define this function we require a more general concept for functions, namely, the concept of *distribution*.‡ When a function, say $f(x)$, is viewed as a distribution, it is defined by the associated integral

$$\int_{-\infty}^{\infty} f(x)g(x)\,dx = D < \infty \qquad\qquad (V\text{-}1)$$

where $g(x)$ is called a *test function* which satisfies some general conditions so that it is suitable to test a given distribution. We are concerned only with the values of D corresponding to different test functions. For this, it may or may not be necessary to know all the values of $f(x)$. Therefore, the class of distributions includes certain functions which are not ordinary functions.

As a distribution, the Dirac delta function is defined by the expression

$$\int_{-\infty}^{\infty} \delta(x)g(x)\,dx = \int_{-\epsilon}^{\epsilon} \delta(x)g(x)\,dx = g(0) \qquad \epsilon > 0 \qquad (V\text{-}2)$$

That is, the value of D is simply the value of the test function at $x = 0$. In order for $\delta(t)$ to be a well-defined distribution, we require that the test function $g(t)$ be continuous at the origin. If, in addition, $g(x)$ is an odd function, then we require $g(0) = 0$. Equation (V-2) shows that $\delta(x)$ is an even distribution (a generalized version of an even function). That $\delta(x)$ is even also can be demonstrated in the following expression:

$$\int_{-\infty}^{\infty} \delta(x - a)g(x)\,dx = \int_{-\infty}^{\infty} \delta(a - x)g(x)\,dx = g(a)$$

Being a distribution, $\delta(x)$ may be a limit of a sequence of distributions. Let $f_n(x)$, $n = 1, 2, \ldots$, be a sequence of distributions and

$$D_n = \int_{-\infty}^{\infty} f_n(x)g(x)\,dx$$

We write

$$\lim_{n \to \infty} f_n(x) = \delta(x) \qquad\qquad (V\text{-}3)$$

if

$$\lim_{n \to \infty} D_n = \lim_{n \to \infty} \int_{-\infty}^{\infty} f_n(x)g(x)\,dx = g(0) \qquad\qquad (V\text{-}4)$$

‡ I. Halperin, "Introduction to the Theory of Distribution", based on lectures by Laurent Schwartz, University of Toronto Press, Toronto, 1952.

Several such limits are given below:

$$\delta(x) = \lim_{\epsilon \to 0} \frac{1}{\sqrt{2\pi}\,\epsilon} \exp\left(-\frac{x^2}{2\epsilon^2}\right) \qquad (V\text{-}5)$$

$$\delta(x) = \lim_{\epsilon \to 0} \frac{1}{2\epsilon}[\mathbb{1}(x + \epsilon) - \mathbb{1}(x - \epsilon)] \qquad (V\text{-}6)$$

$$\delta(x) = \lim_{A \to \infty} \frac{\sin Ax}{\pi x} \qquad (V\text{-}7)$$

In the above examples, the distributions $f_n(x)$ in each sequence are also ordinary functions, but their limit does not exist in the ordinary sense. It exists in the sense of distribution.

The three limit representations of the Dirac delta function, Eqs. (V-5) through (V-7), are quite useful in applied mathematics. In the first representation, Eq. (V-5), the function

$$\frac{1}{\sqrt{2\pi}\,\epsilon} \exp\left(-\frac{x^2}{2\epsilon^2}\right)$$

may be interpreted as the probability density function of a Gaussian random variable, say X, with a zero mean and a standard deviation ϵ (see page 67). As the standard deviation decreases, the probability measure becomes more and more concentrated near the mean. In the limit the probability for $X = 0$ approaches to 1. In Eq. (V-6), the expression

$$\frac{1}{2\epsilon}[\mathbb{1}(x + \epsilon) - \mathbb{1}(x - \epsilon)]$$

may be considered as representing a constant force of magnitude $1/(2\epsilon)$ which is applied on a structure for a time duration 2ϵ. If this time duration is sufficiently short, then the effect of the force is nearly the same as that of a unit impulse. Finally, the function $\sin Ax/(\pi x)$ in Eq. (V-7) is frequently encountered in the theory of Fourier integrals. In fact, it can be written as

$$\frac{\sin Ax}{\pi x} = \frac{1}{2\pi} \int_{-\infty}^{\infty} [\mathbb{1}(u + A) + \mathbb{1}(u - A)] \exp(-iux)\, du$$

Therefore, this function has the interpretation of being the autocorrelation function of a truncated white noise (see page 124). It is also of interest to note that if $\delta(x)$ is considered to be the limit given in Eq. (V-7), then a suitable test function $g(t)$ for this limit must be one of bounded variation in addition to being continuous at the origin.

BIBLIOGRAPHY

Amin, M.: "Nonstationary Stochastic Model for Strong Motion Earthquakes," Ph.D. thesis, University of Illinois, 1966.

Andronov, A., L. Pontryagin, and A. Witt: On the Statistical Investigation of Dynamical Systems, (in Russian), *Zh. Eksperim. i Teor. Fiz.*, **3**:165–180 (1933).

―――: "Selected Works," pp. 142–160, Academy of Sciences, USSR, 1956.

Ariaratnam, S. T.: Random Vibrations of Nonlinear Suspensions, *J. Mech. Eng. Sci.*, **2**:195–201 (1960).

―――: Response of a Loaded Nonlinear String to Random Excitation, *J. Appl. Mech.*, **29**:483–485 (1962).

Barrett, J. F.: Application of Kolmogorov's Equations to Randomly Disturbed Automatic Control Systems, *Proc. First Intern. Congr. Intern. Federation Autom. Control, Moscow, 1960.*

―――: The Use of Characteristic Functionals and Cumulant Generating Functionals to Discuss the Effect of Noise in Linear Systems, *J. Sound Vibration*, **1**:229–238 (1964).

Bartlett, M. S.: "Stochastic Processes," Cambridge, London, 1955.

Batchelor, G. K.: "Theory of Homogeneous Turbulence," Cambridge, London, 1953.

Beer, F. P.: On the Response of Linear Systems to Time-dependent, Multidimensional Loadings, *J. Appl. Mech.*, **28**:50–56 (1961).

Bellman, R.: "Introduction to Matrix Analysis," McGraw-Hill, New York, 1960.

Bendat, J. S.: "Principles and Applications of Random Noise Theory," Wiley, New York, 1958.

―――, L. D. Enochson, G. H. Klein, and A. G. Piersol: Advanced Concepts of Stochastic Processes and Statistics for Flight Vehicle Vibration Estimation and Measurement, ASD-TDR-62-973, Aeronautical Systems Division, Wright-Patterson Air Force Base, 1962.

―――: Probability Functions for Random Responses: Prediction of Peaks, Fatigue Damage, and Catastrophic Failures, *NASA* CR-33, Measurement Analysis Corporation, April, 1964.

Bharucha-Reid, A. T.: "Elements of the Theory of Markov Processes and Their Applications," McGraw-Hill, New York, 1960.

Bisplinghoff, R. L., and H. Ashley: "Principles of Aeroelasticity," Wiley, New York, 1962.

Blackman, R. B., and J. W. Tukey: The Measurement of Power Spectra from the Point of View of Communications Engineering, *Bell System Tech. J.*, **37**:185–282, 485–569 (1958); reprinted by Dover, New York, 1959.

Bochner, S.: "Lectures on Fourier Integrals," English translation by M. Tenenbaum and H. Pollard, Princeton, Princeton, N.J., 1959.

Bogdanoff, J. L., and J. E. Goldberg: On the Bernoulli-Euler Beam Theory with Random Excitation, *J. Aerosapce Sci.*, **27**:371–376 (1960).

—— and F. Kozin: Comment on Reliability of Aircraft Structures in Resisting Chance Failure, *Operations Res.*, **9**(1):123–126 (1961).

—— and F. Kozin (eds.): "Proceedings of the First Symposium on Engineering Applications of Random Function Theory and Probability," Wiley, New York, 1963.

—— J. E. Goldberg, and M. C. Bernard: Response of a Simple Structure to a Random Earthquake-type Disturbance, *Bull. Seism. Soc. Am.*, **51**:293–310 (1961).

——, J. E. Goldberg, and D. R. Sharpe: The Response of Simple Nonlinear Systems to a Random Disturbance of the Earthquake Type, *Bull. Seism. Soc. Am.*, **54**:263–276 (1964).

Bolotin, V. V.: Statistical Theory of Earthquake Resistance of Structures, (in Russian), *Izv. Akad. Nauk SSSR, Otd. Tekhn. Nauk*, **4**:123–129 (1959).

Boyce, W. E.: Random Vibration of Elastic Strings and Bars, *Proc. Fourth U.S. Natl. Congr. Appl. Mech., Berkeley, June, 1962*, **1**:77–85 (1962).

Cartwright, D. E., and L. J. Rydill: The Rolling and Pitching of a Ship at Sea, *Trans. Inst. Nav. Arch.*, **99**:100–135 (1957).

Caughey, T. K.: Response of a Nonlinear String to Random Loading, *J. Appl. Mech.*, **26**:341–344 (1959).

——: Response of Van der Pol's Oscillator to Random Excitation, *J. Appl. Mech.*, **26**:345–348 (1959).

——: Random Excitation of a Loaded Nonlinear String, *J. Appl. Mech.*, **27**:575–578 (1960).

——: Random Excitation of a System with Bilinear Hysteresis, *J. Appl. Mech.*, **27**:649–652 (1960).

—— and H. J. Stumpf: Transient Response of a Dynamic System under Random Excitation, *J. Appl. Mech.*, **28**:563–566 (1961).

—— and J. K. Dienes: Analysis of a Nonlinear First-order System with a White Noise Input, *J. Appl. Phys.*, **32**:2476–2479 (1961).

——: Derivation and Application of the Fokker-Planck Equation to Discrete Nonlinear Dynamic Systems Subjected to White Random Excitation, *J. Acoust. Soc. Am.*, **35**(11):1683–1692 (1963).

——: Equivalent Linearization Techniques, *J. Acoust. Soc. Am.*, **35**(11):1706–1711 (1963).

——: On the Response of a Class of Nonlinear Oscillators to Stochastic Excitation, *Proc. Colloq. Intern. du Centre National de la Recherche Scientifique*, No. 148, pp. 393–402, Marseille, September, 1964.

—— and M. E. J. O'Kelly: Classical Normal Modes in Damped Linear Dynamic Systems, *J. Appl. Mech.*, **32**:583–588 (1965).

Chandrasekhar, S.: Stochastic Problems in Physics and Astronomy, *Rev. Mod. Phys.*, **15**:1–89 (1943).

Chu, H. N., and G. Herrmann: Influence of Large Amplitudes on Free Flexural Vibration of Rectangular Elastic Plates, *J. Appl. Mech.*, **23**(4):532–540 (1956).

Clarkson, B. L., and R. D. Ford: The Response of a Typical Aircraft Structure to Jet Noise, *J. Roy. Aeron. Soc.*, **66**:31–40 (1962).

————: The Design of Structures to Resist Jet Noise Fatigue, *J. Roy. Aeron. Soc.*, **66** (1962).

Corcos, G. M., and H. W. Liepmann: On the Contribution of Turbulent Boundary Layers to the Noise Inside a Fuselage, *NACA* TM 1420, 1956.

Coleman, J. J.: Reliability of Aircraft Structures in Resisting Chance Failure, *Operations Res.*, **7**(5):639–645 (1959).

Coleman, T. L., H. N. Murrow, and H. Press: Some Structural Response Characteristics of a Large Flexible Swept-wing Airplane in Rough Air, *J. Aeron. Sci.*, **25**:515–521, 536 (1958).

Cornell, C. A.: Stochastic Process Models in Structural Engineering, *Stanford Univ. Civil Eng. Dept. Tech. Rept.* 34, May, 1964.

Cramer, H.: "Mathematical Methods of Statistics," Princeton, Princeton, N.J., 1946.

Crandall, S. H. (ed.): "Random Vibration," vol. I, Technology Press, Cambridge, Mass., 1958.

————: Random Vibration of Systems with Nonlinear Restoring Forces, *Proc. Intern. Symp. Nonlinear Vibrations, Kiev, September, 1961,* **1**:306–314 (1963).

———— and A. Yildiz: Random Vibration of Beams, *J. Appl. Mech.*, **29**:267–275 (1962).

————: Random Vibration of a Nonlinear System with a Set-up Spring, *J. Appl. Mech.*, **29**:477–482 (1962).

————, W. D. Mark, and G. R. Khabbaz: The Variance in Palmgren-Miner Damage Due to Random Vibration, *Proc. 4th U.S. Natl. Congr. Appl. Mech., Berkeley, June, 1962,* **1**:119–126, (1962).

————: Perturbation Techniques for Random Vibration of Nonlinear Systems, *J. Acoust. Soc. Am.*, **35**(11):1700–1705 (1963).

———— (ed.): "Random Vibration," vol. 2, M.I.T., Cambridge, Mass., 1963.

———— and W. D. Mark: "Random Vibration in Mechanical Systems," Academic, New York, 1963.

————: Zero Crossings, Peaks, and Other Statistical Measures of Random Responses, *J. Acoust. Soc. Am.*, **35**(11):1693–1699 (1963).

————: The Envelope of Random Vibration of a Lightly Damped Nonlinear Oscillator, *Zagadnienia drgan nieliniowych* (Nonlinear Vibration Problems), **5**:120–130 (1964).

———, G. R. Khabbaz, and J. E. Manning: Random Vibration of an Oscillator with Nonlinear Damping, *J. Acoust. Soc. Am.*, **36**(7):1330–1334 (1964).

———: "The Spectrum of Random Vibration of a Nonlinear Oscillator," presented at the Eleventh International Congress of Applied Mechanics, Munich, September, 1964.

———: Random Forcing of Nonlinear Systems, *Proc. Colloq. Intern. du Centre National de la Recherche Scientifique*, No. 148, pp. 57–68, 1965.

———, K. L. Chandiramani, and R. G. Cook: Some First Passage Problems in Random Vibration, *J. Appl. Mech.*, **33**:532–538 (1966).

Curtis, A. J., and T. R. Boykin, Jr.: Response of Two-degree-of-freedom Systems to White Noise Base Excitation, *J. Acoust. Soc. Am.*, **33**:655–663 (1961).

Davenport, A. G.: The Application of Statistical Concepts to the Wind Loading of Structures, *Proc. Inst. Civil Engs.*, **19**:449 (1961).

———: Buffetting of a Suspension Bridge by Storm Winds, *J. Struct. Div.*, *Am. Soc. Civil Engrs.*, **88**:233 (1962).

Davenport, W. B., Jr., and W. L. Root: "Introduction to Random Signals and Noise," McGraw-Hill, New York, 1958.

Deutsch, R.: "Nonlinear Transformations of Random Processes," Prentice-Hall, Englewood Cliffs, N.J., 1962.

Diederich, F. W.: The Dynamic Response of a Large Airplane to Continuous Random Atmospheric Disturbances, *J. Aeron. Sci.*, **23**:917–930 (1956).

Doob, J. L.: "Stochastic Processes," Wiley, New York, 1953.

Dyer, I.: Response of Plates to a Decaying and Convecting Random Pressure Field, *J. Acoust. Soc. Am.*, **31**:922–928 (1959).

Eckart, C.: The Theory of Noise in Continuous Media, *J. Acoust. Soc. Am.*, **25**:195–199 (1953).

Einstein, Albert: "The Theory of Brownian Movement," Dover, New York, 1956.

Erdélyi, A. (ed.): "Tables of Integral Transforms," vol. 1, McGraw-Hill, New York, 1954.

Eringen, A. C.: Response of Beams and Plates to Random Loads, *J. Appl. Mech.*, **24**:46–52 (1957).

———: Response of Tall Buildings to Random Earthquakes, *Proc. 3rd U.S. Natl. Congr. Appl. Mech.*, p. 141, ASME, 1958.

Etkin, B.: "Dynamics of Flight," Wiley, New York, 1959.

———: A Theory of the Response of Airplanes to Random Atmospheric Turbulence, *J. Aerospace Sci.*, **26**:409–420 (1959).

Feller, W.: The Parabolic Differential Equations and the Associated Semigroups of Transformations, *Ann. Math.*, **55**:468–519 (1952).

————: "An Introduction to Probability and Its Applications," 2d ed., Wiley, New York, 1957.

Fokker, A. D.: Die Mittlere Energie rotierender elektrischer Dipole in Strahlungs Feld, *Ann. Physik.*, **43**:810–820 (1914).

Frazer, R. A., W. J. Duncan, and A. R. Collar: "Elementary Matrices," Cambridge, London, 1946.

Fung, Y. C.: Statistical Aspects of Dynamic Loads, *J. Aeron. Sci.*, **20**:317–330 (1953).

————: The Analysis of Dynamic Stresses in Aircraft Structures during Landing as Nonstationary Random Processes, *J. Appl. Mech.*, **2**:449–457 (1955).

————: "An Introduction to the Theory of Aeroelasticity," Wiley, New York, 1955.

Hasselmann, K.: Random Excitation of Vibrating Systems, (in German), *ZAMM*, **42**:465–476 (1962).

Herbert, R. E.: Random Vibrations of a Nonlinear Elastic Beam, *J. Acoust. Soc. Am.*, **36**(11):2090–2094 (1964).

————: Random Vibrations of Plates with Large Amplitudes, *J. Appl. Mech.*, **32**:547–552 (1965).

Holzer, H.: "Die Berechnung der Drehschwingungen," Springer, Berlin, 1921.

Housner, G. W.: Characteristics of Strong Motion Earthquakes, *Bull. Seism. Soc. Am.*, **37**:19–31 (1947).

Huston, W. B., and T. H. Skopinski: Probability and Frequency Characteristics of Some Flight Buffet Loads, *NACA* TN 3733, August, 1956.

Jasper, N. H.: Statistical Distribution Patterns of Ocean Waves and of Wave Induced Ship Stresses and Motions with Engineering Applications, *Trans. Soc. Nav. Arch. Marine Engrs.*, **64**:375–432 (1956).

Khazen, E. M.: Evaluation of the One-dimensional Probability Densities and Moments of a Random Process in the Output of an Essentially Nonlinear System, *Theory Probability Appl.*, **6**:117–123 (1961).

————: Estimating the Density of the Probability Distribution for Random Processes in Systems with Nonlinearities of Piecewise-linear Type, *Theory Probability Appl.*, **6**:214–220 (1961).

Khintchine, A.: Korrelations Theorie der Stationaren Stochastischen Prozesse, *Math. Ann.*, **109**:604–615 (1934).

Kittel, C.: "Elementary Statistical Physics," Wiley, New York, 1958.

Klein, G. H.: Random Excitation of a Nonlinear System with Tangent Elasticity Characteristics, *J. Acoust. Soc. Am.*, **36**(11):2095–2105 (1964).

Kolmogorov, A.: Uber die Analytischen Methoden in der Wahrschein-lichkeitsrechnung, *Math. Ann.*, **104**:415–458 (1931).

Kozin, F.: On the Probability Densities of the Output of Some Random Systems, *J. Appl. Mech.*, **28**:161–164 (1961).

Kraichnan, R. H.: Noise Transmission from Boundary Layer Pressure Fluctuations, *J. Acoust. Soc. Am.*, **29**:65–80 (1957).

Kramers, H. A.: Brownian Motion in a Field of Force and the Diffusion Model of Chemical Reactions, *Physica*, **7**:284–304 (1940).

Krylov, N., and N. Bogoliubov: Introduction à la mécanique nonlineaire: les méthodes approchées et asymptotiques, translated by S. Lefshetz, "Annals of Mathematical Studies No. 11," Princeton, Princeton, N.J., 1947.

Lampard, D. G.: Generalization of the Wiener-Khintchine Theorem to Nonstationary Processes, *J. Appl. Phys.*, **25**:802–803 (1954).

Langer, B. F.: Fatigue Failure from Stress Cycles of Varying Amplitude, *J. Appl. Mech.*, **4**:A160–A162 (1937).

Laning, J. H., Jr., and R. H. Battin: "Random Processes in Automatic Control," McGraw-Hill, New York, 1956.

Lebedev, V. L.: "Random Processes in Electrical and Mechanical Systems," Moscow, 1958, English translation by J. Flancreich and M. Segal, Israel Program for Scientific Translations, Jerusalem, 1961.

Lee, Y. W.: "Statistical Theory of Communications," Wiley, New York, 1960.

Leybold, H., and E. Naumann: A Study of Fatigue Life under Random Loading, *Am. Soc. Testing Mater. Proc.*, **63**:717–733 (1963).

Liepmann, H. W.: On the Application of Statistical Concepts to the Buffeting Problem, *J. Aeron. Sci.*, **19**(12):793–800, 822 (1952).

———: Extension of the Statistical Approach to Buffeting and Gust Response of Wings of Finite Span, *J. Aeron. Sci.*, **22**:197–200 (1955).

Lin, C. C.: On the Motion of a Pendulum in Turbulent Flow, *Quart. Appl. Math.*, **1**:43–48 (1943).

Lin, Y. K.: Free Vibrations of a Continuous Beam on Elastic Supports, *Intern. J. Mech. Sci.*, **4**:409–423 (1962).

———: Nonstationary Response of Continuous Structures to Random Loading, *J. Acoust. Soc. Am.*, **35**:222–227 (1963).

———: Application of Nonstationary Shot Noise in the Study of System Response to a Class of Nonstationary Excitations, *J. Appl. Mech.*, **30**(4):555–558 (1963).

———: Probability Distributions of Stress Peaks in Linear and Nonlinear Structures, *AIAA J.*, **1**(5):1133–1138 (1963).

———, I. D. Brown, and P. C. Deutschle: Free Vibrations of a Finite Row of Continuous Skin-stringer Panels, *J. Sound Vibration*, **1**:14–27 (1964).

————: On Nonstationary Shot Noise, *J. Acoust. Soc. Am.*, **36**(1):82–84 (1964).

————: Random Vibration of a Myklestad Beam, *AIAA J.*, **2**(8):1448–1451 (1964).

————, T. J. McDaniel, B. K. Donaldson, C. F. Vail, and W. J. Dwyer: Free Vibration of Continuous Skin-stringer Panels with Nonuniform Stringer Spacing and Panel Thickness, *Air Force Systems Command Rept.* AFML-TR-64-347 Part I, Wright-Patterson Air Force Base, Ohio, February, 1965.

————: Nonstationary Excitation and Response in Linear Systems Treated as Sequences of Random Pulses, *J. Acoust. Soc. Am.*, **38**:453–460 (1965).

————: Response of Multi-spanned Beam and Panel Systems under Noise Excitation, *Air Force Systems Command, Rept.* AFML-TR-64-348, Part I, Wright-Patterson Air Force Base, Ohio, February, 1965.

————: Transfer Matrix Representation of Flexible Airplanes in Gust Response Study, *J. Aircraft*, **2**:116–121 (1965).

Love, A. E. H.: "Mathematical Theory of Elasticity," 4th ed., Dover, New York, 1944.

Loéve, M.: "Probability Theory," 3d ed., Van Nostrand, Princeton, N.J., 1963.

Lyon, R. H.: Propagation of Correlation Functions in Continuous Media, *J. Acoust. Soc. Am.*, **28**:76–79 (1956).

————: Response of Strings to Random Noise Fields, *J. Acoust. Soc. Am.*, **28**:391–398 (1956).

————: On the Vibration Statistics of a Randomly Excited Hard-spring Oscillator, *J. Acoust. Soc. Am.*, **32**:716–719 (1960).

————: Response of a Nonlinear String to Random Excitation, *J. Acoust. Soc. Am.*, **32**(8):953–960 (1960).

————: On the Vibration Statistics of a Randomly Excited Hard-spring Oscillator II, *J. Acoust. Soc. Am.*, **33**(10):1395–1403 (1961).

————, M. Heckl., and C. B. Hazelgrove: Narrow Band Excitation of the Hard Spring Oscillator, *J. Acoust. Soc. Am.*, **33**:1404–1411 (1961).

———— and G. Maidanik: Power Flow between Linearly Coupled Oscillators, *J. Acoust. Soc. Am.*, **34**:623–639 (1962).

———— and G. Maidanik: Statistical Methods in Vibration Analysis, *AIAA J.*, **2**:1015–1024 (1964).

Mains, R. M.: Minimizing Damage from Random Vibration, *J. Acoust. Soc. Am.*, **30**:1127–1129 (1958).

Mead, D. J.: Bond Stresses in a Randomly Vibrating Sandwich Plate: Single Mode Theory, *J. Sound Vibration*, **1**:270 (1964).

Middleton, D.: "An Introduction to Statistical Communication Theory," McGraw-Hill, New York, 1960.

Miles, J. W.: On Structural Fatigue under Random Loading, *J. Aeron. Sci.*, **21**:753–762 (1954).

———: Vibrations of Beams on Many Supports, *J. Eng. Mech. Div., Am. Soc. Civil Engrs.*, **82**(Em1):1–9 (1956).

Mindlin, R. D.: Dynamics of Package Cushioning, *Bell System Tech. J.*, **24**:353–461 (1945).

Miner, M. A.: Cumulative Damage in Fatigue, *J. Appl. Mech.*, **12**:A159–A164 (1945).

Morrow, C. T.: Random Vibration, *J. Acoust. Soc. Am.*, **32**:742–748 (1960).

Moyal, J. E.: Stochastic Processes and Statistical Physics, *J. Roy. Statist. Soc. (London)*, **B11**:150–210 (1949).

Myklestad, N. O.: A New Method of Calculating Natural Modes of Uncoupled Bending Vibration of Airplane Wings and Other Types of Beams, *J. Aeron. Sci.*, **11**:153–162 (1944).

Oliver, R. E., and T. Y. Wu: Sled-Track Interaction and a Rapid Method for Track-Alignment Measurement, *AER, Inc., Rept.* TR 114 (114-8-1), June, 1958.

Olmsted, J. M. H.: "Real Variables," Appleton-Century-Crofts, New York, 1959.

Palmgren, A.: Die Lebensdauer von Kugellagern, *Ver. deut. Ingr.*, **68**:339–341 (1924).

Papoulis, A.: "The Fourier Integral and Its Applications," McGraw-Hill, New York, 1962.

———: "Probability, Random Variables, and Stochastic Processes," McGraw-Hill, New York, 1965.

Parzen, E.: "Modern Probability Theory and Its Applications," Wiley, New York, 1960.

———: "Stochastic Processes," Holden-Day, San Francisco, 1962.

Pestel, E. C., and F. A. Leckie: "Matric Methods in Elastomechanics," McGraw-Hill, New York, 1963.

Pfeiffer, P. E.: "Concepts of Probability Theory," McGraw-Hill, New York, 1965.

Planck, M.: Uber einen Satz der statistischen Dynamik und seine Erweiterung in der Quantentheorie, *Sitz. ber.* Berlin A *Akad. Wiss.* 1917, pp. 324–341, 1917.

Powell, A.: On the Fatigue Failure of Structures Due to Vibrations Excited by Random Pressure Fields, *J. Acoust. Soc. Am.*, **30**:1130–1135 (1958).

Pretlove, A. J.: Bond Stresses in a Randomly Vibrating Sandwich Plate: Multi-modal Theory, *J. Sound Vibration*, **2**:1–22 (1965).

Press, H., and J. C. Houbolt: Some Applications of Generalized Harmonic Analysis to Gust Loads on Airplanes, *J. Aeron. Sci.*, **22**:17–26, 60 (1955).

Ribner, H. S.: Boundary-layer-induced Noise in the Interior of Aircraft, *Univ. Toronto UTIA Rept.* 37, April, 1956.

————: Spectral Theory of Buffeting and Gust Response: Unification and Extension, *J. Aeron. Sci.*, **23**:1075–1077, 1118 (1956).

Rice, J. R., and F. P. Beer: On the Distribution of Rises and Falls in a Continuous Random Process, Lehigh University Institute of Research Rept., (1964).

————: Starting Transients in the Response of Linear Systems to Stationary Random Excitation, *J. Appl. Mech.*, **32**:200–201 (1965).

Rice, S. O.: Mathematical Analysis of Random Noise, *Bell System Tech. J.*, **23**:282–332 (1944); **24**:46–156 (1945). Reprinted in N. Wax (ed.), "Selected Papers on Noise and Stochastic Processes," Dover, New York, 1954.

Robson, J. D.: "An Introduction to Random Vibration," Edinburgh at the University Press, 1963.

Rosenblatt, M.: "Random Processes," Oxford, New York, 1962.

Rosenblueth, E., and J. I. Bustamente: Distribution of Structural Responses to Earthquakes, *J. Eng. Mech. Div., Am. Soc. Civil Engrs.*, **86**(EM 2):1–16 (1960).

————: Probabilistic Design to Resist Earthquakes, *J. Eng. Mech. Div., Am. Soc. Civil Engrs.*, **90**(EM 5):189–219 (1964).

Samuels, J. C., and A. C. Eringen: Response of a Simply Supported Timoshenko Beam to a Purely Random Gaussian Process, *J. Appl. Mech.*, **25**:496–500 (1958).

———— and ————: On Stochastic Linear Systems, *J. Math. Phys.*, **38**:83–103 (1959).

Shinozuka, M.: Probability of Structural Failure under Random Loading, *J. Eng. Mech. Div., Am. Soc. Civil Engrs.*, **90**(EM 5):147–170 (1964).

———— and L. Henry: Random Vibration of a Beam Column, *J. Eng. Mech. Div., Am. Soc. Civil Engrs.*, **91**(EM 5):123–143 (1965).

———— and J. T. P. Yao: On the Two-sided Time-dependent Barrier Problem, *Columbia Univ. Inst. Study of Fatigue and Reliability, Tech. Rept.* 21, June, 1965.

Smith, P. W., Jr.: Response of Nonlinear Structures to Random Excitation, *J. Acoust. Soc. Am.*, **34**:827–835 (1962).

Smits, T. I., D. A. Smith, and R. F. Lambert: Crest and Extremal Statistics of a Square-law-derived Random Process, *J. Acoust. Soc. Am.*, **34**:1859–1864 (1962).

Smoluchowski, M. v.: Uber Brownsche Molekular bewegung unter Einwirkung auszerer Krafte und deren Zusammenhang mit der verralgemeinerten Diffusionsgleichung, *Ann. Physik.*, **48**:1103–1112 (1915).

St. Denis, M., and W. J. Pierson, Jr.: On the Motions of Ships in Confused Seas, *Trans. Soc. Nav. Arch. Marine Engrs.*, **61**:280–332 (1953).

Spiegal, M. R.: The Random Vibration of a String, *Quart. Appl. Math.*, **X**(1):25–33 (1952).

Stratonovich, R. L.: "Topics in the Theory of Random Noise," English translation by R. A. Silverman, Gordon and Breach, Science Publishers, New York, 1963.

Stoker, J. J.: "Nonlinear Vibration," Interscience, New York, 1950.

Thomson, W. T., and M. V. Barton: The Response of Mechanical Systems to Random Excitation, *J. Appl. Mech.*, **24**:248–251 (1957).

———: Continuous Structures Excited by Correlated Random Forces, *Intern. J. Mech. Sci.*, **4**:109–114 (1962).

———: "Vibration Theory and Applications," Prentice-Hall, Englewood Cliffs, N.J., 1965.

Timoshenko, S.: "Theory of Plates and Shells," McGraw-Hill, New York, 1940.

Tolman, R. C.: "The Principles of Statistical Mechanics," Oxford, London, 1938.

Trapp, W. J., and D. M. Forney, Jr. (eds.): "Acoustical Fatigue in Aerospace Structures," Syracuse University Press, Syracuse, N.Y., 1965.

Trubert, M. R. P.: Response of Elastic Structures to Statistically Correlated Multiple Random Excitations, *J. Acoust. Soc. Am.*, **35**:1009–1022 (1963).

Tung, C. C., J. Penzien, and R. Horonjeff: The Effect of Runway Unevenness on the Dynamic Response of Supersonic Transports, *NASA* CR-119, University of California, Berkeley, October, 1964.

Van Lear, G. A., and G. E. Uhlenbeck: The Brownian Motion of Strings and Elastic Rods, *Phys. Rev.*, **38**:1583–1598 (1931).

Wang, M. C., and G. E. Uhlenbeck: On the Theory of the Brownian Motion II, *Rev. Mod. Phys.*, **17**:323–342 (1945). Collected in N. Wax (ed.), "Selected Papers on Noise and Stochastic Processes," Dover, New York, 1954.

Wax, N. (ed.): "Selected Papers on Noise and Stochastic Processes," Dover, New York, 1954.

Weidenhammer, F.: Vibrations of Foundations under Random Vibrations, (in German), *Ing.-Arch.*, **31**:433–443 (1962).

Weiner, N.: Generalized Harmonic Analysis, *Acta Math.*, **55**:117–258 (1930).

————: "Extrapolation, Interpolation, and Smoothing of Stationary Time Series," Wiley, New York, 1949.

————: "Nonlinear Problems in Random Theory," Technology Press, Cambridge, Mass., 1958.

Whittle, P.: Continuous Generalizations of Chebyshev's Inequality, *Theory Probability Appl.*, **3**:386–394 (1958).

Wolaver, L. E.: Second Order Properties of Nonlinear Systems Driven by Random Noise, *USAF Aerospace Res. Lab.* ARL-65-61, Wright-Patterson Air Force Base, Ohio, April, 1965.

Yaglom, A. M.: "An Introduction to the Theory of Stationary Random Functions," English translation by R. A. Silverman, Prentice-Hall, Englewood Cliffs, N.J., 1962.

NAME INDEX

SUBJECT INDEX